APPLIED BASIC TEXTILES

Books by GEORGE E. LINTON

CALLAWAY MILLS TEXTILE DICTIONARY (co-author)

CHEMISTRY AND TEXTILES FOR THE LAUNDRY INDUSTRY (co-author)

DAN RIVER MILLS DICTIONARY OF TEXTILE TERMS (co-author)

INTRODUCTION TO TEXTILES

MODERN TEXTILE DICTIONARY

STANDARD TEXTILE FABRICS

TEXTILES: CARE AND TESTING

APPLIED TEXTILES

APPLIED BASIC TEXTILES

NATURAL AND MANMADE TEXTILE FIBERS

APPLIED BASIC TEXTILES

Raw Material, Construction, Color, and Finish
Fabric Analysis
Chemical and Physical Testing of Textiles
Spot and Stain Removal and Care of Clothing

BY

GEORGE E. LINTON, Ph.D.

PROFESSOR EMERITUS, TEXTILE DEPARTMENT, FASHION INSTITUTE;
TEXTILE EDITOR FOR *AMERICAN FABRICS MAGAZINE*, NEW YORK CITY

FIRST EDITION

Fully Illustrated

DUELL, SLOAN AND PEARCE   NEW YORK

First edition

DUELL, SLOAN & PEARCE
AFFILIATE OF
MEREDITH PRESS

Library of Congress Catalog Card Number: 65-23017

MANUFACTURED IN THE UNITED STATES OF AMERICA FOR MEREDITH PRESS

VAN REES PRESS • NEW YORK

To

the Fashion Institute of Technology, which is serving to stimulate research, experimentation, and creative ideas within the apparel and allied fields from fiber to fabric to fashion,

and

to promote greater integration, coordination, and understanding among the textile, apparel, and kindred industries.

Foreword

Textiles and the clothing made from them rank as one of the three major essentials of mankind, and the textile industry is rated second among the twenty-two major industries in the United States with regard to the number of persons employed. Why, then, does the average person or consumer know comparatively little concerning textiles?

Among the reasons are these:

1. There is little carding, spinning, or weaving of textiles in the home.
2. Knowledge of textile fibers, filaments, and fabrics and their properties is not widely disseminated.
3. Most test procedures for evaluating textiles in terms of performance are of comparatively recent origin.
4. Textile terminology as applied to types of fabrics is often misused or misunderstood and is in a continuing state of flux.
5. Many students and teachers of textile subjects in secondary and higher institutions of learning are unable to acquire an over-all mastery of the subject because of a lack of sources and proper organization of textile materials for educational and business purposes.

As one who has devoted many years to the problems of indoctrinating students, teachers, textile mill trainees, home economics groups, and the general public with the knowledge covered in this book by Dr. Linton, I find it most gratifying to have the subjects recognized and set down in black and white by such an eminent authority. This well-balanced, informative, factual book should be of inestimable value to the layman, student, and teacher, the executive and secretary, the textile technologist, mill and department store trainee, and many others.

EPHRAIM FREEDMAN,
Director, Bureau of Standards,
R. H. Macy & Co., Inc., New York City

Contents

Introduction, Aims and Objectives; Fiber Kingdoms; Fiber Identification; Yarn Manufacture—Spun, Filament, and Textured; Parts of a Woven Fabric; Weaving of Fabric and Parts of a Loom; Properties of Woven Cloth; Distinction Between Warp and Filling; Face and Back of Woven Fabrics; Knitting; Hosiery Knitting; Shoe and Stocking Sizes; Felt and Its Manufacture; Plaited, Braided, Lace Fabrics; Nonwoven, Spunbonded, Fiberwoven Fabrics; Stretch Fabrics; Laminated and Molded Fabrics; Standard Textile Fabrics; The Three Basic Weaves and Other Major Weave Constructions; The Language of Color; Types of Dyes Used; Major and Minor Methods of Dyeing and Printing Textiles; Flocking; Permanent Press; Floor Coverings; Tufted Fabrics; Domestics; Factoring.

Textile Testing; The Microscope; Relative Humidity; Fabric Analysis; Quality Control; Physical Testing of Textiles in Detail; Care of Clothing—the Sure Care Symbol; Methods Used to Remove Spots and Stains.

The Textile Fiber Products Identification Act of the Federal Trade Commission (March 3, 1960); Properties and Characteristics of Major Textile Fibers; Who Is to Blame for Faulty Fabrics and Garments? History of Costume; Fashion and Style; Basic Key Words Used in the World of Fashion and Style; Information Sources on Textiles; Selected List of Books on Textiles.

Acknowledgments to Technical Advisers

The author is pleased to make sincere acknowledgment to the following persons whose aid, cooperation, and guidance have made this book possible; their help is greatly appreciated by the author.

Mr. Paul Askew, The Singer Company, Inc., Cobble Division, Chattanooga, Tenn.

Mr. Matthew Babey, Atlas Electric Devices Co., Inc., Chicago, Ill.

Professor Rosa Balenzano, Art Department, Fashion Institute, New York City.

Mr. Cameron A. Baker, Director of Research and Development, Better Fabrics Testing Bureau, Inc., 101 West 31st Street, New York City.

Dr. H. D. Barker, Division of Cotton and Other Fiber Crops, United States Department of Agriculture, Washington, D.C.

Mr. Allen F. Barney, Director, Public Relations, Saco-Lowell Shops, Division of Maremont Corporation, Easley and Greenville, S.C.

Mr. John J. Bosshard and Staff, American Viscose Division of FMC Corporation, 350 Fifth Avenue, New York City.

Mr. Hugh G. Chatham, President, The Fiberwoven Corporation, Elkin, North Carolina.

Mr. Edward Decker, Hess, Goldsmith Company, Division of Burlington Industries, Inc., 1400 Broadway, New York City.

Mr. Walter Dietzsch, Schiffli Lace and Embroidery Institute, Union City, N.J.

Dr. Sidney M. Edelstein, President, Dexter Chemical Company, Inc., 919 Edgewater Road, New York City.

Mr. Richard S. Flood, Vice-president, Glen Raven Mills, Inc., 1430 Broadway, New York City.

Mr. Ludwig Fusser, Technical Manager, General Aniline & Film Corporation, 140 West 51st Street, New York City.

Mr. Ephraim Freedman, Director of the Bureau of Standards, R. H. Macy & Company, Inc., Herald Square, New York City.

Mr. Raymond C. Gagnon, Director of the School of Textiles, International Correspondence Schools, Scranton, Pa.

Professor James L. Giblin, Dean, Southeastern Massachusetts Technological Institute, North Dartmouth, Mass.

Mr. James H. Grant, Advertising Manager, Draper Corporation, Hopedale, Mass.

Mr. Joseph C. Hirsch and Mr. Fred Simmons, Stylists for Manchester Mills, Inc., 1290 Sixth Avenue, New York City.

Mr. Stanley B. Hunt, Director of the Textile Economics Bureau, Inc., 10 East 40th Street, New York City.

Mr. Arthur E. Jerome, President of Arthur E. Jerome Company, Inc., 401 Broadway, New York City.

Mr. Albert E. Johnson, Director of Public Relations for the National Institute of Drycleaning, 101 West 31st Street, New York City.

Mr. Sidney Korzenik, Executive Director, National Knitted Outerwear Association, 51 Madison Avenue, New York City.

Mr. Edward Kuhnel, Secretary, Clupak, Inc., 530 Fifth Avenue, New York City.

Mr. John W. Lane, President, Atlas Devices Company, Inc., 4114 Ravenswood Avenue, Chicago, Ill.

Mr. William H. Lehmberg, President of American Felt Company, Inc., Glenville, Conn.

Mr. Cecil Lubell, Executive Editor for *American Fabrics Magazine*, Doric Publishing Co., Inc., 24 East 38th Street, New York City.

Mr. Harry Mahler, Manager of Industrial Fabrics Market Development, Owens-Corning Fiberglas Corporation, 717 Fifth Avenue, New York City.

Mr. George D. Maynard, Jr., Refined Products Company, Inc., Lyndhurst, N.J.

Professor Ray McCaughey, Head of Knitting Department, Fashion Institute, New York City.

Mr. Alfred H. McCollough and Staff, *Modern Textiles Magazine,* 303 Fifth Avenue, New York City.

Professor Robert A. McWilliams, Textile Division of the Industrial Arts Department, State University College, Oswego, N.Y.

Mr. Christopher J. Moroney, Sales Promotion Manager, The Sanforized Company, a Division of Cluett, Peabody Company, Inc., 530 Fifth Avenue, New York City.

Mr. Richard W. Nelson, Textile Technologist, Beaunit Fibers Division of Beaunit Corporation, New York City.

Professor Arthur Price, Coordinator for Textile Department, Fashion Institute, New York City.

Mr. Charles Reichman, Editor of *Knitted Outerwear Times,* 51 Madison Avenue, New York City.

Mr. Charles H. Rutledge and Staff, Fiber Information Services, E. I. du Pont de Nemours & Company, Inc., Wilmington, Del.

Mr. William C. Segal, Publisher, and Miss Cora Carlyle, Editor and Fashion Co-ordinator of *American Fabrics Magazine,* Doric Publications, Inc., 24 East 38th Street, New York City.

Mr. Lester H. Senholzi, Manager of Greige Goods Department, Eastman Chemical Products, Inc., 260 Madison Avenue, New York City.

Mr. Charles Sinatra, Director of Photography and Visual Aids, American Viscose Division of FMC Corporation, 350 Fifth Avenue, New York City.

Mr. Jacob Solinger, Consultant to the Apparel Industries, 601 West 115th Street, New York City.

Staff of Eastman Chemical Products, Inc., 260 Madison Avenue, New York City.

Staff of The Irish Linen Guild, 1270 Sixth Avenue, New York City.

Mr. J. C. Sutton, President, Cellusuede Products, Inc., Rockford, Ill.

Textile Faculty of the Fashion Institute, New York City—Professors José Alvarodiez, Edna S. Brodie, Allen C. Cohen, Howard Essig, Giles Hopkins, Joseph J. Pizzuto, Joseph Samuels; and Technologist, Joseph Garafolo.

Mr. J. Vernon Wallace, Director, Industrial Relations, Bibb Manufacturing Co., Inc., Macon, Ga.

Mr. Robert Ward, Director, Audio-Visual Services, National Cotton Council, Memphis, Tenn.

Mr. Edwin Wilkinson, President of National Association of Wool Manufacturers, Inc., 386 Fourth Avenue, New York City.

Acknowledgments to Companies and Agencies

APPAREL AND CLOTHING

Professors Ernestine Kopp (Chairman), Adelaide Manno, Renée Rolfo, Edmund Roberts, Josephine Watkins, Fashion Institute, New York City.

COTTON

Bibb Manufacturing Company, Macon, Ga.
Bradford Dyeing Association (USA), 111 West 40th St., New York City.
Callaway Mills, Inc., 295 Fifth Avenue, New York City.
Dan River Mills, Inc., 111 West 40th Street, New York City.
West Point-Pepperell, Inc., 111 West 40th Street, New York City.
Whitin Machine Works, Whitinsville, Mass., Division of White Consolidated Industries, Inc., Cleveland, Ohio.

EDUCATIONAL INSTITUTIONS

Fashion Institute of Technology, New York City.
Philadelphia College of Textiles and Science, Philadelphia, Pa.

FELT

American Felt Company, Inc., Glenville, Conn.

FLAX-LINEN

The Irish Linen Guild, 1270 Sixth Avenue, New York City.

FLOCKING

Cellusuede Products, Inc., Rockford, Ill.
Chemstrand Company, a Division of Monsanto Chemical Company, Inc., 350 Fifth Avenue, New York City.

FLOOR COVERINGS

Mohasco Industries, Inc., Amsterdam, N.Y.
Research Staff of the Carpet Institute, 350 Fifth Avenue, New York City.

GOVERNMENT AGENCIES

Farm Security Administration, Washington, D.C.
Federal Trade Commission, Washington, D.C.
United States Department of Agriculture, Washington, D.C.
United States Department of Commerce, Washington, D.C.

HAIR FIBERS

Strong Hewat & Company, Inc., North Adams, Mass.

KNITTING

Knitted Outerwear Association, 51 Madison Avenue, New York City.

LACE

Metropolitan Museum of Art, New York City.
Schiffli Institute, Union City, N.J.

LAUNDRY SCIENCE

Cohen Consulting Agency, 200 Park Avenue, New York City.

MANUFACTURED FIBERS AND FILAMENTS

Allied Chemical Corporation, Allied Chemical Tower, New York City.
American Cyanamid Company, 111 West 40th Street, New York City.
American Enka Corporation, Enka, N.C.
American Viscose Division of FMC Corporation, 1617 Pennsylvania Boulevard, Philadelphia, Pa.
Beaunit Fibers Division of Beaunit Corporation, 261 Madison Avenue, New York City.
Celanese Corporation of America, 522 Fifth Avenue, New York City.
Chemstrand Company of Monsanto Chemical Company, 350 Fifth Avenue, New York City.
Courtaulds North America, Inc., 104 West 40th Street, New York City.
The Dow Chemical Company, James River Division, Williamsburg, Va.
E. I. du Pont de Nemours & Co., Inc., Wilmington 98, Del.
Eastman Chemical Products, Inc., 260 Madison Avenue, New York City.
Fiber Industries, Inc., Shelby, N.C.
Hess, Goldsmith Company, Inc., Division of Burlington Industries, Inc., 1400 Broadway, New York City.
IRC Fiber Division of Midland-Ross Corporation, Union Commerce Building, Cleveland, Ohio.
New Bedford Rayon Division of Mohasco Industries, Inc., New Bedford, Mass.
Owens-Corning Fiberglas Corporation, 717 Fifth Avenue, New York City.
Union Carbide Corporation, 270 Park Avenue, New York City.
United States Rubber Company, Inc., 1230 Sixth Avenue, New York City.

LAMINATION

Reeves Bros. Inc., 1071 Sixth Avenue, New York City.

NONWOVEN FABRICS

Curlator Corp., East Rochester, N.Y
E. I. du Pont de Nemours & Co., Inc., Wilmington, Del.

PILE FABRICS

Baxter, Kelly & Faust, Inc., Philadelphia, Pa.
Crompton-Richmond Co., Inc., 111 West 40th Street, New York City.
Greenwood Mills, Inc., 111 West 40th St., New York City.

PUBLICATIONS

American Dyestuff Reporter, Howes Publishing Company, Inc., 44 East 23rd Street, New York City.
American Fabrics Magazine, quarterly, Doric Publishing Co., Inc., 24 East 38th St., New York City.
America's Textile Reporter, 286 Congress St., Boston, Mass.
Fairchild Publications, 7 East 12th St., New York City.
Knitted Outerwear Times, 51 Madison Avenue, New York City.
Modern Textiles Magazine, 303 Fifth Avenue, New York City.
Textile Industries Magazine, 1760 Peachtree Road, N.W., Atlanta 9, Georgia.
Textile Organon, Textile Economics Bureau, 10 East 40th St., New York City.
Textile World, McGraw-Hill Publishing Company, Inc., 330 West 42nd St., New York City.
John Wiley & Sons, Inc., 605 Third Ave., New York City.

SILK

George Elbogen & Co., Inc., 450 Fourth Ave., New York City.

TEXTILE ASSOCIATIONS

American Association of Textile Chemists and Colorists, Inc., Research Triangle Park, P.O. Box 886, Durham, N.C., and its publication, *American Dyestuff Reporter*, 44 East 23rd Street, New York City.

American Association for Textile Technology, Inc., c/o New York Board of Trade, 1 Liberty Street, New York City.

American Institute of Laundering, Inc., Joliet, Ill.

American Institute of Men's and Boys' Wear, 1290 Sixth Avenue, New York City.

American Society for Testing Materials, Inc., Philadelphia, Pa.

American Textile Merchants Institute, 1457 Broadway, New York City.

International Silk Association (USA), 185 Madison Ave., New York City.

Man-made Fiber Producers Association, 350 Fifth Ave., New York City.

National Institute of Drycleaning, Inc., Silver Spring, Md.

Textile Research Institute, Princeton, N.J.

The National Association of Wool Manufacturers, 386 Fourth Ave., New York City.

The National Cotton Council of America, Memphis, Tenn.

TEXTILE DICTIONARIES

Callaway Textile Dictionary, Callaway Mills, Inc., La Grange, Ga. (1947).

Dan River Mills Dictionary of Textile Terms, Dan River Mills, Inc., Danville, Va. (Nine editions, 1944–1964).

Modern Textile Dictionary, Duell, Sloan & Pearce, Inc., New York City (1955, 1957, 1963).

TEXTILE TESTING

Atlas Electric Devices Company, Inc., Chicago, Ill.

Bureau of Standards, R. H. Macy & Co., Inc., Herald Square, New York City.

Alfred Suter & Co., Inc., 200 Fifth Ave., New York City.

Mount Vernon Mills, Inc., Baltimore, Md.

United States Testing Co., Inc., 1415 Park Ave., Hoboken, N.J.

TUFTING

Singer-Cobble, Inc., Chattanooga, Tenn.

WEAVING

Crompton & Knowles Corporation, Worcester, Mass.

Draper Corp., Hopedale, Mass.

Philadelphia College of Textiles and Science, Philadelphia 44, Pa.

WOOLENS AND WORSTEDS

Deering-Milliken Company, Inc., 1045 Sixth Ave., New York City.

National Association of Wool Manufacturers, 386 Fourth Ave., New York City.

Strong Hewat & Co., Inc., North Adams, Mass.

Wool-Australian Government on behalf of The Wool Interests, Canberra, Australia.

Wool Bureau, Inc., 360 Lexington Ave., New York City.

TYPING: Margaret M. Linton and Marion L. O'Brien.

Why Make a Career in Textiles?

There are twenty-seven major industries in the United States—agriculture, airlines, apparel, automobiles, automobile suppliers, building trades, capital goods, chemicals, defense contractors, department stores, diversified industries, drugs, electrical, food processors, metals, natural gas, office equipment, oil and petroleum, paper and packaging, railroads, rubber, soap and toiletries, steel, textiles, tobacco, trucking, utilities. Other large industries include mail-order houses, variety stores, general merchandise, grocery, shoe, furniture, and auto variety stores.

The textile industry makes a very creditable showing among the foregoing. In overall size it ranks second; it is fourth in total manufacturing units; first in the total number of employees, directly and indirectly; second in dollar wages paid; and third, behind steel and food, in total value added to raw materials. At present, there are about six thousand mills or plants in this country, and 1.6 million men and women are employed in this industry. Annual wages paid employees amount to about 1.5 billion dollars a year. The number of motors used in textile plants is now close to one million, while installed horsepower is around four million, with many millions of dollars spent annually for machinery. And the amount expended for materials, supplies, containers, etc., is now around two billion dollars on an annual basis.

Less than 40 per cent of the textile mills account for over 90 per cent of the industry's employees. The thirty largest textile companies employ more than 325,000 persons. The twenty largest textile mills do 4.5 billion dollars' worth of business per annum. This is about 20 per cent of industry's total sales.

The three most important needs in our lives are food, shelter, and clothing, followed by transportation. The textiles industry happens to be one of our oldest industries; it is definitely fundamental and meets the great need and demand for clothing and apparel, both as a protection against the elements and in our social, political, and economic lives. As population increases, so will textiles increase; as standards of living increase, so will textiles increase. This industry will go forward to further heights and keep pace with greater buying power, more leisure time, increased travel, and more changes in wardrobes, especially with the correct attire, say, for skiing, golf, tennis, beachwear, resort wear, etc.

Americans are becoming more fashion-conscious, and today fashion and style are truly "big business." The wealthy, the upper-middle class, the lower-middle class, and even the less affluent are all fashion-conscious. The industry with its long history, and its great run of staple and novelty fabrics, is alive, dynamic, and ever changing to achieve greater heights. These factors especially are true since World War II with the advent of new fibers, new yarns, new fabrics, new finishes, new techniques, and new uses for fabrics in clothing and apparel, in the home, and in industry. Textiles keep pace with the advances in our modes of living today. Expanding markets in all phases of our daily lives should be obvious to the casual observer.

The field of textiles is highly competitive, and this has served the industry well in that textile companies of today have to be aware of all the various conditions with which they are faced. Up to this time, the industry has made a most creditable showing. Large and small companies are aware of the fact that management, labor, and business must integrate in all dealings if they are to survive. As a result of this the textile industry is today in a very healthy condition.

The running of a company, large or small, is a cooperative enterprise, and the industry learned this many years ago. There has to be teamwork and cooperation or the plant will have difficulty in surviving, especially so because of the intense competition among mills.

New blood furnished by younger people is necessary to any company in any field of endeavor. Time marches on, and changing conditions keep the industry constantly on the alert along progressive lines. It has been said that "there is something new in textiles every day." This dynamic industry has much to offer persons who become interested in it. Consider for a moment the many facets of textiles from which to carve out a really worth-while career—raw materials, yarn manufacture, designing and styling fabrics, fabric construction, fabric finishing; dyeing and printing of textiles, quality control, physical and chemical testing, new developments and new products; buying, selling, and merchandising; management, personnel directors, public relations, fashion coordinators, advertising, accountants, administrators, supervisors, et al.

The industry is growing constantly, new vistas are being created, and the larger companies are always offering splendid opportunities to new personnel, with excellent practical and theoretical programs. Smaller concerns offer fine opportunities for those individuals who have vision and perspective, and show leadership. Whether the company is large or small, the opportunity is always there for the person who knows his textiles as well as he knows himself. Chances for becoming a business partner are always in the offing. Textiles offer opportunities for those who have the yearning to, in time, go into business for themselves. It is safe to state that "no industry has more opportunities than does the great textile industry." Why not try to make it your career? Think it over well, discuss it with other people, and then come to your decision. If you decide to go into textiles you are not making a mistake—provided you, yourself, "have what it takes."

Some Thoughts on How to Appraise, Read, and Study a Textbook

1. First of all, examine the book casually, thumb through it and form a first impression of it; first impressions are often lasting in nature whether or not in time you find the book does have appeal for you.

2. Note the name of the publishing house, its status in the book trade, the name of the author, and the date of publication.

3. Read well the text on the book jacket to learn of the background of the author; note other books that he has written. Does the author seem to have sufficient background to do the type of book in question?

4. Read the introduction carefully to learn of the underlying philosophy and psychology of the author and obtain a good idea of the comprehensiveness of the book.

5. Then examine the book in detail and form an opinion as to whether you deem the book worthy of your attention and interest.

6. Examine the index very carefully, a most important part in any good book. Note the cross-references, the breakdown of subterms under the major captions and general over-view of this part of the book. The index is very important to a beginning student in any subject, technical or otherwise.

7. The following high points should be noted by the reader: the units or chapters in the one or more parts of the book, the sequence of contents, its setup and continuity, any pictures, illustrations, half-tones, flowsheets included, and company credits given by the author.

8. Check the front material of the book for the list of contributors and companies that have assisted the author in preparing the book.

9. Does the book have an appendix, a most important part of any worthwhile textbook? Also check the bibliography with regard to source material.

10. After a close examination of the book satisfy yourself that the author has written in a clear, lucid, understandable manner. Does he know his subject? Does the book seem easy to read to you?

11. Is the book factual and does it contain a goodly amount of general, as well as specific, information? Any good book should appeal to a serious student and should serve your felt need to definitely learn much from its use. Or is the book one of the so-called "scissors-and-paste" type done by an author who is not well versed in the field or by one trying to write a book outside his or her major field or background?

12. Is the book set up with a self-study and self-testing program which will aid the student in digesting the text? Psychologists are agreed that we retain 10 per cent of what we read, 20 per cent of what we hear, 30 per cent of what we see, but 90 per cent of what we write or underline on paper.

Thus a textbook should also serve you as a workbook. Underline all the items that seem to hold special interest for you. Underlining will aid you in your retention of the basic or core material so essential for examination purposes. Use a red, blue, or ordinary lead pencil for underlining; ink is not suggested.

13. Compare the book at hand with comparable books done in the field. Analyze the books from all angles and then form your opinion as to which one will best serve your purpose. Often textbooks, chiefly semitechnical and technical books, are done by an author with a rather meager background. There has never been a book written and printed that is perfect in all details. Many books, written by authors not too well trained in the particular subject, contain misstatements, errors, faulty setup and sequence, etc.

14. Any well-written textbook should serve the beginning student through to the semitechnical and full-fledged technologist. Any book is an investment to you. Make certain that the investment of your money in a book is for one written by an author who is definitely aware of and fully competent in all the details and ramifications necessary to produce a really worth-while book. It is also suggested that students consult with their teachers or professors on any book that they intend to study.

Conversion Tables of Units and Factors

Length

1 meter = 100 centimeters
1 centimeter = 10 millimeters
1 millimeter = 1000 microns
1 yard = 3 feet
1 foot = 12 inches

1 meter = 1.094 yards
1 meter = 39.37 inches
1 centimeter = 0.3937 inch
1 micron = 0.000039 inch

1 yard = 0.9144 meter
1 yard = 91.44 centimeters
1 inch = 2.54 centimeters
1 inch = 25.4 millimeters
1 inch = 25,400 microns

Weight

1 kilogram = 1000 grams
1 gram = 1000 milligrams
1 mole = 1000 millimoles

1 pound = 16 ounces
1 ounce = 437.5 grains
1 pound = 7000 grains

1 kilogram = 2.2046 pounds
1 kilogram = 35.274 ounces (avoir.)
1 gram = 0.03527 ounce (avoir.)

1 pound = 0.4536 kilogram
1 pound = 453.6 grams
1 ounce = 28.35 grams

Volume

1 liter = 1000 milliliters
1 liter = 1000.027 cubic centimeters
1 gallon = 4 quarts
1 quart = 32 ounces
1 gallon = 231 cubic inches

1 liter = 0.2642 gallon
1 liter = 1.057 quarts
1 liter = 33.815 ounces
1 gallon = 3.785 liters
1 quart = 0.946 liter
1 ounce = 29.573 milliliters
1 U.S. gallon = 0.8327 British gallon
1 British gallon = 1.201 U.S. gallons
1 cubic inch = 16.387 cubic centimeters

Area

1 square meter = 10,000 square centimeters
1 square yard = 1296 square inches
1 square foot = 144 square inches

1 square centimeter = 0.155 square inch
1 square inch = 6.452 square centimeters

TO CONVERT	MULTIPLY BY	TO CONVERT	MULTIPLY BY
meters to feet	3.3	grains to ounces	0.04
feet to meters	0.3	grains to grams	0.065
cubic feet to gallons	7.5	grams to grains	15.43
gallons to cubic feet	0.13	yards to meters	0.9
cubic feet to liters	28.33	meters to yards	1.1
liters to cubic feet	0.035	quarts to liters	0.95
inches to centimeters	2.5	liters to quarts	1.06
centimeters to inches	0.4	gallons to liters	3.78
ounces to grams	28.35	liters to gallons	0.26

Testing Program

This book contains a program for self-testing and group testing; practically every unit contains a testing program. In addition, comprehensive testing in textiles may be found as follows:

APPLIED BASIC TEXTILES

Every man who rises above the common level has received two educations; the first from his teachers; the second, more personal and more important, from himself.

—Edward Gibbon (1737–1794)

Introduction

This text has been constructed in all details to meet the needs of:

1. Teachers.
2. Home economists.
3. Training schools in department stores and textile plants.
4. Students of buying, selling, marketing, and merchandising.
5. Students who pursue textile and apparel construction courses.
6. Others with an interest in the textile, apparel, and allied industries—specific, general, or applied.

There are many specific techniques in studying or teaching textiles. The wide scope of the industry lends itself to many interpretations: abstract, concrete, logical, psychological, the project and job-analysis approach. Studying or teaching the techniques in textiles extends from the vocational high school to graduate work in textile colleges. It is the hope of the author that this book may serve as a source of information to the student, the teacher, or the individual who is engaged in some phase of the textile or apparel industries.

The text should be of interest to those who work in fields allied with textiles—dressmaking, millinery, tailoring, garment machine operating, marketing, consumer education, and distributor education.

The subject matter has been compiled with special emphasis on the integration of factual information on textiles for the students in the wearing apparel and marketing fields. The finished textile fabric is the raw material for the person engaged in the foregoing fields. The book aims to bring about a clear understanding of the making of textile fabrics, how they differ, and the end use of these materials. It has often been stated that "the fabric's the thing." Without knowledge and understanding of the fabric at hand, the terminal use of the goods may be misdirected during the making of garment or accessory.

The facts and the principles embodied in the book are sufficient in scope to train students in the secondary schools and higher institutions of learning for the following types of work:

1. The various phases of the textile, apparel, and marketing industries.
2. Wholesale and retail buying and selling of fabrics and apparel.
3. Homemaking and interior decoration.

The material and text are the result of many years of teaching, experimentation, and research by the author in the Fashion Industries High School, The Fashion Institute of Technology, Hunter College of the City of New York, and New York University.

The contents are organized around a division into the four ways in which textiles differ—namely, in raw material, construction, color, and finish. The working properties and characteristics of textile fibers and the processing of the raw materials into textiles, ending with the finished fabric and its use in industry, are covered in detail.

The majority of topics covered include a self-study and self-testing program that should be of interest to the reader. The identification of fabrics, as well as the physical and chemical testing of textiles, including spot and stain removal and the care of clothing, form a part of the text. This new edition has been thoroughly revised in all details.

THE IMPORTANCE, AIMS, AND OBJECTIVES OF GENERAL AND APPLIED TEXTILES

Importance of Textiles

1. To enable students to purchase in an intelligent manner inner- and outerwear, home furnishings, decorative materials and all other textiles from any of the animal, vegetable, mineral, or manmade fibers.
2. To care for clothing and apparel in an intelligent way.
3. To clean clothing correctly in order to preserve its life and usefulness.
4. To become acquainted with the properties and characteristics of textile materials.
5. To acquaint the student with possible fields of employment—worker, buyer, seller, clerk, converter, designer, stylist, advertising, and color work in textiles.

Aims and Objectives

1. To develop an appreciation for textiles, in its many branches, that will be worthwhile.
2. To develop within the student the need for textile knowledge as it pertains to clothing in the all-important cycle of the material factors in life—food, shelter, clothing, transportation, fuel, tools, accessories, and adornments.
3. To develop an artistic appreciation of environment of the things about us.
4. To develop an appreciation of truth, authority, and honesty in textile materials, the contents, and qualities.
5. To train in the scientific methods of textiles.
6. To develop the powers of observation, inquiry, and inspection.
7. To develop an appreciation of fashion, style, vogue, demand, and conservativeness in our dress, our home, and social qualities.
8. To present specific ways in which the science of general and applied textiles is used in the trade.
9. To develop the proper integration of textiles in everyday life.

FUNDAMENTALS IN STUDYING TEXTILES

The following should be of some help to textile students in laying a foundation for the study of the subject:

1. **The Eight Necessary Material Things in Life**

   a) Food
   b) Shelter
   c) Clothing
   d) Transportation
   e) Fuel
   f) Tools
   g) Accessories
   h) Adornments

2. **The Textile Cycle—From Raw Material to Consumption**

   a) Raw material—wool, cotton, flax, silk, rayon, etc.
   b) Manufacturing—yarn to gray-goods cloth from the looms or frames.
   c) Converting and finishing of cloth—from gray goods to fabric.
   d) Innerwear and outerwear fabric or garment manufacture.
   e) Buying and selling of textiles.

f) Distribution of textiles to the public.

g) Consumption by the public. This includes the economic disposal of consumed textiles, the reworking of cloth to obtain shoddy, paper stock, secondhand clothing, rag rugs, and "export fiber."

3. The Ten "M's" of Textiles

a) Men
b) Material
c) Machinery
d) Money
e) Mill Engineering

f) Management and Methods
g) Manipulation
h) Millwrighting
i) Marketing
j) Merchandising

4. The Periods of Textile Manufacture

a) Family System: to about 1100 A.D.
b) Guild System: 1100 to 1750
c) Domestic System: 1750 to 1850
d) Factory System: 1850 to the present time
e) The Manmade Fiber Era: began about 1900 and now has major proportions
f) Automation: 1950 to the present time

5. Clothing Expenditure

a) 70 per cent for Outer Clothing
b) 20 per cent for Inner Clothing
c) 5 per cent for Accessories
d) 5 per cent for Care and Repair of Clothing

RELATED SUBJECTS IN STUDYING TEXTILES

Philosophy of Textiles

This is a study and knowledge of the principles that cause, control or explain facts and events which pertain to textiles in all of its branches.

Psychology of Textiles

This is the science that treats of the working of the human mind in textiles, fashion and style, vogue, supply and demand, fabrics, apparel, design, symmetry, quality, texture, finish, and so forth.

Economics of Textiles

The study of textiles as they actually are—poor, fair, good or excellent in the many properties and characteristics peculiar to the hundreds of types of cloth. This includes a knowledge of the many uses of textiles in the industrial world.

Ethics of Textiles

This is the study of textiles as they should be. Many textile materials, because of the raw stocks used in manipulation, are not what they should be. An unsuspecting public is often fooled or misled when buying some fabrics or garments. The fine finish of a cloth does not imply that the material is always of high quality.

INSTINCT AND LEARNING IN STUDYING TEXTILES

There are certain factors in the history of education and psychology which may be used, by the careful student, to broaden the knowledge and scope of textile learning and growth. Many of the basic elements of learning may be applied to textiles, in whole or in part.

Instincts As to Purpose Applied to the Values of Textile Learning

a) Self-preservation — The use of clothing and apparel as a covering.

b) Race-preservation — Clothing of many types, national costumes.

c) Instinct to live — Clothing is a necessity here.

d) Mating instinct or instinct to marry — Textiles play an important part here; the special materials essential to small or large weddings and functions call for color, grace, beauty, form, design, vogue, and style.

e) Instincts derived from European court clothes — This instinct, while somewhat apart from the first four, is felt when it is considered that "court clothes" down through the ages have exerted much influence—church vestments, gowns, uniforms, national apparel, pageant fabrics.

The Dicta of Herbert Spencer Applied to the Values of Textile Education

a) Self-preservation — Textiles and clothing are one of the eight necessities of material life.

b) Necessities of life — Clothing as a covering for the body is essential; textiles in the home, office, etc.

c) Rearing and discipline of the family — Textiles and clothing are decided assets in this instance.

d) Training of the social and political relationships — A place for textiles must be found here.

e) Worthy use of leisure time — A study of textiles in its far-reaching branches: design, history, fashion and style, color theory, materials, merchandising, consumption, economics, and so forth.

The Laws of Learning As Applied to Textile Knowledge—The Stimulus-Bond-Response Theory

READINESS: When a bond is ready to something (the circuit) and the act gives SATISFACTION—seeing a green dress may arouse the desire to possess it, or seeing a green dress on a prominent actress may stir the desire for possession.

When the bond is ready and does not act because it gives ANNOYANCE—you do not like the green dress.

The law of readiness presents the stimulus in order to evoke a response—satisfying or annoying. From this:

1. The individual is more apt to buy the things which he has been stimulated to desire.
2. The individual often acquires that information which he is ready to receive or recognize.
3. The condition of readiness is most likely to result in the response of satisfaction or annoyance.

ASSOCIATION

1. When associated with certain places, persons or things, the green dress may become more desirable.
2. When associated with last year's fashions, the green dress becomes less desirable.

EXERCISE: Known also as the LAW OF FREQUENCY, PRACTICE, USE AND DISUSE, REPETITION. The more a given response is linked with a certain situation, the more likely it is to be made to that situation. Negatively, by DISUSE: when a modifiable connection is not made use of over a certain length of time.

1. What we like will satisfy. You may buy the green dress.
2. What we do not like is annoying. You may not buy the green dress.

We may become accustomed to buying new clothes more often if the practice is encouraged and exercised. We learn to wear those materials, colors, and styles which are most often admired on us by others.

We are not likely to buy at stores with which we are not familiar; we buy at stores where we are well received and satisfied.

EFFECT: Satisfying results strengthen a bond and dissatisfaction weakens a bond. The law of effect governs all learning.

If you are finally satisfied, you will buy the green dress.

If you are not satisfied, you will not buy the green dress if there is something about it that you do not like.

A pleasant experience with green cloth may lead to further use of it.

SUMMARY

1. *Readiness:* Comes through the senses.
2. *Exercise:* The action and reaction by the nervous system, the brain, and spinal column action.
3. *Effect:* The motor activity which results from the sensory and nerve action; the final acceptance or rejection, satisfaction or annoyance.

Three Subsidiary Laws of Learning, Applied to Textiles and Apparel

These subordinate laws are linked with the three laws of learning—Readiness, Exercise, and Effect—and may be applied to more or less specific instances when examining, analyzing, and making purchases of some particular article.

MULTIPLE RESPONSE OR VARIED REACTION: An example of this would be the examination and possible analyzing of a fabric or item of apparel whereby close study would reveal several of the characteristics of the article. Varied reaction, for the time being until a decision is reached, would be the study, pro and con, of the properties and characteristics of the item in question. For example, one might select a cotton broadcloth instead of comparable fabrics such as poplin, repp, oxford, or madras, after thorough appraisal. One might select a suiting of tweed rather than a homespun, cheviot, or shetland when the mind is satisfied that this tweed is the better purchase when all things have been considered.

MIND SET OR ATTITUDE: This is the psychological reaction of the mind in finally accepting or rejecting a material or article of apparel. Many things must be considered in this phase before making a decision. Ordinarily these factors, consciously or unconsciously, are considered: the season of the year, the occasions for use of the article, the weight of the fabric or item of apparel, the construction of the goods, the color, and the finish on the fabric.

PARTIAL ACTIVITY: Application of this is when a person does not evince too much interest in the cloth or apparel item. The article just does not appeal to the prospective purchaser. Partial activity becomes full activity if the individual finds, after some study, that it does have appeal and suits his particular needs; or he may reject it altogether because it does not have any appeal.

Laws of Association As Applied to Textiles and Apparel

CONTIGUITY: An example of this law would be the determination as to how a fabric or item of apparel compares with more or less closely allied materials or attire. The basis of this law is that the prospective buyer has received satisfaction and good performance from comparable prior purchases. He must decide, from past experience, as to nearness or approximate nearness the article at hand has with his previous purchases. Although he may have never worn a chambray shirting, he might choose it instead of other shirtings he has worn and which have satisfied him in the past, such as broadcloth, oxford, madras, repp, all of which are contiguous to the chambray shirting.

SUCCESSION: Applied to textiles it may mean that the individual always buys the same type of shirt, sports jacket, topcoat, overcoat, socks, etc. Past satisfaction from good performance and service cause him to continuously "buy the same thing," when making his purchases.

A person may have his suits always made in the same manner and style, irrespective of the prevailing fashion or trend at the time of his new purchase. For example, he may always insist on double stitching in his suit, along with patch pockets, loop belt tunnels, and no vents in the coat.

SIMILARITY: An example of this could be the manner in which a man attires himself year after year, say, in the cut of his suit, set-in sleeves in coatings, partiality to certain colors and patterns, a three-button model, and the continuous use of a tweed, homespun, cheviot, shetland, gabardine, "Dacron" and worsted tropical suiting or sharkskin, etc. This similarity tends to give him peace of mind, a psychological reaction.

ASSIMILATION OR ANALOGY: The capability of the individual to inspect, analyze, and then determine if the fabric meets his own requirements. Apperception or past experience is important in accepting or rejecting the article at hand, along with imagination and reasoning power.

ASSOCIATIVE SHIFTING: This occurs when the person is in a quandary to accept or reject the item. His mind, in the beginning, is not definitely made up as to the exact thing he may finally purchase. He "shifts" from one to another, mulling over in his mind the better and poorer characteristics of all the articles under examination. Induction and deduction are used until he arrives at a decision, pro or con. For example, after due consideration, a lady may finally select a blouse that is asymmetric instead of a rather large selection that included draped, overblouse, peasant, peplum, rhumba, stovepipe, tailored, tunic, or tuck-in.

CONTRAST: The opposite of similarity when applied to textiles and apparel. Prevailing fashion and style, vogue and demand, along with the so-called "new colors and new patterns" are the determining factors which cause the person to constantly go along with the trends of the times in his choice of fabrics and attire, from season to season and year to year.

FREQUENCY: This psychological trait is between contrast and similarity in the choice of fabrics and modes of attire. A person may wear the same type of shirt, suit, coat, dress, blouse, etc., for quite some time and then more or less change his or her plan of attire in cut, fit, trim, color, fabric weight, type of fabric, etc. The individual is also governed by the season of the year, the occasions for its use, the weave in the pattern, and the finish of the goods.

RECENCY: Its application demonstrates that the person is one who always seems to be dressed in the latest fashion, style, whim, or vogue. He is the type "who must be dressed in the latest fashion or style," regardless of whether the item is suitable to his individualism. The results show that the article may be conservative, in good taste, poor taste, and may, at times, run to the outlandish or bizarre type of costume. Women are much more "afflicted with recency" than men because women's wear styles are constantly changing, whereas for almost a century there has been no appreciable change in men's wear.

INTENSITY: This is really the underlying force, since intensity, quality, and determination of the individual cause him to purchase and wear what he deems is best for him irrespective of the prevailing fashion or style. He is the type of person who knows what he wants when he wants it, and is determined to make his purchases on his own and without the "aid" of selling personnel in a store or a tailor who may try to change his ideas of what the person actually desires in a fabric or item of apparel.

The Seven Cardinal Principles of Education As Applied to Textiles

1. HEALTH: Proper clothing, correct garment weight, good fit and body contact to clothes have an effect on health. Proper types of cloths and clothes should be worn at the correct times of the year. Sickness may be caused by too little or too much clothing.

2. **FUNDAMENTAL PROCESSES:** English, reading, writing, and arithmetic are essential to enhance a knowledge of textiles and textile cost systems. A development through a study and analysis of fibers and fabrics is also important.

3. **HOME MEMBERSHIP:** Textiles find a place in the home as well as in art, literature, the social studies, and household arts. Textiles play an important part in making the home cheerful, inviting, and beautiful.

4. **CITIZENSHIP:** Through the social studies, the part that textiles have played in the past in world commerce and industry may be gleaned—the Industrial Revolution, King Cotton, the Mechanical Cotton Picker, the Rise of Manmade Textiles. These and many other important contributions to the world by textiles have served to facilitate modes of living and national betterment, as well as aspiring and unified groups.

5. **VOCATION:** A definite trade or occupation. A goodly percentage of people make their living by services rendered directly or indirectly in the textile field, from raw cotton or wool all the way to the department store and consumer. Textiles show a great range of possible positions to the youth of the land.

6. **LEISURE:** Art, literature, and science may be studied for an appreciation of textiles in its many branches.

7. **ETHICAL PHASE:** The full, true values of textiles—a background to know what cloths should be, the best qualities, etc.

Textile Education Involves Four Adjustments

1. **MENTAL:** The proper attitude toward textiles and textile education which can be developed by analysis.

2. **ECONOMIC:** The economic adjustment, through education, which makes for better and intelligent buying.

3. **PHYSICAL:** An adjustment which makes for appropriate use of the materials and fabrics we use.

4. **SOCIAL:** The chance for individual expression and integration through knowledge of fashion and style, line, color, design, and silhouette. This phase also makes for better integration in society, since the social phase of life is so important in the life of the adult.

Methods Used to Learn about Textiles

1. **IMITATION:** Knowledge may be acquired through imitation. Much is learned by observing and imitating what the better-dressed members of society wear. It has been said that people are slaves of fashion and style, both of which appear in cycles from time to time. What the wealthy, leisure class decrees shall be worn is adopted and utilized by the middle and poor classes.

2. **TRIAL AND ERROR:** This results from experiences with actual fabrics, colors, textures, fashions, and styles. You may buy a suit which, in time, seems to lose its appeal because of blemishes, shabbiness, poor colors, and so forth. The article is soon discarded.

3. **TRIAL AND SUCCESS:** You purchase a textile article. It is not quite up to your requirements, measurements, or standards. Alterations make the fabric or garment suitable for your usage and wear. You will not discard it as it now meets with your approval.

4. **OBSERVATION:** You observe the effects of various fabrics on others by thoughtful analysis; you consider, through observation, the principles and elements of design in relation to the specific, individual type—short, tall, stout, thin, blonde, brunette; in relation to the materials as sheer, soft, transparent, nubby, shiny, stiff, napped, and so on. Then you decide upon your choice. A study is made of the theories of color, color harmony, similarity, or contrasts with complexion, stature, and so on. You

adjust yourself, through observation, to the praise and criticism of friends in the circles in which you move. Advertising does much in attracting you to this or that garment. If satisfied with your resultant purchase, you will look for similar good points in future purchases.

Factors in the Learning Process As Applied to Textile Education

1. REPETITION: Many people have learned to adhere to "a style all their own," year in and year out; and are still well dressed.

2. MEMORIZING: A textile article strikes your fancy. You "memorize" it to the extent that you may purchase it, or the nearest thing to it, the next time you need a similar article. Colors are often memorized.

3. COLLATERAL SKILL: All typists are not secretaries; all cloth is not of the best quality, but it is still cloth. Fortunately, the results of myriad experiments in textiles, and in the advertising field, have shown the increased efficiency of the learning process as applied to textiles. There is collateral skill in knowing how and what to buy in textiles. It is learned. The cut, fit, and trim, the color or shade, the draping qualities, price, accessories, and the psychological effect of the clothes on you do or do not appeal to your friends. These essential requisites may or may not appeal to you. The general make-up of the human form caused by the clothes that you wear does, however, to a great degree, admit of your being accepted or rejected in certain circles. One must learn to dress for the occasion. This embodies collateral skill.

TEXTILES IN RELATION TO OTHER SUBJECTS IN THE CURRICULUM

Biology

There is a close link between biology and textiles. This connection embraces the following: the reflective powers of fibers, principles of transmission, refraction and diffusion of light, the life cycle of the silkworm, study of merino sheep industry, study of the clothes-moth—its habits and methods of extermination, biological conditions which make for the best grades of cotton, wool, and silk, etc.

Chemistry

This subject is akin to textiles when a study is made of the elements which constitute the wool fiber—carbon, hydrogen, nitrogen, oxygen, and sulphur. The chemical phases of textile testing on raw stock, yarn, and cloth are important in the trade today. Much knowledge of chemistry is essential in spot and stain removal. Chemistry is particularly close to textiles with the advent and rise of the so-called "new manmade" fibers which are creating such favorable comment in the market—nylon, "Dacron," Spandex, protein fibers from the soy bean, and zein from corn meal; imitation wool, strong acetate, abraded filament yarn, discontinuous filament yarn, modified viscose staple, acetate staple, strong fibro, high-strength viscose, rayon staple, etc.

Chemistry in textiles has produced pre-shrinking methods for textile materials, permanent finishes, crease resistants, water repellents, air-conditioned materials, sanitized fabrics, etc.

Chemistry is important in that the effects of chemicals on textiles continue to lead to new successes in the field of textiles—the effects of commercial products on fabrics by naphtha soap, oxydol, peroxide, soda, acids and alkalies, and so on.

Physics

This subject aids much in textile testing of materials for tensile strength, wearing quality, finish, flexibility, abrasiveness, bursting strength of knitted fabrics, durability, etc. Physical conditions have a great influence on textile materials, and much research is carried on in this phase of the industry.

History

This subject is easily linked to textiles. Examples of this connection could be: the Industrial Revolution, textiles of the American Indian, history of textiles in the church, development of the cotton, silk, wool, and rayon industries, the sheep industry in America, and so forth.

Economics

The economic status of cotton as a power in the United States, and as a world factor in internationalization, is important because it is considered a "front-page" news item. Other examples of the connection could be: the stages in textile economy from the use of skins, primitive weaving, Indian designs, church-vestment cloths, and homespun fabrics to the highly specialized phases of the textile industry today. The history of textiles, down through the ages, has had much to do with our problems in the social, political, and economic life of today. Other economic subjects that have attracted attention are: southern wealth and northern profit, which led to the War Between the States over the question of cotton and slavery; the development of world trade through the development of machinery, mass production, and uniform sizes; men, material, and money; progressive assembly; job specialization, etc.

Geography

A consideration of the world centers which produce wool, cotton, silk, flax, and other textile fibers will cover the point in question.

Politics

For example, the part played by cotton in connection with the N.R.A. of 1932, at the time of the Civil War, and the maneuvering among nations in a political way to obtain raw materials with which to make synthetic materials as well as to use cotton as a basis for explosives—gun cotton. Cotton has had much to do in this struggle between the "haves and the have-nots."

Religion

The use of textiles down through the ages for utilitarian purposes, appeal to the senses, and in decoration is known to all

Sociology

From the sociological standpoint, textiles are very important in our daily lives. The effect of textiles in some of their forms in fashion and style, vogue, demand, sociological background, and appearance adds much to the human body, to groups of people, and to large areas of people. From this develops the psychological effect as well. Cloths do have an important part to play in the sociological backgrounds of men and nations.

Textiles and courses in textiles, from the standpoint of art and science in textiles, must be considered from the utilitarian angle. Some of these angles are form, outline, silhouette, design, color, pattern, drapability, clinginess, and so on. Taking these points into consideration, it may be said that the aim or purpose of a course in textiles determines the content of information.

Students or teachers studying textiles are naturally practical, and, in some instances, motor-minded with regard to assimilation of technical knowledge. Before they are able to grasp or understand the subject in a positive way, they must have had experience, observation, and a background which will form an apperceptive basis. This is obtained consciously and unconsciously. Special interest groups, with high intelligence quotients, will be interested in a study of one or more of the foregoing subjects briefly discussed. Experience, observation, and background must be directed along the proper channels in order to obtain the fullest understanding of the term "textiles," not only in the broad meaning of the term but in its allied branches—the woolen and worsted trade, the cotton industry, the silk business, the rayon and other synthetic industries, converting of cloth, buying and selling, merchandising, textile economics, and so on.

The clever teacher should be able to integrate what is learned in textiles with her own subject. This is often helpful in keeping interest and attention. The use of objective materials also aids in motivation and development of a lesson, since the "seeing or feeling" of an object does much to arouse the proper stimulus. All of these things can be done in a scientific manner by proper integration of textiles with the particular subject or topic at hand.

FIELDS OF ART WHICH REQUIRE SOME KNOWLEDGE OF TEXTILES

Window Display and Advertising

A knowledge of textiles is essential for interior and exterior display cases and serves as a background for proper balance and symmetry. Clothing, underwear, haberdashery, furniture, hats, and similar displays may be shown to best advantage if the display artist is able to sense the value of appeal to the buying public.

Costume Design

The elements of drapability, form, durability, suitability to the occasion, climate, personality, individuality, machine production, coloring possibilities and age differences are necessary to the artist in this field. A thorough knowledge of the capabilities of materials is very helpful.

Stage Setting and Stage Costume Designing

A study and knowledge of what materials may be employed to give the proper effects are valuable, particularly when the effects desired are used to represent the more expensive fabrics. Durability and ease of manipulation must be considered in obtaining the desired results.

Interior Decoration

The importance of textiles to the interior decorator is obvious. A knowledge of materials will help to obtain proper effects, characteristics, uses, and possible color schemes.

Industrial Designing

Textiles will help to supply the knowledge necessary in the utilitarian phases of materials with relation to friction, tensile strength, texture, waterproofing, fireproofing, heat, dirt, moisture, weather conditions, and so forth. Knowledge of fabrics with their relation to static electricity, strength of fiber or weave construction is often a valuable asset to the industrial designer.

Textile Designing

This broad field includes dress materials, decorative fabrics, useful materials in the home, innerwear, outerwear, textile furnishings in the store, office, school, public buildings, theater, hospital, amusement area, and so forth. Knowledge of attaining design through texture contrasts is often vital to the designer. Textile knowledge will aid considerably to attain a pleasing design that is appropriate in line, color, tone, and texture, and appropriate to the forms upon which the materials are to be placed.

Craft Work and Leisure Time

For individualists, hobbyists, and specialists in textile art, a knowledge of raw material, construction, color and finish, design and texture is helpful.

Textile Study

By studying textiles, the individual is able to express himself, in an adroit manner, with regard to the choice of color, line, tone, texture, balance, fashion, style, and vogue.

TEACHING OF TEXTILES

The Content and Methods

In schools where textile subjects are taught, certain foundations and principles must be adhered to in order to obtain a functional curriculum. Methods must be applied by the instructor of textiles in the lower grades, junior high school, high school, junior college and college, as well as in institutions which teach textiles as a major subject. The latter would include Philadelphia College of Textiles and Science, Lowell Technological Institute, Southeastern Technological Institute of Massachusetts, Clemson College, Georgia Institute of Technology, North Carolina State College, Texas Technological College, Alabama Polytechnical Institute (Auburn), Fashion Institute.

The content of a course in General or Applied Textiles consists of the principles which underlie:

1. The raw material—animal, vegetable, mineral, manmade.
2. The construction of materials—woven, knitted, felt, braided, or nonwoven.
3. The color—dyeing, printing, or methods used to secure a good whiteness in the material.
4. The finish—the type of finish applied to the fabric—harsh, smooth, lustrous, dull, napped, mercerized, embossed, soft, etc.

The applications of the principles involved are emphasized in terms of the student's major interest, as expressed in the course. For example, a course in General Textiles for students in the vocational and manufacturing courses should stress the properties that adapt them for the processes in making textiles. They might include preparation of the raw material, carding, spinning, weaving, and finishing of woven cloth. Close study would have to be made of the machines involved and the treatment of the stock in the various machines with the ultimate goal of a finished product or material constantly kept in mind.

In marketing, merchandising, buying and selling courses, emphasis should be placed on the psychology of selling and in the descriptive properties of the fibers, the structure, the color, and the finish.

Textiles must be considered from the economic law of supply and demand, distribution and consumption. From these phases of textile study, the student will build a splendid vocabulary for the description of items that have to be used as selling points.

In a similar manner, the artistic value of fibers, luster, reflection in color, actual coloring, the design or motif, and the finished article are emphasized.

In clothing, the characteristics of the fibers in warmth, absorption, elasticity, strength, etc., must be given serious consideration. In like manner, much thought must be given to the structure for underwear, linings, overcoatings, dressgoods of all types. The finish, weight, design, drapability, clinginess, washability, launderability, cut, fit, and trim all tend to bring out the style and artistic value of the fabric. Consequently, the teacher must know where and when to instill properly the motivation which leads to interest and attention of a positive nature.

Some of the outstanding methods of teaching the subject of textiles are herewith given:

LOGICAL METHOD: This method is found in textbooks and begins with the fiber or raw material and ends with the woven cloth. It is ideal for textile classes in mill areas where the cloth is made, and in the large city where the cloth is finished into a garment or fabric ready for sale over the counter or from the rack in the department store, clothing store, haberdashery, women's shop, and so forth.

Evening schools in these centers enable students to acquire a knowledge of textiles. The students are employed in the industry in some form or other in the daytime and can further their education at night schools.

This method prepares students for the mill, cutting-up house, the department store, mill office in the mill center or large city, and for buying, selling, merchandising, styling, etc. The student comes in contact with the things taught at night in his business in the daytime. Dressmakers, salesmen, garment machine operators, and residence buyers profit much from this method of instruction.

The method is not well adapted to junior high school or even high school pupils unless a thoroughly experienced teacher handles the class, a teacher who is a graduate of a textile school of college grade and who has had practical experience over a span of years.

PSYCHOLOGICAL METHOD: This method begins with the cloth or fabric. In reality, it is working backwards, but, by doing so, it is better adapted for students in junior high school, high school, the junior college, and even in colleges which give courses in applied textiles. The appeal to the human being by "seeing and feeling" the goods is essential to cause the proper interest and attention by the pupils. They are not interested to any great degree in the mechanical operations necessary to make the cloth; they want to know what the cloth is capable of doing and what can be done with it.

Emphasis must be placed on the finished material, the design, the properties and characteristics of the goods, the style, and other pertinent factors. By doing this, only the basic elementals as to raw material and machine operations to make the cloth must be known. The teacher who uses this method must make the adjustment of tasks integrate with the capacities of the class.

LECTURE METHOD: This method is ideal for the mature type of student of college grade. It is also used in overcrowded classes in high schools, since it is the only means that may be used, in addition to devices and experiments by the teacher, which give the completed picture to the lesson. The method is also used in evening schools, as most of the students seem to have some more-or-less-common background.

This method imparts information quickly, and for pupils with a common background much time is saved in covering the lessons in a course which is usually fairly well crowded with material.

The lecture method is good for students with an apperceptive background. It seems to suffice for "the people in the trade."

By itself, the lecture method is not truly effective. A good teacher should not use more than 25 or 30 per cent of the time in lecturing. The rest of the allotted time should be spent on samples, concrete problems, trends in the trade, questions in forum, proper use of blueprints, if they are used, sketches, models, exhibits, etc. The method is ideal for stimulus toward questions of a provocative nature. The lecturer must know his subject thoroughly; otherwise, class interest and attention will diminish rapidly.

DEVELOPMENT METHOD: This is supplemented by the laboratory or objective teaching methods, and it is the most effective method in teaching textiles. It begins with the experiences of the students, and new knowledge is added to what the students already know. The teacher should ask questions to arouse interest and attention in the beginning of the lesson; questions which should be terse, to the point, plausible, thought-provoking and rather intricate. Answers should be summarized on the blackboard, and a running outline made as the class progresses in the recitation. This method, under the guidance of the teacher as to questions, will encourage the students, who, with their past experience, reasoning power, and observation, will learn much. The use of samples and other aids will add much to the lesson.

THE UNIT SYSTEM OF TEACHING: This method is very good for an entire course of study, since it gives a detailed routine whereby each topic, method or operation is taught separately. It has some advantages in technical classes where detail is essential. Examples of this method could be the study of the card used in carding wool, worsted or cotton. The study of the parts of the machine, the condition of the stock as it enters the machine at the feeding-in end, what happens to it in its course through the frame, and the condition of the fibers as they emerge from the delivery end of the machine, all constitute units in this method of procedure. The purpose, aim, and function of the machine would then be understood by the class, which, of necessity, should be small. The unit system is used in classes in carding, weaving, spinning, finishing, knitting, lace making, etc.

Another use of the method would be a consideration of a group of machines in textile manipulation; the machines would be taken in sequence. For example, in studying cotton, the machines in order would be:

1. Opener Picker Machines
2. The Carding Machine
3. The Sliver Lapper
4. The Ribbon Lapper
5. The Comber
6. The Drawing Frame
7. The Slubber Frame
8. The Intermediate Frame
9. The Roving or Jack Frame
10. The Mule Spinning Frame and the Ring Spinning Frame

This system is ideal for textile high schools and colleges which have a textile department, and for textile schools of collegiate grade.

THE SPIRAL METHOD OF TEACHING: As the name implies, this method causes a grouping of the necessary operations together. It can be used for an entire course of study where much ground knowledge must be taught in a limited time. The spiral method is good for summarizing in preparation for an examination since it is used to stress the high points in the course of study. This method is employed chiefly for mature students with a solid background and understanding. Otherwise, this method does not seem to be effective with other groups because interest and attention will wane and much of the effort on the part of the teacher is lost.

THE OBJECTIVE METHOD OF TEACHING: This ideal method is used by the good teacher who has an awareness of the things about her. The use of objects, crutches, charts, exhibits, and samples aid materially to enlighten the class. The method should be resorted to by a teacher in order to insure a successful termination to a course in textiles.

Most people are visual-minded; seeing something makes a deeper and longer impression and will tend to hold the attention and interest of the class. Concrete work is of vital importance. In this way, the individuality, characteristics, and personality of the teacher are brought to the fore. The ability of the teacher to use the proper underlying psychology and correct philosophy is brought out, and the aims in the textile education can be discerned. The proper use of these "spokes in the wheel of textile education" lead to the "hub of the wheel"—the student who is in school to learn, and who, after all, is very often a keen judge of human nature, his teacher, and the things about him.

The objective method may be employed to good advantage in all textile subjects and subjects allied with it. The motor-minded, technical, vocational student will profit greatly from this method, as well as the academic-minded pupil. Some of the courses in which this method gives much satisfaction to student and teacher are:

1. General Textiles
2. Applied Textiles
3. Cloth Analysis
4. Weave Construction
5. Spinning
6. Weaving
7. Knitting
8. Textile Testing
9. Clothing and Style
10. Jacquard Design
11. Identification of Fabrics
12. Textile Chemistry
13. Color Analysis
14. Economics of Textiles and Clothing
15. Home Economics
16. Millinery
17. Dressmaking
18. Costume Draping Design
19. Hand-decorated Fabrics
20. Art Courses
21. In courses for Buying and Selling, Marketing, Merchandising, Window Display, and Advertising

THE PROJECT METHOD: This is used when the pupil is the center of activity and interest. This interest and activity evolves from the student's attitudes. This method develops the latent and innate abilities that the student may have. Much responsibility rests upon the pupil, and the completion of a project, for the most part, places the teacher in an advisory capacity, and somewhat in the background.

A project is a complete unit of purposeful experience; any episode taken from life may be developed into a project.

A problem is any situation that challenges the mind and invites solution. As long as knowledge and skill are adequate, no problem arises. Problems arise only when there is a conflict of experience.

The project method of instruction extends over a short or long time, dependent on the assignment. The academic abilities, as well as the motor-minded abilities, are called upon by the student in completing the assignment and work. The use of the hands must be linked with the use of the mind, and the laws of learning must be followed to the letter.

In textile, vocational, technical, and trade schools, the method is ideal to complete assignments. The structure of the method may be gleaned from the following arrangement of items:

A *mimeographed sheet* upon which the directions for the projects in the course are listed is used. This would include the length of the course in terms, and the rules concerning the written reports.

General instructions would follow the above introduction.

The details of the report would be listed next.

The time allotment would follow.

A *project sheet* is next in order. This sheet is mimeographed. The following items would appear on this sheet, which has to be read and understood by the student:

The title of the project.

The objective of the project.

The prerequisites necessary to do the work.

Apparatus needed in fulfillment of the project.

Procedure to be followed in doing the assignment.

Results to be obtained and completed by the student follow in order.

Name of the student, class, period, term, room, date, etc., would appear at the bottom of the form.

From experience, this method has proved to be one of the best in methods of instruction for content, development, and responsibility. The students, in this procedure, retain what they have built up and completed. The method appeals to pupils as it gives them an opportunity to develop the proper type of self-assertion and inculcates confidence in them.

Only the experienced teacher, with a broad, general, and sympathetic background, can manipulate this method of teaching to the satisfaction of the students.

CONTRASTS BETWEEN THE PROJECT AND THE JOB SHEET: The project or instruction sheet is defined by Rodgers and Furney of the New York State Department of Education as "one unit of a body of organized teaching material that has been prepared for the student to use under conditions that will insure the greatest amount of directed individual instruction."

The project sheet is specifically for the purpose of supplementing the efforts of the teacher, thereby enabling him to render greater assistance to the individual members of the class. It may be stated that they are used as specific assignments of educational problems that require solution or completion by the student.

The project sheet is a substitute for the lesson plan of the teacher. It is an organized lesson which may be used by the student as a supplement to the demonstration. The instruction sheet is to the student what the teacher's lesson plan is to the teacher. It gives the pupil a definite idea of what is to be accomplished and how it is to be done.

The project or instruction sheet is *not* a factory job sheet. The school or factory job sheet contains usually a short sketch, together with a few specific directions regarding the accomplishment of the job.

The project sheet is an educational factor in the training of the learner.

The job sheet takes for granted a skilled workman rather than a beginner or learner.

On the other hand, the project or instruction sheet may accustom the pupil to the practice of the mill or factory, even if the school cannot approach shop conditions.

There is a cultural background absorbed in the school that is not obtainable in the mill, plant, or factory.

JOB ANALYSIS: This method of teaching has never been accepted as being for the student. It is accepted and encouraged for the use of the teacher in preparing:

1. Course Outline
2. Lesson Plan
3. Project sheets which fit and dovetail with the Course Outline and the Lesson Plan

The student who is unfamiliar with a trade would construe the trade or job analysis as more or less of an incoherent collection of words and instructions. The use of the form is, in reality, up to the discretion of the teacher, and it should include all essential data.

Incidentally, the old method of teaching was through the medium of the job sheet. It is well to remember that the job sheet, and not the job analysis, is being supplanted by the project or instruction sheet. The project method of teaching makes for objective, developmental teaching.

CONTRASTS BETWEEN THE PROBLEM AND THE PROJECT: In the latter, genuine, lifelike situations arise. The enterprise calls for diversified activities and may involve problems. The project cannot be carried out within confining bounds. The project erases departmental bounds, so to speak, of school subjects.

There are six types of projects:

1. Manual	2. Community	3. Excursion
4. Intellectual	5. Aesthetic	6. Athletic

TYPES OF PROBLEMS:	TYPES OF PROJECTS:
1. Selective recall	1. Situation is presented to the class by teacher or pupil.
2. Comparison	2. Agreement is reached to undertake the project and see that it is carried to a successful conclusion.
3. Cause and effect	3. To be analyzed and set up into activities arranged in the order to be undertaken.
4. Statement and explanation	4. Activities are taken up one by one.
5. Classification	5. In the light of experience, the original intent may be changed or the plan may be modified.
6. Opinions as to justice, adequacy, approval, relationship	6. As a project nears completion, the teacher and the class assume a critical attitude toward it. To gauge the degree of success, list the errors, indicate improved procedure for attaining the goal.

A problem may be supposititious; usually a task for a particular period; usually limited to the subject matter of the school; and it may involve little correlation.

THE DALTON PLAN APPLIED TO TEXTILES

Contract One
Week One

PROBLEM ONE   Cloth construction.   Credit 1 & 2

   a) What is meant by cloth construction?
   b) What is weaving? How is woven cloth constructed?
   c) What is knitting? How is a knitted cloth made?
   d) What is felt? What are the characteristics of a felt cloth?
   e) What is braiding or plaiting? How is a shoelace made, and
       what are the characteristics of it?   Credit 3 & 4

Week Two

PROBLEM ONE Spinning and weaving of yarn.   **Credit 1 & 2**
    a) What are the differences between spinning and weaving?

PROBLEM TWO Mount samples of the four standard types of fabrics
on mounting sheet. Place name of each under re-
spective samples.   **Credit 3 & 4**

PROBLEM THREE Woven designs in cloth.   **Credit 5 & 6**
    a) Plain weave
    b) Right-hand twill weave
    c) Left-hand twill weave
    d) Satin weave, warp-effect
    e) Satin weave, filling-effect
    f) Basket weave

PROBLEM FOUR
    a) Paste constructions on mounting sheet for weaves.   **Credit 7 & 8**

Week Three

PROBLEM ONE Determination of warp and filling in woven cloth.   **Credit 1 & 2**
    a) Read mimeographed notes on warp and filling. Take
threads from each system in woven sample and determine
which threads are warp and which are filling. Mount the
respective threads on mounting sheet. Label samples. Pick
out needle and its use demonstrated.   **Credit 3 & 4**
    b) Answer questions on warp and filling noted on the mimeo-
graphed sheet. Use of pick glass demonstrated by teacher.

Week Four

PROBLEM ONE Texture in woven cloth.
    a) Count number of threads per inch, each way, in the three
samples. Use pick glass for this.   **Credit 1 & 2**
    b) Define the term texture, in woven cloth.   **Credit 3**
    c) What is meant by the following terms:
      1. Warp, warp thread, end?
      2. Filling, filling thread, pick?
      3. Define interlacing of threads.   **Credit 4 & 5**
      4. Define the term "ply," after taking sample threads from
each system of yarn.
      5. How many ply in the warp threads? In filling threads?
      6. What is meant by a "square cloth"?
      7. Which cloth, of the three samples, is the best and
strongest—(1) 88 x 80? (2) 76 x 76? (3) 72 x 66?   **Credit 6 to 10, incl.**

NAME OF STUDENT . . . . DATE . . . .   ACCEPTED . . . . .
                                                                   REJECTED . . . . .
                                                                    TEACHER . . . . . .

PART ONE

TABLE OF CONTENTS

Part 1—Unit 1

TOPIC: INTRODUCTION TO THE STUDY OF TEXTILES

The eight material things of life that afford us a living and comfort are food, shelter, clothing, transportation, fuel, tools, accessories, and adornments. All these affect us directly or indirectly. The so-called ten "M's" of industry are men, material, machinery, money, mill engineering, management and methods, manipula-

[1]

tion, millwrighting, marketing, and merchandising. All workers in any industry fit into one or more of these categories. Obviously, there would not be any apparel industry, with marketing and merchandising of apparel, if there were not a textile industry. These latter four industries or businesses are dependent upon one another with textiles as the feeder for the other three.

If one were asked to state what is used to make clothing, there might be answers such as fabrics, goods, cloth, materials, thread, laces, fibers from animals, furs, plants, and so on. These responses in a general way might be considered correct. Therefore, an all-inclusive definition of textiles might be as follows:

TEXTILES: the product of textile work, i.e., manipulation from the raw condition, through to the finished state, of any of the kingdoms of fibers employed by man for this purpose. They include practically all of the materials used in the making of clothing, inner and outer, for the human race all over the world. Textiles also include carpets, rugs, wall coverings, other decorative fabrics. Industrial fabrics made from textiles include canvas, duck, webbing, automobile tire fabric, conveyor belting, filter cloths, and items or articles for airplanes, farm equipment, insulation, publishers' supplies, and a host of other uses.

The word "textiles" comes from the Greek *Textores*, a special or separate class of citizens who carded wool, spun it into yarn, wove the cloth, and then dyed it with various colors.

In quality, textiles range from the very cheapest types of cotton cloths such as cheesecloth, tobacco cloth, muslins, and print cloths to very expensive brocades, brocatelles, damasks, and other Jacquard fabrics done in silk. The types, kinds, and varieties of fabrics make an almost endless chain from the lowest to the highest in texture, finish, weight, price, width, sheerness, or compactness.

In this country the word "textiles" should be pronounced "textills"; in England it is pronounced "textyles."

Courses in textiles are divided into four main groups:
1. Course of study for those who expect to enter into the manufacturing of some form of textiles.
2. Course of study for those who expect to enter the buying, selling, marketing, or merchandising fields.
3. Course of study for those who intend to use textiles in the manufacture of other products.
4. Course of study for those who use textiles as consumers.

The consumer, home economist, and needleworker should have a basic knowledge of textiles for the following purposes:
1. To know and analyze their own needs and to determine purchasing values.
2. To recognize qualities and differences in textile fabrics.
3. To determine the suitability of the different kinds of fabrics for various uses and occasions, in the home as well as for clothing.
4. To know something of cost variation and the comparative values of fabrics.
5. To learn of the properties and characteristics of fabrics in which one might become interested.
6. To learn the standards of good taste in clothing and in home furnishings.
7. To learn how to care for textile fabrics and garments; to know about spot and stain removal from clothing.

The study of textiles for the needleworker goes beyond that of the home economist and the consumer. The sewing machine was invented in 1846; Elias Howe, and his brother-in-law, Nathaniel Banks, a noted Union general in the Civil War, brought out their machine after working on it in Palmer, Hudson, and Boston, Massachusetts. Unbeknown to them, Isaac Singer brought out his machine in the same year. Howe's efforts in this country soon lapsed into oblivion, but the Singer Sewing Machine Company is known today to everyone.

Most schoolgirls know something of a sewing machine. They know that a Number 70 (or 70s) thread is finer than a Number 40 (or 40s) thread in diameter; the higher the number, the finer will be the particular thread. They also know that there are two tensions on a sewing machine—upper and lower.

It is important for those who handle textile fabrics and those who can sew to know as much as possible of the material with which they may be working. The more one knows about fabrics, the more valuable this information will be.

When working with a fabric on a machine, the following points should be kept in mind:

1. TENSION: This will vary with the various fabrics being used.
2. SIZE OF THE NEEDLE: Fine needles are used on fine fabrics, etc.
3. SIZE OF THE THREAD: The finer the fabric being used, the finer will be the thread used.
4. NUMBER OF STITCHES PER INCH: Closer stitches are used on the finer or sheerer fabrics.

Thus, basically, a good sound knowledge of fabrics will make it easier to manipulate cloth into a garment. And this knowledge can be helpful to the thirty-five million women in this country who do home sewing today, in addition to the thousands employed in the needle trades throughout the nation.

Part 1—Unit 2

TOPIC: THE TEXTILE FIBER KINGDOMS

NATURAL FIBERS—ANIMAL

Alpaca	Guanaco	Noil *	Spun silk *
Angora goat hair	Hog hair	Persian cashmere	Suri
Camel hair	Huarizo	Rabbit hair	Vicuna
Cashmere	Llama	Reprocessed wool *	Wool
Cow hair	Mohair	Reused wool *	Worsted
Extract wool *	Misti	Shoddy *	Worsted top
Fur	Mungo *	Silk	

NATURAL FIBERS—VEGETABLE

Abaca	Hemp	Kapok	Ramie
Coir	Henequin	Kenaf	Sisal
Cotton	Istle	Manila hemp	Straw
Flax linen	Jute	Pineapple fiber	Sunn

MINERAL FIBERS (do not burn)

Asbestos	Lurex †	Metlon †	Spun glass
Glass fibers	Metallic	Slag wool	Tinsel

MODIFIED TEXTILE FIBERS

Cyanoethylated cotton	Mercerized cotton	Acetate and rayon staple
Immunized cotton	Non-shrinkable wool	Plexon

* Classed as reclaimed animal fiber for use in textiles.
† Made from aluminum.

[3]

MANUFACTURED OR MANMADE FIBERS

Generic Names and Definitions of Manufactured Fibers: Rule 7 of the Rules and Regulations under the Textile Fiber Products Identification Act lists the generic names and definitions as decreed by the Federal Trade Commission on June 3, 1959, effective March 3, 1960. The purpose of the Act is to "protect producers and consumers against misbranding and false advertising of the fiber content of textile fiber products, and for other purposes." In addition to the definitions, some representative trade names have been added in the respective categories. Under the Rules the generic term is required to be used in conjunction with the fiber name in labeling and advertising textile products.

1. RAYON: A manufactured fiber composed of regenerated cellulose, as well as additional manufactured fibers composed of regenerated cellulose in which the substitutes have replaced not more than 15 per cent of the hydrogens of the hydroxyl groups.

   Rayon—Trade Names

   Briglo, Perlglo, Polynosic, Suprenka, Zantrel of American Enka Corporation;
   Avicolor, Avicron, Avlin, Avril, Avlon, Rayflex, Super L of American Viscose Division—FMC Corporation.
   Fortisan, Fortisan 36 (modified rayon) of Celanese Corporation of America.
   Coloray, Fibro of Courtaulds North America, Inc.
   Dul-tone, Dy-lok, Nupron, Spun-Black, Tyron of Industrial Rayon Company, Division of Midland-Ross Company.
   Newbray, New-Dull, New-Low of New Bedford Rayon Division, Mohasco Industries, Inc.

2. ACETATE AND TRIACETATE: A manufactured fiber in which the fiber-forming substance is cellulose acetate. Where not less than 92 per cent of the hydroxyl groups are acetylated, the term "triacetate" may be used as a generic description of the fiber.

   Acetate—Trade Names

   Celacloud, Celacrimp, Celafil, Celaloft, Celaperm, Celarandom, Celatow, Celatress, Celaweb, Arnel (triacetate fiber) of Celanese Corporation of America.
   Acele of E. I. du Pont de Nemours & Co., Inc.
   Chromspun, Estron, Loftura of Eastman Chemical Products, Inc.

3. ACRYLIC: A manufactured fiber in which the fiber-forming substance is any long-chain synthetic polymer composed of at least 85 per cent by weight of acrylonitrile units ($-CH_2-CH-$).
   $$\underset{CN}{\overset{|}{}}$$

   Acrylic—Trade Names

   A-Acrilan, of Chemstrand Company.
   Creslan, of American Cyanamid Company, Inc.
   "Orlon," of E. I. du Pont de Nemours & Co.
   Zefran, of The Dow Chemical Company.

4. MODACRYLIC: A modified fiber in which the fiber-forming substance is any long-chain synthetic polymer composed of less than 85 per cent but at least 25 per cent by weight of acrylonitrile units ($-CH_2-CH-$).
   $$\underset{CN}{\overset{|}{}}$$

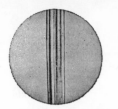

ACETATE FILAMENT

Longitudinal   Cross Section

CUPRAMMONIUM RAYON

Longitudinal   Cross Section

DACRON

Longitudinal   Cross Section

DYNEL

Longitudinal   Cross Section

NYLON

Longitudinal   Cross Section

"ORLON"
Continuous Filament

Longitudinal   Cross Section

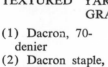

TEXTURED YARN (PHOTOMICRO- GRAPHS)

(1) Dacron, 70-denier
(2) Dacron staple, 96-denier

Right: Filament acetate yarn; textured yarn from it

ACRILAN

Longitudinal   Cross Section

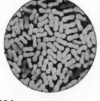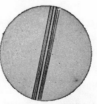

VINYON

Longitudinal   Cross Section   [5]

VISCOSE RAYON

Longitudinal   Cross Section

Modacrylic—Trade Names

Dynel, of Fabrics and Fibers Division, Union Carbide Chemical Company, Union Carbide Corporation.

Verel, of Tennessee Eastman Company, Division of Eastman Chemical Products, Inc.

5. NYLON: A manufactured fiber in which the fiber-forming substance is any long-chain synthetic polyamide having recurring amide groups ($-C-NH-$) as an integral part of the polymer chain.

$$\overset{|}{\underset{O}{}}$$

Nylon—Trade Names

C-Chemstrand nylon (Type 66), Chemstrand Corporation.

Du Pont nylon (Type 66), E. I. du Pont de Nemours & Co.

Nylon (Type 6), Beaunit Mills, Inc., Fibers Division.

Caprolan nylon (Type 6), Allied Chemical & Dye Corporation.

Enka nylon (Type 6), American Enka Corporation.

Firestone nylon (Type 6), Firestone Synthetic Fibers Company, Division of the Firestone Tire & Rubber Company.

IRC nylon (Type 6), IRC Division, Midland Ross Corporation.

National nylon (Type 6), the National Plastic Products Company.

Poliafil nylon (Type 6), Poliafil, Inc.

Lus-Trus nylon (Type 6), Southern Lus-Trus Corporation.

6. NYTRIL: A manufactured fiber containing at least 85 per cent of a long-chain polymer of vinylidene dinitrile ($-CH_2-C(CN)_2-$) where the vinylidene dinitrile content is not less than every other unit in the polymer chain.

Nytril—Trade Name

Darvan (Travis, outside U.S.A.), of Celanese Corporation of America.

7. POLYESTER: A manufactured fiber in which the fiber-forming substance is any long-chain synthetic polymer composed of at least 85 per cent by weight of an ester of dihydric alcohol and terephthalic acid ($p-HOOC-C_6H_4-COOH-$).

Polyester—Trade Names

"Dacron," of E. I. du Pont de Nemours & Co.

Kodel, of Eastman Chemical Products, Inc.

Fortrel, of Fiber Industries, Inc.

Vycron, of Beaunit Corporation.

8. VINYON: A manufactured fiber in which the fiber-forming substance is any long-chain synthetic polymer composed of at least 50 per cent by weight of vinyl chloride units ($CH_2-CHCl-$).

Vinyon—Trade Name

Avisco Vinyon (Vinyon HH), of American Viscose Company, Division of FMC Corporation.

9. VINAL: A manufactured fiber in which the fiber-forming substance is any long-chain synthetic polymer composed of at least 50 per cent by weight of vinyl alcohol units ($-CH_2-CHOH-$) and in which the total of the vinyl alcohol units and any one or more of the various acetal units is at least 85 per cent by weight of the fiber.

Vinal—Trade Name

Vinal, of Air Reduction Company.

10. SARAN: A manufactured fiber in which the fiber-forming substance is any long-chain synthetic polymer composed of at least 80 per cent by weight of vinylidene chloride units ($-CH_2-CCl_2-$).

Saran—Trade Names

Dawbarn, of Dawbarn Brothers, Division of W. R. Grace & Co., Inc.
Velon, of Firestone Plastics Company.
Boltaflex, of Bolta Products Division, The General Tire & Rubber Company.
Saranspun, of The National Plastic Products Company.
Lus-Trus, of Southern Lus-Trus Corporation.
Rovana, of Textile Fibers Department, The Dow Chemical Company.

11. OLEFIN: A manufactured fiber in which the fiber-forming substance is any long-chain synthetic polymer composed of at least 85 per cent by weight of ethylene, propylene, or other olefin units.

Olefin—Trade Names

DLP, of Dawbarn Brothers, Division of W. R. Grace & Co., Inc.
Velon PS, Velon LP, of Firestone Plastics Company.
Boltathene, of Bolta Products Division, The General Tire & Rubber Company.
Wynene, of The National Plastic Products Company.
Polyarns, of Polyarns, Inc.
Pex, of Polymers, Inc.
Reevon, of Alamo Industries, Inc.
Royalene, of Textile Division, United States Rubber Company.

12. GLASS FIBER: A manufactured fiber in which the fiber-forming substance is glass.

Glass Fiber—Trade Names

Fiberglas, of Owens-Corning-Fiberglas Corporation.
Garan, Vitron, LOF, of Johns-Manville Fiber Glass, Inc.
Unifab, Uniformat, Unirove, of Ferro Corporation, Fiber Glass Division.
Pittsburgh, PPG, of Pittsburgh Plate Glass Company, Fiber Glass Division.
Modiglass, of Modiglass Fibers, Inc.

NOTE: Glass Fiber Group: Specially prepared glass marbles are melted in an electric furnace. Melted glass is then extruded through orifices to form continuous filaments, and then drawn to the desired size.

13. RUBBER: A manufactured fiber in which the fiber-forming substance is comprised of natural or synthetic rubber.

Rubber Fiber—Trade Names

Lastex and Laton, elastic yarns; Lactron, extruded rubber thread; and Revere, cut-rubber thread, and a rubber tension tape, all of United States Rubber Company.
Contro or Rolled Latex, of Firestone Tire & Rubber Company.
Darleen, cut-rubber yarn, of Darlington Fabrics Corporation.
Filatex, flat-oval-type rubber yarn, of Filatex Corporation.

14. METALLIC: A manufactured fiber composed of metal, plastic-coated metal, metal-coated plastic, or a core completely covered by metal.

Metallic Fiber—Trade Names

Alistran, of Multitex Products Corporation.
Chromeflex, of Metal Film Company.
Fairtex Type 206, Fairtex with Mylar, of Fairtex Corporation.
Lame, Lame with Mylar, of Standard Yarn Mills.

Lurex, Lurex MM, Lurex MF, Lurex MM-CR, of The Dow Chemical Company.
Malora, Malora with Mylar, of Malina Company.
Metallic Cellophane, of Malina Company.
Metlon Metallic Yarn, Metlon with Mylar, of Metlon Corporation.
Mylar, of E. I. du Pont de Nemours & Co.
Nylco, of Nylco Products Company.
Ultra-Vat, of Metlon Corporation.

NOTE: Metallic Group: Metallic yarns are now made with Mylar ("Dacron") film as well as with acetate film. Mylar metallic yarns withstand higher temperatures and more rugged finishing and laundering than the acetate-type yarns.

15. SPANDEX: A manufactured fiber in which the fiber-forming substance is composed of a long-chain polymer of at least 85 per cent of a segmented polyurethane.
"Lycra," of E. I. du Pont de Nemours & Co.
Vyrene, synthetic elastomer of United States Rubber Company.

16. AZLON: A manufactured fiber in which the fiber-forming substance is composed of any regenerated naturally occurring proteins. Not made in the United States at the present time; formerly known as "semi-synthetic" fiber.

Alginate, from seaweed, England.
Casein fiber, from casein, Belgium.
Enkasa, from casein, Holland.

Fibrolane, from casein, England.
Lanital, from casein, Belgium.
Merinova, from skim milk, Italy.

DESIRABLE QUALITIES IN TEXTILE FIBERS

1. COHESION: The manner in which fibers adhere, cling, or "hang together" in a uniform manner, as in the case of a worsted yarn, or in a more or less conglomerate mass, as observed in woolen yarn.

2. ELASTICITY: The ability of textile fibers to "bounce back" when released from tension or stretch, as noted in woolen yarns.

3. ELONGATION: The ability of fibers in yarns or in fabrics "to go in the direction of the weave." Also means the increase in length from a tensile force: an example of this, the fibers in yarns as they appear in "baggy trousers" on a rainy day, or the sagginess of some woolen fabrics of low texture or pick count.

4. CRIMP: The waves, seen or unseen, in textile fibers; noted especially in wool fibers in which there are "waves within waves," known as serrations, chiefly not observed by the naked eye.

5. FIBER LENGTH: Evenness of length, uniformity, and the staple length of a group of fibers; all these properties are very important in fabric development.

6. FINENESS: May be measured in microns, centimeters, parts of an inch, or in inches. Fiber diameter is very important in the determination of the end use or terminal use of the fibers at hand. Fineness does much to determine the properties and characteristics of the particular fibers, whether to be worked alone or in conjunction with other fibers in blends, mixtures, combinations, etc.

7. FLEXIBILITY: The ability of fibers to bend or flex easily; highly desirable property in many instances.

8. MOISTURE CONTENT: The regain is what the fiber is able to take up or actually regain in moisture after being brought to the bone-dry condition. Moisture content will vary with the several types of fibers used in the textile industry today.

9. POROSITY OR CAPILLARITY: The capacity of fibers to absorb moisture; varies with the several types of fibers in use today.

10. TENSILE STRENGTH: The ability of fibers, yarns, or fabrics to withstand or resist tension; tested by breaking or rupture of yarn or fabric on "tensile-strength machines" or "breaking machines." Strength tests on yards and fabrics are very important in fabric structures today.

11. RESILIENCY: The ability of yarns or fabrics to "bounce back" when crushed in the palm of the hand or otherwise.

12. TWIST SPINNABILITY: The ease with which fibers may be drawn, drafted, doubled, redoubled, attenuated, twisted, and wound from some type of spinning method onto a device for taking care of the newly spun yarn.

TEXTILE YARNS

The word "yarn" is a generic term for an assemblage of fibers or filaments, either natural or manmade, whether twisted together to form a continuous strand which can be used in weaving, knitting, braiding, or plaiting, or otherwise made into a textile material. Spun yarn is the product of the spinning frame characterized by a continuous, evenly distributed, coherent arrangement of any type of fibers of varying or similar staple length, the relative positions of which are maintained by the introduction of a definite lateral twist to produce strength or coherence in the final operation.

Notable exception to the above would be the woolen-type yarn. Here the fibers are distributed at nearly right angles with relation to the continuous length of the yarn. An exception to even spinning would be the addition of noiled fibers to the base stock. Noils do not lend themselves to being properly drawn; in consequence, a rough-texture yarn, desirable for tweeds and shantungs, is produced.

To produce spun yarns, the raw stock must be put through preparatory machinery for even distribution and blending, after which there is carding or combing to achieve parallel fiber distribution; then several attenuating or drawing machine operations follow, ending with the spinning. Yarn in production is called a lap, sliver, and roving, in that order, depending on the type of machine used. Yarns are definitely sized or numbered, based on the number of standard yardage hanks contained in one pound.

Filament yarn is made from various continuous filaments, such as silk and manmade filaments—viscose, acetate, nylon, "Orlon," "Dacron," etc.

TESTING

1. Name five animal fibers; five vegetable fibers; three mineral fibers.
2. Name five reclaimed animal fibers.
3. Name two regenerated textile fibers.
4. List three cellulose-derivative fibers; three protein fibers.

Matching Questions: Place your choice from the second column of words or terms on the blank line provided at the left, if there is a definite connection or association:

1. _____ Nylon		1. Cellulose triacetate
2. _____ Mercerized cotton		2. Modacrylic
3. _____ "Orlon"		3. Polyamide fiber
4. _____ Merinova		4. Acrylic fiber
5. _____ "Dacron"		5. Polyester fiber
6. _____ Arnel		6. Lurex
7. _____ Fortisan		7. Polyacrylic fiber
8. _____ Dynel, Verel		8. Protein fiber
9. _____ Acrilan		9. Mineral fiber
10. _____ Slag wool		10. Saponified acetate fiber
		11. Modified textile fiber

TOPIC: Identification of Textile Fibers by Burning, and by Chemical Tests

Burning tests, as applied to textile fibers or fabrics, are not always valid, but they do have a place in the study and identification of fibers. Some fibers, such as cotton, linen, kapok, viscose rayon, cuprammonium rayon, burn in an identical manner. Some fibers burn rapidly, others not very long before the flame expires; other fibers have the tendency to melt when a flame is applied, as in the case of acetate and nylon. Several fibers give off drippings that can be very painful if allowed to drop onto the body. Safety in handling flame is very important. If a fabric is being burned for identification, yarns from each system should be used in the test. The fringes on fabric can also be burned for identification. Yarns from bobbins, cops, skeins, or tubes can be used for testing. Fabrics to be tested should be about three inches square.

REFERENCE CHART FOR IDENTIFICATION OF SOME MAJOR TEXTILE FIBERS BY BURNING

FIBER	BURNING FLAME	ODOR	RESIDUE
Cotton—Vegetable	Rapid, luminous; yellow glow, afterglow; smokes	Burning paper; pungent, choking	Small, fine, gray, ashen-like, light; charred outline
Linen—Vegetable	Same as cotton, but not quite so rapid in burning	Comparable with cotton	Same as cotton but more of burned residue outline
Mercerized cotton—Vegetable	Like cotton	Like cotton	Like cotton
Wool—Animal	Slowly; sputters; expires quickly	Burning hair or burning feathers	Brittle, bulbular; shiny; hollow beads, easily crushed
Worsted—Animal	Like wool, usually more rapid burning; often depends on yarn and fabric construction	Same as wool	Same as wool
Silk—Animal	Slow, yellowish; sputters; globules	Burning hair or feathers	Brittle bead, easily crushed
Weighted silk—Animal	No flame at all; blackens; smoky	Burning hair, not so sharp as silk; metallic	Skeleton of char outline; flecks
Viscose—Manmade	Like cotton, very rapid burning	Compares with cotton	Compares with cotton
Cuprammonium—Manmade	Same as viscose rayon	Same as viscose; papery odor	Ash formation, easily removed or flecked
Acetate—Cellulose derivative, manmade	Rapid, small sparks; melts, may drip	Acidic, like vinegar	Hard, shiny black bead, not easily crushable
Arnel—Cellulose triacetate	Yellow; rapid; much sputtering	Burning sugar with "resin" odor noted	Hard, dark, gritty; rather easily crushed or flecked

FIBER	BURNING FLAME	ODOR	RESIDUE
Acrilan—Acrylic co-polymer—acrylic	About like wool; supports combustion and melts; smokes	Very little; black smoke may be indistinguishable	Black, gummy, brittle in parts
"Dacron"—Polyester type	Melts before burning; slowly, does not flash	Very black smoke given off	Hard black mass, formerly molten
Dynel—Staple of co-polymer of acrylonitrile and vinyl chloride; modacrylic	Does not support combustion, melts	Very sharp acrid odor, may cause choking	May have some unburned fiber; balance is black, leathery-type mass, brittleness noted
Nylon—Amide—coal, air, and water	No flame; melts, gives off drippings	Like celery	Very hard black bead; sticks before hardening to anything
"Orlon"—Polyacrylonitrile—acrylic	Melts and burns; supports combustion	Like broiled fish	Hard and on order of charcoal
Vinyon—from vinyl resin—vinyon	Melts but no flame	Paraffinlike odor	Hard, dark bead
Fiberglas—glass fibers, from marbles	Does not burn	Does not burn	Does not burn

REFERENCE CHART FOR IDENTIFICATION OF SOME MAJOR TEXTILE FIBERS BY CHEMICAL MEANS

FIBER	IDENTIFICATION
Cotton—Vegetable	Dissolves in 80 per cent cold sulfuric acid bath. Becomes yellow in caustic soda. Bleached by hypochlorites.
Wool—Animal	Completely destroyed by 5 per cent caustic soda solution at the boil. Destroyed by hot sulfuric acid.
Viscose Rayon—Cellulose	Insoluble in acetone (regenerated in manufacture). Swells but does not dissolve in ammoniacal copper solution.
Cuprammonium Rayon—Cellulose	Insoluble in acetone; dissolves in ammoniacal copper solution. Dilute sulfuric acid gives a blue color accompanied by swelling of the fiber.
Acetate—Cellulose derivative	Strong alkalies saponify acetate into a regenerated cellulose which reacts to dyes like viscose rayon. Attacked by strong oxidizing agents. Soluble in acetone, phenol, glacial acetic acid, and other solvents.
Acrilan—Acrylic of copolymer of 85 per cent acrylonitrile and 15 per cent vinyl chloride	Resistant to all acids at room temperatures, and to alkalies. Dissolves in nitric acid, naphtha; insolvent in acetone, benzene, carbon tetrachloride.
Arnel—Staple fiber from cellulose triacetate	Unaffected by mineral spirits or perchloroethylene. Soluble in methylene chloride alcohol mixture. Acetone and chloroform cause Arnel to swell.
"Dacron"—Polyester	Not soluble in acetone or concentrated formic acid. Soluble in hot metacresol. Very resistant to acids; disintegrates in 96 per cent sulfuric acid. Not soluble in acetone or concentrated formic acid. Disintegrates in boiling alkalies; moderate resistance to cold alkalies.

FIBER	IDENTIFICATION
Darvan or Travis—Nytril fiber	Good resistance to acids, better than "Dacron" and nylon and not so good as Dynel and "Orlon." Good resistance to alkalies, not affected by dry-cleaning solvents.
Dynel—Copolymer or vinyl chloride and acrylonitrile—modacrylic	Highly resistant to acids, alkalies, solvents. Immersed in concentrated sulfuric acid without effect. Acetone and other ketones soften the fiber.
Creslan—Acrylic fiber	Good resistance to acids, fair to good to alkalies. Not dissolved or softened by alcohols, esters, ketones, or ethers. Dyes a dark blue with Calco Stain #2 for Identification (American Cyanamid Co.).
Fortisan—Regenerated cellulose—(Rayon)	Reacts similar to cellulose as in case of viscose, cuprammonium, cotton.
Fortisan-36—highly oriented regenerated cellulose—(Rayon)	In general, the same as in case of viscose, cuprammonium, cotton. Yellows around 350° F.
Glass Fibers—specially prepared glass marbles are melted; solution flows through orifices and is extruded into strands or filaments	Do not burn. Attacked only by hydrochloric and hot phosphoric acids. Attacked by hot solutions of weak acids, and cold solutions of strong alkalies. Generally good resistance to other chemicals.
Nylon—Polyamide Nylon 6 and polyamide caprolactam Nylon 66	Nylon 66—insoluble in acetone or boiling caustic soda solution. Soluble in formic acid and xylenol. Nylon 6 —insoluble in acetone or boiling caustic soda solution. Soluble in concentrated formic acid and xylenol, and dissolves slowly in chloral hydrate.
"Orlon"—Acrylic polyacrylonitrile polymer dissolved in dimethylformamide—acrylic	Not affected by glacial acetic acid, chloroform, acetone, or 88 per cent formic acid. Not harmed by common solvents, greases, oils, and some acid salts.
Polyethylene—Polymerization of ethylene under heat and pressure	Monofilament is insoluble in organic solvents at room temperatures; soluble in toluene, xylene, carbon tetrachloride, at 160° F. Very resistant to acids, alkalies, and other chemicals. Floats on water.
Saran—(Velon) Vinyl derivative of vinylidene chloride resin	Insoluble in acetone. Dissolved in dioxan at elevated temperatures. Good resistance to most acids but only fair resistance to concentrated sulfuric acid. Unaffected by most alkalies.
Verel—Modified acrylonitrile fiber—modacrylic	Excellent resistance to chemicals. Partially dissolved by concentrated sulfuric acid and stiffens with acetic and hydrochloric acid, acetone, hydrogen peroxide, and phenol.
Vinyon—Copolymer of vinyl chloride, 80 to 85 per cent and vinyl acetate from 15 to 20 per cent	Vinyon HH is insoluble in acetone and in 90 per cent phenol. Vinyl resin fibers, however, are dissolved by certain ketones and softened by aromatic and certain halogenated hydrocarbons.

REFERENCE CHART FOR IDENTIFICATION OF MANMADE FIBERS AND THEIR BLENDS WITH NATURAL FIBERS BASED ON VARYING DEGREES OF THEIR SOLUBILITY IN ORGANIC SOLVENTS

The following sequential procedure should be of much value to the student of textiles.

For Individual, Unblended Fibers

1. The specimen should first be treated with acetone, which dissolves cellulose acetate, triacetate, and Dynel.
2. An acetone-and-water solution on an 80/20 basis dissolves acetate but not triacetate or Dynel.
3. Triacetate is soluble in chloroform while Dynel is not.
4. The insoluble residue from the acetone test is then treated with boiling glacial acetic acid. This solution dissolves nylon (polyamide) Types 6, 66 and 11. Type 11 is soluble in cyclohexanone, while Types 6 and 66 remain insoluble.
5. Nylon (polyamide) Type 6 is soluble in dimethyl formamide/formic acid—85 per cent in three parts of the former to one part of the latter. Type 66 remains insoluble.
6. The insoluble residue from the glacial acetic test may contain polyvinyl chloride, polyacrylonitrile, or polyester fiber content. Dimethyl formamide dissolves polyvinyl chloride at room temperature, but polyacrylonitrile only at the boiling point. Polyester fibers remain insoluble. These fibers will dissolve in boiling nitrobenzol.

For Blends with Natural Fibers

1. Many blends use only a rather small percentage of manmade fiber stock when blended with the natural fibers. Thus it is necessary after each treatment with a solvent to examine closely and then determine as to whether or not the solvent used has actually dissolved any of the manmade content. The solution should be cooled, if need be, and then diluted with water. If it becomes dull or flocculated, this is the indication that the presence of a dissolved fiber is apparent. NOTE: Use the Table preceding this Table for further individual fiber testing.

READY REFERENCE COMPARATIVE DATA ON MAJOR TEXTILE FIBERS

Elongation of Major Fibers: These will vary at varying temperatures. The following tabulations show elongation at standard atmospheric conditions of 65 per cent relative humidity and 70 degrees Fahrenheit:

FIBER, DRY CONDITION	PERCENTAGE IN ELONGATION	FIBER, DRY CONDITION	PERCENTAGE IN ELONGATION
Acetate	25.00–40.00	Nylon–(reg.)	26.00–32.00
Acrilan	30.00–44.00	Nylon–(staple)	18.00–52.00
Avril (HWM)	5.00– 7.00	Nylon–(HT)	16.00–28.00
Cotton	6.00– 7.00	"Orlon"–(staple)	20.00–25.00
Creslan	32.00	Rayon–(reg.)	15.00–35.00
"Dacron"–(reg.)	19.00–25.00	Rayon–(HT)	9.00–20.00
"Dacron"–(staple)	25.00–36.00	Saran	15.00–25.00
"Dacron"–(HT)	11.00–14.00	Silk	20.00
Dynel	30.00–36.00	Verel	33.00–35.00
Flax/linen	2.00	Vycron	25.00–35.00
Fortrel	30.00–40.00	Wool	25.00–35.00
Glass	2.00	Zantrel–(HWT)	10.00
Kodel	24.00–30.00	Zefran	33.00

Fiber Strength: This is the ability to resist strains and stresses and is expressed as tensile strength (pounds per square inch) or as tenacity (grams per denier). Strength is divided into three categories—high, medium, and low. Data on the major fibers follows:

HIGH STRENGTH			MEDIUM STRENGTH			LOW STRENGTH		
FIBER	DRY	WET	FIBER	DRY	WET	FIBER	DRY	WET
"Dacron"	4.5–7.5	4.5–7.5	Acrilan	2.0–2.7	2.0	Acetate	1.1–1.5	0.8
Flax	6.6	8.4	Cotton	2.0	8.0	Arnel	1.2–1.4	0.8–1.0
Fortisan	8.5	5.5	Creslan	2.7	2.7	Rayon	1.7–5.0	1.0
Glass	6.4	5.8	Dynel	2.5–3.3	2.5–3.3	Vinyon	0.7–1.0	0.7–1.0
Ramie	6.7	8.7	Fortrel	3.7–4.7	3.7–4.7			
Vycron	4.2–6.3	4.2–6.3	Kodel	2.5–3.0	2.5–3.0			
			"Orlon"	2.5	2.1			
			Saran	2.5	2.5			
			Silk	5.0	28.00			
			Verel	2.5–2.8	2.4–2.7			
			Zefran	3.5	3.1			

Heat-Sensitive Fibers: Heat will cause fibers to shrink, soften, or melt, a property that is not peculiar to cellulosic and protein fibers. Chemical composition and structure varies in these fibers, but those listed do have common properties in which sensitivity plays an important part in their end uses; they are thermoplastic in nature—Acetate, Nylon, Polyamide, Nytril, Modacrylic, Saran, Spandex, Vinal, and Vinyon HH:

IRONING TEMPERATURES FOR HEAT-SENSITIVE TEXTILE FIBERS

FIBER	TEMPERATURE	FIBER	TEMPERATURE
Acetate	350–445°F.	Nylon 6	300–340°F.
Acrilan acrylic	325–356	Nylon 66	300–350
Arnel triacetate	482	Olefin fibers	175
Cotton	425–475	"Orlon" acrylic	300
Creslan acrylic	408	Rayon	375–428
"Dacron"	400	Silk	240–300
Dynel modacrylic	225	Verel modacrylic	275
Flax/linen	300–475	Wool	212–275
Kodel	425	Zefran	350

Melting Point of Some Noncellulosic Fibers: The heat sensitivity of textile fibers of thermoplastic base shows that they will soften on heat application. The degree of sensitivity varies with the respective fibers. Melting is actually a separating of the molecules in a fiber, causing them to vibrate with such force that they become separated or melt. Cellulosic and protein fibers will not melt because of the strong attractive forces in the hydroxyl groups in them. The melting points follow:

FIBER	MELTING POINT, FAHRENHEIT	FIBER	MELTING POINT, FAHRENHEIT
Acetate— cellulosic base	500	Nylon 6	420
Acrilan	Sticks at 470, no melting point	Nylon 66	482
		Olefin	230–325, depending on the type of fiber
Arnel— cellulosic base	572	"Orlon"	No practical melting point, sticks at 445
Creslan	Sticks at 468, no melting point	Rayon	Non-melting
"Dacron"	480	Saran	340
Dynel	Does not melt or drip	Verel	About 300
		Vinyon HH	275–330
Kodel	480	Zefran	Sticking point at 490

Moisture Regain of Some Major Textile Fibers: Moisture is the water or other liquid which renders anything moist. Absorbency means to take up or receive by chemical or molecular action. Moisture regain is the percentage which the weight of moisture in a textile material represents of its bone-dry weight. It is sometimes referred to as content. Percentages of moisture regain in the fibers follow, under standard conditions:

FIBER	PERCENTAGE OF MOISTURE REGAIN	FIBER	PERCENTAGE OF MOISTURE REGAIN
Acetate	6.00	Nylon 66	8.00 at 95% R.H.
Acrilan	1.50–5.00	Nytril	2.60
Arnel	3.00	Olefins	0.00
Cotton	6.00–7.00	"Orlon"	2.50 at 95% R.H.
Creslan	1.50 at 70° F.	Rayon—	
"Dacron"	0.50 at 95% R.H.	regular	12.00 at 95% R.H.
Dynel	0.40	Rayon—high	
Flax/linen	6.00–10.00	wet modulus	12.20
Fortisan	10.70	Saran	.10 in 24 hour
Fortrel	0.40		immersion
Kodel	0.40	Silk	10.00 and may reach
Lycra	0.30		28.00
Mercerized	10.00–11.00	Verel	3.00–4.00
cotton		Vycron	0.40
Nylon 6	8.00 at 95% R.H.	Wool	15.00–17.00
		Worsted	10.00–12.00
		Zefran	2.50 at 65% R.H.

Specific Gravity of Some Major Textile Fibers: Density is defined as the mass per unit of volume. Specific gravity is the ratio of the mass of a given volume of any substance to that of the same value of some other substance taken as a standard. Water is the standard for liquids and solids, while hydrogen is the standard for gases. Density and specific gravity are expressed in terms of grams per cubic centimeter.

FIBER IN GRAMS PER CC		FIBER IN GRAMS PER CC		FIBER IN GRAMS PER CC	
Acetate	1.32	Fortrel	1.38	Silk	1.30
Acrilan	1.17	Glass	2.56	Verel	1.37
Arnel	1.30	Kodel	1.22–1.38	Vinyon HH	1.34
Cotton	1.48	Nylon 6 and 66	1.14	Viscose rayon	1.50–1.54
Creslan	1.17	"Orlon"	1.14–1.17	Wool	1.30
"Dacron"	1.38	Polypropylene	0.91	Zefran	1.19
Dynel	1.30	Saran	1.70 plus		
Flax/linen	1.50		or minus 0.05		

TESTING

1. Name three things that should be kept in mind when burning textile fibers.
2. Why should the edges of cloth be raveled prior to a burning test?
3. Cite an instance when a burning test would not be valid; a test that would be valid.
4. Name four fibers that burn practically the same as cotton.
5. Name four fibers that produce a hard bead during or after burning.
6. Explain the differences in burning a pure silk fabric and one that is weighted.
7. What fiber, when burned, gives off the odor of celery? Vinegar? Broiled fish?
8. Name two fibers that will not burn when a flame is applied.

TOPIC: THE MANUFACTURE OF YARN—SPUN, FILAMENT, AND TEXTURED

SPUN YARN

The manufacture of a yarn spun from many short fibers, of the same or vary-ing lengths, requires the positioning of these fibers into a continuous strand with the fibers in a relatively straight, uniform, and parallel, "north-to-south" arrange-ment. The methods used to achieve a yarn from different fibers will vary some-what because they have differences in fineness, length, diameter, resiliency, cohesiveness, elasticity, etc. This treatise uses the manufacture of cotton yarn as the basis for explaining, in a greatly simplified form, the essential steps neces-sary to achieve the objective.

The raising of cotton begins with the preparation of the soil, planting, cultiva-tion, and then picking the ripe cotton bolls. Ginning of cotton follows; there is a first-time ginning of cotton done at the community or the plantation gin, followed by a second-time ginning, also called delinting, which separates the short, tena-cious fibers not removed in the first-time ginning. Delinting is done in the large so-called "cotton cities" of the South, and the product is known as "cotton linters." The baling of cotton for shipment follows, and the American bale weighs five hundred pounds, which includes twenty-two pounds for burlap, cooperage, etc., thereby making a legal American bale have a weight of 478 pounds.

Cotton, when received in the mill in bale form, still contains foreign matter such as chaff, dirt, dried vegetable matter, seedpods, leaves, etc. These wastes have to be removed, of course, and the amount of waste depends chiefly on the grade and quality of the cotton. Cleansing and disentangling of the fibers is the first operation in the mill. The cotton is manipulated by an OPENING PROCESS, where a beater opens up the compressed mass of fibers. Fans aid in the treatment and remove goodly amounts of foreign waste matter, which falls into hoppers provided for this purpose. The opener fan blows the fibers onto a moving apron which carries them to the FIRST or BREAKER PICKER MACHINE. This picking process also uses beaters to further disentangle the fibers and eliminate more foreign matter.

Depending on the final product desired, the cotton may pass through as many as three different picker frames before it is then ready to be fed into the carding machine. The fibers are sent from the last picker in the set in the form of a cotton lap which is about 40–45 inches wide and has a weight of 40–45 pounds.

The CARDING PROCESS begins to orient the fibers into a more parallel arrange-ment, removes the short, undesirable fibers and further disentangles the stock. Most yarns are made from blends of several different lots of cotton to assure in all respects a better, more uniform yarn than would be obtained were the cotton to be only from a single lot of stock which would be the same in characteristics and properties. CARDING is done by the main or master cylinder and a set of re-volving flat bars or flats, both of which are densely covered with fine, bent steel wires wound spirally on the rollers; this wire covering is called "card clothing."

Cotton boll.

A cotton field being dusted or sprayed with insecticide, an arsenic preparation, to destroy the boll weevils, the scourge of the cotton grower.

Cultivating young cotton plants.

Cluster of cotton bolls.

Ripe cotton ready for picking, either by hand or by automatic cotton picker.

Mechanical cotton picker; about 90 per cent of American cotton is now picked by machine.

Picking cotton by hand, a slow, tedious process.

Mechanical cotton stripper.

Courtesy: National Cotton Council of America, Memphis, Tennessee

Courtesy: National Cotton Council of America, Memphis, Tennessee

Ginning of cotton is done at the community gin or on the large plantations in the South. Second-time ginning to produce cotton linters is done in the large cotton cities of the South: Memphis, Galveston, Houston, Little Rock, and elsewhere.

Courtesy: Lee, U. S. Department of Agriculture

Baled cotton from the gin following ginning.

Courtesy: Lee, U. S. Department of Agriculture

Baling ginned cotton, Arkansas.

Courtesy: National Cotton Council of America, Memphis, Tennessee

Placing cotton in the breaker-picker machine.

Cotton ready to be fed into the carding frame. Known as cotton lap stock, it is about 40 inches in width and weighs approximately 40 pounds.

Cotton sliver from the full coiler cans is fed into one or more comparable machines to reduce the sliver into a slubbing form.

Carded web-form cotton at the delivery end of the carding machine. The strand is known as sliver (pronounced slyver).

Drawing the fibers among themselves and twisting them into a roving form or strand. Drawing, drafting, doubling, and redoubling of the fibers are necessary in order to attenuate and produce a finer diameter in the strand as it comes from the delivery end of the frame. Twist is also inserted in the action so that the strand will have increased strength and be able to sustain itself.

Courtesy: National Cotton Council of America, Memphis, Tennessee

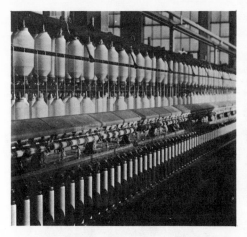

Spinning cotton yarn on the ring-spinning frame: Two ends of roving are fed in as one to the set or drawing rollers and emerge for passage onto the yarn spindles. Final drawing and twisting is applied in the operation. The term "roving" means that the stock being treated is one step removed from being finished, spun yarn. The term is applicable to all fibers in this condition. Spinning embodies final drawing and twisting of the fibers into commercial yarn. The placing of the yarn on some suitable device such as bobbin, cone, cheese, tube, spindle, etc., is done by the final operation in spinning, called winding.

Winding of the cotton from spools onto a warp beam; this is done so that the full beam may be set in the back of the loom and made ready to weave with the perpendicular filling in the weaving action of the loom.

The weaving of cotton cloth on a loom. The shuttle is observed in the shed of the loom in its passage from a shuttle-box on the one side of the loom to the correct shuttle-box on the other side.

Spools of finished spun yarn. Spinning combines three actions: drawing of the fibers, twisting, and winding of the spun yarn onto a suitable device such as a bobbin, cone, cheese, spindle, or tube.

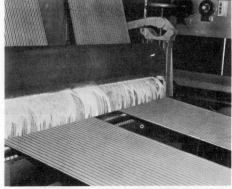

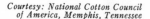

Courtesy: National Cotton Council of America, Memphis, Tennessee

Starch removal and the application of a resin in the finishing of the cloth.

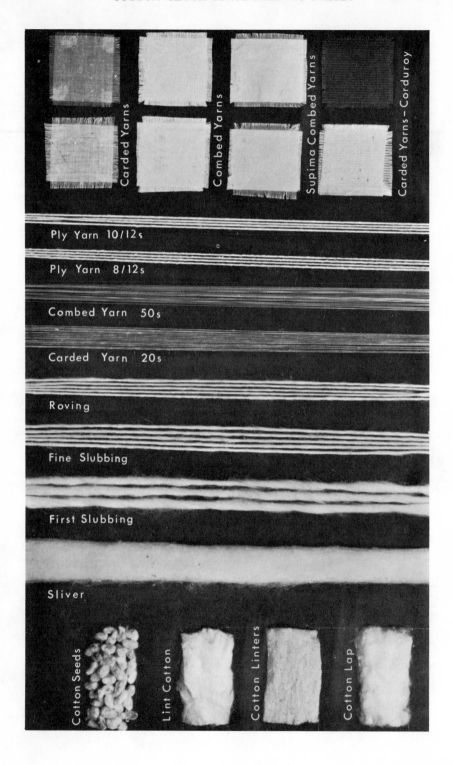

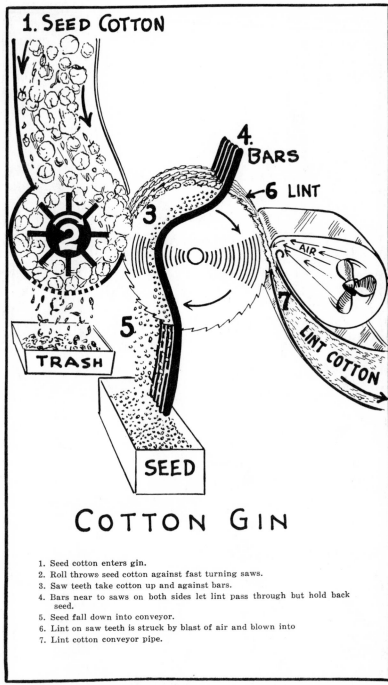

COTTON GIN

1. Seed cotton enters gin.
2. Roll throws seed cotton against fast turning saws.
3. Saw teeth take cotton up and against bars.
4. Bars near to saws on both sides let lint pass through but hold back seed.
5. Seed fall down into conveyor.
6. Lint on saw teeth is struck by blast of air and blown into
7. Lint cotton conveyor pipe.

This drawing and those which follow leave out much detail for the purpose of making more clear the basic principle of operation.

Pages 23-30 Courtesy Bibb Manufacturing Co., Inc., Macon, Georgia

BLENDING FEEDER

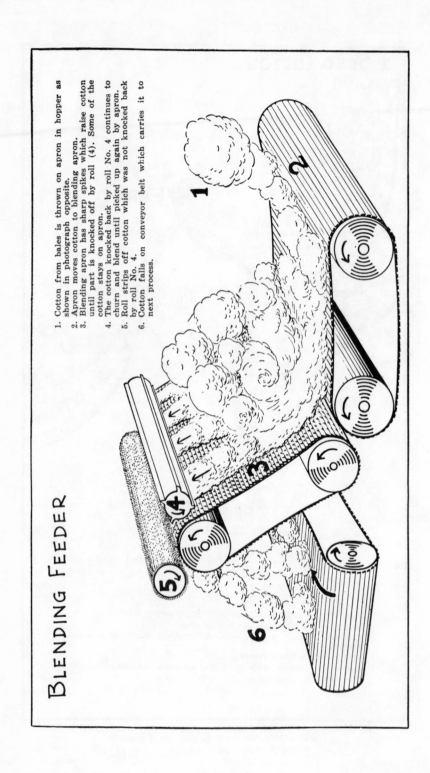

1. Cotton from bales is thrown on apron in hopper as shown in photograph opposite.
2. Apron moves cotton to blending apron.
3. Blending apron has sharp spikes which raise cotton until part is knocked off by roll (4). Some of the cotton stays on apron.
4. The cotton knocked back by roll No. 4 continues to churn and blend until picked up again by apron.
5. Roll strips off cotton which was not knocked back by roll No. 4.
6. Cotton falls on conveyor belt which carries it to next process.

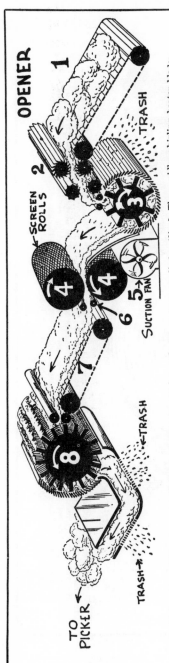

OPENER

1 2 3 4 4 5 6 7 8

SCREEN ROLLS

SUCTION FAN

TO PICKER

TRASH

1. Lint cotton falls on apron and passes between feeder rolls (2) to beater cylinder (3). 3. The rapidly whirling beater blades each take off small tufts of cotton knocking out trash and loosening up the mass. 4. The two screen rolls are made of screen material and air is sucked out of them by the fan (5). This draws the cotton from the beater and condenses it on the surface of the screen rolls from which it is taken and passed on by the small rolls (6). The air suction through the cotton takes out dirt and trash. 7. The conveyor belt (7) passes the cotton to another type of beater. (Many types of beaters are used. Those shown are typical.) 8. From the beater the cotton passes to a conveyor which take it to the next machine which is the picker. (see below)

PICKER

1 2 3 4 5 6

SCREEN ROLLS

TRASH

1. Cotton in a loose mass from the opener enters the picker which is a series of beaters (2) (2) (2) and screen rolls (3) (3) (3) similar to those described under opening, but gradually more refined. 4. At the final output of the beater and screen system the cotton has again been formed into a sheet or "lap." At this point the "evener" operates to feed more or less cotton as may be required to make the lap perfectly uniform as it is wound up into a "lap roll" (5) on the winding rolls (6). From this point the lap roll is taken to the carding process.

CARDING

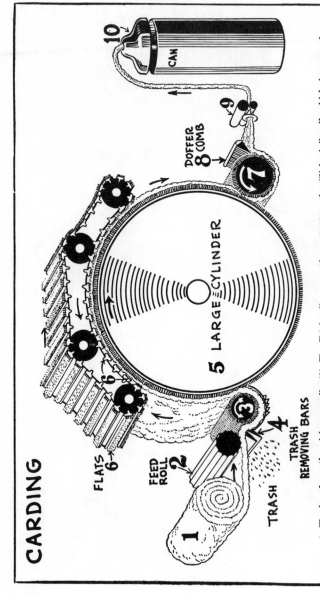

1. The lap from the picker unrolls (2) The Feed roll passes the cotton to the "lickerin" roll which is covered with sawtooth like wire. (3) The lickerin roll passes the fiber against the (4) Cleaner bars and gives it up to the (5) large cylinder which passes between the thousands of fine wires on the surface of the cylinder and on the 6. Flats. The cotton follows the large cylinder to the 7. doffer cylinder which removes the lint from the large cylinder. 8. The doffer comb vibrates against the doffer cylinder and takes the lint off in a filmy web which passes through the 9. Condenser rolls, the coiler head (10) and into the can.

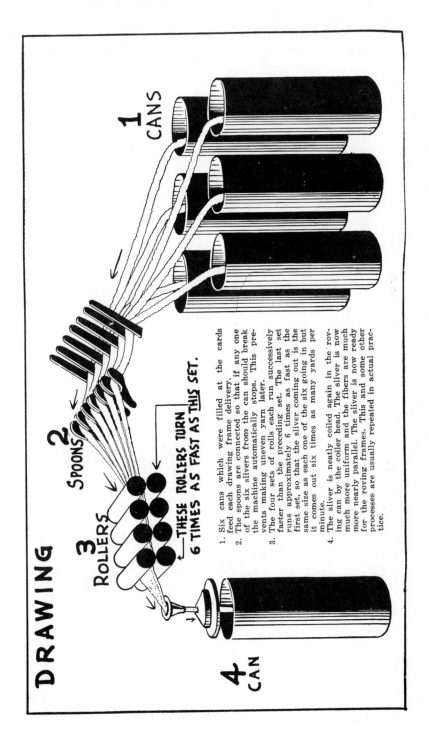

DRAWING

1 CANS

2 SPOONS

3 ROLLERS

THESE ROLLERS TURN 6 TIMES AS FAST AS THIS SET.

4 CAN

1. Six cans which were filled at the cards feed each drawing frame delivery.
2. The spoons are connected so that if any one of the six slivers from the can should break the machine automatically stops. This prevents making uneven yarn later.
3. The four sets of rolls each run successively faster than the preceding set. The last set runs approximately 6 times as fast as the first set, so that the sliver coming out is the same size as each one of the six going in but it comes out six times as many yards per minute.
4. The sliver is neatly coiled again in the roving can by the coiler head. The sliver is now much more uniform and the fibers are much more nearly parallel. The sliver is now ready for the roving frames. This and some other processes are usually repeated in actual practice.

ROVING FRAMES

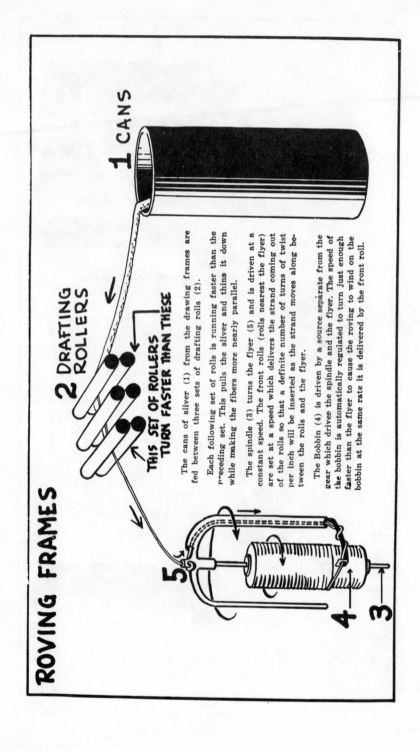

1 CANS

2 DRAFTING ROLLERS

THIS SET OF ROLLERS TURN FASTER THAN THESE

5

4

3

The cans of sliver (1) from the drawing frames are fed between three sets of drafting rolls (2).

Each following set of rolls is running faster than the preceding set. This pulls the sliver and thins it down while making the fibers more nearly parallel.

The spindle (3) turns the flyer (5) and is driven at a constant speed. The front rolls (rolls nearest the flyer) are set at a speed which delivers the strand coming out of the rolls so that a definite number of turns of twist per inch will be inserted as the strand moves along between the rolls and the flyer.

The Bobbin (4) is driven by a source separate from the gear which drives the spindle and the flyer. The speed of the bobbin is automatically regulated to turn just enough faster than the flyer to cause the roving to wind on the bobbin at the same rate it is delivered by the front roll.

SPINNING

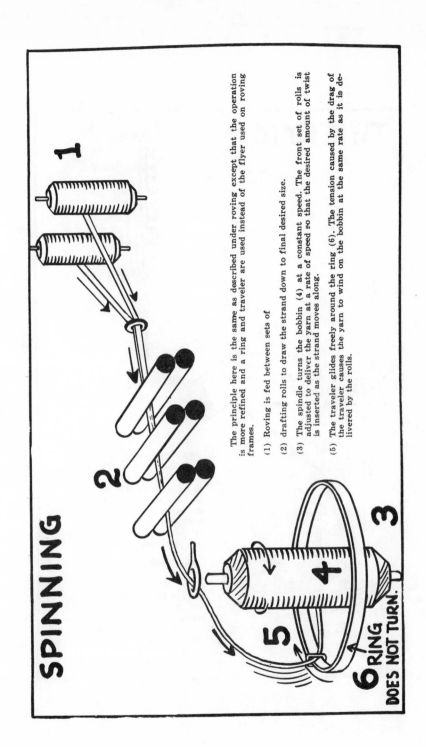

The principle here is the same as described under roving except that the operation is more refined and a ring and traveler are used instead of the flyer used on roving frames.

(1) Roving is fed between sets of

(2) drafting rolls to draw the strand down to final desired size.

(3) The spindle turns the bobbin (4) at a constant speed. The front set of rolls is adjusted to deliver the yarn at a rate of speed so that the desired amount of twist is inserted as the strand moves along.

(5) The traveler glides freely around the ring (6). The tension caused by the drag of the traveler causes the yarn to wind on the bobbin at the same rate as it is delivered by the rolls.

RING DOES NOT TURN.

TWISTING

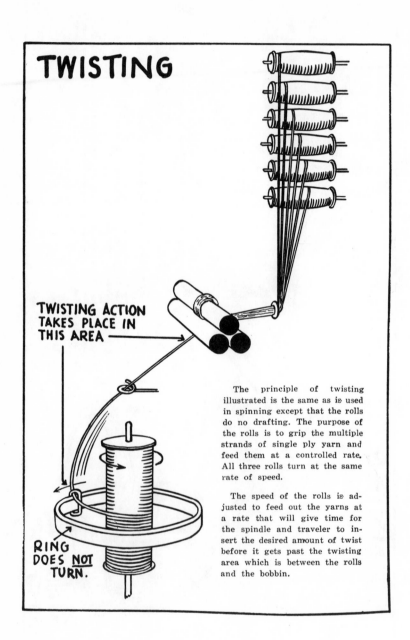

TWISTING ACTION
TAKES PLACE IN
THIS AREA →

RING
DOES **NOT**
TURN.

The principle of twisting illustrated is the same as is used in spinning except that the rolls do no drafting. The purpose of the rolls is to grip the multiple strands of single ply yarn and feed them at a controlled rate. All three rolls turn at the same rate of speed.

The speed of the rolls is adjusted to feed out the yarns at a rate that will give time for the spindle and traveler to insert the desired amount of twist before it gets past the twisting area which is between the rolls and the bobbin.

The fibers are passed back and forth between the cylinder and the flats and, on completion of the action, they are removed from the cylinder by a fancy roller which then feeds the fibers to the doffer roller situated at the front or delivery end of the frame. The fancy roller is clothed with wire an inch or so in length so that this set of wire clothing will penetrate easily and well into the cylinder wire, take out the carded fibers, and then present them to the doffer roller.

The web of cotton fibers which extends the entire width of the rollers is then converged into what is called a SLIVER. This sliver is then passed through a steel trumpet device on its way to the coiler cans, which are filled with the newly made sliver. The sliver is in a continuous strand of cleansed fibers with no twist present at all; it is soft, bulky, and fluffy, and if not compressed, is about one inch or so in diameter. The size may be compared with the diameter of a man's thumb.

The stock then goes to the DRAWING OPERATION following carding. A drawing frame has four pairs of rollers, with each successive set from back to front having an increased speed; thus the back rollers will go the slowest, the two sets of carrier rollers somewhat faster, with the front set of rollers having the highest speed. By means of this action the fibers are drawn among themselves, drafted, and they become more parallel. In the operation, six slivers are fed into the drawing frame at one time, and they are converged so as to produce at the delivery end of the machine a single sliver made up of the component fibers from the six slivers. The resultant sliver will have about the same weight as those fed into the machine, but its length will be about six times greater than that of the individual sliver. To attain this, there would have to be a draft of six on the frame, which means that the overall speed of the front set of rollers as compared with the back set and the carrier rollers would be six times as fast. The fibers have been doubled, redoubled, drawn, drafted, and attenuated, by which is meant the reducing of the diameter of the slivers fed in caused by the actual drawing of the fibers among themselves in the operation to thereby deliver a longer single sliver at the delivery end of the frame.

The SLUBBER FRAMES are next in line, and they reduce by drawing and drafting the stock into what is known as SLUBBING. Also known as FLY FRAMES or SPEEDER FRAMES, the number of frames used varies from two to five, according to the fineness of the yarn to be spun. These frames draw out the strand, set twist into it, and wind the slubbing onto a bobbin. The diameter of the slubbing may be compared with that of a lead pencil. The last frame in a set of slubber machines is called the ROVING FRAME. More twist is added to the strand to make the fibers more compact and stronger, as well as to further attenuate the strand. Roving, generally speaking, may be compared in diameter with that of the lead in a pencil.

The term "roving," irrespective of the type of fiber being manipulated, always means that the stock "is one step removed from being finished spun yarn." Two rovings are fed into the SPINNING FRAME. Spinning may be defined as the final drawing, twisting, and winding of the yarn onto a suitable device such as a bobbin, cheese, cone, tube, pirn, spindle, etc. The foregoing operations are for CARDED COTTON YARN. There is a better type of yarn called COMBED YARN, which is superior in all respects when compared with CARDED YARN.

In the combing process a number of card slivers are set side by side to form a lap. Done on a SLIVER LAPPER MACHINE, the process is usually known as a

RIBBON LAPPER FRAME. Several ribbon laps are then placed in parallel formation to provide the COMBER LAP. These two treatments have converted the sliver into a form suitable for the combing operation. The COMBER is usually made up of eight compartments, and each one thoroughly combs the stock, takes out the short, undesirable, immature fibers, and causes the fibers to become uniform, straight, and parallel. The suitable combed fibers are removed from the respective compartments and condensed into sliver form. The eight resultant slivers are then combined into a sliver made suitable as to weight and appearance by the settings on the frame. This is the combed sliver ready for drawing, and from this point the procedure is similar to that of the carded fiber to make spun yarn.

Because of these additional processes, the longer staple of the fibers, and the higher quality of the stock, combed yarn is more expensive when compared with carded yarn; it is stronger, smoother, softer, more lustrous, and can be spun finer in yarn diameter and count of yarn for use in better-quality fabrics.

Incidentally, in the better-quality combed yarn all fibers under one and a quarter inches could be removed, and in slightly lower quality the combers could be set to remove those fibers less than one inch in length. A carded yarn of very good quality could have all fibers less than three-quarters of an inch in length removed; this is, generally speaking, about as much actual carding that a card frame can accomplish. Most carded yarns use a staple of one-half-inch length and longer.

The reader should keep in mind that any fibers not too long for processing on these machines may be used. Thus the foregoing explanation applies to yarns of any fiber content spun on the carded or the combed methods or systems. If, for example, a 100-per-cent manmade fiber, in staple form, is processed on the cotton system, then the cleanliness of the combed yarn will not exceed that of carded yarn because manmade fiber stock does not contain the amounts of foreign matter found in cotton that is to be made into spun yarn.

The spinning of wool fibers differs to some degree from cotton spun yarn. The yarn spinner, of course, is aware of these differences, but the basic concepts are quite similar. In the cleaning of wool fibers a different approach is necessary. The shorn wool or fleece is very matted and dirty, and it contains natural oils such as the yolk, suint, or dried and wet perspiration, along with considerable amounts of chaff, burs, grass, pebbles, and so on. The grease fleece is scoured and washed well to remove the yolk which, when purified, becomes lanum or lanolin —the basic ingredient in ointments and salves, grease paints, certain cosmetics, shoe polish, shaving creams, et al. The suint, when removed, a form of potash, is much used for fertilizer. Scouring is usually done in an acid bath, which does not injure the fibers, and vegetable matter present is removed by a carbonizing action. Scoured wool is usually white to yellowish-white in color cast or shade. Cotton is cleaned mechanically, while wool is cleansed by chemical means.

WORSTED YARNS, except for some technical differences in the construction and settings on the machinery, and some differences in names, follow the same path as combed cotton yarns. The differences are caused by the nature of the wool fibers as to length, diameter, cohesion, elasticity, and outer fiber surface when compared with the cotton fiber. Comparable with combed cotton, worsted yarns are processed through opening, picking, carding, combing, drawing (gilling for worsted), roving, and spinning processes to produce yarn. The product of the worsted comb is called TOP instead of COMBED SLIVER, the term given to cotton. Another major difference is that the chief determination in the selection of the raw stock to be used for combed cotton is length, whereas the main determination in selecting wool fibers for worsted yarns is the fineness of the fibers and the amount of crimp (serrations or waves, seen and unseen) present in the fibers being graded.

The woolen method of carding uses a set of three or four cards which produces a roving form instead of a sliver. The roving is fed directly to the wool-spinning frame, either on a mule frame or on a ring-spinning frame, bypassing the drawing and roving operations used in cotton. Since the purpose of drawing is to parallel the fibers and make a more uniform sliver, and because the purpose of roving is to make a suitable strand ready for the spinning frame, it should be noted that a woolen spun yarn is rather bulky, uneven, fuzzy, and with the fibers in the yarn "running at all angles." Actually, it may be stated that a wool yarn is a more or less conglomerate mass of fibers manipulated into a yarn.

Worsted yarn is strong, very uniform with parallel fibers, has a high number of turns of twist per inch, and is smooth and capable of being used in high, compactly textured fabrics. The quality of woolen and worsted yarns may vary from high to low in quality and price, all depending upon the grade of the basic stock used as the raw ingredient.

Woolen and worsted yarns refer to a system of spinning and do not imply a fiber content. Thus practically any of the manmade fibers in staple or short-fiber form may be spun on the cotton, woolen, or worsted systems. Variations, of course, exist, and these are known and observed by the yarn spinner. Manmade fiber yarns can be made from tow (sliver form) as well as from the staple stock of these fibers. Thus, while the concepts are comparable, the variations occur because of the very nature of the respective fibers being processed.

TESTING

1. Define the following terms: (a) fiber; (b) strand; (c) sliver; (d) tow; (e) slubbing; (f) roving; (g) spun yarn; (h) drafting of fibers.
2. Explain the principles of carding fibers; combing of fibers.
3. List five differences between a woolen yarn and a worsted yarn.
4. What three phases in spinning of yarn are performed on a spinning frame?

FILAMENT YARN

The term "filament" may have three meanings or interpretations:

1. The single filament or unit which is extruded by the silkworm in spinning its cocoon, the length of which may run from three hundred to about sixteen hundred yards. Actually the silkworm produces two filaments at one time, which are cemented or glued together by the sericin or silkgum, exuded by the silkworm in action. The filaments are then "spun" into yarn.
2. A fiber of indefinite length, such as a filament of acetate, rayon, nylon, etc. The filament may be miles long.
3. A single strand, for example, of rayon-spinning solution as it is exuded from a spinnerette orifice (very small hole or opening) and coagulated in an acid bath or other medium; also true of other manmade filaments.

Manufacture of filament yarn of manmade fibers is based on the principles and methods used by the silkworm and the subsequent cocoon from which the filament is obtained. These principles were noted by the pioneers in the possible manufacture of manmade fibers along the lines of the filament produced by the cocoon—Dr. Robert Hooke (1664), René de Réaumur (1724–52), F. Gottlieb Keller (1840), George Audemars (1855), Sir Joseph Swan (1860), Count Hilaire de Chardonnet (1885–89), and others.

The manufacture of viscose rayon, now the oldest method still in use, may be taken, generally speaking, as representative of the processes and methods used in the manufacture of manmade fibers. There are some modifications and deviations used in the manufacture of the other manmade fibers to suit their particular characteristics and properties.

Briefly, in the manufacture of viscose rayon, purified cellulose is made into a solution and is then regenerated (solid-liquid-solid) into yarn by chemical procedures. Stretching produces high-tenacity types of manmade fiber yarns. The filaments can be cut into suitable lengths to give the staple fiber for blending with natural and other manmade fibers.

Viscose Method—Cross and Bevan

a) The product from which all rayon is made is called cellulose. This is obtained by the reduction of cotton linters, spruce, or other high Alpha-cellulose woods to a pulp, the same as in the manufacture of paper.

b) The pulp is bleached and pressed into sheets which resemble blotting paper. This is done in the pulp mill.

c) In the rayon plant, the sheets are soaked in alkali, caustic soda, and then shredded. The machine which actually does the shredding into flake form is called a Pfleiderer.

d) Aging of the flake or alkali crumb form follows, a great secret in the making of rayon.

e) Carbon bisulfide (disulfide) is added to the crumbs to produce the orange crumb, cellulose viscose xanthate; the latter word comes from the Greek, meaning "orange."

f) Further treatment with a dilute solution of caustic soda follows and the mass is again aged. It is during this procedure that the mass slowly turns into the liquid called viscose, which has the color and consistency of honey.

g) The viscous or viscose solution is then forced through spinnerettes which are submerged in a dilute acid bath. The alkaline viscous solution reacts with the acidic bath which neutralizes the alkalinity. The action causes the cellulose content of the viscose solution to harden into filament.

   A spinnerette may be called a type of nozzle, usually about the diameter of a dime, through the face of which are bored a number of beveled holes or orifices which average from two one-thousandths of an inch to five one-thousandths of an inch. Through these minute holes the viscose solution is forced to form the filaments which comprise one strand of yarn. Spinnerettes are made from a combination of iridium and platinum; they are rather expensive.

h) After the filament is finally formed in the atmosphere, it is passed around a feed wheel, twisted, and then passed into a revolving feed box where it winds itself into what is known as a rayon "cake." This form resembles an angel food cake and is made possible by the revolving motion of the feed box.

i) On completion, the "cake" is removed from the container.

From the Aging Cellar to the Spinnerette

1. Pipe from aging cellar to conduct the viscose solution.
2. Area and box above the aging cellar.
3. Pump to draw the viscous solution from aging cellar. This pump forces the solution through the filter which removes foreign particles.
4. Filter pipe to filter.
5. Filter.
6. Pipe to conduct the filtered solution to the spinnerette.
7. The spinnerette: This is a thimblelike device that has many minute holes or orifices, through which the solution is forced. The minute portions of the spinning solution are strongly alkaline. They harden as they come in contact with the hardening or acid reverting bath to form the filaments of rayon.

THE VISCOSE BOX METHOD OF MAKING RAYON: SPINNING BOX

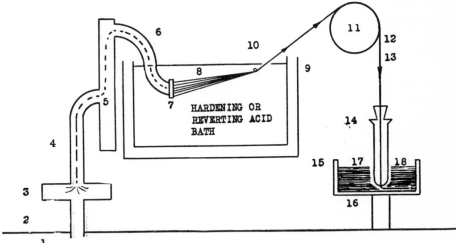

From Spinnerette to Spun Yarn

8. Filaments as they leave the spinnerette. They are gathered together in the hardening bath and are led around a small guide roller that is in the acid bath. From this small roller, the filaments are led into natural atmospheric conditions. By this time, they are hardened or coagulated. No mechanical twist has, as yet, been given the filaments.
9. Tank.
10. Yarn.
11. Revolving feed wheel around which the yarn is passed.
12. Twist is applied to the filaments from the feed wheel to the outlet at the bottom tip of the glass funnel, number 18.
13. Thread taking the twist turns that are necessary—mechanical action.
14. Glass funnel or tube that raises and lowers in the revolving feed box, number 15.

[35]

15. Revolving feed box.
16. Shaft to revolve the feed box.
17. Rayon "cake" being made by the revolving motion of the feed box.
18. Yarn coming from the outlet of the glass funnel and led to the cake form. On completion of the cake, the yarn is removed from the container.

TESTING

1. Give two meanings of the term "filament."
2. What is a spinnerette? An orifice?
3. Name three pioneers who gave food for thought with regard to the possibility of making manmade (synthetic) textile fibers.
4. Define the term "regeneration."
5. Explain what is meant by a viscous solution.
6. What is meant by a cake of yarn?

TEXTURED YARNS

They are made of continuous filaments and are modifications of these filaments in that the filaments do not lie parallel to one another. Fabrics made of these yarns have greater covering power and are softer than materials made from untreated filament yarns.

STRETCH YARNS are also modified versions of continuous filament yarns and are classified as TEXTURED YARNS. Some of these, however, do not have stretchability.

HIGH-BULK YARNS are spun yarns made by blending high-shrinkage staple fibers with staple fibers of low shrinkage. Strictly speaking, they are not textured yarns since they are made from staple stock and not from continuous filament. Bulk yarns provide a soft, flufflike effect or an opaque effect on certain woven and knitted cloths.

Articles made from the foregoing yarns are form-fitting to the body without pressure. The yarn effects are obtained in several ways—twisting, untwisting, false-twisted stretch, and by the use of air jets, heat, dry heat, crimping, curling, straining, and looping.

Advantages of bulked yarns and stretch yarns follow: These include soft, appealing hand, retention of air, absorbency, conductivity of perspiration, rather dull surface effect, varying amounts of stretchability, low specific gravity, ease of washing and rapid drying, and good resistance to wear and abrasion. Most products which use these yarns come in one size, thereby making them economical for both the manufacturer and the consuming public. Generally speaking, these yarns have about the same uses in trade, such as for men's, women's, and children's stockings and socks, undershirts, T-shirts, men's shorts, light winter-wear fabrics, blankets, swimsuits, decorative fabrics, leotards and slacks, carpeting, foundation fabrics, and for certain industrial fabrics.

Some of the Major Yarns in This Group

Agilon: The texturing method is done by heat-setting over a blade. There is alteration of strain within the filaments so that when released from tension they have a tendency to curl. The yarn is made on modified standard textile equipment, of a non-torque nylon or "Dacron" filament yarn used alone or in combination with other yarns, chiefly cotton. A product of Deering Milliken Research Corporation, Spartanburg, South Carolina.

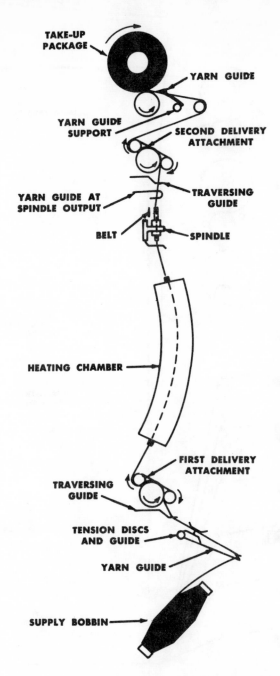

TAKE-UP PACKAGE

YARN GUIDE

YARN GUIDE SUPPORT

SECOND DELIVERY ATTACHMENT

YARN GUIDE AT SPINDLE OUTPUT

TRAVERSING GUIDE

BELT

SPINDLE

HEATING CHAMBER

FIRST DELIVERY ATTACHMENT

TRAVERSING GUIDE

TENSION DISCS AND GUIDE

YARN GUIDE

SUPPLY BOBBIN

Courtesy: Whitin Machine Works,
Whitinsville, Massachusetts

Schematic string-up diagram of whitin A.R.C.T., type FT-1 machine for false twist in textured yarn.

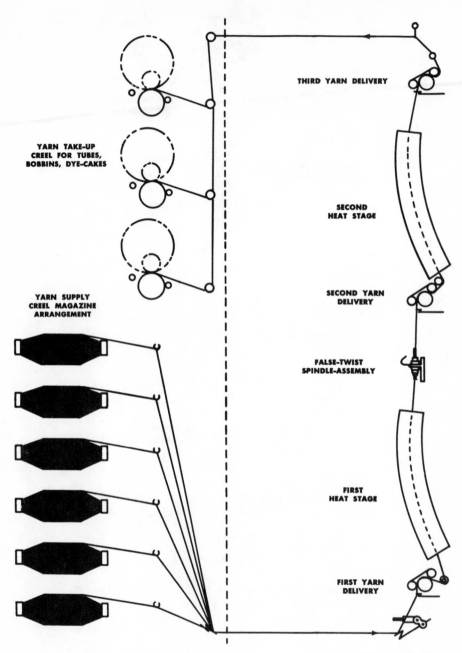

THIRD YARN DELIVERY

YARN TAKE-UP
CREEL FOR TUBES,
BOBBINS, DYE-CAKES

SECOND
HEAT STAGE

SECOND YARN
DELIVERY

YARN SUPPLY
CREEL MAGAZINE
ARRANGEMENT

FALSE-TWIST
SPINDLE-ASSEMBLY

FIRST
HEAT STAGE

FIRST YARN
DELIVERY

Courtesy: Whitin Machine Works,
Whitinsville, Massachusetts

Schematic string-up diagram of whitin A.R.C.T., type FTF machine. For most stretch-woven fabrics the stretch yarn is produced using the first process stage only with the second heat zone inoperative.

TYPE F. T. 3.

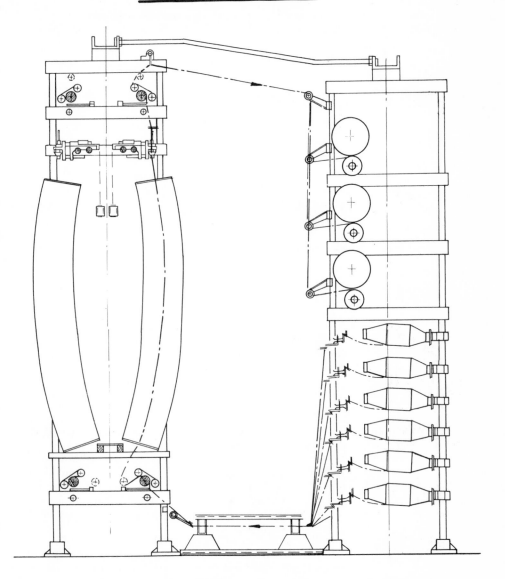

Advanced stretch yarn machine for production of high modulus yarns at speeds of 250,000 rpm. Equipped with separate yarn supply and take-up creels; magazine tailed for uninterrupted production. Has yarn-cutting device to prevent yarn lap-ups and minimizes operator's patrol duties. Stop motions are at each spindle position, and optional spindle drive arrangement permits simultaneous production of S-twist and Z-twist on each machine.

Antron 24: This trilobal nylon yarn is changed in the process of manufacturing before the final molecular structure is set up. A product of E. I. du Pont de Nemours & Co., Wilmington, Delaware.

Ban-Lon: This is a crimped yarn in which unprocessed filaments are textured or crimped and then thermo-set in a stuffer box. The principle of stretch yarn is not involved, and the yarn presents a smooth surface texture. Applied to any of the thermoplastics, Ban-Lon gives a soft, appealing hand. Joseph Bancroft & Sons Company, Wilmington, Delaware, owns and controls the patents associated with the yarn (Textralized) and the fabrics and garments made from yarn under specific standards (Ban-Lon).

SOME EXAMPLES OF TEXTURED YARNS

Coiled

Peaked crimp effect

Rounded crimp effect

Curled

Curled over heated blade

Heated gears provide the crimp

High bulk—stretched and relaxed principle

High twist—not highly elastic

Lofted effect from use of air jet

Stretch core—retains good elasticity

Synfoam—twist and untwist method

Stuffing box used for crimp

BCF Nylon: In this product of the Du Pont Company, the yarn is altered in the process of manufacturing before the final molecular structure is set up.

Cumuloft: Done by the application of modified crimp to the thermoplastic yarn in a continuous process at specific temperatures. There are three types of Cumuloft made by The Chemstrand Company, New York City—regular, deep dyeing type, and ultra deep dyeing type. Deep dyeing and ultra deep dyeing Cumuloft have modified dyeabilities. When combined with regular Cumuloft, they bring about two and three color effects with acid and disperse dyes in a single dye bath.

Fluflon: Of high bulk and high stretchability, the method may be applied to any thermoplastic fiber. The method of manufacture is continuous, taking the raw yarn as received all the way through to produce finished ply yarns for the trade. Licensor of the method is Leesona Corporation, Warwick, Rhode Island.

Helanca: Product of the Heberlein Patent Corporation, New York City. This company produced the first commercial stretch yarn in 1947. Helanca is a registered trademark of the company for a nylon or a polyester yarn made under license grant. Continuous filaments are specially engineered to create millions of microscopic curls, obtained through a torque (or tension) technique. The filament is first coiled like a spring and then is heat-set and twisted counter to the coil. The curls formed by this reverse plan open and close to give the stretch; the finer or lighter the denier, the greater will be the stretch.

Not all "stretch yarns" are Helanca. In order to bear the name of Helanca, the yarn must first be approved and then undergo continual tests in the Heberlein Testing Station, High Point, North Carolina. Thus Helanca is the only torque yarn with universal quality standards because the specifications are kept uniform and constant among the licensees. Quality control is also exercised over fabrics and finished products bearing the Helanca trademark and made by the licensees.

Helanca: This is the conventional and false-twist nylon and "Dacron" textured yarns used in woven and knit fabrics.

Helanca High Test: Maximum stretch yarns of nylon and "Dacron" used in hosiery, swimwear, and leotards.

Helanca NT: Non-torque nylon-textured yarn with considerable stretch and a soft appealing hand; used much in woven and knit fabrics.

Helanca SP: High-elastic stretch yarn of nylon used in woven goods; very popular in ski ensembles.

Helanca SS: Highly bulked nylon yarn which has limited stretch and provides a smooth, even surface-texture effect in woven and knit goods.

Helanca SW: A textured nylon yarn with the false-twist modified to give low stretch in effects such as bouclé or crepe in knitted fabrics.

Mylast: The crimp is inserted into the yarn, to give a surface effect that may be either smooth or creped. Product of Clarence L. Meyers & Co., Philadelphia, Pennsylvania.

Saaba: Obtained by an annealing process on the Universal down-twister, which is equipped with a heating chamber and feed rolls. Involves the removal of stretch from a false-twist stretch yarn. Surface texture may be bouclé, chenille-like, or smooth. Licensor is Leesona Corporation, Warwick, Rhode Island.

Shape-2-U: Owned by Burlington Industries, Inc.; the yarn results from a twisting and untwisting method.

Skyloft: A product of American Enka Corporation, New York City, the yarn passes through an air jet which causes the filaments to become wavy and intertwined. Another product of the company is ENKALOFT, which is modified in a post-process treatment.

Spunized: Filament yarns are crimped in a batch and the equipment includes a heat-setting chamber. This smooth-textured yarn is made by Hartford Spinning Company, Unionville, Connecticut.

Superloft: This highly twisted yarn is made in continuous process in which dry heat is used. False twist spindles reverse the direction of the twist as the yarn is being wound onto a bobbin or cone. Comes in single and in ply yarn. Licensor is Leesona Corporation, Warwick, Rhode Island.

Synfoam: Owned by Synfoam Yarns, Inc., the yarn is made on the twist-and-untwist method. Nylon and "Dacron" crepe fabrics are made from the yarn, which also finds much use in upholstery fabrics.

Taslan: Produced through a bulking process which imparts a particular texture different from standard textile yarns. The hand, loftiness, covering power, yarn texture are such that these properties are permanent and do not require special handling or care. As a full-textured yarn, it is distinctively different when compared with regulation spun yarns or continuous filament yarns. The method can be applied to any thermoplastic fiber. The product of E. I. du Pont de Nemours & Co., Inc.

Tycora: This trademark of Textured Yarn Company is applied to several processes used in the modification of continuous filament yarn. Tycora yarns have soft hand, high dye affinity, strength and durability, bulkiness without added weight, and they are nonpilling.

Welderstretch: Twisted combinations of stretch nylon yarn with cotton, rayon, worsted, and spun nylon, "Orlon-dyed," and "natural Orlon" are used in the various yarn compositions. Product of the Blackwelder Textile Company, Inc., Cherryville, North Carolina.

Whitin ARCT FT-1, and *Whitin ARCT FT-3:* Treats any thermoplastic yarn highly twisted, heat-set, and untwisted in a continuous process. Necessary machinery is made by ARCT, and is sold by Whitin Machine Works, Whitinsville, Massachusetts. Developed in conjunction with Deering Milliken Research Corporation, Spartanburg, South Carolina.

Whitin ARCT FTF: Any thermoplastic yarn highly twisted, heat-set, untwisted, relaxed, and then heat-set a second time in a continuous process. Necessary machinery is made by ARCT, and is sold by Whitin Machine Works, Whitinsville, Massachusetts. Developed in conjunction with Deering Milliken Research Corporation, Spartanburg, South Carolina.

CORE YARN: A thread or yarn made with a core or center of another, different yarn. It is made by winding one yarn around another so as to give the appearance of one made solely from the visible outer yarn. The core in the yarn is all, or nearly all, covered by the shell or outer yarn. Core yarns afford increased strength. The core yarn is often one in which the core has been "cheapened" by the use of an inexpensive yarn, often a waste yarn, to reduce the price of the yarn.

One use of this type of yarn is in blanketing and "woolen" bathrobe cloth wherein the outer yarn is a softly spun "filling-type yarn" which will develop a good nap in the finished goods. Sometimes instead of a low-twist yarn being used, a soft-twist roving stock is used as the shell. Cotton core yarns are popular in some cloths since they are inexpensive and give the fabric the necessary strength to make a rather rugged cloth.

Recently core yarns have come into favor with the rise of textured yarns and those used in stretch fabrics. Spandex fibers are now used much as the core while several of the manmade yarns of various types are used in the shell or outer yarn. For example, Lycra and Vyrene Spandex yarns, or rubber yarns such as Contro, Filatex, Lactron, Lastex, Laton, etc., would serve as the core in a particular yarn while yarns of cotton, wool, silk, nylon, acrylic, modacrylic, acetate, rayon, triacetate, polyester, etc., would be wound spirally around the core yarn to give the desired plan or novel strength effect on the yarn surface.

TESTING

1. Define a stretch yarn; a textured yarn; a high-bulk yarn.
2. Name five articles made with stretch yarns.
3. What is the name of the first stretch yarn to be produced?
4. Differentiate between a coiled yarn and a curled yarn.
5. List five advantages of bulked yarns and stretch yarns.
6. With what stretch yarn is "Textralized" associated?
7. Give two possible examples of core yarn with regard to the specific yarns that could be used.
8. Name two Spandex fibers; two rubber yarns.

Part 1—Unit 5

TOPIC: NAMES AND DEFINITIONS OF THE PARTS OF A WOVEN FABRIC

A fabric begins with a fiber, the smallest unit in a piece of material. Fibers are made into yarns, which are used to make woven, knit, plaited, braided, or lace materials. Any cloth, fabric, material, or textile product obtains its individuality from the fiber, yarn, construction, method of coloring, and finishing.

Animal fibers are obtained from sheep, the silkworm, and a number of other animals such as the camel, llama, alpaca, vicuna.

Vegetable fibers come from cotton, flax, ramie, jute, hemp, etc.

Mineral fibers are obtained from asbestos, slag wool, glass, metallic sources, etc.

The manmade fibers—the general term now applied to the cellulosic and the non-cellulosic fibers—are products of the ingenuity of man. For example, viscose rayon and cuprammonium or Bemberg rayon are known as cellulosic fibers. Acetate, which is made from the same base as rayon but has different properties and characteristics, is known as a cellulose-derivative fiber. Acetate and rayon are true cellulosic fibers, while the non-cellulosic fibers include nylon, "Dacron" polyester fiber, "Orlon" acrylic fiber, Dynel, Acrilan, Kodel, Creslan, saran, Verel, Zefran, and others. These fibers have also been referred to as specially manmade fibers, test-tube fibers, synthetic fibers, true synthetic fibers, and chemically made fibers in the past.

All fibers have distinctive qualities and characteristics that influence the appearance, the usefulness, and the performance of the finished material. From the foregoing list of manmade fibers it will be observed that scientific advances have enabled man to produce in laboratories a variety of fibers whose qualities and characteristics can be controlled for different end uses, or terminal uses. These fibers are much used in all kinds and types of fabrics for the apparel, decorative, and industrial fabric trades.

Thus, whatever the fabric in question, there are certain basic terms and definitions that the reader should understand. These follow:

1. FIBER: The smallest unit in a woven, knit, plaited, braided, or lace material. Fibers are the smallest units in felt and nonwoven fabrics as well. Yarns are not used in the manufacture of felt and nonwoven materials. See Units 13, 15.

2. FIBRIL: Pronounced "fybril," it refers to a fine or very fine fiber.

3. FILAMENT: This is a fiber that is indefinite in length; it may be miles long, such as filament of acetate or rayon. Filament can be cut into short lengths known as staple for use with the natural fibers of a more or less definite length such as wool, worsted, cotton, and linen.

4. STRAND: It is a single fiber or filament; the term also implies a number of yarns or threads composed of fibers or filaments which, when taken together, constitute one of the parts, portions, or plies that are twisted together to form a cord, rope, or the like—a rope of twisted strands.

5. THREAD: Thread is made from yarn but yarn is not made from thread. It is a highly specialized type of yarn used for some definite purpose such as sewing, basting, embroidery work. Thread is plied to give it added strength when it is being manipulated. Three-ply and six-ply thread are two of the common threads in use today.

6. YARN: A generic term for an assemblage of fibers or filaments, either natural or manmade, twisted together to form a continuous strand which can be used for weaving, knitting, plaiting, braiding, the manufacture of lace, or can be otherwise made into a textile material.

7. PLY-YARN: Two or more yarns that have been twisted together. Ply-yarn, such as automobile tire fabric, may have nine, ten, or eleven ply.

8. DENIER: Briefly, by the use of the factor-formula method, it is the weight of 9,000 meters (9,846 yards) of filament or strand in grams. Thus, if 9,000 meters weigh 150 grams, the denier is a 150-denier. The higher the denier number, the heavier will be the filament.
   NOTE: The terms "fiber," "fibril," "filament," "yarn," "thread," denier," "ply-yarn," and "strand" should be fully understood as to their correct and specific meaning when speaking of each one with respect to its usage in regard to diameter, length, yarn or thread count or size, etc. There seems to be the tendency to use some of these terms interchangeably, especially when discussing the use of the foregoing terms in the manmade fiber field. For example, fiber, filament, and strand are often confused, as well as yarn, thread, and denier. Yarn, denier, and filament are also often confused and used incorrectly.

9. WARP: The yarns which run vertically or lengthwise in woven goods.

10. FILLING: The yarns which run horizontally or crosswise in woven cloth.

Courtesy: Crompton & Knowles Loom Works, Worcester, Mass.

Courtesy: American Viscose Corp.; A. Devany, Inc.

Weaving figured fabric—Jacquard

Weaving pile fabric

11. CLOTH: It is made from some raw material, constructed, may or may not be colored, and may or may not be finished for the final effect. Other names for cloth include fabric, goods, material, and stuff.

12. SELVAGE: Each side edge of a woven fabric and an actual part of the warp in the fabric. Other names for selvage include listing, selvedge, self-edge, raw edge.

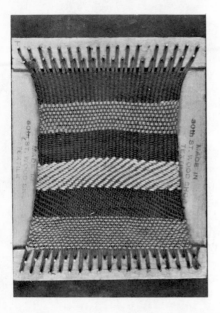

Simple kindergarten or pocket loom with various weave formations. "Anyone can build a loom; everyone can weave fabric."

13. WEAVE: The manner in which the yarns interlace according to some plan or motif decreed by a fabric designer.

14. KNITTING: The interlooping of a system of yarn or yarns, a loop with a loop. Lengthwise direction is the wale, crosswise is the course.

15. PLAITING, BRAIDING: To interweave or intertwine, such as the plaiting or braiding of one's hair, or narrow strips of material as in the case of a braided rug or a shoelace.

TESTING

1. Define the following terms: fiber, filament, yarn, thread, ply-yarn.
2. Give two other names by which cloth is known.
3. Of what advantage is a selvage on woven goods?
4. Why is selvage considered as a part of the warp arrangement in a cloth?
5. What do wale and warp have in common in fabric? Filling and course?
6. How does yarn differ from thread?

Part 1—Unit 6

TOPIC: THE WEAVING OF FABRIC AND THE PARTS OF A LOOM

Weaving is the interlacing of two systems of yarn at right angles. It is the most important way of making cloth. About 80 per cent of all fabric made is woven, either by hand or by power loom. The warp is the system of yarns or threads which runs vertically or lengthwise in the goods. Warp is often referred to as warp ends, or ends. The filling is the system of yarns or threads which runs crosswise or in the horizontal direction in the material. Filling is often referred to as filling picks, or picks.

The warp yarn is wound evenly, snugly, and uniformly onto the warp beam or roll. Filling yarn is placed into the fabric, in most instances, one pick at a time. Some pile fabric is made with a top shuttle and a bottom shuttle working simultaneously, in a double-shed loom. See Unit 26.

In the beginning, weaving was done by passing the filling yarns over and under the warp threads, a very slow and tedious process. Today, warp yarns are separated into a top set of threads and a bottom set of threads. This formation is called the shed of the warp in the loom. The filling pick passes through this shed from one side of the loom to the other side. Hand-weaving of fabric is still a very slow process when compared with the high production obtained on power looms today. Crompton & Knowles Corporation, Worcester, Massachusetts, and the Draper Corporation, Hopedale, Massachusetts, the two major loom manufacturers in the United States, make broad looms with a shuttle speed of about 250 or more picks per minute.

THE THREE MAJOR MOTIONS OR ACTIONS ON ALL LOOMS

These are shedding, picking, and beating-up. The minor or auxiliary motions are the take-up, let-off, and pattern. The first three motions are linked together as follows:

1. SHEDDING MOTION: The separating of the warp ends into an upper and lower system of threads to permit the shuttle to pass through the space that has been formed. The warp ends are drawn through heddle eyes in the correct manner and in the turning over of the crankshaft of the loom, a shed is formed with each turn.

2. PICKING MOTION: The actual passing of the shuttle through the shed of the loom. The shuttle passes over the lowered ends of the shed and under its raised ends. The shed permits the shuttle to pass through it and thereby makes it possible for the shuttle to deposit the pick or filling yarn.

3. BEATING-UP: The actual beating into place of the loose pick that was placed in the shed of the loom in the picking motion. Beating up makes each deposited yarn a component part of the woven cloth. The reed beats this pick into place with each consecutive turn of the crankshaft.

THE THREE AUXILIARY OR MINOR MOTIONS ON ALL LOOMS

1. TAKE-UP MOTION: The motion is positive when the sand roller moves a fractional part of an inch in direct ratio to the take-up wheel. The motion is semipositive when the sand roller is not definitely controlled.

2. LET-OFF MOTION: The motion is frictional when there is a definite amount of warp allowed to leave the warp beam according to the beating up of the lay of the loom. It is positive when the lay and the let-off work in two ratios, taking up just as much as is let off.

3. PATTERN MOTION: Not found on all looms, but generally used on machines where more than one color is desired. It is found in the following ratios:

From a 2 by 1 box loom to a 7 by 1 gingham loom.
From a 2 by 4 box loom controlling three colors.
From a 4 by 4 box loom controlling seven colors, pick and pick type.

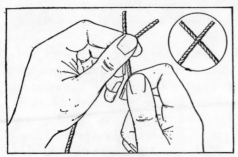

Fig. 1. Cross the two ends, making certain that the end from the *left* hand is in front of the end from the *right* hand.

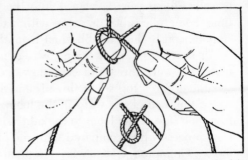

Fig. 2. Swing the yarn in the *right* hand over the *left* thumb and in back of the two ends.

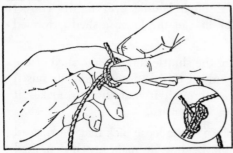

Fig. 3. Now swing the same yarn around only the *right*-hand end.

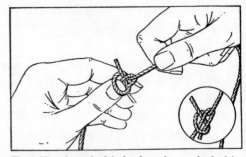

Fig. 4. Push the *right*-hand end with the *right* thumb—

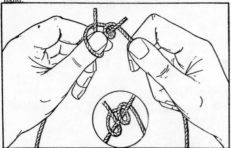

Fig. 5. —through the loop made by the *left* thumb.

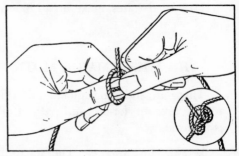

Fig. 6. Now clamp the *left* thumb on the yarn in the *left* hand and pull hard with the *right* hand.

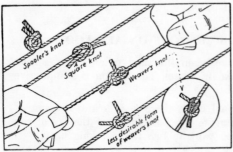

Fig. 7. The result is the weaver's knot. Other knots are shown for comparison.

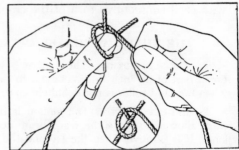

Fig. 8. The alternative method, less desirable because both ends are on same side of completed knot. Substitute this diagram for Figs. 2 and 3.

OTHER PARTS OF A LOOM

Warp Beam or Warp Roll: The roll upon which all warp ends are uniformly, snugly, and evenly wound. For certain types of weaving—double cloth, terry toweling, pile fabric weaving, etc.—two or more warp beams are used on the loom.

Whip Roll: It is placed above the warp beam and guides the warp ends as they come up from the warp beam on their way to the lease rods and heddles. This guide roller is in the same flat plane with the breast beam and selvage edges. The arrangement makes weaving possible.

Warp: The total number of threads or ends which make up the entire warp in the loom. The warp is always under tension.

Ends: The individual yarns which, when taken collectively, make up the warp.

Lease Rods: Two wooden or glass rods set between the whip roll and the harness frames. These rods help to keep the lease in the warp threads. For example, all even-numbered warp ends may pass over the back lease rod and under the front lease rod; all odd-numbered warp ends may pass under the back lease rod and over the front lease rod. By this arrangement of warp threads, the lease rods aid considerably in finding broken warp ends, keeping the ends under control and preventing possible gnarling, tangling, and rolling of the warp ends. In addition the rods cause the ends to enter the heddle eyes on the harness frames in an even, uniform manner.

Heddles: Usually made of fine pressed steel wire, they have a hole or eye in the center through which the respective warp ends are drawn.

Harnesses: The wooden frames upon which the heddles are placed by means of a top-heddle loop and a bottom-heddle loop. The harnesses form the shed in the loom when some of them are raised while others are lowered.

Reed: The comblike device through which the warp ends are drawn after leaving the heddles and the harnesses. Reeds are usually made of fine pressed-steel wire, and the spaces between these wires are known as reed splits or reed dents.

The reed prevents the warp ends from gnarling or tangling with one another; it keeps the warp ends level, straight, and true and serves as a control for the ends being fed in evenly to the newly woven cloth. The reed by its to-and-fro action beats the loose filling pick lying in the shed of the loom into its proper place in the woven goods. The reed is parallel with the whip roll and lease rods, and is at right angles to the selvages.

Temples: Devices at each edge of the cloth to keep woven fabric at the proper width in the loom during weaving. Another purpose is to keep the warp ends at the correct width and angle so that they will weave at right angles with the filling yarn; acts as an auxiliary to the reed in this respect.

Shuttle and Bobbin: The shuttle passes through the warp shed formed by the raising and lowering of the ends in the warp.

The filling yarn is wound on a bobbin which sets in the shuttle. This yarn is unwound and left in the shed as the shuttle passes through in going from the shuttle box on the one side of the loom to the shuttle box on the other side.

The reed then beats the loose pick in the shed into the cloth.

Breast Beam: The bar, wooden or otherwise, at the front of the loom over which the cloth passes on its way to the cloth roller. This beam runs parallel with the reed, lease rods, and whip roll; these four parts of the loom must be parallel to produce cloth because of the fact that the warp must interlace at right angles with the filling to make woven fabric.

Cloth Roller: A roller across the front of the loom, below the breast beam, onto which the newly woven material is wound.

Each piece, bolt, or cut of cloth is taken from the cloth roller when the correct cloth yardage has been woven.

Cut lengths of cloth will vary considerably, dependent upon local conditions. Sixty to eighty yards seems to be the length desired for woolen and worsted goods; forty to fifty yards for rayon and cotton goods. There is no cut-and-dried rule as to what a cut length should be in actual yardage.

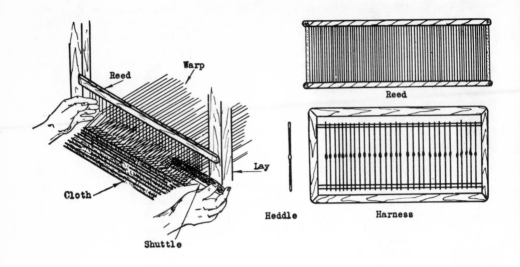

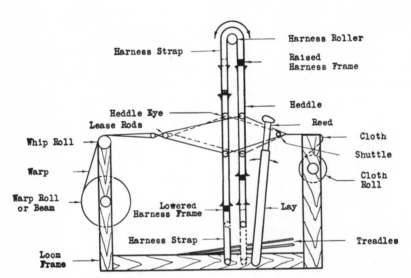

Mali Technology to Produce Fabric

In 1952, Heinrich Mauersberger, Limbach, East Germany (Karl Marx Stadt, Germany, D.D.R.), invented a new method of producing fabric which has had a meteoric rise in fabric-producing circles throughout the world. First production, however, was not achieved until 1959. The name, Malimo, is derived from the first two letters of the inventor's name, "MA," and the first two of his home town, "LI," thus, MALI. The distributor in the Free World for the machines is Crompton-Knowles-Malimo, Inc., a division of Crompton & Knowles Corporation, Worcester, Massachusetts.

There are three types of Mali machines—Malimo, linked with the word "melton"; Malipol, linked with the word "pile"; and Maliwatt, derived from the word "watt," which means a batting or wadding.

MALIMO: Warp and filling are present in the fabric and woven characteristics are apparent: the goods are ravel-free and very tear-resistant. The warp ends are laid on top of the filling, which is fed in continuously to the machine. Up to 150 filling yarns are fed in from a creel and laid out in filling formation. The mechanism of the frame allows the insertion of the equivalent of 4,000 to 4,500 picks per minute.

The warp ends and the filling picks are connected by a third system of yarn (thread), and it sews or stitches (interlaces) the two systems, warp and filling. Thus, different from conventional looms, the insertion of the filling yarn is no longer a speed-controlling factor. The sewing stitches have a speed of twelve to fourteen hundred per minute and the stitch length is adjustable between 1.5 mm. and 3.0 millimeters. Production on this frame ranges from two to three yards a minute, and any woven length within reason may be made. The frame is 63½ inches wide, and fabric made can be given either a knit or a woven effect; all fabric has the properties of woven goods.

Yarns used are fed in from beams or creels; if creels are used, all preparatory processes in manipulation are eliminated. Warp and filling are under considerably less tension than in an ordinary loom, and this permits the use of yarns with less twist, and slashing of warp is not necessary.

Possible production on heavy goods, for example, can run as high as a hundred yards an hour. These goods include winter coatings (melton, kersey, beaver, etc.), bath mats, heavy dressgoods, imitation furs, etc.

MALIPOL: If it is desired to produce corduroy or velveteen on the machine, there is a head motion attachment available which uses a backing fabric and the filling is sewn to this backing in processing. About one hundred yards an hour may be obtained on the frame. The product is known as Mali-corduroy or Mali-velveteen.

In the production of pile fabrics on Malipol, the machine uses the backing fabric for presentation to the needle elements. Pile sinkers on one side of the goods cause the sewing of the pile yarn to form the pile effect of the desired height. This type of goods, however, does not support pulling out or shredding, since the pile yarns are knit onto the back of the fabric. From eleven to twelve hundred stitches per minute are applied and machinery efficiency ranges from 85 to 90 per cent. Stitch lengths can be adjusted to suit any purpose of construction. Blankets, carpetings, and comparable heavy goods can be made easily on this type of machine.

MALIWATT: This type frame uses a fiber batting or wadding, or a carding machine web formation. Sewing thread is used to compact and interlace the web used into actually a nonwoven fabric. Conventional or ordinary finishing equipment is used to finish the goods—napping, shearing, cropping, printing, etc. Many uses have been found for coating applications and insulations. Laminations to other products, textile or nontextile, give interesting effects. The machine may have a width of one hundred inches and speeds of better than one thousand stitches per minute are obtained. Stitch lengths are adjustable between 2.1 and 4.2 millimeters. Production yield is from 120 yards to about 250 yards per hour dependent on local conditions and the type of fabric desired. Numerous lining and interlining materials are made on this type frame.

In summary, the major advantage of Mali machines is high production speeds which, however, limits the styling of basic fabric types. Fabric runs on production amounts to many thousands of yards in sequence.

Box loom fabrics, weave effects, color effects, twills, dobby motifs, etc., are not produced on the frames because of the manner in which the filling yarns are placed into the fabric in manipulation. New effects, however, not possible on a loom or a knitting frame, are achieved on Mali machinery.

Currently available machinery is now up to 14 gauge and capable of producing fabrics with a very wide range, from 5.5 ounces per square yard up to 20-ounce weights.

Possible Defects in Cloth

The following will show the number of possible defects that may be found in woven goods:

1. Barry or barre marks.
2. Bleeding colors.
3. Broken pattern.
4. Broken ends or picks.
5. Cloudy goods.
6. Cockled cloth.
7. Coarse ends or picks.
8. Creases.
9. Crocking.
10. Cut listing or selvage.
11. Dead colors.
12. Double picks.
13. Ends out.
14. Floats.
15. Hair in filling—fuzziness.
16. Harness skips.
17. Hitch backs.
18. Holes.
19. Kinks.
20. Loose picks.
21. Loose selvages.
22. Mispicks.
23. Mixed filling.
24. Narrow width.
25. Oil stains.
26. Overwidth.
27. Reed marks.
28. Rolling selvage.
29. Section marks.
30. Shear marks.
31. Shiners.
32. Skipping.
33. Shuttle marks.
34. Slugs.
35. Specky goods.
36. Sluff-offs.
37. Sand roller marks.
38. Start-up marks.
39. Thick stripes.
40. Thin stripes
41. Tender goods.
42. Tight picks.
43. Tight selvages.
44. Torn selvages.
45. Uneven cloth.
46. Washer wrinkles.
47. Weaving over or under.
48. Weaving slack.
49. Wrong draws.
50. Uneven double and twist.

TESTING

1. Name the six motions of a loom. Shedding, picking, and beating-up (major); let-off, take-up, and pattern motion (minor or auxiliary).
2. Name the three chief motions in weaving. Shedding, picking, beating up.
3. Explain the function of each motion.
4. Name the parts of the loom which form the flat plane to make weaving possible. The two selvage edges, whip roll, breast beam.
5. Of what value is the selvage in a woven cloth?
6. How would you recognize selvage in a woven material?
7. How may the selvage differ from the body of the woven cloth?
8. What is another name for selvage? Listing, self-edge; sometimes spelled "selvedge."
9. Why is warp yarn in the loom woven under tension?
10. Why would warp yarns, rather than filling yarns, be sized? Because the warp yarn is under tension and has to withstand the rigors of weaving, wearing, and chafing. The warp must also have greater tensile strength than the filling for obvious reasons, as observed in weaving.
11. What are names of the three parts of a full filling bobbin? Nose, body, and heel.
12. How would reed marks mar cloth? Faulty reed wires cause the warp ends to make slight deviations or angles rather than enter the fabric straight, true, and at right angles with the filling yarn.

13. Are all woven cloths, from the simplest and the cheapest to the most intricate and expensive, made on the same principles of weaving on the loom? Yes, from cheese-cloth or printcloth to silk brocade and damask.
14. What changes would occur in weaving if the take-up rate were increased? Light, shaded effects would appear in the cloth, and the texture would be affected in the filling direction. If the take-up rate is changed it is also necessary to correspondingly check the let-off motion; otherwise cockled cloth will result.
15. Name and describe five parts of the loom.
16. Name five defects that may occur in woven fabrics, and describe each of these.

The Largest Loom in the World

This loom was built by Lansdowne Steel & Iron Company, Inc., at the Goodyear Aerospace Corporation, Akron, Ohio, under contract for the Manufacturing Technology Division, Air Force Materials Laboratories, Wright-Patterson Air Force Base, Akron, Ohio. The loom weaves stainless steel yarns into expandable appendages that can be used for the recovery of boosters and other reentry vehicles. The cost to build the loom was $750,000. The expandable fabrics in their uses include shelters for astronauts, expandable and rigid components for a bullet-shaped reentry vehicle for use in space programs, and for inflatable antennas for mobile ground forces. It is known as the "Airmat Loom."

The loom weighs 150 tons, is 125 feet long, 80 feet wide, and 20 feet high. Nylon gears are used and no lubrication is necessary. The harness motion has two dobby head motions, one on each side of the loom, to drive even-and odd-numbered harnesses, and a four-position Jacquard head motion that weaves along and synchronizes with the dobbies.

The take-up motion, instead of the usual motion used on conventional looms, has a drawbar that pulls the finished fabric straight out from the reed. The weaving is automatic and stop-motion controlled. Woven fabrics run up to eight feet in thickness, and in any width in three-foot increments, the usual width being from three to twenty-one feet.

Pickage is from 2.7 up to 16 picks a minute, while maximum cloth density is 200 by 200 yarn ends per inch on a 1.5 millimeter yarn. Minimum construction is 25 by 25, and the diameter of yarns used ranges from .0015 to .032 of an inch. There are six harness frames on the looms and plain, twill, or satin constructions can be used. Production is from a thousand to fifteen hundred square inches per hour. Steel and other metallic yarns are woven on this loom.

There are two harness beams used for the warp yarn. Sections for beams, harnesses, and reeds are made in units of three to six feet so as to use all the reed splits, dents, or space. The loom uses the drop-yarn feed-in from conventional creels and can weave up to 102,000 ends of yarn.

Seven motors are required to run this fabulous loom and right-hand and left-hand electric assemblies are interconnected through gear reducers and are coupled to the lay of the loom (the movable loom action when the loom is weaving fabric) and the Jacquard cam shafts. The main drives also power the let-off motion as fabric is being produced, the dobbies, filling inserter, and a selvage shuttle.

The loom weaves three-dimensional fabric which consists of two layers of woven fabric connected by a series of drop yarns that are woven as integral parts of the two surface fabrics. Air space between the top and bottom fabric, the height of the drop yarns, may run as high as eight feet.

Reflected light highlights some of the thousands of strands that go into the loom. At bottom right, an engineer inspects a sample of a finished Airmat segment, with the metallic drop threads stretched between the outer surfaces.

Courtesy: R. & D. Division, Wright-Patterson Air Force Base, Dayton, Ohio

Gears that control the vertical movement of the thousands of strands being woven into Airmat are checked by a technician.

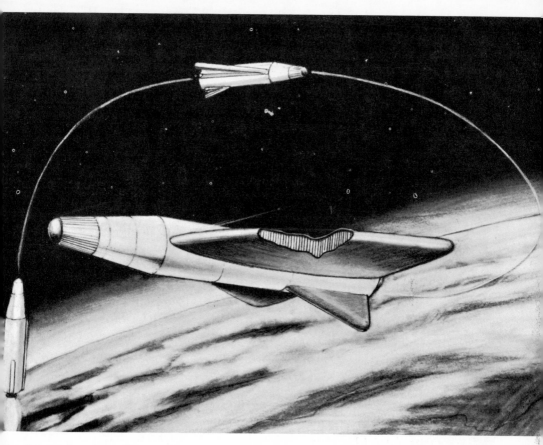

An artist's concept illustrates the method of recovering expended rockets through use of expandable wings and fins that would be packaged during the initial stages of flight and would deploy as the object returned to earth, creating a navigable craft. Goodyear Aerospace Corporation announced installation in June 1964 of a huge Airmat loom, built under contract to Research and Technology Division, Wright-Patterson Air Force Base, that can produce the expandable appendages.

Thickness and shape of the fabric are controlled during fabrication by changing the length of the drop yarn. Internal pressuring gases are retained between the two surface fabrics by impregnating the fabric with an elastomer. Truly this loom is one of the marvels of our time and will contribute its share in future developments in the exploration of space.

Part 1—Unit 7

TOPIC: Properties and Characteristics of Woven Cloth

HOW TEXTILES DIFFER

There are four ways in which textiles differ:

1. Raw Material: wool, cotton, acetate, nylon, "Dacron," asbestos, etc.
2. Construction: woven, knitted; plaited, braided and/or lace; felt, and nonwoven fabrics, etc.
3. Color: red, blue, gray, brown, natural, neutral, pastel shades, etc.

4. Finish: boardy, cashmere, ciré, clear, crepe, crisp, cropped, de-lustered, dull, duplex, even, face-finished, glazed, glossy, harsh, lustrous, mercerized, moiré or watermarked, moss, napped, natural, pebble, plain, reversible, rough, satin-like, satiny, semi-finished, sheared, smooth, soft, starched, stiff, surface-finished, undressed, uneven, embossed, etc.

Some fabrics are used for innerwear, others for outerwear, and there are decorative fabrics such as brocade, brocatelle, damask, Jacquard fabrics, tapestry, certain types of cretonne, some duplex fabrics, furniture fabric, curtain material. There are also fabrics used in the industrial world such as canvas and duck, rayon or nylon tire cord, webbing, conveyor belting, and automobile upholstery fabric.

SOME ADVANTAGES OF WOVEN CLOTH

1. Firm construction: typewriter ribbon, duck, webbing, overcoating.
2. Durable if closely woven: serge, broadcloth, many types of outerwear.
3. Launders well: underwear of many types, washable dressgoods.
4. Drapes well, will not sag, and holds shape: satin and other ideal fabrics for evening wear, French worsted, tricotine, cavalry twill.
5. The only type of cloth that will drape with a natural flare: satins made of silk, rayon, acetate; high-quality worsted for women's wear apparel; soft sheers of wool, rayon, or nylon.
6. Can be pleated and tucked very readily: serge, cassimere, many other types of dressgoods made from the major fibers. Accordion pleats and box pleats present a good effect on certain woven goods, whereas many other types of textile fabrics cannot be pleated in a satisfactory manner.
7. Can be cut and draped on the bias: evening wear, slips, dresses.
8. Has greater tensile strength than other types of material: for example, the shoulder strap webbing on an army haversack must have a tensile breaking strength of two thousand pounds (one ton). It is made of cotton or nylon webbing.
9. Withstands chafing and friction well: men's wear suiting must meet these tests; topcoatings and overcoatings, underwear, etc.
10. May be colored by any of the major methods of coloring: piece-dyed, yarn or skein-dyed, stock-dyed, cross-dyed, printed.
11. Especially suited for detailed and intricate printed designs: splash prints, fourteen-color prints, photographic prints, etc.
12. Woven construction makes possible many types of finish.
13. Woven constructions make possible many uses: innerwear, outerwear, household fabrics and cloths, decorative materials, industrial fabrics.
14. Certain weave constructions permit finer detail of pattern than is found in knitted, plaited, braided, or felt cloth, generally speaking: Jacquard patterns showing pastoral scenes, noted personages, buildings, etc. A Jacquard loom can be made to reproduce any picture.
15. Close constructions can be made waterproof: gabardine, tackle twill, raincoating, Zelan-treated fabrics, Scotchgard-treated fabrics, etc.

SOME POSSIBLE DISADVANTAGES OF WOVEN CLOTH

1. Is not generally elastic when compared with knitted fabrics.
2. Is not really form-fitting; woven socks have not yet been produced.
3. After continued wear some woven fabrics will develop an undesirable shine—garments made of serge, cassimere, whipcord, tricotine, elastique.
4. Generally more expensive to manufacture than other types: Some textile fabrics have sold as high as two hundred dollars per yard for coating or evening wear material. Much decorative fabric is often very high in price.

5. Very sheer woven fabrics may slip or pull at the seams: slips cut on the bias; certain dressgoods may slip when washed.
6. Will show wrinkles readily: Many dressgoods will not stand up in hot weather and require frequent laundering. Handkerchiefs wrinkle easily.
7. Yarns of uneven size appear as defects in woven goods that have been finished: often noted in apparel or in goods bought over the counter in the department store.
8. Usually not porous. Some summer materials are made porous; but in general, woven textiles are not classed as being porous when some plaited, braided, or knitted fabrics are considered.

Some Thoughts That Should Be Kept in Mind Relative to Woven Fabric

1. The many advantages of woven cloth result in its widespread use in the fabric and garment fields.
2. There is a very wide range possible as to design, motif, or pattern.
3. Woven goods are the most durable in the long run.
4. Many woven fabrics and garments will launder easily and well, can be made "good-as-new," may be drycleaned, given many types of finishes.
5. The proper care of all types of clothing is very important in our economic and social life. Most of the clothing we wear is of woven construction.
6. Woven fabrics when made into garments may be form-fitting or form-revealing. Garments may be tailored to exact measure or they may be loose with regard to fit.

TESTING

Make a list of ten textile materials or products that have been woven and are used in the home. Write not more than five lines on each of these on its advantage or utility purpose. Some materials that might be included are sheeting, handkerchief linen, dishtoweling, upholstery, shirting, carpeting, neckwear, nightwear.

Part 1—Unit 8

TOPIC: Determination of Warp from the Filling in Woven Fabric

Any rectangular figure has a length and a width. This is true of fabric as well. The student in textiles, apparel, merchandising, and home economics should have a good knowledge of the basic features found in a woven material. These include the distinction between the warp and the filling, and the determination of the face of the goods from the back of the fabric. When a fabric is being used to make a garment, it should be obvious that the warp direction of the fabric is stronger and that the cloth should be manipulated with the warp direction of the cloth running vertically. In dressmaking one often hears the expression, "the grain in the cloth." A thread is pulled in order to straighten the grain-line, and the thread drawn should be a filling yarn so that the grain-line may be made even.

Aids in the Distinction between the Warp and the Filling

1. Garments cut in the warp direction will give better wear.
2. There is less shrinkage in the warp or vertical direction.
3. Filling or horizontal threads have the tendency to stretch more when compared with warp ends or threads. Difficult to overcome in some fabrics in the cut-fit-trim trade.
4. To know the direction enables one to cut in the direction which is more desirable in tailoring—the warp or vertical direction in most instances.
5. A means to aid in identification of the face of the material.

6. Serves as an aid in testing fabrics in many physical tests resorted to in textile testing.
7. Used as an aid in laying out fabric on the cutting table.
8. For proper hanging purposes, as well as for true balance of the garment, the pattern of every part of the garment must be placed accurately on the material—in the warp, vertical, or true bias direction. Some printed materials, however, because of the motifs or stripes, should be used on the cross-graining for balance, the proper hang of the garment, and for the suppleness of the material.
9. Many collars, yokes, belts, and cuffs are cut on the cross-grain in order to avoid excessive stretching.
10. Accurate measurements can be made on the proper grain-line.
11. Most garments are cut in the warp direction because:
    (*a*) Warp threads are stronger.
    (*b*) The garment will hang better.
    (*c*) The garment will fit and wear better.
12. Many style lines are better adapted to the warp grain.
13. Proper grain-line lends for contrast in trimming.
14. The draping and the pleating quality of each grain varies.
15. True bias is absolutely essential for bias binding; off-grain will not stretch on a garment in a smooth manner.
16. The lengthwise or warp grain is usually used through the center front of the garment because of the strengh needed.
17. When matching checked material, the lengthwise grain squares and the crosswise squares often vary slightly in size.
18. When an operator receives a bundle of cut work, the two sections which are to be joined may be of such shape that it is difficult to judge which seams are to join together. A knowledge of grain-lines will be of value to the operator:

Examples:

Skirt-front   Skirt-back

join together

lengthwise
grain

Some Rules to Be Used in the Determination of the Warp from the Filling

1. The selvage or listing runs in the warp or vertical direction in a woven fabric and is a component part of the warp. A woven cloth has a selvage to protect the edges of the material in the processes of weaving, dyeing, and finishing. A good selvage produces the effect of a frame around a picture and usually indicates a quality fabric.
2. The set of yarns with the greater or harder twist is the warp. Added tension is necessary to the warp threads since they must withstand the rigors of weaving in the loom. Filling yarn is under little or no tension as it comes off the nose of the filling bobbin. Examples include blankets, dressgoods, overcoatings, shirting.
3. The regularity and number of one parallel set of yarns usually indicates that this set is the warp. Filling yarns in a woven fabric are usually coarser and fewer in number and are sometimes irregular.
4. Stripes run in the warp or vertical direction in woven goods. Examples include awning stripes, banjo stripes, suiting, baseball uniform cloth, Bengal stripes, chalk stripes, curtaining, dressgoods, madras and other shirting fabric, neckwear fabric, pin stripes, striped trousering, ticking, toweling.

5. When several sizes of yarn are used in a fabric, it usually implies that the basic yarns are in the warp while the fancy, decorative, or novelty yarns are in the filling. This effect is observed in some curtaining, decorative fabrics, bedspreads, some novelty dressgoods, brocade, brocatelle, damask, tapestry.
6. Some fabrics in which novelty or fancy yarns are used will reveal that these yarns are used in the warp in order to give decoration, a novelty effect, or an attractive surface appearance to the material. This may occur in some types of women's wear coating, decorative fabrics, and some dressgoods. Whether the effect of novelty or fancy yarns is to be in the warp or in the filling direction depends, to considerable degree, on the particular cloth and its terminal use.
7. When one system of yarn is entirely two-ply and the other is single, the two-ply system is usually considered as the warp. This is observed in cloths where the preponderance of the fabric is warp which covers up the filling, as in the case of gabardine, whipcord, and some woolen suiting fabrics.

CAUSES OF REED MARKS IN THE WARP DIRECTION

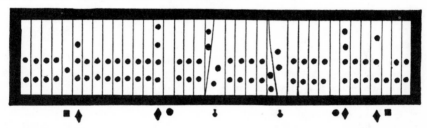

The diagram above illustrates the causes of reed marks in the warp direction. This reeding plan is for two warp ends per dent or split.

● — Skipped dent . . . no ends reeded in the dent; causes a light line in the warp direction seen when the cloth is held to the light.

■ — Light dent . . . when less than the required number of ends has been reeded; causes a line reed mark in the warp direction.

◆ — Swollen dent . . . in addition to the regular number of ends drawn through the split, the threads from a split on either side of the dent have been likewise drawn through; causes a cord effect in the warp direction that is difficult to correct.

⦙● — Loose, bent or worn reed wire . . . reed wires bend and cause a spreading or a crowding of the respective warp ends; cause the ends to enter the woven goods at a slight angle rather than an absolute right angle with the filling pick. Lines appear in the goods as a result, but usually they can be removed in the finishing of the goods.

8. The nap or fur on a material runs in the warp direction, comparable with the fur on a cat's back, and a man's beard—smooth on the downward stroke and rough on the upward stroke. Examples include pile fabrics of many types, carpets and rugs, melton, kersey, beaver, broadcloth, and several types of women's wear winter coating.
9. Bulkier yarn is used for filling. Often found in drapery and upholstery fabrics, boys' and girls' apparel, and in low-cost women's.wear ensembles and coating.
10. The lower grade of yarn in the one system of yarns implies that this system is the filling. Yarn of this type is in low-cost coatings for women's wear, some face-finished fabrics, some union fabrics, and low-quality woolen suitings.
11. Several fabrics may be rather easily identified as to the warp or the filling in that they have rounded or cylindrical yarn in the filling direction. Fabrics in this group might include poplin, rep, broadcloth, fuji, luana, oxford shirting, faille, taffeta; grosgrain, bengaline, ottoman, ribbon—warp-rib weave fabrics in which the rib or cord always goes in the filling direction.

[59]

12. Reed marks in cloth go in the warp direction since the reed is a comblike device usually consisting of a top and a bottom rib of wood into which are set thin flat strips of rather fine pressed steel wire. Carpets, rugs, and heavy industrial fabrics are woven on looms equipped with an iron reed which has a low number of splits to the inch.

The spaces between the reed wire are called reed dents or reed splits. The count or number of a reed is determined by the number of dents to the inch—a 24-reed would have 24 splits to the inch.

The reed is set in the raceplate of the loom and, when in operation, beats the loose filling pick into its component place in the cloth, and keeps the warp ends even, uniform, straight, and true. In this way the warp and filling interlace at right angles.

Reed-mark imperfections can be observed in many silks, rayons, and light-weight cottons when the fabric is held to the light. These marks, because the finishing of fabrics is an art and a science, may not show in finished materials.

TESTING

1. Define the following terms: warp, filling, selvage.
2. Of what value is the selvage in a woven fabric?
3. Explain why warp yarns are usually stronger than filling yarns.
4. Name five fabrics that show stripes in the warp direction.
5. Name two cloths that may use a warp of varying size or diameter.
6. Name three materials which are recognized by the nap on the face of the goods.
7. Name three cloths in which reed marks might be easily seen.
8. List five fabrics identified by their cylindrical filling yarn in cloth.
9. Define the following terms: skipped dent, swollen dent, light dent.
10. Name three decorative fabrics.

Part 1—Unit 9

TOPIC: DETERMINATION OF FACE FROM BACK OF WOVEN FABRIC

Every fabric must have two sides, the face and the back, or the right side and the wrong side. In some fabrics there is a vast difference between the face and the back, while in others the face and back are very similar or practically the same in effect and appearance. Some other materials may even be classed as reversibles, since it makes little or no difference which side of the material is used as the face or the back. The following information should be of importance to the reader in the question of determining the face from the back of a cloth.

1. Unless the face of the material is used throughout, there may be a different shade-of-garment appearance caused by difference in color or by a difference in design. (If the sleeve, for example, is made from the back of the goods and the rest of the garment is made from the face of the goods, the sleeve will make the garment an imperfect, or a second.)
2. Direction of design in the material: Stripes, plaids, checks, floral effects should be in proper alignment and proper matching.

If each stripe or block effect were of a different color, a matching problem would arise—all parts of a garment should match.

3. Surface effect or texture:
   (*a*) Lustrous satin face as against a dull back-of-fabric effect. The former is used as the body of the garment; the latter may be used for cuffs, collar, lapels, trimming, etc.
   (*b*) Raised designs on face, such as sprigged dimity, dotted Swiss, and flock-dotted fabric should have raised effect on face of goods.
   (*c*) Twill fabric. Care should be exercised that all parts of a garment have twill running in correct directions. A suit made of right-hand twill serge or gabardine would be spoiled if the sleeve, for example, were made inside out and and had a left-hand twill effect used for the face.
   (*d*) Knots, blemishes of several types, press marks, flaws in weaving, flaws from dyeing—all should, unless it is possible to remove them altogether, be brought to the back of the goods so as not to show on the face of the goods and possibly spoil the surface of the face of the material.
4. Satin will clearly show the fact that the face has much finer construction and finish when compared with the back of the goods.
5. Velvet or corduroy demonstrates that the pile on the face makes it more attractive than the reverse side.
6. Colors are usually brighter on the face of the fabric.
7. Ribbed or corded fabrics are more pronounced on the face.
8. The design of a woven or a printed cloth will be more attractive on the face.
9. Medium and heavyweight fabrics have the better finish on the face.

Rules to Aid in the Determination of Face from Back of Fabric

1. The face and the back of some fabrics are the same and may be classed as reversible. Examples include canvas, duck, burlap, bagging. Handkerchief linen, which might be included, can be identified by the manner of hemming or stitching —the back or underside is hemmed or stitched.
2. With the exception of plaid-back overcoatings, plaids appear on the face of the material. Examples may include dress silks and rayons, umbrella fabric, overplaids made with double cloth construction, ribbon, novelty fabrics.
3. Face-finished fabrics have the more attractive side as the face of the goods. Examples include beaver, bolivia, bouclé, broadcloth in the woolen trade, camelhair fabrics, chinchilla, kersey, melton, montagnac, Saxony, tree-bark, Whitney finish, zibeline.
4. Some cloths are made so that only one side may be considered as being suitable for the face of the fabric. Long floats, knots, extra yarn stitching on the back make these fabrics unsuitable for use as the face of the goods.
5. Some silk fabrics, such as crepe-back satin and rib-back satin, are so constructed that either side may be used as the face of material, although the lustrous side is the real face. These cloths may go into garments which have the satin side as the face while trimming, lapels, pockets, bandings may have the darker side as the face.
6. With the exception of duplex or registered prints, printed materials have that side as the face which shows the clearer pattern effect. Cretonne, shirting, prints of many types, chintz, dressgoods, decorative fabrics are examples.
7. Fabrics which are decorated with fancy yarns would use the side which shows these yarns to advantage as the face of the material. Nubs, bright spots of color from the use of novelty yarn, fancy yarn effects and laminated yarns would be examples. Fancy effects are noted in some suiting and dressgoods, coating, vesting fabric, draperies, some shirting materials.
8. Cloth made with twill or diagonal lines, when held to the light or with the warp vertical or lengthwise, will show that side to be the face which has the lines running from the lower left-hand corner of the fabric to the upper right-hand corner of the goods. This is right-hand twill direction; it may be stated that about 80 per cent of twill-woven fabric is made with right-hand twill construction. Examples may include cassimere, charmeen, covert, diagonal suiting, elastique, cavalry twill, tricotine, gabardine, serge, Poiret twill, straw car seating, tartan plaid, twillcord, whip-

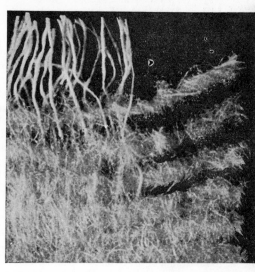

1. THE SELVAGE TEST ... the selvage, the edge of a piece of woven goods designed to prevent unraveling, runs in the warp direction of the fabric. A good selvage which is found on any cloth of full width produces the effect of a frame around a picture and usually indicates a quality fabric.

2. THE TWIST TEST ... the set of yarns with the greater or harder twist is the warp. Added tension is necessary to the warp ends since they must withstand the rigors of weaving in the loom. Filling yarn is under little or no tension. Found usually in shirting, serge, overcoating and dress goods.

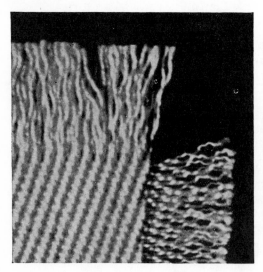

3. THE REGULAR NUMBERS TEST ... the set of yarns which is most numerous and regular. This set is the warp. Filling yarns in a woven fabric are usually coarser and fewer in number. Sometimes they are irregular. Found in shirting cloth, serge, overcoating.

4. THE STRIPES TEST ... stripes run in the warp or vertical direction in woven goods. Examples include awning stripes, banjo stripes, suiting, baseball uniform cloth, Bengal stripes, chalk stripes, curtaining, dress goods, madras, shirting, neckwear fabric, pin stripe suiting, ticking, toweling.

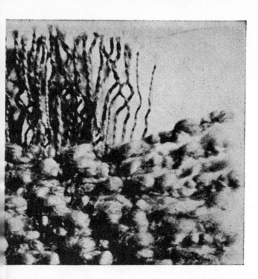 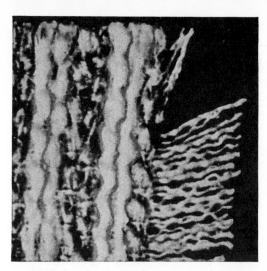

5. THE VARIED YARN SIZE TEST . . . if several sizes of yarn are used in a fabric, usually the basic yarns are in the warp while the fancy, decorative or novelty yarns are in the filling. This is found in some curtaining, decorative fabrics, bedspreads, brocade, brocatelle, damask, tapestry.

6. THE FANCY YARN TEST . . . novelty or fancy yarns are sometimes used in the warp to give decoration, a novelty effect or an attractive surface appearance to the material. Whether the effect of fancy yarns is to be in the warp or filling direction depends on the cloth and its terminal use.

7. THE TWO PLY-ONE PLY TEST . . . when one system of yarn is entirely two-ply and the other is one-ply, the two-ply system is usually considered as the warp. Fabrics fitting in this classification are gabardine, whipcord and some woolen suiting. In these cases, the warp covers up the filling.

8. THE NAP OR FUR TEST . . . the nap or fur on a material, smooth on the downward stroke and rough on the upward, usually runs in the warp direction. Examples include pile fabrics of many types, carpets, rugs, melton, kersey, beaver, broadcloth, velvets, velveteen, women's winter clothing.

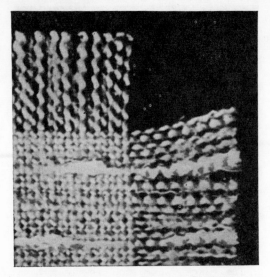

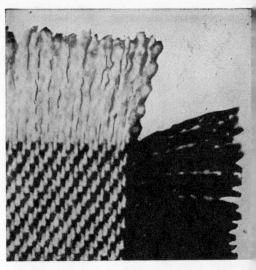

9. THE BULKIER YARN TEST . . . bulkier yarn is used for filling. It is often found in drapery and upholstery fabrics, boys' and girls' apparel and in low-cost women's wear ensembles and coating.

10. THE YARN QUALITY TEST . . . the lower grade of yarn in a woven fabric is usually the filling. Conversely, the better yarn is the warp. Yarn of this type is in low-cost coatings for women's wear, some face-finished fabrics, some union fabrics and low quality woolen suitings.

DETERMINATION OF FACE FROM BACK OF WOVEN FABRIC

1. REVERSIBLE FABRICS . . . There is no difference between the face and the back of these fabrics. Examples include canvas, duck, burlap, mail bagging. Handkerchief linen is somewhat of an exception because the back of the fabric is hemmed or stitched.

2. PLAID FABRICS ... With the exception of plaid-back overcoatings shown above, plaids are always on the face of the material. In this category are found dress silks and rayons, umbrella fabrics, overplaids made with double cloth construction, ribbon and novelty fabrics.

3. FACE-FINISHED FABRICS ... The face on these goods is the more attractive side of the material. Beaver, bolivia, bouclé, broadcloth in the woolen trade, camel-hair fabrics, chinchilla, kersey, melton, montagnac, Saxony, tree-bark, Whitney fabric, and zibeline are examples.

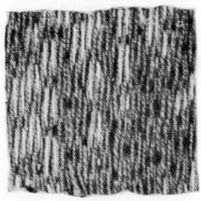

4. ONE-FACE FABRICS ... Only one side of such fabrics is suitable for the face of the fabric. Long floats, knots and extra yarn stitching on the back make these sides unsuitable for use on the face of the goods.

5. DOUBLE-FACED SILKS . . . Either side may be used as the face of such material, although the lustrous side of the material is the real face. In many garments, the satin side of the crepe-back satin or rib-back satin, for example, is the face while the trimming is the darker side.

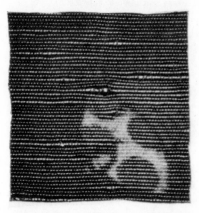

6. PRINTED MATERIALS . . . With the exception of duplex or registered prints, the face is that side with the clearer pattern effect. Cretonne, shirting, prints of many types, chintz, dressgoods and decorative fabrics are examples.

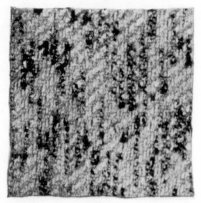

7. FANCY YARN DECORATED FABRICS . . . Such decorations are always shown to advantage on the fabric face. Nubs, bright spots of color from the use of novelty yarn, and laminated yarns are examples. Fancy effects are common in types of suiting, dressgoods, coating, drapery and shirting.

8. RIGHT HAND TWILL CLOTH . . . The face is that side of the fabric which has the lines running from the lower left-hand corner to the upper right-hand corner. About 80% of all twills are right hand.

9. LEFT HAND TWILL CLOTH . . . The face is that side of the fabric which has the diagonal lines running from the upper left-hand corner to the lower right-hand corner. Among left hand twill fabrics are denim, drill, jean and middy cloth, galatea, nurses' uniform cloth and some British worsteds.

10. RIBBED OR CORDED FABRICS . . . The face is the more pronounced side of the cloth in most instances. Fabrics of this type include Bedford cord, bengaline, corduroy, tweeduroy, piqué, ribbon, Russian cord and shirting.

Courtesy: American Fabrics, Reporter Publications

cord. The angles of the twill lines may be 15, 20, 27, 45, 63, 70 or 75 degrees; the 45-degree twill is the most popular, and considerable fabric is made from the 63-degree twill angle.

9. Some few fabrics will have a left-hand twill on the face of the fabric; that is, the twill line will run from the upper left-hand corner of the goods to the lower right-hand corner of the material. Some cloths in which left-hand twill may be used include denim, drill, jean and middy cloth, galatea, nurses' uniform cloth, some cotton lining, some cotton twills which repeat on third, fourth, fifth, sixth, and eighth harnesses in the loom. Most British imports in the woolen and worsted field are made with a left-hand twill on the face.

10. Ribbed or corded fabrics are more pronounced on the face than on the back of the cloth. Examples include Bedford cord, bengaline, corduroy, Tweeduroy, pique, ribbon, Russian cord shirting.

TESTING

1. What are the two surfaces of a piece of cloth called?
2. Why are some cloths known as "face-finished fabrics"?
3. Name four face-finished fabrics.
4. How is cloth rolled in the mill? When bought by the piece over the counter in the store? Selvage-to-selvage and folded face-to-face. The outside of the bolt or cut is the back of the goods—this is done to protect the face of the material.
5. Define a reversible fabric. Name two.
6. Name five fabrics made with a right-hand twill weave.
7. Name five fabrics made with a left-hand twill weave.
8. Name three fabrics made with a plaid or tartan design.
9. How is the face of a serge fabric distinguished from the back?

TOPIC: KNITTING

In 1589 William Lee, a graduate of St. John's College, Cambridge University, England, and a Presbyterian minister of the gospel, invented the first knitting frame or machine. It could knit only woolen stockings and it was not until 1598 that he was able to produce silk stockings on his frames. He presented the first pair of these stockings to Elizabeth I (1533–1603), queen of the United Kingdom from 1558 to her death in 1603.

The knitting industry has progressed from the old-time hand-manipulative methods to a complex, highly sophisticated tape-programmed fabric-manufacturing system. In recent years, this great industry has made phenomenal strides and today is one of the leading and most progressive segments in the entire textile kingdom of industries. Its meteoric growth can be attributed to the following causes:

1. The rise of the manmade fibers and filaments which have fostered the development of modified filament and high-bulk yarns for surface appeal, effect, and interest; new stretch properties and characteristics which provide greater performance and durability for the consumer.
2. Advances made in chemical finishing of fabrics in various forms to reduce fabric shrinkage and to better provide care requirements to the consumer.
3. The development and engineering of knitted fabrics for an almost endless chain of fabrics for use in apparel, clothing, and industrial purposes.

Knitting is the art and science of constructing fabric by the interlooping of yarn loops by the use of needles, a "loop within a loop." The most essential unit in a knit fabric is the loop or stitch.

SOME BASIC KNITTING DIAGRAMS

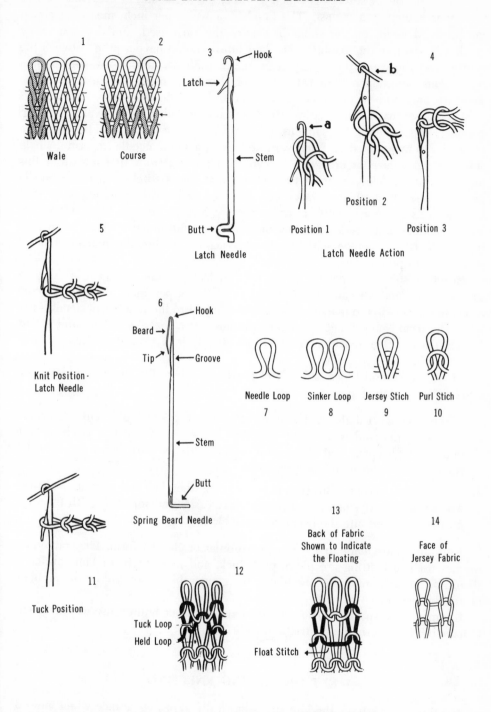

1 — Wale 2 — Course

3 — Hook, Latch, Stem, Butt — Latch Needle

4 — Latch Needle Action — a — Position 1, b — Position 2, Position 3

5 — Knit Position - Latch Needle

6 — Hook, Beard, Tip, Groove, Stem, Butt — Spring Beard Needle

7 — Needle Loop 8 — Sinker Loop 9 — Jersey Stich 10 — Purl Stich

11 — Tuck Position

12 — Tuck Loop, Held Loop

13 — Back of Fabric Shown to Indicate the Floating — Float Stitch

14 — Face of Jersey Fabric

Courtesy: Diagrams nos. 1–25 copyright property of the National Knitted Outerwear Association, 51 Madison Avenue, New York; used with permission of Mr. Sidney S. Korzenik, executive director and counsel, and Mr. Charles Reichman, editor for the Knitted Outerwear Times.

A vertical row of stitches is called a WALE; the horizontal or crosswise row of stitches is known as a COURSE. The number of wales per inch, measured across the fabric, depends on the count or size of the yarn used, and the number of needles per inch in the machine. The knit fabric should have a ratio between the courses and the wales that is equal to or up to 50 per cent more courses than wales. This ratio depends upon the type of fiber stock used, the yarn, the fabric structure, and the type or method to be used to finish the product.

There are two main divisions in the knitting industry. In warp knitting, parallel yarns are used, the same as in loom weaving for woven goods, which are presented to many needles. Each yarn knits with a single needle to form a single stitch in the course or crosswise direction in the material. In contrast to this method, weft or filling knitting uses a yarn that forms stitches on every needle on the frame. A number of yarns may be used to increase production in weft knits with as many as ninety-six or even more feeding stations being set in the large machines in use today. For instance, a frame with ninety-six yarn feeds may be said to be a machine with ninety-six machines within the one machine—a great boon to production.

In filling knits, the spacing of the needles in the frame can be expressed in several ways, and all can be converted to "needles per inch." The term "cut" refers to the cuts in the machine frame and is equal to the number of needles per inch. The term "gauge" (gg) refers to the number of needles in one and a half inches. Thus a 30-gg machine is equal to a 20-cut, or to twenty needles per inch in the machine bed or frame.

There are several types or kinds of needles used by the industry today. The two most important types are:

1. LATCH NEEDLE: It finds much use in the coarser types of fabric, although some fine-gauge material is made by this type of needle. There is a latch on this needle which opens and closes as it works, with the yarn being fed into the frame to form the actual knitting loops.

2. SPRING-BEARD NEEDLE: This type of needle is used on fine and very fine knitting. The spring-beard, small as it is, works very easily and smoothly with the yarn as it is being fed into the frame to make cloth.

Knit fabrics are made in a flat or in a tubular or circular form. The commoner stitches used in knitting are plain, purl, tuck, and miss-stitch. In knit fabrics it should be borne in mind that the higher the gauge, the higher will be the number of needles per inch.

Compound or special-purpose needles are in rather limited use and do seem to have fabric construction restrictions.

WEFT OR FILLING KNITTING

In fabric of this type, the knit stitch has a different appearance when viewed from the opposite side; therefore, these concise definitions should be kept in mind:

KNIT STITCH: Occurs when a yarn is pulled toward you through a previous loop.

PURL STITCH: Occurs when a yarn is pulled away from you through a previous loop or when you view a knit stitch from the back of the goods.

TUCK STITCH: It is made when the needle receives a new yarn and does not lose its old loop. The accumulated yarns must be knitted off the needle at some later time.

MISS-STITCH: Also known as a "float stitch" or a "welt stitch." It is made when the needle holds the old loop and does not receive a new yarn; that is, a needle is held in a nonworking position as the yarn is fed or guided to the needles that are working. (See pages 69 and 72.)

These foregoing stitches are used in various combinations to produce the basic fabrics and fabric constructions with a great many surface effects and patterned designs. There are actually three basic fabrics and machines in the weft knit goods manufacturing process—the fabrics are jersey, rib, and purl, as shown on pages 69 and 72.

Development of a Pattern or Construction

This is accomplished in knit fabric in several ways. In addition to ordinary horizontal stripes, some of the major constructions follow:

PLATING: There are two loops in every stitch which, when properly arranged, will have one loop on the face of the stitch and the other loop on the back of the material. The loops may be formed from yarns of different fibers or yarns, and different colors. Plating is accomplished by yarn positioning, with the upper yarn being placed behind or on the back of the stitch.

USES OF THE METHOD

a) REINFORCEMENT: Cotton face and nylon back (socks).
b) COLOR EFFECT: Red face and blue back (sweaters).
c) COST REDUCTION: Wool face and cotton back.
d) PROPERTIES: Filament yarn face and spun yarn back (socks).

STITCH TRANSFER: Transferring or "decking" is an operation of moving loops from one or more needles to needles in the same or in the opposite bed. It can be accomplished by manual or automatic operations for the development of *design texture* (pelerine or eyelet, lace, half-point, cable). Also, *fabric shaping* can be accomplished by single-needle narrowing and single-needle widening (full-fashioned sweaters).

INTARSIA: Solid color or intarsia designs or motifs show the same colored yarn on both face and back of the color area. Horizontal striping areas will always be solid; vertical stripes or geometrical designs will have a clear joining on the face in the case of rib, or one- or two-wale overlap of color joining in jersey, purl, and rib only on the back. The advantages of solid-color motifs are good color definition, more than one color may be used in the same course, and light-weight fabric and the characteristics pertinent to the fabric are maintained (sweaters and socks).

TERRY: This is a type of plated fabric which has two yarns in each stitch. The terry effect, comparable with the woven fabric, is obtained by drawing the back yarn into a longer sinker loop than the face yarn which forms the base or foundation fabric (napped fabrics, beachwear).

PILE: Sliver knitting is a method of knitting both yarn and fiber into a fabric to provide an exceptionally deep pile effect. A miniature carding machine is situated at each knitting feed which delivers parallel fibers to the last roll (the doffer roller) of the card. The needles rise and enter the wire clothing of the doffer roll, thus actually "scraping" the fibers into the needle hooks.

SOME BASIC KNITTING DIAGRAMS

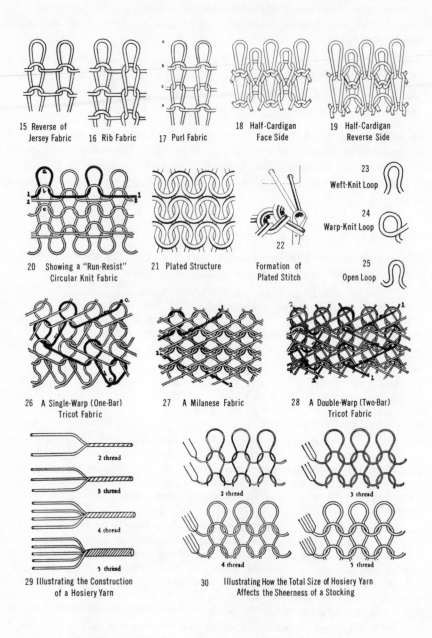

15 Reverse of
Jersey Fabric

16 Rib Fabric

17 Purl Fabric

18 Half-Cardigan
Face Side

19 Half-Cardigan
Reverse Side

20 Showing a "Run-Resist"
Circular Knit Fabric

21 Plated Structure

Formation of
Plated Stitch

22

23
Weft-Knit Loop

24
Warp-Knit Loop

25
Open Loop

26 A Single-Warp (One-Bar)
Tricot Fabric

27 A Milanese Fabric

28 A Double-Warp (Two-Bar)
Tricot Fabric

2 thread

3 thread

4 thread

5 thread

29 Illustrating the Construction
of a Hosiery Yarn

2 thread

3 thread

4 thread

5 thread

30 Illustrating How the Total Size of Hosiery Yarn
Affects the Sheerness of a Stocking

Diagrams nos. 26–30 used by permission of Beaunit Fiber Division, Beaunit Corporation, 261 Madison Avenue, New York City.

A backing yarn is fed as the needles descend, thus locking the fibers into the knitted stitch. The average pile height is one-half the fiber staple length. The density of the pile is regulated by the card delivery speed and the sliver weight per yard. The fabric is split open for dyeing and finishing. Some of the more recent machines developed for this type of work use color sliver at various feeds and through needle control can develop figured color pattern effects of pile (pile coats and rugs).

NEEDLE SETOUT: The removal or deactivation of needles for long periods of time during the course of knitting is referred to as "drawn" needles, the needle setout arrangement (sweater cuffs).

RACKING: The lateral or side-to-side movement of the needle bed and/or the needles is known as "racking" and it is used in purl and rib fabrics. Racking for fabric design is generally restricted to one bed, either the front or the back bed.

    The racked effect inclines the stitch, reduces the elasticity, and causes the fabric to become more compact. The movement of the back bed to the left will incline the front-bed stitches to the right. Fabrics may be shaped to some extent by the operation of racking (sweater and collar trimming).

KNIT AND MISSING: This procedure provides the following:

    a) Developing the designs in color.
    b) Developing the design in construction.
    c) Developing run-resistant fabrics.
    d) Provides a fabric that is narrower than one made with tuck stitches.
    e) Provides a cloth lighter in weight than is possible with tuck stitches.
    f) Provides a fabric with less elasticity in the width.

KNIT AND TUCKING: This procedure provides the following:

    a) Developing the designs in color.
    b) Developing the design in construction.
    c) Provides a fabric that is wider than plain jersey or knit-and-miss fabrics.
    d) Reinforcement and strengthening fabric parts.
    e) Provides mock fashion marks.
    f) Can produce open textures and lace effects easily and well.
    g) Can increase the weight-unit area without changing the size or count of the yarn or the length of the stitch.

LAID-IN: There are two ways to obtain this effect:

    1. STANDARD OR CONVENTIONAL LAYING-IN: This is done on one set of needles by tucking and missing on several feeds or rows of the fabric.
    The purposes of this construction are:

        a) To incorporate heavier threads than would be normally used on the machine.
        b) To introduce novelty yarns that are irregular in diameter. In this manner they can be made to combine with the ground structure without being drawn through any knitted loops.
        c) To restrict a yarn to the back of a fabric such as rubber or elastic yarns, yarns for brushing, and reduced yarn consumption.
        d) To develop a figured motif of floats through the sequences of tucking and missing.

    2. FLEECY OR DOUBLE-FACE PLUSH: This is a type of goods which uses one set of needles with tucking and missing, but there are two knitting yarns which form two ground loops in each stitch.
    The laid-in threads pass between the two yarns and do not appear on the true face side of the material. The advantage of the fleecy construction is that it provides a clearer texture on the technical face and a more secure binding of the yarn, especially in the case of the manmade fiber group of yarns.
    The fleecy type of fabric is preferred when the technical face of the goods is

worn outside, as in the case of sweat shirts, and when a brushed or raised surface is required with manmade fiber yarns, such as noted in a nylon fleece fabric.

DROP STITCH: Fabrics under this caption are constructed to control the degree of un-looping of certain stitches and to provide for opening needle latches when necessary. The drop stitch construction is generally limited to jersey and rib fabrics for either fabric design or for the separation of rib fabric pieces (knit shirts and dress fabrics).

ELASTIC INSERTION: Two points should be observed in this type of work:

a) One-way stretch fabric incorporates a rubber thread into the fabric of laying-in on jersey or between the beds on a rib machine, and provides horizontal stretch.

b) Two-way stretch fabric must knit the elastic yarn into the stitch. This method is used on rib machines, thereby incorporating the elastic on the back needles either to all or else according to a patterned sequence. On jersey machines, the rubber will show on the face of the fabric so that it must be planned as part of the pattern and possibly stocked in various colors (girdles and swimwear).

INTERLOCK: This is a special kind or type of eight-lock fabric, but it is generally described as a double one-by-one rib with crossed sinker wales. The fabric has a smooth surface on both sides, possesses good wearing qualities, has less elasticity than ribs, and does not develop prominent ribs when stretched in the horizontal direction. Fancy fabrics in this category are made with color arrangements, needle setout, tucking, missing, and combinations of the foregoing (sweaters and underwear).

DOUBLE KNIT: Fabrics made on a rib- or interlock-type machine usually have sixteen or more needles per inch, patterning control of the dial needles or interchangeable dial sections, as well as some form of patterning mechanism to control the cylinder needles. The simpler forms of the fabric are practically reversible, light in weight, possess stability to resist stretch, will lie flat, and do not easily ravel (suits, shorts, slacks).

WRAP KNITTING: This method involves a principle of feeding a yarn to a small group of needles. The yarn may be fed to one needle, thereby making a one-wale vertical stripe on an intermittent feed of yarn to produce the design effect. A limit of thirty needles causes the yarn to be placed in the fabric in a vertical direction. Alternate knitting feeds place or set in a conventional knitting course (outerwear).

Patterning of Needle Control Systems

The mechanism used to control the needles is related to the methods of pattern selection such as used in weaving fabric. Thus:

a) DIRECT NEEDLE BUTT SELECTION: Uses a cam or a shaft system.

b) TRICK DRUM SELECTION: Chain or dobby-loom system or method.

c) JACQUARD SELECTION: Jacquard head-motion system to produce fabric.

d) PATTERN WHEEL SELECTION: No equivalent exists in this instance.

The Needle Cam Device

This is used to actuate the needles in the knitting sequence. By operating on the butts of the needles or push jacks, the cam "positions" the needles to the desired knitting, tucking, missing, transferring, or cast-off heights. The possibilities for fabric design are very limited and the motif will be placed vertically in the goods.

The Trick Drum Unit

This is composed of a drum, steel pegs, or flat tricks with removable teeth, and a series of selector plates. Each peg in the drum pushes a selector plate, which is in direct contact with the jacks in the needle cylinder. When a jack is pressed, the deactivation of the needle takes place insofar as all needles will knit unless stopped by the butt on the trick drum through the selector to the jack.

This patterning system is the only one which employs this negative technique. Patterns are changed by a rearrangement of the position of the pegs or replacement of the tricks in the drum. The cylinder jack arrangement determines the number of needles controlled, which is usually the number of pegs in the height of the drum. If a jack has one butt and each jack has its butt at a different level, then all needles will be controlled separately. If the jack arrangement is in the form of a chevron, or a "V," the design width is nearly doubled, but the fabric pattern will be in a systematic formation.

The motif will be placed or set vertically in the material. The height of the pattern will be controlled by the number of pegs or slots in the circumference of the drum. It is possible to control the drum movement or indexing so that the drums may stop or index at the rate of one or two slots at a time.

The Jacquard Selection Method

This procedure can be accomplished through several mediums. For example, by the use of perforated paper, film roll, metal flat cards, or by metal or plastic ribbons. By means of appropriate mechanisms, the holes punched in the cards will actuate levers whose functions are to raise the needles, by means of cams, to the knitting or "functional" height.

The patterning of fabric is unlimited, since the needles are individually controlled with a repeat size equal to the machine width and the length regulated by storage facilities for the cards.

Jacquard effects are seen in dresses, sportswear, and sweaters. The operation, generally speaking, is rather slow and more costly than the other methods of knitting used at the present time.

The Pattern Wheel Selection Method

This is used in circular knitting; a helical or spiral gear-type mechanism is used to control the needle movement. The pattern wheel, in a sense, is an extension of the cam raceway. There are two- and three-position-type pattern wheels.

The two-position wheel can control only knit-and-tuck, knit-and-miss, or tuck-and-miss at any one feed, whereas the three-position wheel can control all needle heights at the feed.

Pattern wheels are used on jersey and rib machines. The meshing of the wheel and the needle butts produce a gear ratio which may return to its original starting place after one revolution of the machine cylinder or as many as one hundred revolutions. The repeat width will be the wheel length or multiple of the wheel, and the height is controlled by the feeds and gear ratio or by the "remainder" needles.

Some Major Terms Used in Weft Knitting

CIRCULAR KNITTING: The fabric is produced on a circular machine to provide tubular fabrics such as girdles, hosiery, and undershirts.

FLAT KNITTING: The fabric is made by having the needles arranged in a straight line to produce scarves, collar trims, and beltings.

NEEDLE LOOP: A loop in knitted fabric which has been drawn through a previous loop by a needle.

SINKER LOOP: A loop that connects two adjacent needle loops.

FEED: The area of a knitting machine where the needles operate to receive the yarn as it is fed into the frame.

NEEDLE HOUSING

a) CYLINDER: A slotted cylindrical housing for needles in a circular knitting machine. The cut of a cylinder is the number of needles in one inch of the circumference of the cylinder.

b) NEEDLE BED: A flat slotted plate in which the knitting needles slide.

c) DIAL: The horizontal needle housing in circular machines of the rib and the interlock type.

d) N.P.I.: The number of needles per inch in the cylinder or needle bed. Sometimes referred to as the "cut" and often mistakenly called the "gauge."

SINKER: A device on a circular knitting frame used to hold down fabric.

JACK: A tempered steel blade, with either high or low butts or both, whose primary purpose is to actuate the movement of the latch knitting needles when they are in action.

WARP KNITTING

The development of warp knit fabric is more concerned with how the yarn is presented to the needle, since the machine is built to perform the knitting function on all needles. The yarns are threaded through a frame or guide bar comparable with the ordinary harness used on a weaving loom. This bar "shoggs" or moves the yarn to the right or to the left of the needle and in front of or behind the needle during each successive knitting cycle.

The thread movement and the stitch appearance may be defined as follows:

a) OVERLAP: Thread movement on the hook or beard side of the needle; the yarn will appear on the fabric face as a loop.

b) UNDERLAP: Thread movement on the back side of the needle; the yarn will appear on the fabric back as a horizontal or diagonal yarn float.

c) OPENLAP: This stitch is created when the yarn makes an overlap, followed by an underlap in the same direction as the overlap or no underlap at all.

d) CLOSEDLAP: This is a stitch created when the yarn makes on overlap followed by an underlap in the opposite direction of the overlap.

e) COURSE: This is made by the yarn making one overlap and one underlap. (See pages 69 and 72.)

One-Guide Bar in Warp Knitting

Two points should be closely observed here:

1. A fully threaded bar produces a fabric that may run; it has fabric properties similar to weft-knit jersey and horizontal bars of inclined stitches which serve as an identifying characteristic. (See page 72.)

2. A partially threaded bar is used to produce mesh and run-resistant fabrics. Since each needle must receive a yarn to make a fabric, this method makes it necessary for the yarn to be wrapped around two needles, thereby producing a severe strain on the yarn. Incidentally, it is a rather difficult method in fabric manufacture.

Two-Guide Bars in Warp Knitting

The following should be noted carefully:

1. Fully threaded bars can either move in the same direction and the same distance, thereby producing a plated fabric with the properties of a single bar fabric, or the guide bars can be made to move different distances in the same direction in order to make a fabric with two yarns in each stitch from different parts of the warp to give a runproof material.

2. Fully threaded bars moving in opposition to each other can either move the same distance to make the wale in the goods erect and symmetrical, or at different distances such as the standard construction used in industry for "tricot jersey." In this instance, one guide bar (back) moves between two needles and the other guide bar (front) moves among three needles to make a fabric that is runproof. In this type of work it should be noted that in the alternate courses the stitches are slightly inclined. (See page 72.)

3. One fully threaded bar and one partially threaded bar will produce cordlike effects either in vertical-stripe formation or in horizontal-stripe-herringbone effect or motif. The cord develops because some stitches in the fabric have two yarns per stitch, thereby affording thicker texture than other stitches which have only one yarn per stitch.

4. Partially threaded bars will generally provide mesh or net motifs in the goods; whenever a yarn is missing from the warp and the wales are not cross-connected, the opening or mesh will be developed.

5. One fully threaded bar which makes the normal overlaps and underlaps while the other bar makes only the underlaps. The back guide bar, which underlaps only, will "lay-in" a thread between the needle and the knitting or front guide bar. This allows for incorporation of novelty yarns, elastic yarns, and materials that will not knit (to form loops) or stabilize the fabric, since the yarn is placed in a reasonably straight or parallel formation and no stitches are formed on this thread.

6. One fully threaded bar which makes the normal overlaps and underlaps while the other bar will make either knits (overlaps and underlaps) or "lay-ins" for part of the fabric and then will swing between the needles without making either overlaps or underlaps. This construction will provide raised welts or pleats in the goods.

Multi-Guide Bars

The use of three or more guide bars will encompass any of the previously mentioned methods of thread movement to create the fabric pattern. WARP KNIT FABRICS are usually classified by the one machine construction into the following groups listed:

TRICOT FABRICS: The French verb *tricoter* means "to knit." The term "stocking-net," as applied to warp-knitted materials irrespective of the motif, often refers to a flat knitted material that is not tubular. The meaning, however, should not be construed to imply a flat machine-knit fabric. TRICOT FABRIC is more expensive than circular knitgoods and is less inclined to stretch. Texture is classed as thin, since it can be made on one, two, or three bar frames. Tricot is made on spring-beard needles and has from one to four warps or thread systems and these warps are mounted in a stationary position. INDUSTRY STANDARD MACHINE is twenty-eight needles to the inch, or a 28 gauge (gg).

RASCHEL FABRICS: They are made on latch needles. There are from one to thirty-two warp or thread systems, and the warps are mounted in a stationary position. INDUSTRY STANDARD MACHINE is based on a two-inch width in a 36 gauge, which is the same as an 18 gauge in the one-inch-width measurement.

MILANESE FABRICS: They can be made on either the spring-beard or the latch method. There are two warps or thread systems, with the warps being moved continually during manufacture in a lateral movement to the needle bed. The warps move always in the opposite direction with the full-threading or color arrangement to produce a runproof fabric and one which shows "biased plaid effects." INDUSTRY STANDARD MECHANISM does not at the present time actually exist; however, a one-inch measure is usually agreed upon to serve as the gauge. Milanese fabrics are known for their high gauge, light weight, fineness in texture, and appealing hand.

Some Major Terms Used in Warp Knitting

RACK: A unit of measure of 480 courses for fabric production and costing calculations.

RUNNER LENGTH: The number of inches of yarn from a warp to make one rack of fabric.

QUALITY: The number of inches of fabric made by knitting one rack.

FULLY THREADED BAR: The arrangement of the warp threads so that each yarn guide hole has a yarn and each needle in the machine receives one thread.

PARTIALLY THREADED BAR: PARTIALLY THREADED BAR: The arrangement of the warp threads in a repeat sequence, that is, three yarn guides threaded and one yarn guide empty, or one guide threaded and one guide empty.

SOME GENERAL PROPERTIES AND CHARACTERISTICS
OF KNITTED FABRICS

Knitgoods are elastic, may be flat or circular, may ravel or run.

Some fabrics have porosity and may tend to sag with wear.

Knit fabrics may be form-fitting or form-concealing.

Outerwear fabric in garments provides good to excellent wear and service to the wearer. Can withstand rugged wear and usage.

A knitting machine gives a much higher production of fabric when compared with that of a weaving loom.

Much knit clothing is ideal for travel, since it is packed easily and well, and, generally speaking, takes up less space than other types of apparel and clothing.

Knit apparel is usually priced lower than comparable articles in the woven field and very often seems to give as good or even better service.

Production of major knitting machines, in courses per minute:

(a)	Tricot lingerie:	1,000 courses.	(d)	Seamless hosiery:	200 courses.
(b)	Yard goods:	600 courses.	(e)	Fancy purl stitch	
(c)	Sweater fabric:	240 courses.		and cable stitch	
				machines:	50 courses.

MAJOR TYPES OF KNIT FABRICS

Individual companies in the knitting industry, because of machinery requirements and the specialization in the field, are divided into three major branches: (1) outerwear; (2) underwear; (3) hosiery.

Outerwear concerns manufacture fabrics for use in dresses, shirts, sportswear, sweaters and swimwear. Underwear companies provide fabrics for infants' underwear, men's and boy's underwear, lingerie, and sleepwear. Hosiery includes socks, stockings, and tights.

Sweaters

Originally, a sweater was a heavy woolen garment that would cause one to perspire. At present, it is a knitted outer garment on the order of a jacket, heavy or light in weight, and made in many styles. Worn by men, women, and children, sweaters are of the coat or slip-on type, and may or may not have sleeves.

SWEATERS, MEN'S AND BOYS'

There are three types:

1. PULLOVER: This is usually a long-sleeved garment with either a crew-, V-, or turtleneck collar.

2. CARDIGAN: This may be finished with button or zipper closures, and is chiefly made with long sleeves. The name comes from the Earl of Cardigan, who led the famed "Charge of the Light Brigade" in the Crimean War, 1854–1856, when Russia opposed France, Great Britain, Sardinia, and Turkey.

3. SLEEVELESS: There are three types of this sweater:
Sleeveless pullover: This garment is identified by its V-neck.
Buttoned front: This sleeveless garment is often called a knitted vest.

Jerkin: It is usually a V-neck pullover garment consisting of a front made of woven fabric, and the back, neckline, and pocket trims of knit fabric. Some jerkins may also have button or zipper closures down the front. In such cases, it is called a vest. It should be, however, distinguished from the vest of all-knit fabric.

SWEATERS, WOMEN'S AND MISSES'

There are four basic types:

1. SLIPON, PULLOVER: It is made with any type of neckline treatment, while the sleeves may be long, short, three-quarter or batwing. Necklines include crew-neck, turtleneck, bateau, square, V-neck, Peter Pan, etc. All except the Peter Pan and bateau are as their names imply. The bateau is a boat-shaped line, while the Peter Pan shows a pert, smart collar with rounded edges.

2. CARDIGAN: In women's wear, it is usually a button-front garment. There is a wide variety of neckline treatments. There may be a high-neck closure, plunging V, or rounded collar. Most cardigans have long sleeves though some short-sleeve types or batwings are on the market.

3. SHRUG: An abbreviated sweater somewhat on the order of a bolero. It may or may not have a button closure. The sleeves are usually three-quarter, although some have short sleeves.

4. JACKET: It is usually of the cardigan type but is made with heavier yarn, and invariably has no closure device. It may or may not have a collar, and is usually adorned with patch pockets. A crest or similar adornment is often seen on this garment. It is of hip length and the sleeve length is long. One type of this jacket is the "cruise jacket."

Knitted Shirts, Men's and Women's

There are seven basic types:

1. BASQUE: A crew-neck pullover with short or long sleeves, depending on the season, with a horizontal stripe treatment in two or more colors.

2. GAUCHO: A short, widespread collar treatment on a knitted outerwear garment.

3. PLACKET: A two- or three-button effect underneath the collar on a pullover shirt. Very often the placket and collar contrast with the color of the body of the shirt.

4. POLO: A crew-neck, short-sleeve garment usually of solid color with contrasting rib trimming around the neckline and at the sleeve end. The name comes from its resemblance to the garments worn by polo players.

5. T-BLOUSE: A smart, dressy type of T-shirt worn by women.

6. T-SHIRT: This is a plain, unadorned crew-neck garment designed for outerwear, and resembling the U. S. Navy skivvie shirt.

7. MISCELLANEOUS: A wide variety of collar treatments is used to vary polo shirts, most of them coinciding with the currently popular styles used in men's dress shirts.

TESTING

1. Define knitting, wale, course, gauge.
2. How many needles per inch would there be in a 30 gauge? In a 54 gauge?
3. What are the essential differences between a latch needle and spring-beard needle?

4. What is the basic principle involved in making knit fabric?
5. What causes runs in some knit fabrics?
6. Describe weft or filling knitting.
7. Define the following stitches: knit stitch, purl stitch, tuck stitch, miss-stitch.
8. What is meant by the term "plating"?
9. Define the term "intarsia."
10. Define the term "double knit."
11. Discuss Jacquard knit fabrics.
12. What is the difference between circular knitting and flat knitting?
13. Differentiate between weft or filling knitting and warp knitting.
14. How does warp knitting differ from wrap knitting?
15. What does the term "tricot knit," or "tricot fabric," mean to you?
16. Explain the term "rack."
17. List five properties of knit fabrics.
18. Name the three major types of knit fabrics.
19. Describe in detail one type of a man's sweater. One type of a woman's sweater.
20. Name and describe two types of sweaters worn by men, women, and children.

BASIC CHARACTERISTICS OF WEFT KNITTED FABRICS

	JERSEY OR PLAIN	1 x 1 RIB	1 x 1 PURL
MACHINE:	1 set of needles 1 needle bed Needle Bed: Straight or Circular	2 sets of needles 2 needle beds Needle Bed: Straight or Circular Offset Needle Tricks	1 set of needles 2 needle beds Needle bed: Straight or Circular Directly Opposite Tricks
FABRIC:	Plain	Plain and Rib	Plain, Rib, Purl
CONSTRUCTION:	All stitches are going in the same direction. Distinct face and back.	All stitches in one wale are in same direction and adjacent wale can go in the opposite direction.	All stitches in one course are in the same direction and alternate courses are different.
RAVEL:	Either end	Top down	Either edge
DROPSTITCH:	Up or down	Down	Up or down
ELASTICITY:	Good	Best	Best
CURL:	Toward back— Selvedge Front—Top and Bottom	None	None
APPEARANCE:	Face Back The technical face, the knitside of the stitch, can be represented by an "X." The back is identified by an "O."	Either side may be used as the face of the goods. X O X O X O X O X O X O X O X O	Either side may be used as the face of the goods. O O O O X X X X O O O O X X X X

See Pages 69 and 72.

Courtesy: American Viscose Corporation

Interlocking knitting   Circular knitting   Full-fashioned knitting

Aveco knitting machine—knits 168″ fabric

F.N.F. knitting machine—knits 84″ fabric

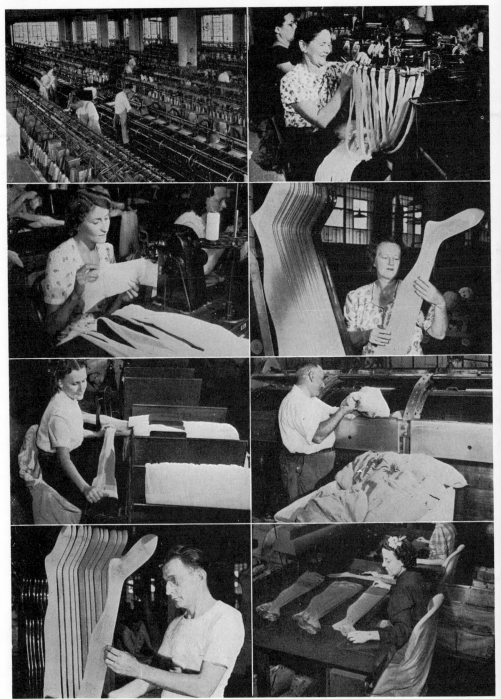

Courtesy: Chadbourn, Gotham Co., Inc.

Hosiery knitting machines
Seaming stocking
Inspection before dyeing
Blocking process

Closing toe of stocking
Preboarding
Hosiery dyeing
Final inspection

TOPIC: HOSIERY KNITTING

One of the largest and most active departments in a department store, specialty shop, neighborhood store, or haberdashery is the hosiery department. It is estimated that in the United States women buy from twelve to fifteen pairs of stockings a year. Sales in men's and children's hosiery are voluminous. Types of hose or hosiery include sheer type, service type, socks, anklets, full-length stockings, knee-high type, and the stretch stocking.

Considerable knowledge should be available to the consumer with regard to hosiery. Many terms used in the language of hosiery should be known to the layman. These are covered in detail below. New developments are constantly coming to the fore in the hosiery industry. For example, a popular knitting machine today uses 474 needles in the frame and is capable of running 12-denier nylon yarn very easily. The consumer should know something of the excellent heat-treating results obtained in nylon yarns and stockings as full-fashioned and fashioned or seamless hosiery, and in stretch stockings as well.

Knitting Gauge. This means the actual number of needles in 1½ inches in a knitting machine. Thus:

45 gauge means 45 needles in 1½ inches, or 30 needles per inch.
51 gauge means 51 needles in 1½ inches, or 34 needles per inch.
60 gauge means 60 needles in 1½ inches, or 40 needles per inch.
66 gauge means 66 needles in 1½ inches, or 44 needles per inch.
72 gauge means 72 needles in 1½ inches, or 48 needles per inch.

Each needle knits one wale in a vertical row of stitches, while a course is a row of horizontal stitches or loops that extend crosswise in the fabric.

The higher the gauge, the finer will be the fabric, but this does not mean that the stocking will be sheerer. For example, a 72 gauge with 15-denier yarn would be heavier or less sheer than a 45 gauge with 15-denier yarn because of the greater number of stitches in the former per square inch of fabric.

In nylon knitting, the most commonly used gauge-denier setup follows:

45 gauge will use a 40-denier and heavier sizes, if necessary.
45 and 51 gauge will use a 30-denier size yarn.
51 and 60 gauge will use a 15-denier or finer yarn.
51 to 72 gauge will use a 15-denier or finer denier size.

The Parts of a Knitted Stocking

WELT: This is the hem or garter top and it is of heavy or reinforced yarn to withstand the garter strain. In women's hosiery this is generally made of double fabric.

RUN STOP: This consists of a narrow band, generally one course wide, of locked stitches to prevent runs from extending into the leg of the stocking, and usually placed either at the end of the welt or shadow welt.

FASHION MARKS: These are visible as small dots or raised portions in the fabric wherever the stocking has been narrowed for fashioning purposes and are caused by the placing of the inwardly transferred stitch on a needle which already holds a stitch.

BOOT OR LEG: The area between the end of the welt or the shadow welt and the ankle.

SEAM: The row of small stitches that join the selvages of flat-knit hosiery.

HIGH SPLICING: The reinforced portion of the stocking above the shoe line.

HEEL: The portion of the stocking widened to form a heel pocket, generally reinforced. In the case of sandals, for example, the heel is the location of the added width to actually form a "heel cup." It is usually reinforced to provide strength and wear.

SOLE: That part of the stocking generally reinforced and extending directly under the instep from heel to toe. Incidentally, in full-fashioned hosiery made by the single-unit method, there is no definite line of demarcation between the heel and the sole.

TOE: The portion over the toe area of the foot narrowed or shaped to fit the toe, generally reinforced. If, however, it is not reinforced, it is still the toe of the article.

Full-Fashioned Hosiery

This is knitted flat and it is shaped during the knitting by the inward transfer of the selvage stitches, usually two at a time, on each side in order to provide the correct shape to properly fit the leg.

The narrowings are always located at the calf, heel, and toe, and generally above the knee just below the shadow welt.

In stockings made by the single-unit method the fabric is also widened at the instep to form a heel pocket. This widening is usually over one needle at a time and may be made at the selvages when it is invisible or some wales away from the selvages, in which case a gore line is visible in the heel. The latter method provides a better-fitting stocking. The selvage edges are then joined by a seam.

Seamless Hosiery

Also known as circular-knit hosiery. Knitted circular or tubular, it is recognized by the absence of the fashion marks. The use of stretch yarns in hosiery has been the cause for the increase in demand of seamless stockings. It should be borne in mind that stretch yarns are also used in full-fashioned hosiery as well.

One of the advantages of circular-knit hosiery is that it will fit very well on the leg in all respects and does give improved wear to the consumer. Coming in three sizes—large, medium, and small—the seamless stocking is also aided by the fact that the heat-setting of the manmade fiber used, nylon, has been of great aid for increasing production. Seamless stockings present no problem in fitting at any time, a great impetus to their increased consumption.

Mock Fashioning Marks

These are achieved by varying the tensions at the various parts of the stocking. Mock seams may be introduced to simulate full-fashioned hosiery. This type of seam can be recognized since it does not extend into the welt or sole areas of the article. The seam will appear as a small hole (tuck stitch) rather than as a raised mark as in the narrowing. Full-fashioned hose is usually the better-fitting stocking as compared with other types because of its method of construction.

Incidentally, there is one type of stocking on the market that is not made with knitting construction. It is made of lace, which is produced by an interlacing of yarns or yarns at any angle. The lace used is usually Queen Anne's lace and it is cut and then sewed into a stocking. It is used for opera-length stockings.

TESTING

1. Define gauge. How many needles per inch in a 66-gauge stocking?
2. Which of the following denier sizes of hosiery yarn is the finest in diameter: 15, 20, 30, 40?
3. Define the following terms: boot or leg, fashion marks, heel, high splicing, run, stop, seam, sole, toe, welt.
4. Discuss full-fashioned hosiery as to how made and compare it with circular-knit or seamless hosiery.
5. Discuss mock fashioning marks.
6. If you have worn stretch hosiery made with nylon yarn, give some reasons as to why you do or do not like it, as compared with full-fashioned hosiery.

TOPIC: Shoe and Stocking Sizes

Trouble is often encountered in the proper determination of shoe and stocking sizes. The following explains the synchronization between these two items:

Shoe Sizes and Methods of Numbering

The following chart covers the numerals and the widths used in establishing shoe size:

NUMERALS	WIDTHS
000	AAAA
00	AAA
0	AA
1	A
2	B
3	C
4	D
5	E
6	EE
7	EEE

The reading of shoe sizes may be discerned from the following plan:

WIDTH	SIZE	HALF SIZE
3	6	5
3	7	0
4	10	0
1	10	0
5	12	0
0	6	5
2	9	5
4	9	0

The half size is denoted by the symbol "5." The full size is denoted by the symbol "0," under the half-size caption.

Thus, for example, 5 12 0 is a 12 E.   0 6 5 is a 6½ double A.   2 9 5 is a 9½ B.   4 9 0 is 9 D.

Another Method Used to Figure Shoe Sizes Is the French Method

Use the number "32" as the so-called dummy number:

36 would be a size 4.   38 would be a size 6.
37 would be a size 5.   39 would be a size 7, etc.

Thus the figure "37000" would be interpreted as a 5 quadruple A.

391 would be a 7 A.
36— would be a 4½ size. The dash "—" is used to indicate the half size. Thus
361— would be a 4½ A.
391— would be a 7½ A.
384— would be a 6½ D.

Another Method Known as the Blind Method

"3" is the blind number; then follows the size, then the width.
The dash "—" is used for the half size.
Note that, as in the above box-chart, A is 1, B is 2, C is 3, and so on.
Thus, 383— would be interpreted as 8½ C.

3110— is an 11½ double A.
364— would be a 6½ D.

Another Blind Method

For the size, divide the second and third numbers in the number chain by 2 and add 0 for the full size. Add a 5 for the half size, if the shoe is a half-size make.
NOTE: As above in the box-chart, A is 1, B is 2, EE is 6, and so on.
NOTE: In this method the width comes first in the number chain.
Thus the numbers 3143 would mean a 7½ C.

5105 would mean a 5½ E.
0140 would mean a 7 double A.
2180 would mean a 9 B.
4225 would mean an 11½ D.
1085 would mean a 4½ A.

Stocking and Shoe Size Chart

STOCKING SIZE OF 8 SHOE SIZES	SIZE OF 8½	SIZE OF 9	SIZE OF 9½
2C	3AAA–EEE	4½A–D	5E–EEE
2½C–EE	3½AAA–EEE	5AAA–D	5½A–EEE
	4AAA–E	5½AAA–AA	6AAA–D
	4½AAA–AA		

STOCKING SIZE OF 10 SHOE SIZES	SIZE OF 10½	SIZE OF 11	SIZE OF 11½
6½AAA–A	7E–EEE	8C–EEE	10C
6E–EEE	7½B–EEE	8½B–EEE	10½
6½B–EEE	8AAA–B	9AAA–C	11
7AAA–D	8½AAA–A	9½AAA–C	
7½AAA–A		10AAA–B	

Stocking Types

TYPE A: for short, small, or slender legs—
Sizes 8, 8½, 9; 27½ to 28½ inches long.
Sizes 9½ and 10; 28½ to 29½ inches long.

TYPE B: for average legs of medium proportions—
Sizes 8½ and 9; 29½ to 30½ inches long.
Sizes 9½ and 10; 30½ to 31½ inches long.
Sizes 10½ and 11; 31½ to 32½ inches long.

TYPE C: for long or plus-proportioned legs—
Sizes 9½ and 10; 33 to 34 inches long.
Sizes 10½, 11, 11½; 34 to 35 inches long.

TYPE D: adjustables and new—for longer or amply proportioned legs—
Sizes 9½ and 10; 34 to 35 inches long.
Sizes 10½, 11, and 11½; 35 to 36 inches long.

TESTING

1. Determine the shoe size in each of the following:
   A. 4 10 0.   B. 5 12 0.   C. 3 7 5.   D. 4 9 0.   D. 2 9 5.
2. Using "32" as the dummy number find the shoe size in each of the following:
   A. 391.   B. 384.   C. 36—.
3. Using "3" as the dummy number, determine the following sizes from the data given:
   A. 383—.   B. 3110.   C. 364—.

Part 1—Unit 13

TOPIC: FELT AND ITS MANUFACTURE

Wandering tribes evolved the art of making felt long before spinning and weaving were discovered or invented. The patron saint of the great felt industry is St. Feutre of Caen, France, and he has held this honor for more than one thousand years. Legend has it that he made a pilgrimage from Caen to the famous Benedictine Shrine of Mont-Saint-Michel in the Diocese of Avranche, Normandy, France, founded in the year 708.

The pilgrimage was made in the eighth century, and on the long, rough road to the abbey, St. Feutre placed some "grease" wool, plucked from a nearby sheep along the road, in his sandals to relieve his tired, painful feet. On examining the wool at the end of the long day's journey, he noted that the scales and serrations, peculiar only to wool fibers, aided by heat, pressure, and moisture, had interlocked to form a matted layer of wool "fabric." Thus, felt was born, a very important segment in the lives of all peoples today.

Properties and Characteristics of Felt

1. Felt is a three-dimensional fabric; it is made by an interlocking of fibers.
2. It is a good shock absorber.
3. It is easy to shape, since it is a homogeneous admixture of interlocked fibers, contains no yarn in its content, and is not woven or knitted.
4. The edge of the material will not fray or ravel, and it is always clean and neat.
5. Felt is durable and will hold considerable amounts of moisture and water.
6. Felt may be blocked; it may be draped with care.
7. Tensile strength will vary considerably depending on blend, density, and construction.
8. Holes cannot be remedied in felt.
9. It is sound-absorbing and may be drycleaned.
10. Thickness varies from $\frac{1}{32}$ inch to 3 inches.
11. It may be porous or dense and of high or low permeability depending on thickness and density.
12. It does not go back to its original shape on release from tension.
13. It has little elasticity but will retain it longer than rubber.
14. Felt will not tear in a straight line.
15. Can be made into smooth fabrics.
16. Can be made into exceptionally light fabrics.
17. Has high resiliency.
18. More impervious to water than any other fabric.
19. Has no selvage or listing.
20. Retains given shape.
21. Has high thermal insulating properties.
22. Provides warmth.
23. Weight ranges from 3 ounces per square yard to 65 pounds per square yard.
24. Easy to cut into shape since it is formed into a solid mass and is not woven or knitted.
25. May be mothproofed, fireproofed; made water-repellent, fungi- and mildew-resistant.

Felt Products

1. Banners, pennants.
2. Coverings.
3. Ear muffs for aviators.
4. Felt hats.
5. Felt slippers.
6. Filters.
7. Football pads.
8. Gun wads.
9. Helmet wadding.
10. Insoles.
11. Oil seals.
12. Piano hammers.
13. Surgical pads.
14. Swabs.
15. Washers.
16. Wicks.
17. Glass and metal polishing wheels and laps.

Felt May Be Made of

1. Camel and goat hair.
2. China cotton.
3. Other cottons.
4. Cow and rabbit hair.
5. Flocks and other mill wastes such as card strippings, shear wastes, willow wastes.
6. Reprocessed or new wool.
7. Reused wool.
8. Shoddy, mungo, extract wool.
9. Short staple wool noils, the most important fiber for felt.

TESTING

1. Why does wool fabric felt? "Because it is a fabric built up by the interlocking of fibers by a suitable combination of mechanical work, chemical action, moisture and heat, without spinning, weaving, or knitting. Felt may consist of one or more classes of fibers—wool, reprocessed wool, and reused wool, with or without admixture with animal, vegetable, and synthetic fibers." (From the Felt Association and ASTM Definition of Felt. See Wool Products Labeling Act, 1939.)
2. Why is the best felt made from wool fibers?
3. Name ten properties or characteristics of felt.
4. Name five felt materials.
5. What causes wool to shrink in laundering or washing?
6. Why is it not necessary for felt fabric to have a selvage?
7. What is the purpose of mixing cotton with wool fibers in the making of felt? Cotton is used to give added strength in certain uses for felt.

INFORMATION ON THE MAKING OF WOOL FELT

1. **Wool:** Obtained from the sheep fleece.
2. **Sorting:** Sheep fleeces are sorted into particular grades; from four to twenty grades of wool may be obtained from the same fleece, depending on the rigidity of the sorting and the type of fleece involved. The higher the quality of the fleece, the greater will be the number of grades sorted.
3. **Scouring:** This removes yolk, suint, and remaining foreign matter from the wool. Leaves wool in whitened condition.
4. **Blending, Oiling, Mixing:** The various grades of wool are chosen and laid down layer upon layer, each layer being sprayed with oleic oil or some similar type of oil. After the blend has been built up, it is then torn down and the varying grades and types of stock selected are thoroughly mixed and made ready for the next operation.
5. **Carding:** This parallels the fibers to marked degree, takes out much foreign matter that may still be in the wool, and also removes the short, undesirable fibers from the lot. Carding puts the stock in a manageable condition for further manipulation.
6. **Crossing:** This operation takes the carded webs of wool, supported on lattice aprons, and feeds it to an endless canvas apron from several directions.
7. **Hardening:** The first felting treatment afforded the wool is initiated at this point when the fibers are felted by the application of heat, moisture, pressure, and vibration.
8. **Felting and Fulling:** These are effected by mechanical pressure agitation with chemical stimulus to cause the actual felting of the fibers to considerable degree.
9. **Washing:** This will clean the stock and remove any soluble impurities prior to further manipulation.
10. **Dyeing:** This is done in the piece-dye kettle or kier. Water-soluble aniline dye-stuffs are used to obtain standardized shades.
11. **Drying:** This operation stretches the material to the proper width, and the moisture is removed by passing the felt fabric through circulating hot-air dryers under controlled conditions.
12. **Shearing:** The removal of fuzzy, protruding fibers is done by the rotating blades of the shears, which work on the principle of a lawn mower. Smooth surface is the result of this action.
13. **Calendering:** The pressing and the ironing of the felt under heated cylinder rollers to produce the desired finish on the fabric.
14. **Inspecting:** Keen optical inspection of the felt for flaws and blemishes which may be remedied or removed. The felt is also checked for weight, thickness, width, length, color, and general quality.
15. **Cutting:** Precision die cutting of the felt into the desired size demanded by the trade.

16. **Testing:** This is done in accordance with ASTM D-461-Methods of Testing Wool Felt, required specifications. Testing is carried on continuously to insure the best type of product obtainable and to meet the needs of industry.
17. **Shipping:** The packaging of the finished felt product according to the desires of the customers' specifications, and the delivery to transit carriers.

Courtesy of American Felt Company, Glenville, Connecticut.

WOOL FELT HAT BODIES

The felt hat industry as a whole is divided into two parts, the so-called back shop, where hat bodies are made, and the front shop where these bodies are blocked, finished, and trimmed to make the finished hats as we wear them. We may further divide these two categories. Back shops may make either wool felt hat bodies or fur felt hat bodies, while the front shops will make either men's hats or ladies' hats.

While there are a number of integrated hat factories in the country making both bodies and trimmed hats, the usual procedure is for the back shop to make and sell bodies to their customers, who then carry out the front-shop operations and in turn sell trimmed hats to wholesalers or retailers. The reason for this is fairly obvious when a study of hatting is made. In the first place a back shop requires much heavy and expensive machinery and therefore considerable capital for its setting up, maintenance, and operation. This is not true in the case of the front shop, which may vary in size from the small home millinery store, with one woman making and selling the total output, to the very large mass production units finishing thousands of dozens of hats a day for mail order houses and large consumers. Secondly, there is the problem of selling. The back shop, producing only partially finished goods, must sell to the manufacturers, while the front shops will sell to wholesalers, retailers, or direct to the consumer. Thus it may be seen that two very different types of selling units must be maintained if one company is to sell the production from both the back shop and front shop. There is also the problem of finding sufficient skilled labor for back-shop operations in the same locations with skilled front-shop labor.

The felt hat industry in the United States in 1964 produced over six and one quarter million dozen felt hat bodies, or more than seventy-five million individual hats. Of these, four million dozen were wool felt and two and one quarter million were fur felt. The average cost of a fur body is considerably more than that of a similar wool body, this being due chiefly to the cost of the raw material which goes into the manufacture of the body.

Since the volume production of the wool body is so much greater than fur, let us consider first the manufacture of wool hat bodies from the raw material to the finished product. Wool as it comes from the sheep is a matted, greasy, tangled mass of fibers of all lengths. The first operation to be performed on the wool is to degrease it. This removes the body grease and some of the dirt. Next it is combed by one of several processes that divide the wool into long staple fibers, knowns as "tops," and used in worsted, and short staple fibers known as "noils," which are perfectly suited for the manufacture of wool felt.

Depitching is a process for removing the paint, tar, and other pitchy substances from the fiber. It is accomplished by the use of various chemical solvents that dissolve the paint and tar and yet have no effect on the wool noils. Neither do these solvents have any effect on vegetable matter, leaves, twigs, and other material that the sheep is bound to pick up in the course of its wanderings. Thus it is necessary to soak the wool in a bath of sulfuric acid, which literally burns the extraneous material, but again causes no harm to the fiber. After about an hour in the acid bath, the wool is partially dried by squeeze rolls or in an extractor and then goes to a dryer. The heat turns the already burned vegetable matter into carbon, which can be broken up and dusted out. In some cases, especially where the stock is to be used for light or white hats, the wool must be visually inspected and small dark particles removed by hand.

No wool hat can be properly made of only one kind of wool, therefore it is necessary to properly mix and blend in the right proportions as many as six or eight different types. These lots, which weigh up to eight hundred pounds, are first dumped into a bin and blended by hand, then run through a picking machine. The picker accomplishes three purposes, namely: it breaks up the large lumps of stock into small pieces, it mixes the various types of stock, and it mixes into the stock a very small amount of liquid emulsion. The latter is to cause the wool to card better. The stock has now been properly cleaned, mixed, picked, and prepared for carding, which is really the first hat-making operation.

Carding consists fundamentally of combing and straightening the individual fibers. In actual practice the stock is fed into the card in the proper amounts by a mechanical feeder. It is picked up by drums known as cylinders, workers, and strippers, which are all revolving. The surfaces of these drums are covered with literally millions of fine, sharp wires that act as combs. Around one cylinder, sixty inches in diameter, are arranged numerous sets of workers and strippers, which are respectively seven inches and two inches in diameter. The wool goes onto the cylinder first. It is picked up by the worker, from which it is stripped by the stripper and then deposited again on the cylinder. The cylinder carries it a short way to the next worker, where the stock goes through the same routine. After going through a number of these worker-stripper combinations, the stock comes from the card in the form of a very thin, continuous, gossamerlike web, which can vary in width from twelve inches to two feet. It will perhaps give an idea of how thin this web is when we realize that it takes about sixteen square feet of it to weigh only one ounce.

This web is reeled off the delivery end of the card onto a revolving wooden form made in the shape of two cones jointed bottom to bottom. The form not only revolves but also oscillates, causing the web as it rolls onto the form to crisscross back and forth, covering the entire form with successive layers. At the proper time, a knife is forced down against the middle of the form, and as the form revolves under the knife the wool is cut, allowing a large soft woolen cone to slide off each end of the form. Thus two hat bodies are formed. The weight tolerance allowed at this point is merely a small fraction of an ounce and small pieces of carded web are added to or removed from the bodies to make the weight right. Much care must be exercised when the bodies are just carded as they are now in their most delicate condition and may easily tear if not handled properly. Carded bodies are very carefully inspected before any other work is done, for two reasons: first, a poor body at this stage will generally be a poor body all the way through the shop, and second, a body which is not good here may be recarded with no loss of material, whereas if it goes through any further operations, the stock may not be reused and is therefore a loss.

Besides being fragile and soft, the bodies are now about twice as large as the finished body should be. The many operations between carding and the dyeing or coloring are devoted primarily to making the felt hard and to shrinking the body, or fulling it, as it is called. Shrinking is a well-known phenomenon and is undesirable when present in finished woven or knitted goods, but the hatter during the manufacture of his product does all he can to increase shrinking. There are four requisites to produce shrinking, namely: heat, motion, moisture, and pressure. Acid, a fifth item, does not in itself cause shrinkage, but when present with the other four acts as a catalyst and facilitates fulling. Therefore the hatter sees that varying amounts of sulfuric acid are present in his fulling operations.

Hardening is, strictly speaking, not a fulling operation but must be done so the body will be in condition to receive the terrific pummeling it gets during the shrinking operations. Side hardening, as the name implies, consists of hardening the sides of the body, while tip hardening does the tip. A gentle flow of steam is introduced through a perforated plate onto and into the body (heat and moisture). Another plate with a roughened surface is clamped down on the body (pressure). This board is attached to a cam mechanism which causes it to oscillate with a short, fast stroke (motion). There are a number of different mechanisms and types of hardening machines, but they all use the same principles of heat, moisture, motion, and pressure.

The hat bodies, as they leave the hardening room, are the same overall dimensions as when they went into the room. But they no longer are soft and fluffy; they are about the consistency of a thick blanket. Each manufacturer has his own particular procedure and method of routing bodies through the fulling operation, so without going into detail of any specific routing, we will consider one at a time the different types of fulling machines which may be used singly or in combination with any or all other types.

The multiroller type of fulling machine consists of a horizontal bank of ten or more four-inch rollers in a frame. Above this is a similar bank of rolls in a frame which is free to move up or down, thus pressing the bodies which are fed in between the banks of rolls. All the rolls are driven so that, as they rotate, the hat bodies will be carried through the machine. Both the upper and lower bank of rollers are attached to cams which cause them to oscillate from side to side, the lower bank moving to the right while the upper moves to the left. The rolls of this type of machine have a surface which has a tendency to hold the felt. Thus a kneading action takes place within the machine as the hat bodies travel through it. The bodies are either wet before they enter the machine or are subjected to a shower of hot water as they pass between rolls. Here again we have the four requisites—heat, moisture, pressure, and motion.

The Mezzera machine is a type of multiroller with certain refinements. The roll surfaces are usually harder and either grooved or knurled. While the lower bank of rolls oscillates from one side to the other, the upper rolls are individually sprung and are mechanically driven up and down, thus giving not only a kneading action but a pounding action as well. The feeding and operation is similar to the multiroller. In many cases two or more of these are connected by roller conveyors so that bodies will travel through several machines with only one feeding. This type of machine gives good felting under controlled conditions but is expensive to use because of the necessity of feeding each body individually and of all the handwork in turning and straightening the bodies.

The bumper or fulling mill, as it is sometimes called, gives a very violent action and is generally used only after the bodies have been partially shrunk on a multiroller-type machine. The bumper consists of a large boxlike container into which the bodies are dumped. Two big wooden hammers are so constructed that they may be driven mechanically to pound the bodies. Because of the design of the box and the hammers, the batch of bodies slowly revolves in the box, thus presenting new surfaces to the hammers as they pound up and down. Bumping is an inexpensive and fast way of shrinking felt, but the operation cannot be as closely controlled as in the multiroller-type machine. During the operation hot water is run over the mass of bodies, so again we have the four necessary elements for felting—heat, moisture, pressure, and motion.

The twister is one other type of machine in common use which is generally considered in the class of fulling machines. The twister does not in a true sense shrink the hat bodies but hardens the felt   thout changing the overall size. For this reason, it is usually used after the coloring operation, which has a tendency to soften and open the felt. In this operation several bodies are dipped in hot water and rolled up in a canvas. This roll is then fed into a tube which carries the roll axially between four grooved rolls. The design of the machine and the grooves in the rolls are such that the roll of bodies is carried through the machine and given a kneading action. This process is repeated until the felt is firm and hard.

The dyeing of wool hats takes a great deal of technical knowledge and experience. Although the bodies may be handled in lots of up to one hundred pounds, a considerable amount of machinery and equipment is necessary. The acid dyes used, which will dye animal fibers but not vegetable matter, must be thoroughly mixed in the correct proportions for the desired color. The same dyestuffs may be used in different proportions to give entirely different colors. For example, certain grays and beiges are made from the same dyestuffs but in different proportions. The procedure for dyeing a lot of hat bodies is, roughly, as follows: warm water is run into a tank until steam pipes along the bottom of the tank are covered. The powdered dyestuffs, mixed by a predetermined formula, are dumped into these three or four inches of water, which is then brought to a boil by the steam and is agitated to thoroughly mix dyestuffs. The tank is then filled with water while a drum which revolves in the tank is filled with hat bodies. The average drum will hold from seventy-five to one hundred dozen bodies. A wetting agent is added to insure penetration and a leveling agent to insure even dyeing, and the whole mixture is brought to a boil over a half-hour period. The actual dyeing takes something over an hour, at which time a certain amount of acid is added to set the colors. At the end of another fifteen minutes, the bodies are dyed and the operation is completed.

Under two headings "Stiffening" and "Blocking," the next departments, there are really seven different operations consisting of brim stiffening, crown stiffening, blocking, shaping, rollout, extracting and drying.

The object of stiffening bodies is to get into the felt a predetermined amount of stiffening material such as shellac. The operation is done in two parts, as the brims of the bodies as a general rule must have five or six times as much shellac as the crown. The liquid shellac is made up in a very concentrated solution and diluted with water to give the desired degree of stiffness. The bodies are dipped in this solution and then squeezed between rolls which are very much like an ordinary clothes wringer. When an operator is stiffening crowns, he dips the body all over in a weak solution before running the body through the squeeze rolls. When doing brims, he only dips the brims in the shellac. This solution is so much stronger than the crown stiffening that the slight amount of crown stiffening that gets on the brims when the hat is dipped all over is negligible..

There is another machine sometimes used to stiffen brims which is more or less automatic. The brim of the body is placed between two slightly conical rolls. As these rolls turn, the body revolves and shellac automatically flows onto the brim for a certain length of time. When the cycle is completed, the machine stops automatically.

The bodies which have been in cone shape through all the preceding operations must now be blocked out into the rough shape of a hat. The blocking machine that stretches the crown from a narrow tip to a full-rounded crown has a set of six metal fingers which open and close on the felt, stretching the tip. The shaping is done immediately following the blocking and consists of pulling the body over a wooden block. Felt has a tendency to creep back to its original shape after the blocking, but the body is left on the wooden form for about half a minute, which is just long enough for it to obtain a set.

The rollout machine is used if a wide brim is wanted. Two conical rolls stretch the felt as the brim is run between them.

The bodies, although they may have been extracted twice in large centrifugal extractors, still have a certain amount of moisture in them. This moisture, which must be completely removed before the pouncing operations, is taken out in steam dryers. The dryer may be either the stationary type in which the bodies are placed on racks, or it may be an endless chain type which automatically carries the racks in, through, and out in a predetermined cycle.

The final operation in the making of a wool hat body is the pouncing or smoothing of the surface of the felt. The operator, or pouncer, sits in front of a lathe, which consists of a wheel about six inches in diameter and three inches wide, turning at a high speed. The wheel is so designed that strips of sandpaper may be attached to its surface. In operation, the pouncer forces the surface of the body against the sandpaper, thus sanding the felt. The action of the sandpaper is such that it cuts off the ends of the fibers which are naturally uneven. It also cuts down any thick places in the felt and gives the felt surface a nice feel and handle. While suction hoods around the wheels remove much of the pouncing dust caused by the cutting action of the paper, some of this dust is driven into the felt. In order that this may be removed, the hat bodies are placed in dust boxes which tumble the bodies and beat them. There is also a suction connected to the dust box to carry off the loosened dust.

The wool hat bodies are now ready for the final inspection, weighing, packing, and shipment to the front shop, where they will be blocked, trimmed, and finished for the eventual consumer.

FRONT-SHOP OPERATIONS

Those parts of hat manufacturing having to do with the transformation of bodies into finished hats are known as the front-shop operations. These operations may be roughly divided into two parts: (first) the finishing, consisting of blocking, finishing, pressing, ironing, leuring, etc.; and (second) the trimming, such as sweat-lining band, bow, binding, slicking, and packing. Since there are so many varied ways of accomplishing these operations, only an idea as to the principle involved will be given.

Blocking, done on metal or wood dies, with the aid of steam or heat to soften the shellac, transforms the body to the desired shape. Many of the blocks or dies are extremely intricate, as one may gather by inspecting the current trends in millinery.

Finishing, done either before the hat is removed from the block, or as a separate operation later, is another sandpaper operation, similar to pouncing, done to improve the surface of the hat. Ironing and leuring (wiping with powder or grease) improves certain finishes and gives a better feel to the felt. Under some conditions the hat is pressed in a hydraulic press to help it hold its shape. The edge of the brim must be rounded some time during the course of the finishing, and if the hat is to have a welt, the edge of the brim is folded over and stitched.

In the trim room, the hat is dressed up and receives a band and bow, sweat band, edge binding if called for, linings in the case of some men's hats, and feathers, veils, flowers, and so on in the case of millinery.

Before they are packed, all hats receive an inspection and touch-up. Men's hats are flanged or have the brims pressed and millinery is slicked and steamed to bring out the best in the finish.

It it a far cry from the original wool or fur as it comes to the hatter to the brilliantly colored and stylish headgear on the store counter; but when the hundreds of operations that have taken place are considered, it is not unbelievable.

Courtesy of Merrimac Hat Corporation, Amesbury, Massachusetts, and New York City.

FUR FELT HAT BODIES

Fur fibers obtained from animals such as the beaver, hare, nutria, rabbit, and other types of hare are ideally suited for the manufacture of fur felt hats after cleaning, grading, and carroting operations have been performed. Wool is clipped from sheep time and again with no harmful effect to the animal but to obtain hatter's fur, the hare or rabbit must be killed and the pelt taken. In most European countries, the meat of the animal is used as food after the removal of the pelt, thus making economically sound the breeding and raising of rabbits and other such animals. Because of this and the fact that our climate is unfavorable, most of our hatters' fur comes from abroad.

The skins as received by the fur cutter are covered with a thick pile of fur through which stand the longer, coarser hairs. After being sorted and graded, the skins are cleaned by being tumbled with damp sawdust in a large drum. This tumbling also removes some of the natural grease present in the skins. The pelt may be run through a clipping machine which will cut off these long hairs, or it

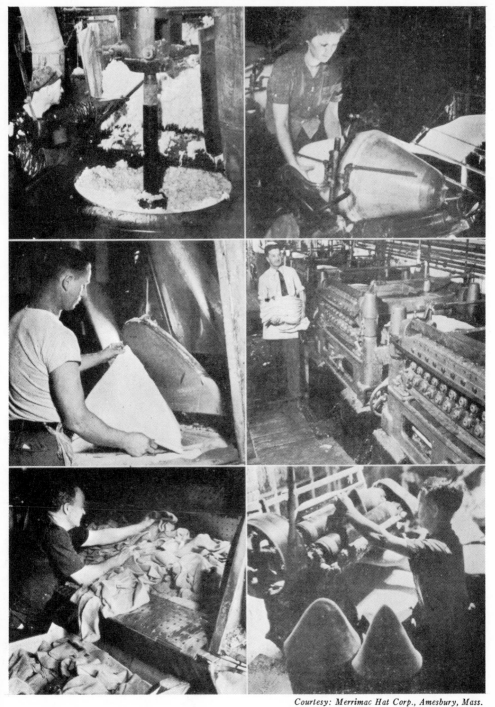

Courtesy: Merrimac Hat Corp., Amesbury, Mass.

Extraction after carbonizing (wool)   Shaping wool on cone forms (wool)
Side hardening operation (wool)   Mezzera machines (wool)
Loading dyeing machines (wool)   Stiffening operation (wool)

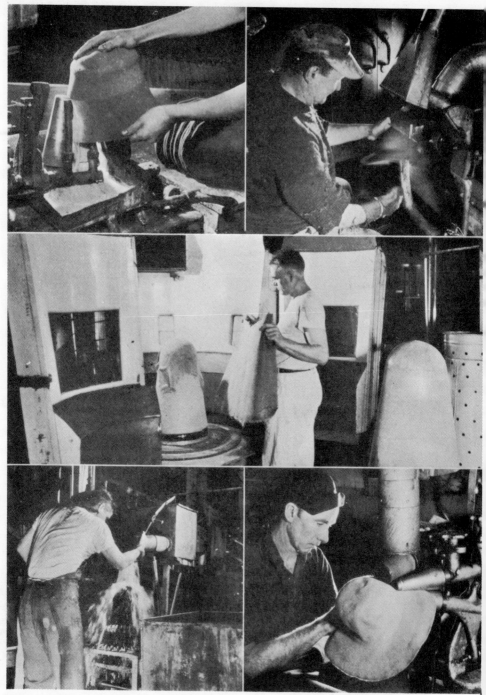

Courtesy: Merrimac Hat Corp., Amesbury, Mass.

Shellac stiffening (fur or wool)   Water blocking (fur)

Covering hat formed with burlap (fur)

"Pouncing" operation (wool)   "Pouncing" the brim (fur)

may be passed over revolving rollers which snatch and remove the long hairs. Certain skins receive neither the plucking nor clipping and the resultant mixture of hair and fur is known as "unpulled."

Fur fibers are covered with barbs which are similar to the scales or serrations of the wool fiber. In their natural state, the barbs are closed, lying close to the surface of the fiber, and before the fur will felt properly, the barbs must be opened by a process known as "carroting." In the past, carroting was done with a solution of mercuric nitrate, a chemical very apt to violently affect those working with it. From this condition arose the old saying "as mad as a hatter." The laws of most states now prohibit the use of the mercury carrot, which has been replaced by a new non-mercury carrot. The liquid carroting material is brushed into the fur and allowed to work for a short period of time, after which the skins are carried by a conveyor belt through a dryer. A brushing operation now removes any loose dirt and opens any fibers which may have been stuck together due to the carroting.

The actual cutting is done in an extremely interesting machine which literally cuts the skin from the fur rather than the fur from the skin. During the operation, the skin is shredded and disposed of in a separate compartment. The fur, on the other hand, may be routed in one of two ways, either onto an endless belt inspection table, where it is inspected and sorted by hand, or into the chamber of a blower. Over 90 per cent of the hatters' fur cut today is done by the latter method and goes into a blower, where the light, clean fur is kept suspended and circulating by a stream of air and the dirty, heavy particles and the small pieces of skin which may have become mixed with the fur drop to the bottom and are carried away. The fur is carefully weighed, packed, and labeled, and is now ready for the fur back-shop operations.

As in the case of the wool body, it usually takes several types and grades of fur to make a hat body. These various furs are weighed out in the proper amounts and fed into mixers and blowers whose job it is to thoroughly mix the blend and open the mass of fibers. A small amount of this mix, just enough for one hat, is then weighed by hand and fed onto the feed belt of the former.

The fur former consists of a large cylindrical enclosure open at the top and with a door in the front. On the floor of the former is a round turntable with a hole in the center through which a strong suction is created by exhaust blowers. In operation, a perforated metal cone is placed on the turntable over the hole, and the door is shut. The feed belt presents the fur into the enclosure near the top from where it is sucked down onto the revolving cone. Adjustable vents in the sides of the former control the air coming from around the edges and, when properly adjusted, will determine the lay of the body. The lay is the relative amount of stock on the tip or brim. When this snow storm of fur is completed and all the fur is on the cone, the door is opened and the next part of the operation carried out. In the so-called wet former, a spray of warm water is turned on the body as the cone continues to revolve. The cone is then removed, tipped upside down, and the body removed. In the dry former, a wet burlap is draped around the body while still on the cone and a perforated metal cover put over the burlap. The cone, body, burlap, and cover are then removed and submerged in a tank of hot water for about half a minute. The cover and burlap are then removed, the cone is tipped upside down, and the body stripped off.

The body, about three feet high and two feet in diameter at the bottom and very soft and tender, is rolled in burlap and presented to the hardening machine.

Fulling or shrinking of fur bodies is the same in principle as wool fulling, although the machines are of different design. Heat, moisture, motion, and pressure are as necessary here as in the wool back shop.

The hardening machine consists of two or more slatted rolls so placed that a trough is formed. The bodies are rolled in burlap and the roll is placed in the trough. The slats on the rolls give a kneading action as the rolls revolve. The hats are placed in the hardener numerous times, being unrolled and rerolled a different way between each machine operation. Hot water is sprayed on the rolls as the bodies are being hardened.

Starting, the next operation, is very similar to the hardening, with the exception that the rolls revolve faster than in the hardening machine and the bodies are dipped in hot water between each operation in the machine. The bodies will shrink from five to eight inches during this operation.

The Type-A fur machine, another version of the multiroller, uses hard rubber rolls upon which boiling water continually pours, and has a return conveyor to bring the bodies back to the feeding end. The bodies are fed in groups of about sixteen into the machine. When the return conveyor brings them back to the feeder, they are reentered, but in another position. Even shrinkage will result only if the bodies are fed alternately tips and then corners. Here again the usual shrinkage amounts to from five to eight inches.

The Type-B fur machine, again a multiroller type, is often used after coloring to harden the felt and bring the body down a small amount to its final size. In this case the Type-B machine would correspond somewhat to the twister as used in wool.

The coloring of fur bodies is carried out much as the coloring of wool bodies. However, a different type of kettle is sometimes used. It consists of a large oval open kettle in the bottom of which is a tunnel. A propeller in this tunnel keeps the liquid dye moving from one end of the kettle to the other while the bodies are kept in one place by screens. Here the dye moves while in wool the bodies move.

The stiffening is done in the same manner as in wool, the only exception being that, as a general rule, fur bodies require no shellac in the crowns.

The tip stretching and brim stretching are done in the same manner as the wool body, but water blocking, an extra operation not used on wool, is done at this point. The body, just out of a tank of hot water, is placed in the machine, the crown being over an expandable metal form and the brim being gripped at its edge by thirty-five to forty metal fingers. A ring of the correct size fits down over the crown to make a sharp corner where the brim joins the crown. By means of two levers, the operator causes the crown block to expand, stretching the crown of the body and at the same time causing the fingers to pull the brim out to any desired width. The levers are locked in this position, holding the felt, and several gallons of cold water are dumped on the body to set the felt.

Drying is done in a stationary or conveyor chain dryer and the bodies are ready for the final operation, pouncing.

Although the fur-pouncing operations are done on different types of machines, the results are similar to wool pouncing. Brims are pulled under a conical roll covered with sandpaper by two rubber-covered conical rolls. If both upper and under brim are to be done, the body is turned and the other surface presented to the sanding wheel. The crowns are usually pounced on a very interesting and almost human machine, consisting of a slowly revolving block on which the body is pulled, and a swinging head holding a sandpaper belt. Through an intricate cam mechanism, the swinging head presses the sandpaper belt, which is running at high speed, against the hat body, and then swings about the body, allowing the paper to work on all sections of the crown. Besides this regular finish, there are many special finishes such as suede, velour, chamois, etc. To produce these finishes, special machinery and special techniques are required.

The fur bodies are now ready for final inspection, packing, and shipment.

Courtesy of Merrimac Hat Corporation, Amesbury, Massachusetts, and New York City.

TOPIC: PLAITED, BRAIDED, AND LACE FABRICS

Recall to mind the braiding or plaiting of a little girl's hair, or the making of a pair of horse reins for a child, and you have the principle of the manufacture of fabrics in this group. The three basic terms—knitting, netting, and knotting—come from the same Anglo-Saxon root, *cnyttan*. This means "to tie with a knot, to intertwine, to weave into a network with needles, or to join in a close manner." The root indicates the various methods used in the manipulation of a single yarn for the purpose of making elastic and pliable yarns, threads, and fabrics.

The term "lace" comes from the old French *las*, by way of the Latin *laquens*, which means a noose, or to ensnare—rather well adapted to lace. A single yarn can produce a plaited or braided fabric or article, since it will interlace, entwine, and twist in several directions to produce a porous material or lace. It should be kept in mind that one yarn may be used to make a lace, and that the action is like that of several yarns entering the machine; this action is used in knitting as well.

A crude form of meshed cord for ornamentation was used in Peru over four thousand years ago. Ancient Egypt used a form of lace to cover mummies. In the days when Rome was at its height, the term "lace" merely implied the cord which holds by being tied or interwoven; in time, however, lace came to mean the open-work fabric made of interwoven threads. Today, such threads may be made of cotton, linen, silk, metal, lastex, rayon, acetate, nylon, wool, and similar fibers or filaments. The threads can be braided, plaited, twisted, interlaced, or looped to make some type of material.

Lace was well known in the early Christian era, and lacemaking took on impetus through the Middle Ages, chiefly in Europe. The work was done in convents and monasteries. By the sixteenth century, Flanders, France, and Italy had good lace industries; and it may be stated that lacemaking in the modern sense began around the year 1500.

In 1533, Catherine de Médicis became consort of Henry II, king of France. This illustrious lady of a famous family of Italy brought the art of making lace to France. Venice, however, remained the center for the heavier types of lace, such as needlepoint or point lace. France soon began to develop and produce the lighter types of lace which produced a new grace and delicacy, as shown by Alençon, Argentan, and Chantilly. Lace soon was being made in special motifs for particular purposes.

During the sixteenth century, Belgium and Flanders developed handmade laces and became leading centers in the industry. Frans Hals, Raphael, and Velázquez received wide acclaim for their paintings because they portrayed lace to advantage. Lace guimpes, headdresses, and ruffs made their paintings popular and their prestige high, by showing the fashions and vogues of their era.

A very remarkable woman, Barbara Uttmann, of Annaberg, Germany, who had learned lacemaking in the old centers of Liége and Bruges in Belgium, brought the art to the Harz Mountains area in Germany in 1561. She was particularly adept in making Brussels or Brabant lace, Binche, Flanders, Mechlin, and Valenciennes.

Queen Elizabeth, during the same century, because of close contact and good relations with the courts of France, brought lace to England. Aprons, gowns, and ruffs soon became the rage, and she is given credit for the introduction of the lace handkerchief into England. Lace began to be used in a lavish way on the Continent and in the British Isles. Men used lace cravats, lace cuffs and collars, and boots of all types were even trimmed with lace, while lace towels were used to wipe razors. By the end of the century people of affluence wore thick ruffs of lace around the neck. Each ruff was about six inches thick and extended twenty-one inches or so from the neck. Spoons measured about two feet in length so that the wearer of a ruff might eat without soiling the lace.

By the end of the century, fashions and styles changed considerably with the advent of the industry in many centers in Europe. England, France, and Italy began to use lace in dress in many ways. As lace became more plentiful, the vogue for it grew, and all classes of people began to wear it. Lace was now a mark of distinction and prestige. The rich and the poor had something in common, but not for long. Laws were passed by the various countries which forbade the use of lace by the common people. This irksome edict caused a furore throughout Europe. In due time the laws were finally repealed through the valiant efforts of a Jesuit, Father Regis. For his work he is the patron saint of the lace industry to this day.

During the reign of Louis XIV (1643–1715) in France, lace became a top performer. Schools and workshops were founded in many French cities and towns, and many of these are still known for their lace work. Lace was official court dress at all time. Jean Baptiste Colbert, prime minister for Louis, stated that "the fashion of lace is to France what the mines of Peru are to Spain." He was instrumental in bringing many lace workers to France from other countries, chiefly Italy. Colbert established the first school for lacemaking in Alençon. France and Italy soon outstripped England in lace manufacture, so much so that England imported much lace from these nations, since it could not make enough lace to supply the demand. By the eighteenth century, lace had really arrived, and it expressed the heights of extravagance.

LACES

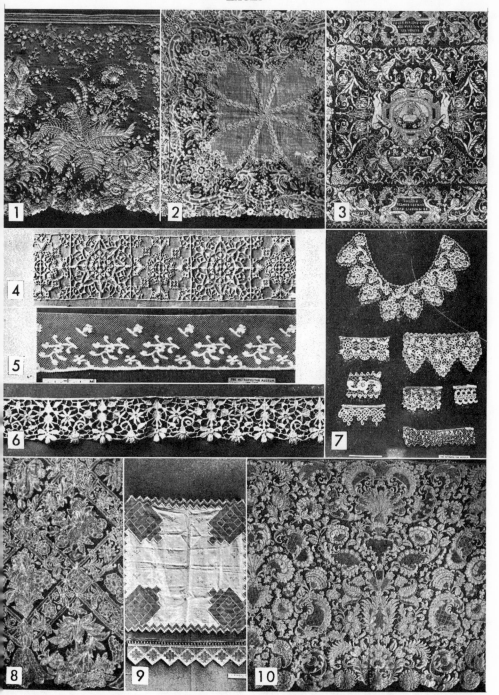

1. Brussels United Lace; 2. Bobbin Lace, 14th Century; 3. Lace Network, 18th Century Italian Fahnestock Collection; 4. Needlepoint Laces, 19th Century Italian Border Reticello; 5. French Bobbin Lace, Late 18th Century Valenciennes Strip; 6. Italian Needlepoint, 15-18th Centuries Border—Punto In Aria; 7. Crochet Laces, 19th Century Irish; 8. Brussels Lace; 9. Lace Cutwork, 14th Century Hardanger; 10. French Needlepoint, 18th Century.

French Lace—18th Century Needlepoint—Point d'Alençon
French Lace—18th Century Needlepoint—Point d'Alençon
Italian Lace—17th Century—Fischback Collection

Crocheting, netting, knotting, and tatting, kindred techniques to lacemaking, also received acclaim. Definitions for these follow:

1. CROCHETING: Separate loops are thrown off and finished by hand successively. In knitting, the entire series of loops that go to form one length, round, or circumference are retained on one or more needles while a new series is being formed by a separate needle. Crocheting may be done by hand or by machine.

2. NETTING: The knotting of threads into meshes that will not ravel. Chinese-type lace and fish net have a knot at every intersection. Knitted fabric may ravel or disentangle and the yarn may be used over again to make another fabric. Netting is done by hand or by machine.

3. KNOTTING: The actual knotting of the parts of one or more threads so that they will not slip or loosen. Bows, laces, and other types of mesh or porous work are examples of knotting. May be done by hand or by machine.

4. TATTING: It is used to make banding, edging, or insertion, which is lacelike in formation in the finished condition. It is done by means of a small shuttle manipulated by the individual. Machine tatting is also done.

There are two distinct groups of laces today—handmade and machine-made or real lace, classified as follows:

1. Needlepoint Lace 3. Crocheted Lace
2. Pillow or Bobbin Lace 4. Darned Lace

Needlepoint Lace: It is the most expensive and most difficult type of lace to make. Made with a needle, the first step is to sketch the pattern on parchment which is then stitched down upon two pieces of linen. The thread is then laid on the leading lines drawn on the parchment and fastened to the parchment here and there by stitches. The solid parts are filled in by the needle with buttonhole stitching. The meshes or ties are manipulated so as to link the different parts into the one fabric. A knife is then passed between the parchment and the linen, thereby releasing the completed lace.

HANDMADE LACES: NEEDLEPOINT

1. ALENÇON: The name comes from the city in France where it was first made. Alençon is still a leading world center for lace making. Birds, flowers, pastoral scenes, and vases form the background of Alençon. The groundwork of this lace is hexagonally shaped in mesh construction of double-twisted thread.

2. ROSE POINT: Resembles Venetian point lace.

3. VENETIAN POINT: Floral patterns typify this lace, in which the design is marked with regular open-worked fibers or vine effects. Belgium is the center for this type of lace today.

Bobbin Lace: It is made on pillows and often referred to as pillow lace. A twisting and plaiting action brings the threads into the motif. The pattern is first drawn on a piece of paper and pricked with holes which determine where the pins shall be placed for guiding the thread. The pattern is then fastened to a pillow from which hang the threads of the bobbins; these are twisted and plaited about the pins to form the fabric.

There are two types of bobbin lace:

1. UNCUT THREAD LACE: The outstanding types of this single-piece lace include Binche, Cluny, Malines, Old Flanders, Point de Lille, Point de Paris, common Torchon, and Valenciennes. The meshes are hexagonal, round, or square; from these types the motif is developed. Heavy outline threads are employed to set off the design.

2. UNITED LACE: Individual details are combined to give the finished fabric. Black and white Chantilly, Blonde, Bruges Duchesse, and Brussels Duchesse are the more popular types. Relief motifs are a feature in these laces.

Coarse Flanders and Point d'Angleterre are made from a combination of needle-point and bobbin point. The latter term was originally used for very fine Flemish lace of the 18th century. Other names for bobbin lace are bone and pillow.

HANDMADE LACES: BOBBIN

BRUSSELS: A fine type of pillow lace which is not made in one piece on a pillow. The ground is worked around the pattern which has been worked beforehand.

CHANTILLY: First made in this city in France, it is now made with silk, rayon, or cotton. The feature of this lace is the double ground with fillings of baskets, flowers, or vases.

CLUNY: Paddle or wheel effects are features of this popular lace which was first made in this city in France. The lace is coarse and strong.

DUCHESSE: Fine net ground in which the patterns are in raised work. This popular lace is made chiefly in convents and convent schools in Belgium.

HONITON: Originated in town of this name in England; made chiefly, at present, in Belgium and France. Flower patterns, especially the rose and the thistle, appear on open groundwork.

MALTESE: Supposed to have been first made in Malta, the lace is known for the Maltese cross in the pattern.

MECHLIN, MALINES: Light and very fine threads typify this lace, in which the ground pattern is linked together with bud and flower effects. It is on the order of Brussels, but the hexagonal mesh is smaller.

TORCHON: An inexpensive, stout, rugged lace known for its simple patterns. The ground is coarse, threads are rather loose; often referred to as beggar's lace.

VALENCIENNES: Commonly referred to as Val, the mesh is diamond shape. First made in Valenciennes, France, the best grades are now made in Ypres, Belgium. Some of the lace requires as many as one thousand bobbins on the same pillow.

Crocheted Lace

There are two types:

IRISH: Made with a crochet hook, it is not as fine in texture as needlepoint.

SYRIAN: Resembles Irish crocheted lace and is used chiefly for handkerchiefs.

Darned Lace

A chain stitch outlines the motif on a background of net or some other suitable fabric. There are two types:

ANTIQUE: A heavy linen thread is used in a large, rectangular, knotted-mesh effect.

FILET: A square mesh in which the patterns are made with animal and tree effects.

MACHINE-MADE LACES

ORIENTAL: This fine net is made with a heavily embroidered edge.

PRINCESS. Made of machine-braid on a machine-made net; put together by hand.

SHADOW: A fine mesh ground in which shadowlike patterns of finer mesh are seen.

COMPARISON OF MACHINE-MADE AND HANDMADE LACES

1. There are irregularities in handmade lace, since the patterns do not repeat in exact, perfect order.
2. Handmade lace can be raveled without trouble.

3. Machine-made Cluny, Torchon, and other bobbin laces, when observed through a magnifying glass, show uneven threads and the use of two sizes of thread instead of one.
4. Cotton lace may be distinguished from linen lace by tipping the end of the respective threads. Cotton threads will become fuzzy and protrude; linen threads will taper to a point.
5. Insert a pin into threads of the pattern of machine-made lace and observe that it is possible to slide the threads back and forth; this is not possible in handmade lace.
6. Machine-made lace has a flat, dull appearance.

Lace Machines: Strange as it seems, England was the country that actually developed machine lacemaking. England, of course, was the keystone in the rise of the Industrial Revolution and the Machine Age. England needed more lace and decided to supply this want by machine rather than rely on imports from the Continent. The old stocking frame, or knitting machine, was invented by William Lee, a Presbyterian minister, in 1586. At the time, net machines were being used in France, and a few of these machines were used in England. From such use it was believed that the making of lace could be greatly augmented by machine production. In 1802, Robert Brown of England perfected a frame to make nets of all sizes. These were used as a background into which the lace motifs could be worked by hand. With great interest mounting, new developments and inventions were in the offing.

In 1808, the first true lace machine was made in England by John Heathcoat. His frame was for "bobbin-net" and it attracted much attention, not only in England, but on the Continent. In 1813, John Leavers, another Englishman, brought out the principles of his machine, which included the making of a fancy pattern simultaneously with the background of net in the fabric. His machine revolutionized the industry. England forbade exportation of the machines. Some few were, however, smuggled into France, and by 1826 the British patents had expired. The advent of the Leavers frame added the equivalent of about fifteen million dollars to the annual business done in England, a considerable amount in those days.

The Jacquard loom made its debut during the years 1801 to 1804. This loom controlled each and every warp end in the weaving operation whereby a single yarn could be raised or lowered at will by the use of his system of cards used for controlling the entire warp. It was now possible to reproduce any motif at all—pictures, foliage, pastoral scenes, buildings.

Taking the principles from this marvelous revolutionary loom, the lace machine inventors developed a card system of their own in 1824. By punching the cards according to a plan denoting the motif to be woven, they were able to translate their designs onto the cards, and then reproduce the most intricate patterns formerly made by hand with the Leavers machines. Nottingham, England, soon became the machine lace center of the world for machine-made lace. England had outstripped and outwitted the lace areas on the Continent.

Soon after these machines came in, Calais, France—still a great lace center—made sensational progress in machine-made lace, so much so that Calais soon was known as "Clef de France" (Key to France), and "Capitale de la Dentelle" (The Lace Capital). It did not take very long for some of the staple laces still known today to become prominent. These include Alençon, Binche, Chantilly, and Point de Paris. Handmade lace, obviously, was soon outdistanced by the machine-made type with regard to production. A Leavers machine is something to behold. It weighs sixteen to twenty tons, and takes up at least five hundred square feet of floor space.

Machine-made lace, around the time of Heathcoat and Leavers in England, began in St. Gall (St. Gallen), Switzerland, and Plauen, Germany. They are still great centers. The laces made in these areas were perfected by the "burnt-out method," whereby a chemical was used to destroy the animal fiber in the lace, leaving the cotton unscathed and the article intact.

The machines of Nottingham embody several features, listed below:

1. The patterns are made on the principle of the cards used for weaving Jacquard fabric on a power loom.
2. The same warp is used as the one used to make woven cloth on a loom.
3. Spools of yarn furnish the motif. There is no filling yarn used in the strict sense as in making woven material.
4. Fine yarn is wound on small brass bobbins which are then set in frames called carriages, to dart back and forth while spiraling around and tying in the warp yarn and the yarn from the spools used for the motif.
5. The tensions on the machine must be watched closely for tautness or looseness of the fabric as it is being made.
6. This machine, thirty feet wide, can be set so that eight to ten curtain fabrics can be made at the one time. Each fabric is controlled by the Jacquard head motion for the motif, to give detailed accuracy.

Dress laces are usually made on the Leavers machine which, while it works on the principle of the Nottingham machine, has a number of differences that make it ideal for manufacturing this product.

It was not until after the turn of the present century that the United States began to make machine-made lace. Up to 1905 we imported practically all the lace used in this country. In 1909 England rescinded its ban on exportation of lace machines: duty-free importation was allowed for lace machines that might be brought here. This was a great boon to the industry, since the duty had been 45 per cent. Protected by tariffs that ranged from 40 to 90 per cent, the industry began to gain impetus and has thrived here ever since.

Nottingham machines were set up in Bridgeport, Connecticut; Paterson, New Jersey; Scranton, Wilkes-Barre, and Philadelphia, Pennsylvania. The latter city until a few years ago was the lace center of America. Incidentally, today the lace center in this country is Rhode Island, where well over three-quarters of the production is made.

There were five inventions in the nineteenth century that greatly improved machine lacemaking with regard to the fabric produced, to the use of less labor, to increased production, and to lowering of the price of the lace products.

1. 1835: Thomas Alcock perfected the Go-Through System of working the carriages on the frames.
2. 1841: Hooten Deverill, a great English inventor, applied to the Leavers machine the Jacquard motion acting on the warp threads in independent bars. This was fifteen years after the Jacquard application had been first made on a Leavers frame.
3. 1849: James Oldknow, English inventor, perfected the perforated steel bar.
4. 1875: By this time Alcock's Go-Through System was in universal use, since some improvements had been effected.
5. 1891: W. H. Smith brought out his porcupine roller attachment, which was widely hailed in the trade.

As previously noted, lace is the result of a twisting process. The product is finished for proper size, correct motif and type, and matching. Optical inspection of lace is very important. Major laces include curtain and table laces, filet net, novelty effects, combination effects, rough-weave and shadow-weave effects.

As used in dress, lace is suitable for a girl of eight or a woman of eighty since it has an elegance that sets off one's appearance. It looks well on all types of women—tall or short, slim or stout. Lace adds grace and charm to the wearer, and may be used either for daily wear, tailored dresses, or in evening wear. Handkerchiefs with lace, and collar and cuff sets, might be in the wardrobe of every woman.

Some Basic Terms Used in the Lace Industry

1. ALLOVER EMBROIDERY: This is thirty-six inches or more in width, and the motif is embroidered over the full width of the fabric. Cotton, linen, nylon, rayon, and silk serve as the yarns, while the fabric base may be organdy, plain dimity, cambric, longcloth, pique, etc. The product is without scallops on each side, and is made in white and pastel shades and colors suitable for everyday wear. This type of embroidery is used for blouses, dress fabrics, pillow covers.

2. ALLOVER LACE: A lace one yard or more wide, devoid of scallops, and with the design spread over the entire width. Many types of design motifs and color shades are used for the fabric, which is made into day and evening dresses.

3. BEADING EDGES: Refers to embroidery or lace in which the edges are perforated or open, so that ribbon may be drawn through and pulled up to give a ruffled effect.

4. BEADING GALLOON: A band used on some embroidery and lace, having both edges scalloped. It comes in varying widths, with openings in the center for ribbon to pass through, as shoulder straps in underwear, or to adorn dresses.

5. BEADING INSERTION: A straight edge applied to both sides of embroidery and lace, with openings in the center to permit ribbon to be pulled through and gathered or ruffled. Used on baby clothes, children's dresses, carriage covers, shoulder straps.

6. BOBBIN FINE: Machine-made lace, on the order of shadow lace, in which heavy threads outline the motif.

7. BOBBIN SPOOL: A spool with a head or flange on both ends. It holds the yarn or thread for spinning, weaving, or sewing.

8. BRIDE: A small strip or connection which links the details of ornamentation in lace. It may consist of threads overcast with buttonhole stitches, or of twisted or plaited threads. The English equivalent of this French term is "pearl-tie."

9. CORDONNET: The yarn, thread, or cord that outlines a lace motif.

10. HARDANGER LACE: This city on the Hardanger Fjord in southwestern Norway is famous for its lace, made by its women. The origin of this lace is very old: worked with colored silks on a fine gauze netting, it was made in Persia and other Asiatic countries for many centuries. Materials for making Hardanger include scrim or loose-textured linen, a pair of very sharp scissors, a tapestry needle, and pearl cotton.

    This lace is based on the principle of the square and is geometric in form. The stitches include kloster, Swedish weaving stitch, woven bars with picots, festoon stitch, lace stitch, Holbein technique, feather stitch, kloster blocks, diagonal kloster blocks, and fagoting stitch.

11. INSERTION: A section used on lace or embroidery for joining two pieces of fabric together; both sides are straight, and it is reinforced with extra threads to make sewing easier and to provide more strength.

12. LACE FABRIC: Sheer lightweight material with a doup or mock leno weave. Made in white and pastel shades, it finds use in summer dressgoods; this cloth gives good service, launders easily and well, and withstands rugged wear. It is not a true lace.

13. LACE FRAMES: The complex machines used to make lace—also known as bobbinette frames and warp net frames.

14. LACE SPRIG: A piece of lace fabric appliquéd to a net foundation.

15. LACE TIES: The connecting threads used in lace manufacture.

16. LACEWORK: Usually implies open-work hosiery which has been knitted.

17. LACE YARNS: Doubled yarns made from good to high-quality cotton yarns which range from 60's up to 240's in yarn size or count. Lace yarns are hard-twisted and usually gassed or singed to add smoothness and luster. Sheen and general appearance of lace yarns are very important since they add to the beauty of the material produced.

18. TOILE: The heavy filling or design of a lace motif in contradistinction to the background.

19. VEININGS: These are used to join the various parts of materials; they are useful as well as ornamental. Width is from ⅛ inch to ½ inch. In French called *entredeux*, which means "between two."

20. VRAIE: French word for "true"; used to designate lace that is real, true, or hand-made.

LAUNDERING OF LACE

Lace will retain its shape better if it is pinned or fastened to a piece of muslin prior to washing. Old and delicate lace should be protected by placing it in a muslin pillow slip during washing. Lace should not be rubbed; instead, the suds should be allowed to soak the material clean. Rinse lace in the container and remove for drying. Press on the wrong side.

SCHIFFLI EMBROIDERY

Embroidery is defined as ornamental needlework, or the art of producing such work. It is different from lace in that it is the ground material which is embellished by motifs, whereas lace means the use of a cord or thread to fasten a network of threads arranged in some figure or design. Embroideries are still extant that were made in the eighteenth century. Egypt, Greece, Italy, Persia, and Syria were known for their early embroidery work. One of the great productive results of the Industrial Revolution in England was the machine carding of fibers, the spinning of yarns, and the weaving of fabrics. This upheaval in the eighteenth century changed the mode of living in practically all respects and its effect is still apparent. Increased yarn production from spinning frames had a great effect on handmade products, especially with regard to lace; something new had to be developed to offset the losses incurred by machine-made lace. The cities and towns in Switzerland had been known for centuries for their handmade laces. Three centers were in the Lake Constance area—St. Gall, Appenzell, and Inner-hoden. The women there decided to do embroidery work by hand and from this the great "schiffli" machine was conceived and developed, one of the marvels of the present age. St. Gall became the clearing house for the work done in Switzerland and many thriving businesses in embroidery were built up. The industry became a "grandmother-to-mother-to-daughter" matter. The first school to teach the art of embroidery was set up by the Swiss government in 1889 in Appenzell. This area is still well known for its work in this field. The rise of schiffli embroidery is interesting and fantastic.

Courtesy: Walter Dietzsch, Schiffli Lace and Embroidery Institute, Jersey City, New Jersey

Schiffli machine.

In schiffli embroidery, multiply an ordinary single-needle home sewing machine by 684 and produce with the resulting machine three-dimensional motifs which resemble the finest hand embroidery in fine colors and designs, and you have an idea of the capabilities of the schiffli frame. The actual schiffli lace and embroidery machines are made in two lengths—ten and fifteen yards—and may weigh as much as twenty tons. Yet these huge machines can produce delicate lace and embroidery that outlast the very fabric they embellish.

Contrary to a popular belief, there never was a Mr. Schiffli. The name is derived from a Swiss dialect of German and means "little boat." It is thus called because the shuttle containing the bobbin is shaped like a tiny ship's hull and is the distinguishing part of the embroidery machine. In the schiffli process, as the machine's many needles penetrate the fabric, a shuttle or "little boat" on the back of the fabric ties the loop of thread from each needle directly into the cloth.

Versatile, adaptable, and beautiful, schiffli laces and embroideries are used in both men's and women's apparel and on many household items as well. Found on lingerie, beachwear, shoes, umbrellas, gloves, millinery, shirts, neckties, lampshades, slipcovers and tablecovers, they are also used on leather coats and jackets. Schiffli products are found in every price range. They are found on cocktail dresses and aprons; on clothes for tiny tots and for great-grandmothers.

One of the more fascinating products of the schiffli industry is Venice-type lace. In this process, a sheer silk-and-gum fabric is used as a base for applying an embroidered design with the schiffli machine. The embroidered cloth is then placed in an acid bath which eats out the silk and leaves only the embroidered design. The result is lace.

The schiffli lace and embroidery industry began here about one hundred years ago when Swiss immigrants brought their craft to the United States and settled in a six-square-mile area atop the Palisades of northern New Jersey overlooking the Hudson River. Gradually 550 plants were erected, and today they produce 95 per cent of schiffli laces and embroideries in the United States as well as the rest of North and South America. Because the Swiss were so impressed with the locality's resemblance to their homeland, they settled there with their families and skills. The area has become known as "little St. Gall" after the world-famous embroidery center in Switzerland. Financially, the schiffli industry represents a $75,000,000 business. There are 1,250 machines in the six-square-mile area in New Jersey. Although today it is completely Americanized, many native-born Swiss are still employed in the industry.

TESTING

1. What is meant by a geometrically-designed motif? A symmetrical pattern?
2. Name four products made by braiding or plaiting.
3. At what angles do the yarns go in a woven fabric? In a lace material?
4. How might a curtain lace differ from a table lace?
5. Give some reasons for the continued popularity of lace among women.
6. How is pillow or bobbin lace made? Point or needlepoint lace?
7. Name two European lace centers.
8. Define embroidery. How does it differ from lace?
9. Where is the lace center in the United States?
10. Define crocheting, netting, knotting, tatting.
11. Discuss some of the features of the Nottingham lace machine.

12. Give three comparisons or differences between machine-made lace and handmade lace.
13. Explain the following terms: allover lace, beading insertion, bride, cordonnet, lace ties, veinings, vraie lace.
14. Discuss schiffli embroidery.

REFERENCES: *Leavers Lace*, by H. G. Truman and E. F. Walker, American Lace Manufacturers Association, Inc., Providence, Rhode Island; *The Story of Lace and Embroidery*, by David E. Schwab, Fairchild Publications, Inc., New York City; *Schiffli Lace and Embroidery Institute*, by Walter E. Dietzsch, Jersey City, N.J.

TOPIC: NONWOVEN FABRICS, SPUNBONDED FABRICS, BONDED FABRICS, FIBERWOVEN FABRICS

The American Society for Testing Materials, Philadelphia, Pennsylvania, defines a nonwoven fabric as "a textile structure produced by bonding and/or interlocking of fibers, accomplished by mechanical, chemical, thermal, or solvent means, and combinations thereof. The term does not include paper or fabric which are woven, knitted, tufted, or those made by wool and other felting processes."

It may also be stated that a nonwoven fabric is a web or sheet of textile-type fibers, bonded together by the application of narrow stripes or patterns of adhesive material, or autogenously bonded by chemical activation of the surface—either through chemical action or heat in the case of thermoplastic fibers. One of the main considerations in this type of material is that the expanses of the web have freedom of fiber movement, since the bonding material is in minor proportion to the fiber content, or the adhesion is self-developed from the fibers themselves.

The nature of the fibers is such that they constitute the important property of a sheet of this type, and the unification material serves only to hold the fibers in place so that advantage may be taken to the fullest degree of the physical properties of the fibers.

The fibers in a nonwoven fabric may be oriented preferably in one direction or they may be laid in a random manner. Manmade fibers in the fabric are crimped during manufacture and may be from a half inch to six inches in staple length.

HISTORY OF NONWOVEN FABRICS

Nonwoven fabrics were first produced about 1942, when a few thousand pounds of cellulosic fiber were used to make the first fabrics. Developed from waste fibers of various types, the products were of disposable nature. Since this beginning, there has been a tremendous development in the qualities of the raw stocks used and a meteoric rise in the uses for fabrics of this type. There were eight manufacturers in the field in 1942, and the number has risen to about forty at the present time.

The Product Information Service of E. I. du Pont de Nemours & Co., Inc., in conjunction with their experimental and research laboratories, has released some interesting information on the subject of the developments in the field.

Nylon has received much acclaim as a base fiber because of its compressional recovery and its tear and tensile properties. Fabrics made with this base, as well as from other manmade fibers, resist acids, alkalies, mildew, and rot. Along with "Dacron" polyester fiber and "Orlon" acrylic fiber, these bases add higher strength and toughness, and "Dacron" in particular increases resistance to high temperatures. Dimensional stability and good electrical properties are also apparent, along with fast drying time and resistance to sunlight deterioration.

Nonwoven fabrics consist of two major components—the web and the binder: all fabrics have to rely on the base fiber used in the web, and the bonding agent. There are two major methods used for the web formation which is ultimately bonded into the nonwoven fabric. These follow:

Method 1: The fibers are blended and carded in order to obtain a lightweight web. The web can also be fed into a lapper machine which continuously crosses and folds the web, so that the fibers lie in one direction or cross at angles. A random orientation can be obtained by use of a multiple lap arrangement.

Method 2: An air stream blows the fibers and deposits them in a random manner on a rotating screen. The fiber web is then obtained by doffing or taking the sheet off the screen and depositing the stock on a conveyor to insure uniformity, so that when bonding is applied there will be equal strength in all directions.

BONDING AGENTS USED FOR NONWOVEN FABRICS

There are two methods used at the present time: resin and thermoplastic.

Resin Bonding: This method is the more popular, since it can be applied directly to the web from an aqueous dispersion as soon as it leaves the web-forming equipment. The dispersion may be applied in spray form, foam form, or by printing or padding onto the web. The web is then dried and heat-cured, and may be calendered. Drying and curing are done on cans or in curing ovens. Temperatures range from 200° to about 400° F. Rebonding is often done to further strengthen the finished fabric.

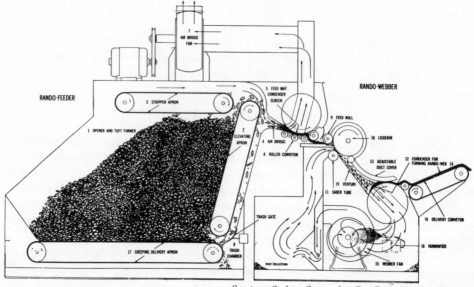

Courtesy: Curlator Corporation, East Rochester, New York

Thermoplastic Bonding: A thermoplastic fiber with a lower melting point than the base fiber is blended with the latter in the formation of the web. The web is either hot-calendered or embossed, at the softening point of the thermoplastic fiber, thereby causing bonding to take place. The bonding agent constitutes from 10 to 30 per cent of the weight of the finished fabric.

NONWOVEN FABRIC PRODUCTION

Beginning in 1950 with the advent of the Rando-Feeder and the Rando-Webber machines, the Curlator Corporation of East Rochester, New York, made rapid strides in the production of textile fabrics that are not woven or knitted. Nonwoven fabrics were manufactured previously by two major processes: (first), by felting certain animal fibers; and (second), by using conventional carding frames, garnetting machines, and cross-lappers, or by laminating the card webs of fibers. The latter method is carried out by spacing several cards over a conveyor line where each card in the set delivers its web, being carried by the conveyor, to produce the necessary web weight by lamination.

Description of each of the foregoing methods follows:

1. Felt is a fabric of wool, fur, or hair obtained by the matting or interlocking of the fibers together under heat, moisture, and pressure. These animal fibers become matted by mechanical entanglement aided by the interlocking scales or barbs peculiar to such fibers. The method, still widely used today in the production of felt, has been used for many centuries. Vegetable and manmade fibers are devoid of any interlocking scales and consequently do not respond to conventional felting methods. Manmade fibers are felted by mechanical interlocking, as on a needle loom, and by subsequent shrinking to desired thickness and hardness by heat or chemical action.
2. Product-web with a parallel lay of fibers is obtained when the card or the garnetting machine webs are laminated longitudinally to give the composite web structure. Thus, there is a parallel orientation of the fibers which produces a wide difference in the parallel tensile strength when compared with the cross tensile strength in the bonded web product.
3. The cross-lapping of the card or the garnett webs affords a means for more nearly equalizing the 90-degree strength with the longitudinal strength. Full equalization of the strength and properties, of course, through 360 degrees of arc is not obtainable.
4. Random orientation of the fibers at the time of the web formation does provide for equal tensile strengths through 360 degrees of arc in a two-dimensional plane. Rando-Web tests have proved that a high degree of performance can be achieved.

The Curlator Corporation, in its research on the feasibility of investing capital in the nonwoven machine industry, noted that the random lay of fibers and the equal physical properties in a two-dimensional plane through 360 degrees of arc had to be the basic consideration. Fiber formations had to be studied to the finite along with the specific requirements for precision and perfection in product webs. Deep study and attention had to be given to the manmade staple fibers and to the vegetable fibers, as well. As time went on in research, trial and error became trial and success. Negative results often produced positive answers.

Curlator designed its well-known "B" machine, which was integrated as far as possible to practical mill operation. Their random lay achieved its success and its superiority over the old-time conventional means of obtaining web in its being able to obtain a high degree of perfection by doffing the fibers from the "opening" cylinder by means of an air stream which permitted free disposition of the individual fibers onto a condenser cylinder or screen. Unless certain fundamental and complex principles are adhered to, the matters of air-doffing, travel, and the delivery of the fibers in a free state to the screen or cylinder can give much trouble and considerable loss in time, energy, and investment.

After the company developed the random lay and obtained a high perfection in the physical properties of the fibers through 360 degrees of arc, other problems of major proportions developed—the problems of the opening of the fiber and the necessity of increasing production rate. After these points were met and conquered, it was possible to obtain webs from many kinds of fiber which have a pre-opening that would produce apparent carding sliver quality in one-half to one-ounce webs. The special design of the Curlator machine's licker-in nose bar and the feed-roll combination is such that the working cylinder, flats or rolls, doffing cylinder, and saw-toothed comb on conventional cards are not involved at all.

Quality webs from the major staple fibers, including the manmade, are now obtainable in a very wide range of products on the Rando-Feeder and on the Rando-Webber.

For high-quality webs the production rate is from one to three pounds per hour per inch of machine width for weights that range between one-half and three ounces per square yard, irrespective of the type of web-forming machinery used. Of course, the user of the equipment must judge the relation between the product web quality and the production rate when his competition and his market are taken into consideration. Selection of fibers, denier size, blending components or ingredients, pre-opening, bonding the treatment of his product, all must be given close study and attention.

Careful increase of pre-opening will prove fruitful to the manufacturer before feeding to the Rando-Feeder and the Rando-Webber in the case of certain fibers; for example, by proper controls such waste fibers as cotton shoddy, wool shoddy, mungo, jute, garnetted thread waste, and reclaimed tire cord fabric may be made into mats or webs ranging from one up to twenty-four ounces per square yard at a production rate as high as 7.5 pounds per hour per inch of machine width. The manipulator must know the qualities desired, the fibers being used, the principles of good blending, the rates of production, and the end use to be made of his product.

A great advancement that has done much for the acceptance of nonwovens is in the chemical field with regard to bonding: the "merger" between the web manufacturers and the technical knowledge of the chemical manufacturers has brought about an entirely new vista for consideration. The chemical bonding agents now being used have stepped up the acceptance and use of these fabrics. Thus, nonwovens have an improved appearance as well as improved physical properties. In addition, the former harsh or boardy fabrics are now being rapidly replaced by fabrics which possess "hand" and drape, when needed; strength and washability problems are being met and progress is being made. Strength in the fabrics is now obtainable, as well as other properties that only a few years ago were deemed impossible to obtain. Fiber producers are taking a markedly increased interest in the nonwoven fabrics, and training units for personnel have been set up in some of the larger companies. With further research in the science and the engineering phases in producing better nonwoven fabrics, the future for this branch of the great, versatile textile industry seems assured.

USES OF NONWOVEN FABRICS

APPAREL:
Absorbent liners; aprons and bibs; diapers; facing material; inter-linings for bathing suits, dresses, foundation garments, shoulder pads; padding for handbags, quilted garments, suitings; women's skirts.

HOME
FURNISHINGS:
Dishcloths; draperies, dustcloths; hospital sheeting; napkins; table-cloths; tissues; towels; vacuum cleaner bags; window shades. Most of these are for a single use and disposable.

INDUSTRIAL:
Backing material for maps, oilcloth, plastic films, quilting; bagging and wrapping material; bags and containers for certain materials such as desiccants; casket lining; disposable industrial cleaning cloths; electrical and cable insulation; filters for air, chemical, and dairy uses; high-pressure laminates; insulation materials; packaging; padding; polishing and wiping cloths; tea bags.

MEDICAL AND
SANITARY:
Bandages; bed pads and sheetings; bibs; covers of many types; dressings; tissues. Most of these are for a single use and are disposable.

RESEARCH IN NONWOVEN FABRICS

Nonwovens as yet have not presented any great threat to woven fabrics except in the short-use, disposable articles. In interlining and foundation garments, non-woven fabrics have come into their own because of superior properties and not from any advantage in price, since this is often more than in woven fabrics. Filter fabrics made from manmade fibers set in a random arrangement have come to the fore, since these fabrics permit filtered air or liquid to pass through the minute openings very readily. Needle-punched felt has increased greatly in use because fabrics in this category afford great strength without the use of a binder or an adhesive.

A machine has been developed that can trim and slit nonwoven fabric at a speed up to 750 yards per minutes. Binder ingredients are being improved constantly. Further research is being made in the blending of thermoplastic and thermosetting fibers for better bonding; in the arrangement of fibers for particular strength and thickness in certain fabrics; and in improved curing of the fabric for a specific end use.

RESEARCH IN BONDING AGENTS

There are today a rather limited number of thermoplastic binder fibers available. However, in the long run these binder fibers may be the most efficient way to produce a durable nonwoven fabric that will have a pleasing "hand" and a good drape. Fiber sources, binder manufacturers, and nonwoven fabric producers are aware of the need for binders which will give to fabrics the full range of possibilities that are apparent in the basic fibers. Thus, improved binders and the methods for their application will be stressed in future experimentation and research. Work is being done in the evaluation of various binding materials and their possibilities, in methods used for reinforced plastic, backing for coating fabrics, and backing for tufted carpeting.

Du Pont has stressed the use of the newer manmade fibers in nonwoven fabrics because of their special characteristics which enhance the possibilities of nonwoven fabrics, practical and desirable in many new, novel, and diverse applications. Properties of nonwoven fabrics have reached the point in development where they can be altered to suit some definite purpose. Bulk is the leading functional property in nonwoven fabrics; they may have at least twice as much bulk and covering power as a woven fabric of equivalent weight—a decided advantage in many possible applications.

By means of both fiber content and type of bonding agent applied in the manufacture of nonwoven fabrics, the following characteristics have been achieved:

Appearance: Paperlike, feltlike, wovenlike.
Strength: Varied from thinness of paper to thickness of a bulky cloth.
Porosity: Very wide in range from minute to considerable spaceage.
"Hand": From soft to hard or boardy in feel.
Fabrication: May be sewn, glued, or heat-bonded.
Raveling: Absence of fraying or raveling.

THE FUTURE FOR NONWOVEN FABRICS

Research at present is very secretive in all areas of approach. The industry will unquestionably grow considerably within the next few years. The potential for nonwoven fabrics is such that it will not only affect textiles but will also make inroads on the chemical, paper, plastics, and rubber industries.

To date these bonded fabrics have acquitted themselves very well, thereby assuring subsequent success in the future. When it is considered that the industry may be said to be only twenty years old and still in its infancy, the volume in production in this short span of time has been meteoric. Annual consumption and sales total are increasing. At present, yearly volume is about one hundred million dollars. In the woven field, the narrow and the broad goods types of fabrics will feel the impact of nonwoven fabrics as time goes on.

On the other hand, it should be borne in mind that bonded fabrics for many years to come will not cut too much into the woven goods field in textiles. Comparing at present the two fields of endeavor, nonwoven fabrics account for less than 3 per cent of the total textile consumption. This may reach 5 per cent in another three years, and in the more or less distant future may attain 7 per cent in total production and consumption.

Continued research and development will be made in both the disposable and nondisposable products. Possible new uses may be in the shoe industry, in the bookbinding trade, in printed materials for outerwear, disposable work clothing for the industrial and medical fields. Work will have to be done on the question of fashion and style for apparel uses, improved seam strength, heat-sealing properties, improved hand, and controlled reproducible quality. Bonded fabrics lend themselves more than any other textile material to engineering for terminal use and to automation. Thus nonwoven fabrics have emerged as a new industry; there will possibly be a 100-per-cent volume increase in less than five years; the possibilities and potentialities are without limit, and these fabrics lend themselves to the most advanced and efficient processing methods—true automation.

Thus will arise new production, distribution, and consumption, and these will make new jobs to be filled by alert and competent persons who should be aware of all details and angles pertinent to nonwoven products of all types. Management and marketing techniques will have to be developed for merchandising these products. All of these aspects should minimize the question of risk and maximize the success of investments and efforts expended in this new and fast-growing field.

PROPERTIES AND CHARACTERISTICS OF NONWOVEN FABRICS

1. Fibers in a nonwoven fabric may be oriented preferentially in one direction or they may be laid or set in a random manner.
2. All fabrics must rely on the base fiber or fibers used in the web, and in the bonding agent applied to the fibers.
3. Random orientation of the fibers is obtained by the use of a multiple lap arrangement.
4. High production in trimming and slitting nonwoven fabric has now reached 750 yards per minute.
5. There is no system of yarn or thread used to make nonwoven fabrics; they have no warp and no filling as in woven fabrics, or loops as in knitted materials.
6. Physical and aesthetic properties of the fabrics cover a wide range, depending on the fiber or fibers used, and, to considerable degree, on the resin or fiber used as a binder.
7. An important functional property is bulk. A nonwoven fabric has at least twice the bulk and covering power of a woven cloth of equivalent weight—often a distinct advantage.
8. In appearance, the fabrics may be paper-like, felt-like, or woven-like. Strength may vary from that of paper to a woven fabric. And a fabric having equal strength in all directions can be obtained through a random orientation of the base fibers used.
9. Porosity comes in a wide range.
10. Hand may run from hard to soft.
11. Nonwoven fabrics will not ravel or fray.
12. In fabrication the fabrics may be sewn, glued, or heat-bonded.
13. Some major uses include skirting, backing for vinyl coating, electrical insulation, apparel interlining, and containers.

SPUNBONDED FABRICS

SPUNBONDED is a generic term coined to differentiate it from other textile materials. SPUNBONDED FABRIC is a sheet structure made by a technique integrated with the manufacture of the fibers which compose the sheet. It is made with continuous filament of "Dacron" polyester formed into a sheet or web and then bonded into position. "Reemay" is the name of this product of E. I. du Pont de Nemours & Co., Inc., Wilmington, Delaware. It is not a substitute, low in price or otherwise, for any other comparable product which finds use in textiles, apparel, and in industry.

The filaments are bonded together at the crosspoints and these bonds hold the fibers together in the sheetlike structure. This provides a uniform appearance and good cover or hiding power coupled with high porosity. The product comes in sheets, tapes, and laminates. Microphotographs of the structure reveal that they are fine webs of randomly arranged continuous filament fibers. Use of this type affords high tear and tensile strength. Random arrangement gives the structure about the same properties in all directions.

Spunbonded can also be made with crimped filaments which afford flexibility and comfort. In these materials the binder concentration is relatively low, and this is an important item in engineering products with good balance of flexibility and strength.

[117]

Three weights of "Reemay" spunbonded polyesters (enlarged).

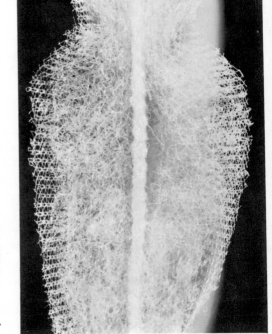

Cross section of a "bra cup" material incorporating shaper of "Reemay" spunbonded polyester. "Reemay" is the dense structure in center of picture; fiberfill is of "Dacron" polyester and it is used between "Reemay" and nylon tricot covering fabric.

Courtesy: E. I. du Pont de Nemours & Co., Inc., Wilmington, Delaware

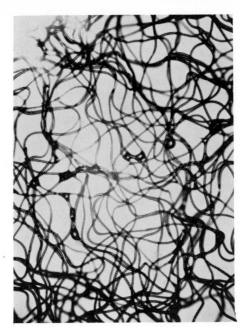

Courtesy: E. I. du Pont de Nemours & Co., Inc., Wilmington, Delaware

Straight fibers   Crimped fibers

Photomicrograph of "Reemay" spunbonded polyester. Field of view in each illustration is less than 0.01 inch square.

The fabric is used for interlinings in blouses, shirts, sportswear, shape liners for brassieres, and uniforms. Interlining used is of the lightweight type. Heavier weights are used as substrates, that which is laid or spread under some other substance, in several coating and laminating applications, such as bookbinding, wallpaper, and backed leather to provide high tear strength. There is excellent adhesion in the coating, and the product is inherently mildew- and rot-resistant.

Porosity of the material permits effective rubber penetration in tire-chafer application, thereby blocking any air wicking. Interlinings are ideally suited for washable and wash-and-wear-garment applications, as in blouses, brassieres, dresses, and shirts. Good assistance is given to the shell fabric in keeping a neat appearance in critical garments, as in the collars, cuffs, and front facings in coats and jackets, after repeated wearings and washings. Low shrinkage, good maintaining of stiffness, and minimum seam puckering also feature the material. Spunbonded interlinings also give good whiteness retention, ease in ironing, and quick drying is a decided asset.

When used as a base material for pyroxylin-coated bookbinding, "Reemay" gives high tear strength, good coating adhesion, clear embossed patterns, and provides a smooth blanking to give a good printing surface. There is also a neat appearance at book hinges and corners, and a long hinge life is assured with its use.

TESTING

1. How is a nonwoven fabric a development from a felt fabric?
2. What is the principle of the bonding of the fibers in the fabric?
3. Nonwoven fabrics consist of two major components—the web and the binder. Discuss each of these in detail.
4. Define random orientation of the fibers used.
5. Explain resin binding; thermoplastic binding.
6. Name three uses for nonwoven fabrics in apparel; in home furnishings; for industrial use; for medical and sanitary use.
7. Explain the principles of the Curlator Corporation machines—(a) the Rando-Feeder; (b) the Rando-Webber.
8. Discuss the future of nonwoven fabrics in the textile world as to their potential and possible impact upon woven and knitted textiles.
9. List five uses of nonwoven fabrics in the following fields—(a) apparel; (b) home furnishings; (c) industrial uses; (d) medical and sanitary uses.
10. Compare or differentiate between a nonwoven fabric and one that is spunbonded.
11. What fiber is used in the manufacture of "Reemay"?
12. Where does the actual bonding occur among the filaments in the material?
13. List five uses of "Reemay."
14. Why is "Reemay" ideal for use in bookbinding?

Courtesy of Curlator Corporation, East Rochester, N. Y., and E. I. du Pont de Nemours & Co., Inc., Wilmington, Delaware.

BONDED FABRICS

Bonded fabrics made their debut in 1962, made possible by new developments in chemistry and textile technology. Research and development in the field of these fabrics brought forth a new group of adhesives found to be ideal for the work. These are made from acrylic or urethane bases. A permanent bonding was developed so that two fabrics could be bonded to each other to perfection. A laminated fabric is a face cloth which has a backing of polyurethane foam. Unveiled in 1958, these fabrics are known as "foambacks" in Great Britain. They provide insulation and bulkiness without adding weight to the fabric, a good buying factor for the consuming public. A bonded fabric is a development from a laminated fabric. In the bonded fabric a foam is used, not necessarily as an insulator but as an adhesive that disappears in the processing. This is called "flame bonding." Another technique which is very popular is to eliminate the foam entirely and to substitute a wet adhesive. Bonded fabrics seem to have a drape and the flexibility not possessed by the foam sandwich laminates.

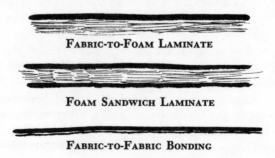

FABRIC-TO-FOAM LAMINATE

FOAM SANDWICH LAMINATE

FABRIC-TO-FABRIC BONDING

Courtesy: American Fabrics Magazine, Doric Publishing Co., Inc., New York

Bonding may, in this instance, be considered as a finishing process since it unites two previously constructed fabrics, and the final, commercial product is made in the finishing. Today fabric-to-fabric bonding is practically synonymous with the use of tricot-knit for the lining fabric. Acetate or nylon are the two agents used, the latter when washability is needed.

Within the last decade the textile world has come up with some fantastic advances, as attested to in wash-and-wear, stretch fabrics, Permanent Press, fiber-woven fabrics, molded fabrics, and spunbonded fabrics. Bonded fabric is the latest addition to this group of new and exciting developments, all of which have great appeal to the consumer. This group of new horizons has increased production of manmade filaments and fibers, has made great yardage of fabric necessary, has increased the buying of clothing and apparel of all types and kinds, and has also been a boon in the home-furnishing fields.

Wet-Adhesive Bonding

Two fabrics are bonded together by the use of a wet adhesive, a water-soluble acrylic base. The adhesive is applied to the underside or back of the face fabric, which is then joined to the liner by passing through rollers. It then enters the first heating stage, which expels the solvents and creates a preliminary, but not a permanent, bond known as "green tack." This term implies that at this point it is not yet ripened. It then passes through a second and more critical heat-curing stage which effects a permanent bond that is strong enough to withstand washing and drycleaning. This treatment calls for very exacting controls in order to avoid any possible degeneration of the bond because of over-curing or under-curing.

Foam-Flame Bonding

The adhesive used is polyurethane foam. By applying a gas flame to the foam, it is burned off and becomes tacky on one side so that it then adheres to the face or first fabric as passage occurs through the rollers.

The combination is then cooled and flame is applied to a second cloth, the liner fabric. By this time the foam has been burned off from an original thickness of 40/1000 inch to one of about 15/1000 inch. Important to this process is the tension control of the rollers and the control of the flame so that both sides of the foam are equally burned off.

The method is often resorted to when the face fabric is light in weight, which necessitates a building up or support for it. The foam achieves this, but in doing so reduces the drapability property. There may also be present the tendency to take on a yellowish cast. This process is not recommended for white goods, since there may be a "show-through" or a "strike-through" of the foam.

Criteria for Best Results from the Bonding Formula

Results depend upon the type of adhesive used, the amount used, the pattern of the adhesive application, and the curing temperature used. Good Bonded Fabric should have the following properties: washability and drycleaning, no loss in drapability, "breathability" should be retained, and there should not be any stiffening of the fabric. In addition, there should be no odor, no chemical breakdown or damage to the fibers, no "strike-through" of the adhesive; and

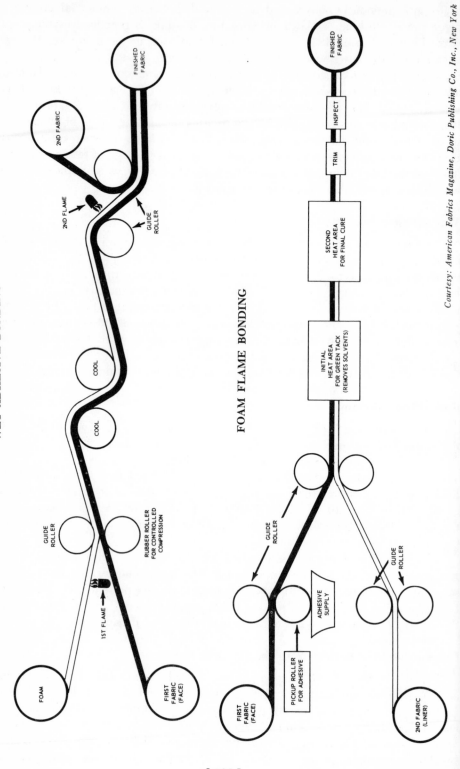

WET ADHESIVE BONDING

FOAM FLAME BONDING

Courtesy: American Fabrics Magazine, Doric Publishing Co., Inc., New York

[122]

resistance to discoloration. Shrinkage on woven goods should be limited to 3 per cent; on knitgoods, to 5 per cent.

Coin Standards

Coin Sales Corporation, New York City, is the licensee to many companies for its Coin (registered trademark) Standards. All features of the Collins & Aikman Certifab' (registered trademark) are included. Coin Standards are used for the effective bonding treatments developed by Coin Sales Corporation for use in the United States and for foreign licensees in carrying out its Quality Assurance Program. These standards are expressed in terms of PEEL BOND STRENGTH, both wet and dry. This strength is the basic factor used to measure quality and the durability of the bond. Tests are done on the Scott Model X5 Tensile Strength Tester; Scott Testers, Inc., Providence, Rhode Island.

THE STANDARDS	UNITED STATES	UNITED KINGDOM AND EUROPE
Dry	16 ounces	20 ounces
Drycleaning—Wet	4 ounces	5 ounces
Hot Laundered—Wet	4 ounces	6 ounces

It should be noted that differences in test standards between the United States and the United Kingdom and Europe are based on habit patterns and consumer expectations in different areas.

Properties of Bonded Fabrics

These include appealing and excellent hand, crease-resistance or crease-retentiveness, resiliency, nonraveling edges, excellent stability, ideal stretch and recovery; they may be used to provide insulation, and are found in sheer and lightweight fabrics and garments as well as in the heavyweight category; they are ideal for permanent press garments, etc.

USES

These fabrics, it may be said "run the gamut" and are used in practically all types of apparel—blouses, coating of varying weights, all types of dressgoods, lingerie to rainwear apparel, shirts, shorts, skirts, trousers, etc. At present, these fabrics are extremely popular with home sewers.

BASIC TERMS USED IN BONDED FABRICS

BONDING: Usually refers to fabric-to-fabric bonding in contradistinction to fabric-to-foam bonding (lamination). There are two basic types of fabric-to-fabric bonding, the wet-adhesive method and the foam-flame method, both named for the two types of adhesives used in the processes.

COMPATIBLE SHRINKAGE: Refers to the need for the face fabric and the liner to have the same or closely similar shrinkage ratios so that there will be no puckering in the bond.

CURING: The process by which a chemical adhesive is set permanently to the fabric by the use of heat.

DENIER: A length-weight measurement of specifically 1 gram per 9,000 meters of yarn. Thus, if 9,000 meters of yarn weigh 100 grams, the yarn is known as a 100-denier yarn. Consequently, the higher the number of the denier size, the coarser or greater in diameter will be the yarn in question. A 100-denier yarn will be finer than, say, a 150-denier yarn, and there will be more yardage per pound in the 100-denier yarn. Denier is used to figure the yarn sizes of silk and manmade filaments and fibers. The denier was an old coin of France and weighed .05 grams. The legal denier weight is used for a yarn length of 450 meters or 492.2 yards, in standard procedure and calculation for yarn sizes or counts.

DOUBLE KNIT: A fabric knitted with a double stitch on a double needle frame to provide a double thickness. It is the same on both sides and has excellent body and stability.

EDGE ROLL: The usual curl or roll that develops at the edges of a single-knit fabric, making it rather difficult to handle since it does not lie completely flat.

FACE FABRIC: That side of a bonded fabric used as the face of a finished garment or other textile product.

FOAMBACK: Term used in Great Britain to denote that a fabric has been laminated to a backing of polyurethane foam.

FOAM-FLAME BONDING: One of the two basic methods used in fabric-to-fabric bonding. The foam takes the place of an adhesive and is made sticky or tacky by heating with a gas flame. In the manipulation the foam thickness is burned off from 40/1000 inch to about 15/1000 inch. This method is much used in building up face fabrics.

GREEN TACK: The preliminary bond created by the first stage in curing in the wet-adhesive process. In this condition, the bond is not yet fully cured and is still "green" or not ripe.

LAMINATION: Refers to the joining of a face fabric to a foam backing.

LINER: That side of a bonded fabric used on the inside of a finished garment as the lining. Ideal for use as a liner is a 55-denier acetate tricot-knit fabric or one made of a 40-denier nylon.

PEEL-BOND STRENGTH: Refers to the actual force needed to peel or separate two layers of a bonded fabric from each other. It is expressed in terms of ounces of pull per one inch width of the bonded fabric. This is a durability and quality test of the bond and is made on the fabric in both dry and wet conditions. See Coin Standards.

PUCKER: The uneven surface caused by differential shrinkage in the two layers of a bonded fabric during processing, drycleaning, or washing.

REVERSIBLE BONDED FABRIC: This means that two face fabrics have been bonded together so that the two sides may be used interchangeably. There are, however, some limitations in this area. It is not advisable, for example, to bond to stiff fabrics such as a nylon taffeta, since stiffness would be increased in the bonding; the same holds true in the case of two hard-faced or hard-twisted yarn worsteds.

SANDWICH LAMINATE: A composite fabric in which a layer of polyurethane foam has been laminated or "sandwiched" between two fabrics; one would be the face cloth, the other one would be a lining. Fabrics in this category are used for heavy outerwear.

SINGLE KNIT: A fabric knitted on a single-needle machine. This fabric has less body, substance, and stability when compared with double knit.

SKIN-SIDE COMFORT: A decided advantage of bonding in that the lining side of the bonded fabric can be made appealing, comfortable, and pleasing when worn next to the skin irrespective of how rough, scratchy or uneven the face may happen to be.

STABILITY: That property of a bonded fabric which prevents sagging, slipping or stretching. This is conducive to ease of handling in manufacturing and helps to keep its shape in wear, drycleaning, and washing.

STRETCH AND RECOVERY: A very important property of knit fabric when bonded to tricot-knit. It develops the ability to return quickly to its original position after stretching and being released from tension.

STRIKE-THROUGH: This means that the adhesive can be seen through the fabric. Every effort should be made to avoid this in fabric-to-fabric bonding.

THERMOPLASTIC: The ability of a textile fiber to become plastic under heat and therefore able to be set into a predetermined shape.

TREE BARK: A rippled or wavy effect which sometimes appears on a bonded fabric only when it is stretched in the horizontal direction or width-wise. It is caused by bias tensions which happen when two distorted or "skewed" fabrics are bonded.

TRICOT: The French verb which means "to knit" (*tricoter*).

WET-ADHESIVE BONDING: One of the two basic methods used in the fabric-to-fabric bonding. The most popular adhesive is a water-based acrylic compound. After application to the fabric, it is then cured by a heat treatment which creates a permanent bond without reducing any of the draping qualities of the face material or affecting softness of hand.

YIELD: The number of yards of tricot-knit or similar fabric obtained from one pound of the yarn used to make the cloth.

TESTING

1. Differentiate between a laminated fabric and a bonded fabric.
2. Describe flame bonding.
3. Name two fibers ideal for use in tricot-knit fabrics which are used in the bonding process.
4. Describe wet-adhesive bonding.
5. Name five criteria essential to the best results from the bonding formula.
6. Define the following terms: (1) denier; (2) single knit; (3) double knit; (4) green tack; (5) liner; (6) peel-bond strength.
7. What is meant by a "reversible bonded" fabric?
8. Define the term "strike-through."
9. Discuss Coin Standards.
10. List five uses of bonded fabrics.

Courtesy of William C. Segal, Publisher, and Cecil Lubell, Executive Editor, *American Fabrics Magazine*, Doric Publishing Co., Inc., New York City.

FIBERWOVEN FABRICS

Fiberwoven fabrics, a development of the Chatham Manufacturing Company and the Fiberwoven Corporation, Elkin, North Carolina, were unveiled in July, 1964. The idea for these fabrics was conceived by Dr. Alexander Smith, a former professor at the Massachusetts Institute of Technology, Cambridge, Massachusetts. Dr. Smith did the mathematics for the project and was assisted by a physicist, a mechanical engineer, and an electrical engineer.

The batt, which is made continuously and, therefore, has no definite length, is fed into the machine in batt-fiber form in the manufacturing process, and barbed needles are manipulated into it, thereby entangling the fibers around the barbs. The barbs pick up the fibers and push them into the batt, the procedure relying on cooperating pairs of barbed needles. The top needle of the set or pair descends and pushes the loops of fiber into the batt. Then it pulls upward and out of the batt, which advances in its progress through the machine. The bottom needle of the set then comes into play and pushes the upward loop through the top loop to form a chain of entangled fibers. Thus the entire sets of needles, top and bottom, perform the work involved. About 26,000 needles are used in this machine, which is ten feet in width and approximately twelve feet in height. The needles, of course, go in two directions.

The batt can be composed of any of the major textile fibers, natural and/or manmade. It may be set up in layer formation. Any type of fiber can be used for the outside, as well as for the inside, in this "sandwich formation." For example, the outside might be wool or acrylic fiber while the inside is made up of rayon, lower in cost than wool or any acrylic. Fiber lengths may range from one to four inches in staple length, and in denier counts of yarn the range may run from 1- to 18-denier. Batts can be made by Air-Lay Equipment, Rando-Webbers, such as used in the manufacture of nonwoven fabrics, or by woolen or worsted carding machines.

A few threads, all in one direction, serve as carrier yarns for the batt, which does not have any strength. It is the needling which builds the strength into the fabric. These yarns do nothing for the fabric, and their only purpose is to aid in feeding the batt into the machine. The batt should have evenness in its structure, since the smoother and more uniform the batt, the better will be the resultant blanket or other product made by this method.

Tests show that Fiberwoven blankets provide better-balanced strength than a conventionally woven blanket. The fabrics do not have to go through the essential operations in making woven blankets—raw stock, grading, blending, oiling, mixing, carding and spinning of the yarn, and finally the weaving of the blanket. Napping on a woven blanket is done only on the filling yarn, which is soft-spun, has little twist in it, and is bulky in nature. Napping also causes the blanket to lose some strength, and as it wears down, the yarns are often observed in the structure. There is also some little loss of strength in Fiberwoven blankets, but it is uniform and as it wears down, "you see more of the same." No exposed yarns are seen.

Final results in a comparison of both types of blanket reveal that the Fiberwoven blanket provides somewhat more warmth because it has a better form of insulation, a loftier hand or feel, and gives longer wear to the consumer. Fabrics may be made heavier or lighter, stronger or weaker, harsher or softer, as the demands require. There is also less shrinkage especially when rayon, a low-cost fiber, is used; shrinkage is reduced about 50 per cent.

There are two great savings in goods of this type. Firstly, in labor requirements; it takes from 350 to 400 operatives to make one million blankets in one year on conventional textile equipment. In the same span of time the same number of blankets can be made by about 50 employees. Secondly, wastes in the manufacture of woven blankets range from around 18 per cent to about 25 per cent from raw wool to finished goods. Fiberwovens have wastes from about 12 per cent to around 15 per cent, and most of this total can be reclaimed for future usage. Their manufacture may be said to be a one-step operation from raw fiber stock to the needled blanket.

Electronics play an important part in the machinery used; each line has more than one mile of wiring, and synchronization is very important. The company has a licensing program for licensees, since the equipment is not for sale. Several items must be determined by licensees dependent upon the construction desired for production. These include needle size and shape, shape of the barbs and the barb location, angle of penetration, rate of the advance of the cloth, number of needle punches per square inch, etc.

Conventional chemicals can be used for surface treatment of the fabrics. The material stands up very well in all types of sewing. Potentials of Fiberwoven fabrics include carpet and rug backing, floor covering, trunk liners, upholstery fabrics, and other heavy goods. Embossed finishes are possible on the fabrics.

TESTING

1. Discuss the principles involved in the manufacture of Fiberwoven blankets.
2. Explain the formation of the batt used in fabrics of this type.
3. Discuss the needle action in manipulation of the batt into fabric.
4. Why may carrier threads be used in the batt?
5. Compare the properties of a Fiberwoven blanket with a loom-woven type.
6. Name and discuss two great savings in the manufacture of Fiberwoven blankets.
7. Define the term "sandwich blend" or "sandwich formation."
8. List five items that should be closely checked prior to fabric construction.

Courtesy of Hugh G. Chatham, President, Chatham Manufacturing Company, and Fiberwoven Corporation, Elkin, North Carolina.

TOPIC: STRETCH FABRICS

Stretch fabrics have a long history when knitted fabrics are considered, since by the nature of the knitting process they are stretchable. Woven fabrics are spoken of as being rigid. When knitted fabrics are made with stretch yarns, their stretch factor is improved because the yarn used, as well as the construction, affords, in most instances, great stretchability. More important, however, is the factor of recovery. Good stretch yarns recover rapidly and enable knitted fabrics to return quickly to the original shape with little or no sign of any distortion.

When woven fabrics are made with stretch yarns, or otherwise processed, they take on a hidden stretch dimension without changing the traditional appearance of the woven goods. Rigidity is lost, and they become stretchable in the warp, the filling, or, in some instances, both ways. And, as with knitgoods, they are able to recover quickly after being stretched out of shape.

The already stretchable knit fabrics can have greater stretch by the modern stretch-yarn technique of recovery. To previously rigid woven goods these yarns add stretchability and recovery. These modern yarns can be produced quickly and economically when compared with the more complicated process of winding a rigid fiber around a core of elastic rubber, the process used in making elasticized yarns for foundation fabrics.

During World War II, the world suffered a great shortage of wool. Heberlein & Company, A. G., Wattwil (pronounced "Vattvil"), Switzerland, offered a substitute for wool by crimping rayon yarns. Following the war the company, after much research and development, adapted the process to nylon, setting the twist in the yarn with heat and then twisting it in the opposite direction, so that the continuous filament took on the properties of a spring. In 1947, Helanca unveiled its first nylon stretch yarn under the name HELANCA.

Austria, Germany, Switzerland, and some of the other countries in Europe are skiing centers, natural areas for the use of stretch yarns in various items of ski apparel. Thus, the first success of these yarns, fabrics, and apparel began in the early 1950's. The well-known Olympic skiing man-and-wife team of Willy and Maria Bogner in West Germany is credited with developing stretch ski pants. The groundwork for further progress in stretch clothing was greatly enhanced in 1959, when Emilio Pucci of Florence, Italy, brought out his stretch fabrics and garments. Emilio Pucci is one of the most remarkable personages in the world today, a sort of modern Leonardo da Vinci. He is a marchese, a member of the Italian Chamber of Deputies, and the greatest designer of the boutique. Incidentally, the word "boutique" actually means a shop, goods, or fabrics—a shopkeeper. The word has become foremost in the fashion field today, and despite its many interpretations, implies a garment of taste, charm, and simplicity "made from goods in a shop." Pucci is probably the leader in fantastic sports- and leisure-wear fashions. The Palazzo Pucci in Florence is over one thousand years old and it is from this palace that he originates and shows his wares. He is also a pilot, an Olympic skier, sports car driver, wine producer, and, incidentally, a graduate of Reed College, Portland, Oregon, where he earned a master's degree in political science.

His definition of fashion is interesting. "Fashion is the essence of modern life. It is movement. We must capture it, yet give it freedom. It is the vision of tomorrow realized today. Color is the 'X-quality' of fashion, and it should harmonize well in all design."

His showings of nylon and silk stretch garments were at once acclaimed throughout the fashion and sports worlds. Men, women, and children became interested in his developments which afforded both power in the fabric and greater comfort in the contortions of the human body. Pucci garments were made with stretch only in the warp direction, the "north-south direction." Shortly thereafter, garments came into the market with filling stretch, the "east-west direction," as well as in both directions—warp and filling.

There are two types of stretch in stretch materials:

1. POWER STRETCH: This provides fabrics with increased snap and "muscle power," greater extensibility and quicker recovery than those observed in ordinary fabrics. This type stretch is essential in athletic clothing, foundation garments, ski wear, swimwear, and the more professional types of active sportswear such as football pants.
2. COMFORT STRETCH: This is applied to apparel used in daily wear to allow ease and greater comfort to the wearer. Clothing does not necessarily need power stretch, but comfort and power in these articles do give greater satisfaction to the individual. Other end uses of comfort stretch include bed sheets, slip covers for use in home furnishings, upholstery, and transportation fabrics.

A concise definition of STRETCH YARN implies that it is a thermoplastic continuous filament yarn which has been modified or conditioned so as to afford high strength in yarn elongation and with rapid recovery.

Three basic principles are used to provide stretch yarns of today. They are:

1. HEAT STRETCH yarn—based on the principle of a steel spring.
2. ELASTOMERIC yarn—may be compared with a rubber band.
3. PIECE GOODS STRETCH yarn—wherein the proper shrinkage can be made in the width of the goods in the filling direction.

HEAT-SET STRETCH YARN

The best-known and most widely used today, it is a development of the Heberlein patents used throughout the world. The company in the United States is Heberlein Patent Corporation, New York City, and it licenses the users of the methods.

Heat-set stretch yarns consist of either nonelastic, continuous-filament manmade fibers which are thermoplastic, or nonelastic staple length natural fibers, both of which have been made stretchable through reformation by the heat-set coil, crimp, or curl methods.

The Coil Type

This is made on the FALSE-TWIST METHOD, whereby continuous filament yarn, such as nylon, is fed into the machine and given about seventy-five turns of twist per inch at a twisting rate of anywhere from 40,000 to 350,000 revolutions per minute. As it is twisted, it passes through a heater box which sets the twist at temperatures of 350° F., up to 465° F. Emerging from the heater box it is untwisted. As the yarn attempts to return to its original twist, it pulls itself into tiny, resilient COILS.

The Stuffer-Box Type

This consists basically of compressing the filaments into a confined space in a heated chamber known as the STUFFER BOX, where the filaments are heat-set in their crimped condition and then withdrawn. Strictly speaking, these are considered to be more of a "bulk yarn" than a regulation "stretch yarn." The yarns present a random zigzag CRIMP.

The Knife-Edge Type

This method sets a curl into the yarn by heating and then drawing it over a knife edge at an acute angle. The spiral direction reverses in a random formation along the yarn, thereby producing a balanced torque-free (twist-free) yarn, a CURL yarn.

In the doubling of stretch yarns it should be borne in mind that when the yarn leaves the false-twist spindle it has actually a built-in torque or twisting force in either the "S" or the "Z" direction, depending on which way the spindle was rotated. To overcome this twist and to create a balanced yarn, the usual practice is to double or ply an "S" yarn with a "Z" yarn. Obviously, the yarn strength is increased to give better performance and service to the consumer.

It is also possible to obtain a balanced single yarn in the one continuous operation on a machine equipped with two heater boxes and two twist heads rotating in opposite directions. The well-known Helanca NT (Helanca No Torque) is a balanced yarn of this type; so is Agilon of Deering Milliken Company, New York City. This is a crimped type of yarn made on the knife-edge method.

Polyester yarns now popular in the stretch-yarn field include "Dacron," Fortrel, and Vycron. Twisting of these filaments is done in the same manner as nylon.

ELASTOMERIC YARN STRETCH

A chemical definiton of synthesis is the forming or building up of a more complex substance or compound by the union of elements or the combination of simpler compounds or radicals. A radical is an atom or group of atoms regarded as an important constituent of a molecule, which remains unchanged and behaves as a unit in many reactions. A chemical definition of synthetic is that it pertains to compounds formed in a chemical laboratory as opposed to those of natural origin.

Father Julius A. Nieuwland (C.S.C.) Ph.D., professor in organic chemistry at the University of Notre Dame, South Bend, Indiana, was the pioneer in the development of synthetic rubber. The du Pont Company, Wilmington, Delaware, perfected its synthetic rubber in 1931 under the trademark name of DuPrene.

Shortly thereafter the generic name "neoprene" was given the product. Royalties were paid by the company to Notre Dame for the use of the catalytic agent perfected by Father Nieuwland which was necessary for use in the manufacture of neoprene. Neoprene, however, was solely the development of the research group of the du Pont Company. Thus it may be said that the beginnings of what is today known as the true elastomeric textile fibers, the spandex fibers, were born in the 1930's.

The major elastomeric yarn stretch fibers include "Lycra," Spandelle, Vyrene, Duraspan, Glospan, and Interspan. In 1947, du Pont made Fiber K in pilot plant production, the forerunner of its present-day "Lycra." From 1950 to 1957 foundation fabrics were made with Fiber K. Vyrene, the spandex fiber of the United States Rubber Company, made its debut before 1960. During this year full-scale production of "Lycra" was begun in the du Pont plant in Waynesboro, Virginia, following a thorough trade evaluation which proved very encouraging and fruitful. The fiber has been a sensation since its appearance on the market. In 1963, Firestone Tire & Rubber Company announced its spandex fiber, Spandelle.

The stretchability of the spandex fiber for yarns in this category is caused by the chemical or the molecular structure and not by a mechanically imparted configuration of the filament as in the case of the heat-set yarns. Thus, this type yarn, comparable with a rubber band, may be extended to about 500 per cent of its length without any breakage.

Spandex is made from polyurethane which, in compliance with the definition decreed by the Federal Trade Commission, Washington, D.C., must make up at least 85 per cent of the fiber content. Polyurethane is the same chemical substance used widely as a foam in transportation fabrics, bedding, and a host of laminated fabrics. Spandex, as such, goes back to World War II in its specific origins, when search began to find a "snap-back" manmade fiber that would replace the then scarce true rubber and which would be as durable or more durable than true rubber.

Core-Spun Yarns

Core-spinning of spandex yarns has taken on increasing importance within the last few years. Core-spinning is done when an elastic filament is fed into the twisting zone of the spinning frame under predetermined tensions. A yarn is produced whose core is the elastic filament, with the outer surface sheathed or covered with any of the basic textile fibers used in the spinning. Formation of the sheath fibers may be spiral or in random formation. When the tension is removed from the spandex core it will return to its normal length, pulling the sheath fibers into a more compact formation.

The use of as little as 5 per cent to 10 per cent spandex can produce a yarn of high stretch and excellent recovery. Elongation degree can also be controlled from a low percentage up to one as high as 200 per cent, depending upon the yarn construction. Core-spun yarn takes on a better appearance, appeal, and hand irrespective of the fibers used as the casing of the core yarn—acrylic, polyester, as well as blends of cotton and wool. The core yarn, because of the methods of manipulation used, does not appear on the surface of the fabric.

It should be kept in mind pertinent to stretch yarns that the lower the total denier of the yarn used, the greater will be the stretch potential. Thus, a 60-denier yarn will "give" more than a 120-denier yarn. The fewer the number of filaments in yarn of a given denier, the greater will be the resistance to extension, the quicker will be the recovery, the crisper the hand or feel, and the higher the percentage of the original yarn strength retained.

Stretch in Fabrics

A stretch fabric is a true example of an engineered material. Engineering, along with "imagineering," determines the processing methods and ultimate results. The amount and degree of stretch in the yarns as well as the styling of the garments are important factors, since aesthetic value, performance, and cost have decided bearings on the terminal use of both fabric and garment. Continuity and uniformity from raw material to finished garment must be watched closely at all times.

A shirting, for example, made with stretch yarns will "give" at the elbows and the shoulders without any apparent strain on the fabric. Garments of this type have good surface effect and texture, afford comfort, and durability and moisture absorptivity are enhanced. These factors are especially beneficial in pajamas, sportswear, and undergarments.

Warp stretch only was used in the first fabrics and garments to use stretch yarn. The horizontal stretch in cloth made its first appearance in the early 1960's. In addition, much of the fabric today is made with the popular "two-way stretch," as noted in foundation garments. Filling-stretch fabrics seem to be better adapted to the movements of the human body in flexing when compared with the warp-stretch fabrics; the former provides the greater flexibility and ease of movement.

PIECE-GOODS STRETCH

Stretch to fabrics in this category comes after the goods have left the loom. Stretch is provided for by MECHANICAL STRETCH, since it involves compacting the width of the goods by chemical treatment and setting. The method is rather simple and inexpensive; results seem to improve hand and performance. SLACK MERCERIZATION is another fabric stretch method that is very popular. It is applied to cotton and cotton blends and was developed in the Textile Research Laboratories of the United States Department of Agriculture. The method involves the shrinking of the fabric without tension, actually in a slack formation, in a bath of sodium-hydroxide (caustic-soda) solution. Treatments are carried out at room temperatures, and strength of the bath may vary from 25 per cent to 55 per cent. The weave used and the compactness of the woven fabric have to be considered when making a determination for the correct shrinkage.

If only filling shrinkage is desired, the warp is held under tension during the shrinking process, or it may be restretched later on. Once the shrinking has been completed, the goods are then further chemically treated. The method has proved to be satisfactory in all respects and especially so in the blends of cotton with polyester, rayon, and even flax fibers. Performance depends on the precise finishing techniques to stabilize shrinkage against multiple launderings.

Cotton Stretch

All-cotton stretch is used extensively at the present time—corduroy, denim, etc.—because of its economy, simplicity of production, and satisfactory price. It is made largely on the slack-mercerization method, since the durability of its stretch factor depends on a concise, precise finishing technique to stabilize it against multiple launderings.

Wool Stretch

Considerable progress has been made with wool-stretch fabrics. For example, J. P. Stevens & Company, Inc., New York City, has developed its patented "PLUS-X" to control wool-stretch goods. It involves the setting of a permanent accordionlike crimp into a wool or a wool-blend cloth prior to the dyeing and finishing of the goods. The method provides excellent durability and performance, improves the hand and appearance, and gives wrinkle resistance to the finished goods. The process changes the molecular structure of the fiber in the treatment.

Burlington Industries, New York City, also has its process, which is the patented "RESTORA." It is described as the "first 100 per cent wool stretch fabric to be made without any chemical change in the molecular structure of the fiber." Special spinning and weaving techniques, along with novel finishing techniques, allow for elasticity in both warp and filling directions.

Advantages of Textured-Stretch Yarns

These include obtaining the proper and desired stretch in fabrics because of the particular yarns used; the increased coverage and opacity of the fabrics; improved hand, surface appeal, and interesting textures; surface effects of interest, such as pebble, crepe, crepon, etc.; and the obtaining of lighter, bulkier, and more resilient yarns and fabrics without added weight to the material.

Advantages of Stretch Fabrics and Apparel

1. Better fit, greater comfort, more shape retention, and longer wear.
2. Improved wrinkle resistance to the fabric or the garment.
3. Greater surface appeal and interest; stronger consumer appeal.
4. Greater flexibility in designing these fabrics.
5. Fewer sizes and alterations needed.
6. Seam puckering greatly reduced in articles of apparel.
7. Less tailoring to shape.

The end use for which a fabric is to serve determines the amount of stretch to strive for in the manipulation of the goods. Generally speaking, the following figures cover the major types of apparel and garments:

TYPE	PERCENTAGE OF STRETCH	PERCENTAGE OF UNRECOVERABLE STRETCH
TAILORED CLOTHING	15 to 25 per cent	Not more than 2 per cent
SPECTATOR SPORTSWEAR	20 to 35 per cent	Not more than 5 per cent
FORM-FIT GARMENTS	30 to 40 per cent	Not more than 5 per cent
ACTIVE SKI WEAR	35 to 60 per cent	Not more than 6 per cent

FLEXIBILITY OF STRETCH NEEDED IN GARMENTS FOR HUMAN BODY FLEXING

BACK FLEX	Across the back	13 to 16 per cent
SEAT FLEX	Across the seat	4 to 6 per cent
ELBOW FLEX	Vertical or north-south	35 to 40 per cent
	Horizontal—circumference	15 to 22 per cent
KNEE FLEX	Vertical or north-south	35 to 45 per cent
	Horizontal—circumference	12 to 14 per cent

Some Uses of Stretch Fabrics

COTTON

1. **Industrial Fabrics:** Converter tops and head liners on automobiles.
2. **Household:** Contour sheets, draperies, slip covers.
3. **Wearing Apparel:** Brassieres, casual wear, blouses, and dress shirts, gloves, infants' and children's wear, knitgoods of many types and varieties, linings for men's coatings, men's suitings, pajamas, ties and tie linings, uniforms, and many sportswear articles.

WOOLEN: These fabrics are used chiefly in some types of apparel such as coatings and jackets, hose and hosiery, ski pants and slacks, woolen shirtings for cold weather.

Sewing on Stretch Fabrics

The following points should be observed:

1. Preshrinking of fabric should be done with a steam iron.
2. Determine the way that the stretch goes in the fabric when cutting a pattern. Sharp scissors should be used when cutting in the correct direction of the stretch.
3. Pins should be set in the same direction as the stretch direction.
4. If possible, use nylon thread because of its elasticity and strength.
5. Pinking shears should be used to finish off the seams.

Testing of Stretch Fabrics

Standard stretch tests have been developed to evaluate knitted and woven stretch fabrics for such end uses as tailored garments, sportswear, and ski wear. In these tests, the percentage of stretch is determined while under a standard load, and the growth, or unrecovered stretch, is recorded after one-half minute, one hour, and sixteen hours. It is important that the growth figure be low, as otherwise a fabric will show a baggy, distorted condition.

TESTING

1. Define five of the following terms used in stretch yarns and fabrics:

   a) Action stretch.   d) Comfort stretch.   g) Spandex fibers.
   b) Power stretch.   e) Core-spinning.   h) Slack mercerization.
   c) Chemical stretch.   f) False-twist.   i) Yarn configuration.

2. Define plastic; thermoplastic.
3. Discuss the work done by Father J. A. Nieuwland, University of Notre Dame, in the development of synthetic rubber.
4. Trace the origin and the history of stretch fabrics.
5. Explain the following terms used in Twist-in-Yarn: (a) S-twist; (b) Z-twist; (c) Zero-twist; (d) Cable-twist.
6. Name three spandex fibers in use at the present time.
7. What is meant by a core yarn?
8. Why are core yarns of much importance in stretch fabrics today?
9. What is meant by "east-west stretch"? By "north-south stretch"?
10. How does a torque yarn differ from a non-torque yarn?
11. Explain the fatigue factor in stretch yarns.
12. What is the name of the base from which spandex fibers are made?
13. Name three polyester fibers that may be used in stretch yarns.
14. Define cotton stretch; wool stretch.
15. List five advantages of textured stretch yarns.
16. Name four advantages of stretch fabrics and apparel.
17. Name five items of innerwear or outerwear that can be made of stretch fabrics.
18. Give three points that should be observed when sewing on stretch fabrics.

Courtesy of E. I. du Pont de Nemours & Company, Inc., Wilmington, Delaware, and *American Fabrics Magazine*, Doric Publications, Inc., New York City.

DICTIONARY OF BASIC TERMS USED IN STRETCH FABRICS

BACK TWISTING: Twisting a yarn, single or ply, in the reverse direction to the previously set direction, whether S-twist or Z-twist, in the original direction of twist.

BODY FLEX: The degree of bending in the different parts of the human body. The term is used with regard to the determination in the amount or degree of stretch in fabrics necessary in any garment to give the proper amount of give or flex.

CABLE TWIST: A cord, rope, or twine construction in which each successive twist runs in the opposite direction from the preceding twist. This type is S-Z-S or Z-S-Z.

CHEMICAL STRETCH: Stretch imparted to fabrics by chemical means after the cloth has been woven and is being finished for commercial use. This is usually a filling or east-west stretch, since the fabric is shrunk horizontally and then set permanently in this state. Also known as "mechanical stretch" and "slack mercerization."

COIL, CRIMP, CURL: Terms used to denote the type of configuration given to a yarn such as nylon, polyester, etc., in order to afford stretchability.

CONFIGURATION: The relative disposition of the elements or the parts of some object or thing; the external form or appearance resulting from this disposition. For example, in textured yarns used in the textile industry, the original fibers or filaments will take on a new configuration because of treatments given the yarn in processing. These treatments which can be made permanent may be done by the use of heat, heated blades, stretching, true twist, false twist, etc. (See Stretch Yarn, Heat-set; Texturizing; Configuration, Yarn.)

CONFIGURATION, YARN: A manmade continuous filament given treatment in processing to cause it to take on a new configuration such as coil, crimp, or curl and thereby become stretchable. (See Configuration.)

ELASTOMERIC: A substance which owes its stretchability to the chemical or molecular structure contained therein. Examples are natural rubber, synthetic rubber, spandex, "Lycra," Vyrene.

FATIGUE FACTOR: The weakening of a stretch yarn in which some of its ability to recover after stretching has been lost. This "tired" or fatigue yarn can result from twisting the yarn at "revolutions-per-minute" speeds that are too high for the length of the heater box which sets the configuration of the yarn.

FIBERS, BI-COMPONENT: Continuous filament manmade fibers that have two related components with each component having a different rate or degree of shrinkage. This variance affords a crimped configuration which causes the yarn to become stretchable.

PLASTIC: Any material, natural or synthetic, which may be fabricated into a variety of shapes or forms, usually by the application of heat and pressure. A plastic is one of a group of organic compounds, synthesized from cellulose, hydrocarbons, proteins, or resins, and capable of being cast, extruded, or molded into various shapes. From the Greek word *plastikos*, which means "fit for molding."

PLUS-X: Patented process of J. P. Stevens & Company, Inc., New York City, for imparting stretch to all-wool and wool-blend fabrics. The process applies a permanent, accordionlike crimp to the fabrics prior to dyeing and finishing of the goods.

RESTORA: Burlington Industries owns this patented process which imparts stretch to all-wool fabrics without any chemical change in the molecular structure of the wool fibers. The process is capable of providing elasticity in both warp and filling in the goods.

RIGID FIBER OR FABRIC: Merely refers to a fiber or fabric that is not stretchable.

SHEATH FIBERS: The fibers which form a coating or sheath around the elastomeric fiber used in core-spinning of yarn. The fibers are usually wound in spiral formation around the core yarn, but random sheathing is also employed.

[134]

SLACK MERCERIZATION IN STRETCH FABRICS: Originally developed on all-cotton stretch fabrics, it can now be applied to blends of cotton and manmade fibers used in some fabrics. The procedure involves the shrinking of the fabric without any tension (slack) in the mercerizing bath of sodium-hydroxide (caustic-soda) solution. Often resorted to in the manufacture of filling or horizontal stretch fabrics.

SPANDEX: Elastomeric fiber owing its ability to stretch to its chemical or molecular structure. There must be at least 85 per cent segmented polyurethane in the fiber; this is the same chemical substance much used as a foam in transportation fabrics, bedding, and laminated fabrics of many types.

SPINNING, CORE: A spinning method wherein a base or core yarn is encased by a group of staple fibers, usually in a spiral formation. On removal of tension the staple or outside fibers are pulled into a more compact formation around the core yarn used. In stretch fabric yarn spinning the yarn will become stretchable to the degree or extent of the predetermined tension of the elastic core filament used.

SPINNING, INTIMATE BLEND: Cut spandex fibers blended with tow or cut staple fibers to produce a stretch yarn at the fiber-producer level.

STRETCH, ACTION: (See Stretch, Power.)

STRETCH CATEGORIES: There are two: (1) comfort stretch; (2) action stretch or power stretch. (See Stretch, Comfort; Stretch, Power.)

STRETCH, COMFORT: Stretch fabrics have either comfort stretch or power stretch or action stretch. Comfort stretch describes the stretch fabric used in apparel and clothing for daily usage. The stretch factor runs up to about 30 per cent. (See Stretch, Power.)

STRETCH FABRIC STABILIZATION: Stabilizing or setting the dimension of a "mechanical-stretch" fabric after it has been shrunk. Obtained by the use of appropriate chemicals and heat.

STRETCH, FILLING: Also known as horizontal or east-west stretch, the term means that the stretch factor has been given only in the filling direction of the goods, with the warp remaining rigid.

STRETCH, KNITTED: Manufacture of a knitted material with stretch yarns. Obviously, all knit fabrics have give or stretch, but a stretch knit material compared with a regulation knitted cloth will recover quicker and possess a greater holding power because of the stretch yarns used in the construction.

STRETCH, MECHANICAL: Also known as chemical stretch and slack mercerization, it is that type of stretch imparted to the fabric after it has been woven.

STRETCH, PIECE GOODS: An "overall" term which describes the various and sundry types of stretch fabrics in which the stretch factor has been applied to the cloth following weaving rather than to the yarn prior to weaving of the goods.

STRETCH, POWER: There are two basic categories pertinent to stretch fabrics—comfort stretch and action stretch or power stretch. Power stretch applies to stretch fabrics which have more snap, liveliness, and "muscle power," along with more extensibility and quicker recovery. This power factor ranges from 30 to 50 per cent and is ideally adaptable for athletic clothing, foundation fabrics, ski wear, swimwear, and the more professional types of sportswear such as football pants. (See Stretch, Comfort.)

STRETCH RECOVERY: Ability of a stretch yarn or fabric to recover its original position after having been stretched.

STRETCH, WARP: In a stretch fabric it means that the stretch in the goods is only in the warp direction; also referred to as vertical or north-south stretch. (See Stretch, Filling.)

STRETCH, WOVEN: Woven fabric made with stretch yarn in it. Generally speaking, woven goods are classed as firm or rigid, but the use of stretch yarns affords stretchability to an otherwise rigid construction. The stretch may be in the warp north-south), filling (east-west), or in both warp *and* filling directions.

STRETCH YARN: A thermoplastic continuous filament yarn which has been modified to afford high stretch to the yarn elongation and rapid recovery.

STRETCH YARN DOUBLING: Combining an "S-twist yarn" with a "Z-twist yarn" to obtain a double or plied yarn free from torque. Torque is the movement of forces which cause rotation or twisting as done with cord, wire, or yarn. (See Torque versus Non-Torque Yarns; Torque Yarn.)

STRETCH YARN, HEAT-SET: A yarn with an irregular configuration which is then set into this formation by the use of heat treatment. Usually applied to thermoplastic manmade fibers, it can also be imparted to natural fibers that have been made thermoplastic through some chemical treatment.

S-TWIST: A yarn or cord has "S" twist if, when held in a vertical position, the spirals conform in slope to the central portion of the letter S. Formerly called left-hand or clockwise twist.

SULFONE CHEMICALS: They change the molecular composition of the cotton fiber by cross-linking; used to give permanent stability to a mechanical stretch fabric.

TEXTURIZING: When a smooth continuous manmade-fiber filament is given a new and permanent configuration which results in a textural surface of appeal on the fabric woven with these textured yarns.

THERMOPLASTIC: Any plastic material which is permanently fusible and soluble. A thermoplastic plastic is one that will soften when exposed to certain heats and will harden again when the source of heat is removed.

THROWING: While not exactly the same treatment given to wool, worsted, cotton, or flax, throwing means the actual twisting, without drawing, of the continuous filaments of silk and manmade fibers. Textured yarns for use in stretch and comparable fabrics are manipulated in this manner. A throwster is one who has a throwing business and processes silk or manmade filaments as noted above.

TORQUE: Applied to present-day stretch yarn, nylon for example, it is a yarn that has been twisted and then subsequently heat-set. Helanca and Chadalon are examples.

NON-TORQUE: A stretch yarn that has been made by curling or crimping rather than twisting. Agilon and Ban-Lon are examples. The word "torque" means that the movement of forces causes rotation or twisting, as in the case of twisting cord, wire, or yarn.

TWIST, FALSE: In processing a heat-set stretch yarn it is passed through a false-twist spindle, and twisting begins at this time. When emitted from the spindle the twist is automatically removed; hence the term "false-twist." The yarn, however, retains "a memory" of its twisted position or torque and seeks to return to that position. It is therefore wound or taken up under tension to prevent it from curling. The torque in the yarn is balanced later on in processing by doubling it with another yarn whose "remembered" twist goes in the opposite direction; thus, a yarn with an "S-twist" and a "Z-twist."

ZERO TWIST: Sometimes referred to as "no-twist." The thrower (spinner) may request that cuprammonium yarns be supplied with no-twist. This is rarely done, however; usually one to five turns per inch are given the yarns. Viscose and acetate yarns with from three to five or six turns per inch are normally supplied to the thrower; this twist is known as "tram twist" or "filling twist."

Z-TWIST: If the spirals of a yarn or cord conform in slope to the central portion of the letter "Z," the twist is known as Z-twist. Formerly known as right-hand or counterclockwise twist.

Courtesy of Cecil Lubell, Executive Editor, *American Fabrics Magazine*, New York City.

TOPIC: LAMINATED AND MOLDED FABRICS

LAMINATED FABRICS

Lamination is the term used when two or more layers of material are held together by the adherence of one fabric or material to another by the use of a plastic binder, an adhesive, some other suitable compound, or by the application of heat. The fabrics are bonded to polyurethane foam. It is possible to bond fabric to fabric, fabric to foam, simulated leather to fabric, and leather and simulated leather to the foam. One side of the fabric is made from one material, with the reverse another material. The method is comparable with that used to make plywood.

In textile fabrics the combining process is usually achieved by actual gas heating of the foam used to a point where it becomes adhesive, sticky, or tacky, and then forcing the shell material to adhere or bind to it so that when the cooling treatment is finished there is a firm bond to the fabric used. For example, "laminated jersey" has become a generic reference to jersey fabric that has been backed and bonded with a synthetic foam of the type known as "Curon" or "Scottfoam." There are several methods constantly under development, most of which use cold adhesive sprays and then combine the lining or backing fabric to the shell.

Foam laminates have good to high tensile strength and elasticity that prevents bunching at pressure points under stress, and they will recover and retain their shape and insulation properties. They are "breathable" materials that allow moisture from the body to escape, giving greater comfort to the wearer. They are resistant to perspiration, mildew, bacteria, and fungi; they are nonallergic and nontoxic; are not damaged by fluids, soaps, and detergents; are quick-drying and flame-resistant; will not deteriorate; and will outlast practically any garment.

Drycleaning and wet cleaning depend on the type of fabric used, the method and the condition of the bonding, the binder or adhesive used, and the garment construction.

Laminated urethane foam fabrics provide warmth with less weight and bulkiness. Fabrics that were never engineered for outerwear may now be laminated and used as outerwear garments. Discoloration of the foam may occur if the foaming chemicals are not completely removed at the proper time in processing during manufacture.

The chemical industry makes many adhesives for use in laminating urethane foam to fabric. They range from cold-setting, water-based rubber to high-temperature-cured resins. The most widely used types of adhesive include vinyl chloride-based solutions, acrylonitrile rubber mixtures, synthetic latex water-based solutions, and combinations of these three.

Examples of laminated fabrics in garments include coats and jackets, rainwear, sportswear, and many other types of apparel for men's, women's and children's wear. Woolens, worsteds, cottons, manmade-fiber fabrics, etc., are often laminated, as they are in such types of cloth as broadcloth, corduroy, flannel, denim, poplin, velveteen, etc.

MOLDED FABRICS

Acrylics, modacrylics, polyesters, nylons, and polyolefins are classed as thermo-formable (heat-formable) fibers. They can, by themselves or in certain types of blends with other fibers, by the application of heat and force or energy, be deformed into shapes which have dimensional stability in use. Woven, knitted, non-woven fabrics and felt made of these thermoformable fibers may be molded. A molded fabric may be defined as one which can be shaped or formed by a system of molding, whereby the fibers of the yarn in the fabric are drawn, attenuated, or stretched; the molded area of the fabric has significantly greater area than its original plane from which it was drawn.

Molded fabrics have had continued success in the textile and apparel industries. With the exception of rayon (viscose and cuprammonium), all other man-made fibers are thermoplastic in nature, and it is this property which permits the necessary molecular change when heat and pressure are applied. Thus, molding may be applied to a fluffy pile fabric or to leatherlike flat fabrics.

Three methods are used in heat-shaping or forming of the fibers. They are:

1. Compression-Forming Method

Two molds, or a male and a female die, may be used to produce more complex and intricate designs and shapes. The process is comparable with plug molding. Because of the pressure developed, the shaped article is usually stiffer and glossier than those formed by the plug method or the modified vacuum method.

2. Modified Vacuum-Forming Method

The fabric is preheated to a pliable or formable temperature and is deformed into the desired shape. A plug assist may be used to cause the fabric to conform to the molded shape. An elastic impermeable membrane is placed on one side of the fabric with a vacuum on the other side in order to achieve the closest conformation to the shape of the mold. Either male or female molds may be used.

3. Plug-Molding Method

A cooled or heated mold of any shape, reasonable size or design is forced into a fabric which has been preheated.

Molded fabrics will retain their shape permanently, are unaffected by washing, wear, heat or moisture within normal, reasonable limits. The "newness" of a product is literally molded into it. This revolutionary phase in fabric development and engineering in apparel makes molded fabrics ideal for brassieres, swimwear, stuffed animals, gloves, shoes, transportation fabric, slip covers, upholstery, headgear, etc.

TESTING

1. Define lamination; plastic; binder; adhesive.
2. Name two popular types of foam used in laminating fabrics.
3. What are two advantages of laminated fabrics?
4. List five examples of laminated fabrics in garments.
5. Define the term "thermoformable."
6. What is meant by a molded fabric?
7. Which manmade fiber cannot be made thermoformable?
8. Three methods are used for heat-shaping or forming of fibers that can be used in molded fabrics. Name them.
9. Describe one of these methods.
10. List five products in the field of molded fabrics.

TOPIC: Résumé of the Standard Types of Fabrics

The following composite information is for ready reference on eight basic types of textile fabrics:

TYPE	HOW RECOGNIZED	WORKING PROPERTIES
WOVEN	Yarns interlace at right angles; warp is vertical; filling is horizontal.	Used the most; strongest cloth for inner and outerwear; drapes well; is durable unless woven loosely; is made in all fibers, dyed, printed or bleached; may be a woven design.
KNITTED	One system of yarn interlooping: a loop within a loop.	Is manufactured quickly; may sag with wear; is elastic; form-fitting; may be porous; comes in wide fabric range for innerwear and outerwear.
FELT	Made from a mass of fibers that are interlocked by heat, moisture, pressure, pounding; with stiff felt, shellac is used. Yarn is not used in felt.	Contains no system of yarn; has varying tensile strength; retains a given shape, is substantial in weight; may be rough, smooth or soft to feel; has no selvage; seldom seen in stripes; holes cannot be mended; least lustrous of the standard materials.
PLAITED, BRAIDED, AND/OR LACE	Yarns may go in any direction, one system of yarn being interlaced to obtain the effect desired.	Open work in pattern is not always durable; not easy to launder; designs are geometrically or symmetrically balanced; serviceable when given good care, as with net and lace; not suited for general use.
NONWOVEN	Web or sheet of textile-type fibers bonded together by application of narrow stripes or patterns of adhesive material or by bonding fibers through chemical activation of the surface or by heat if thermoplastic fibers are used. Yarn is not used in this fabric.	Oriented in one direction or laid and set in random manner; functional property of bulkiness; may be paperlike, felt-like, or of a woven type. Porosity comes in wide range; hard to soft texture. Will not ravel or fray, may be sewn, glued, or heat-bonded. Wide range of uses.
STRETCH	Great stretch in one or both ways; stretch yarns not easily identifiable in goods; resilient, smooth or bulky with surface appeal and good texture effects; appealing hand or feel; light, medium, or heavy in weight.	Good "muscle power"; hidden stretch dimensions; form-fitting to give ease and comfort to wearer; excellent recovery on release from tension. Filling stretch better suited to body movements than warp stretch. Very flexible. Usually made with spandex or rubber as the core yarn, which is surrounded by a sheath of cotton, worsted, nylon, etc. yarn; provides very interesting effects.
LAMINATED	Foam sheet attached to one or two fabrics; if two materials used, they are usually of different types. Usually soft, spongy hand and effect.	Provides warmth with little added weight or added bulkiness. Garments have good flexibility and are aided by laminating for better fit.

TYPE	HOW RECOGNIZED	WORKING PROPERTIES
MOLDED	Molded area has greater area than its original plane from which it was drawn; this is revealed on examination of the article. Product may be fluffy, pilelike effect or a flat material.	Better fit and greater ease in movement of the body; affords more comfort to wearer. Retains permanent shape.

Some Woven Cloths: Beaver, broadcloth, brocade, canvas, cheviot, duck, cavalry twill, covert, crepe, handkerchief linen, homespun, gabardine, Jacquard, kersey, mackinac fabric, melton, muslin, organdy, percale, satin, shetland, taffeta, tricotine, tweed, voile, waffle cloth, webbing, wigan, whipcord.

Some Knitted Cloths: Baby clothes, bathing-suit fabric, jackets, jersey, mignonette, Milanese, neckwear, scarves, socks, stockinette, stockings, sweaters, topcoating, tricot-knit, tricolette.

Some Felt Cloths: Banners, blackboard erasers, felt slippers, insoles, packing, padding of many types, pennants, piano hammers, washers, all types of headgear.

Some Plaited or Braided Materials: Bedspreads, counterpanes, doilies, gauzy geometrical or symmetrical porous materials, insulation, lace, net, runners, shoelacing, trimming, veiling. Schiffli embroidery and Leavers lace machines produce all types and kinds of these products.

Some Nonwoven Fabrics: Aprons, diapers, facing material, interlinings, women's skirts, tablecloths, towels, vacuum cleaner bags, basket and casket lining, bagging and wrapping material, bed pads, covers, tissues, insulation.

Some Stretch Fabrics: Power Stretch: Athletic clothing, foundation garments, football pants, ski wear, swimwear. Comfort Stretch: Blouses and dresses, casual wear, gloves, knitgoods of several types, infants' and children's wear, linings such as for men's coatings, pajamas, shirting and sportswear, slip covers in home furnishings, undergarments, uniforms, upholstery.

Some Laminated Fabrics: Men's, women's and children's coats, jackets, and sportswear of many types; topcoating, overcoating, windbreakers; velvet, velveteen, broadcloth, corduroy, flannel, denim, poplin, etc.

Some Molded Fabrics: Effect found in better fitting effect in men's, women's, and children's outerwear garments—jackets, coats, sportswear, topcoats, overcoatings, mackinac jackets, etc.

EXAMINATION ON THE STANDARD TYPES OF FABRICS

Completion-Type Questions   50 points

1. Corduroy, velvet and velveteen are _____ fabrics.
2. Knitted cloth is made by _____ of yarn.
3. Selvage is found in _____ fabric.
4. Another name for selvage is _____.
5. Carroting is a treatment given to fur fibers for use in _____.
6. John Heathcoat invented the first _____.
7. _____ fabric used for hats must be blocked.
8. Wool fibers will _____ in a natural manner.
9. _____ are found on fur fibers when treated with mercuric nitrate and will because of this treatment open up.
10. Shoelacing is a _____ material.
11. Two systems of yarn that interlace at right angles make _____ cloth.
12. Veiling is a _____ material.
13. The oldest method of making cloth is _____.
14. _____ cloth is the best for shock absorption.
15. Open pattern work is found in _____ material.

16. Plaited fabric is _____ in strength when compared with woven cloth.
17. Lace is a form of _____.
18. Shellac is used in making _____.
19. Carding is a process in the making of _____ felt.
20. Leur is a brushing pad used on _____.

True or False Type Questions   50 points

1. _____ Felt has no elasticity.
2. _____ Holes are easily remedied in felt material.
3. _____ Comparatively speaking, felt has little tensile strength.
4. _____ Knitted cloth is the strongest type of fabric made.
5. _____ There would be 45 ribs in a 45-gauge stocking, per inch.
6. _____ All knitted material is made in circular form.
7. _____ Knitted fabric will hold the crease better than woven cloth.
8. _____ Some woven cloth has the tendency to shine with wear.
9. _____ Knitted garments have the tendency to sag with wear.
10. _____ Leuring is a treatment used in the making of plaited fabrics.

EXAMINATION ON UNIT 1 THROUGH UNIT 18

True-False Questions   25 points

1. _____ Knitted fabric is made by an interlacing of two systems of yarn.
2. _____ Selvage is an actual part of the warp.
3. _____ Lace is made by an interlacing of yarn at any angle.
4. _____ The smallest unit in a woven fabric is the yarn.
5. _____ Another name for listing is self-edge when speaking of the vertical edges of woven goods.
6. _____ A fiber is a filament of indefinite length.
7. _____ Thread is a specialized type of yarn used for a definite purpose.
8. _____ Kapok, hemp, henequin, and istle are vegetable fibers.
9. _____ Llama, alpaca, cashmere, mohair, and ramie are all animal fibers.
10. _____ Glass fibers leave a soft black bead when burned.
11. _____ Bemberg rayon and cuprammonium rayon are synonymous terms.
12. _____ Weighted silk burns quicker than true silk.
13. _____ The three chief motions on a loom, in order, are shedding, beating up, and picking.
14. _____ Spring-beard needles are the only type used to make knit fabrics.
15. _____ Ciré, mercerized, duplex, and satin-like are types of finishes.
16. _____ Stripes in fabrics usually run in the vertical direction.
17. _____ Nap on a fabric runs up and down on the face of the goods.
18. _____ Slag wool is a low-quality wool fiber.
19. _____ That system of yarn with the greater twist would usually be the warp in a woven fabric.
20. _____ Bulkier yarn is usually the filling yarn in a woven material.
21. _____ In a plaid-back fabric, the plaid effect is usually the face of the material.
22. _____ A skipped dent in a reed means that there is not a single end drawn through it.
23. _____ Wale in knit fabric compares with the warp in woven cloth.
24. _____ Filling yarn in woven fabric compares with the course in knit goods.
25. _____ Most twill-woven fabric is left-hand in direction on the face of the material.

[141]

Matching Questions

Place the number before the second column of terms or words on the blank line provided to the left where there is a definite match or link:

1. _____ In felt fabric	1. Plain, rib, purl, tuck
2. _____ Knitted fabric	2. Operation in making hat bodies
3. _____ Stocking of 45 gauge	3. Melton, kersey, beaver
4. _____ Hardanger	4. May have considerable porosity
5. _____ Connecting threads	5. Often seen on taffeta
6. _____ Face-finished fabrics	6. Having 30 needles to the inch
7. _____ Moiré or watermarking	7. Known as lace ties
8. _____ Stitches in knitting	8. Holes cannot be fixed
9. _____ Leuring	9. A type of lace
10. _____ Denim	10. Made with left-hand twill weave

Completion Questions on the Loom and Weaving of Fabric

1. The motion on a loom which feeds in the warp evenly for weaving is called the _____.
2. The _____ motion causes newly woven fabric to be wound evenly on the cloth roller by indirect driving in this action.
3. The _____ keep all warp ends even, straight, and true at all times.
4. Heddles are set on the _____.
5. It is possible to have as many as _____ colors in the filling color arrangement in a plaid material as it is woven on the loom.
6. The filling stop motion is set in the _____ of the loom.
7. The reed in a loom is firmly held in its place by the _____.
8. Mispicks in weaving fabric go in the _____ direction.
9. The _____ keep the edge warp threads at right angles as cloth is being woven in the loom.
10. The group of a few picks in woven fabric between the temples and where the last pick has gone into the newly woven fabric is known as the _____.

Identification Questions

a) One of the terms in each of the following questions is out of place; it is not connected with any of the other terms. Place the number of the out-of-place term on the blank line provided to the left:

1. ___	1. Raw material	2. Construction	3. Finish	4. Strength
2. ___	1. Heddles	2. Shuttle	3. Loop	4. Harness cords
3. ___	1. Gray goods	2. Course	3. Ribbed	4. Tricot knit
4. ___	1. One way	2. Napped	3. Two-ply	4. Usually on face
5. ___	1. Sized	2. Strength	3. Warp	4. Crepe effect
6. ___	1. Velvet	2. Velveteen	3. Pique	4. Corduroy
7. ___	1. Terry cloth	2. Carpeting	3. Plush	4. Face finish
8. ___	1. Swollen	2. Bent	3. Skipped	4. Reed cap to hold reed
9. ___	1. Hair fiber	2. Virgin wool	3. Re-used	4. Re-manufactured
10. ___	1. Whip roll	2. Breast beam	3. Selvage	4. Lease rods
11. ___	1. Full-fashioned	2. No yarn used	3. Felt	4. Nonwoven fabric
12. ___	1. Picker stick	2. Lug strap	3. Shoe	4. Shuttle box on loom
13. ___	1. Square cloth	2. 72 x 60	3. 64 x 64	4. Pick count is same
14. ___	1. Appliqué	2. Schiffli	3. Filling	4. Embroidery
15. ___	1. Spring needle	2. Wale	3. Course	4. Latch needle

b) In each of the following questions, one term or word is the correct answer. Place the number before your choice on the blank line provided to the left:

		1.	2.	3.	4.
1. ____	Animal fiber	1. Flax	2. Burlap	3. Cashmere	4. Asbestos
2. ____	Vegetable fiber	1. Llama	2. Alpaca	3. Jute	4. Vicuna
3. ____	Cellulosic fiber	1. Silk	2. Nylon	3. Acrilan	4. Bemberg rayon
4. ____	Polyamide fiber	1. Nylon	2. Dynel	3. Verel	4. "Dacron"
5. ____	Acrylic fiber	1. Arnel	2. "Orlon"	3. Fortisan	4. Fiberglas
6. ____	Will felt	1. Cotton	2. Wool	3. Cashmere	4. Mohair
7. ____	Most used fiber	1. Rayon	2. Acetate	3. Cotton	4. Nylon
8. ____	Felt operation	1. Gauge	2. Burling	3. Perching	4. Carroting
9. ____	Knit fabric	1. Jersey	2. Kersey	3. Schiffli	4. Tricotine
10. ____	Reversible	1. Voile	2. Chintz	3. Cretonne	4. Handkerchief
11. ____	Longest filament	1. Silk	2. Rayon	3. Flax	4. Rayon staple
12. ____	Shortest fiber	1. Linen	2. Worsted	3. Cotton	4. Ramie
13. ____	Tears unevenly	1. Woven	2. Felt	3. Knitted	4. Organdy
14. ____	Most popular	1. Twill	2. Satin	3. Plain	4. Basket
15. ____	Highest texture	1. Poplin	2. Duck	3. Sheeting	4. Typewriter ribbon fabric

Essay Questions: Select five of the following topics, and write an essay of about 150 to 175 words on each one of your choice: 100 points

THE TOPICS:

1. The Parts of a Woven Fabric from Fiber to Fabric.
2. Textile Fabrics Which Have the Greatest Appeal to Me.
3. Determination of Warp from Filling in Woven Fabrics.
4. Determination of Face from Back in Woven Materials.
5. Why I Like Lace.
6. Schiffli Embroidery.
7. The Importance of Knitted Fabrics for Everyday Wear.
8. Textiles as an Economic Factor in Our Daily Life.
9. How Textiles May Help Me in My Career.
10. The Value of Textiles to a Student of Merchandising.
11. Why I Would Like to be a Designer of Woven Fabrics.
12. Why I Would Like to Design Printed Textiles.
13. The Reasons Why I Would Like to Know More about Textiles.
14. Any topic of your choice in the field of textiles.
15. Why the Subject of Textiles Appeals to Me.
16. Why the Subject of Textiles Does Not Appeal to Me.

Part 1—Unit 20

TOPIC: THE THREE BASIC WEAVES IN WEAVE FORMATION

PLAIN, TWILL, AND SATIN WEAVES

There are three basic weaves from which it may be stated all other weave constructions are derived, directly or indirectly. These weaves which form the foundation for other woven designs or patterns are plain, twill, and satin.

All woven goods have two systems of yarn or thread that weave or interlace at right angles.

Threads that run vertically or lengthwise in a material are called warp, ends, or warp ends.

Threads that run crosswise or horizontally in a material are called filling, picks, or filling picks.

The manner in which threads actually interlace is called weaving. Woven cloth designs are plotted on design paper. This squared paper is arranged so that the vertical or up-and-down lines represent the warp; the horizontal lines, the filling.

3

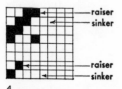

4

A raiser is a painted block on the design paper. It indicates that the warp end is raised over the filling pick at the point of interlacing.

A sinker is an unpainted block and signifies that the filling pick is over the warp end at the point of interlacing. In other words, the warp end is under the filling pick at that point of interlacing.

In plotting or laying out ordinary weave constructions the warp is painted on the design paper, the filling is not.

The term "repeat" is used to designate the size of the weave and the number of threads that the weave may contain in both the warp and the filling direction. Weaves may be repeated on paper any number of times within reason.

Interlacing Arrangement of Plain, Twill, and Satin Weaves

(Black lines—Warp; Shaded lines—Filling)

PLAIN WEAVE   TWILL WEAVE   SATIN WEAVE

5   6   7

$\dfrac{1}{1}$ plain weave

4 repeats high,
4 repeats wide.

$\dfrac{2}{2}$ right-hand twill

2 repeats high,
2 repeats wide.

8 end, shaft or harness satin weave, base or counter of 3; filling float of 7.

1 repeat high,
1 repeat wide.

Cross-Section of Plain, Twill, and Satin Weaves

The warp, shown by the wavy lines, interlaces over and under the filling picks which are shown by the black blocks.

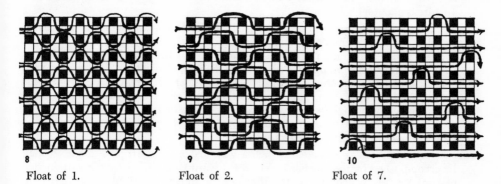

8
Float of 1.

9
Float of 2.

10
Float of 7.

Plain Weave: There is only one plain weave, and it repeats on two warp ends and two filling picks. The construction is one raiser and one sinker on each thread. The second thread weaves the opposite of the first. The effect is a checkerboard. When the first thread is "up," the second thread is "down." The plain weave is written $\frac{1}{1}$ and is read as "one-up and one-down."

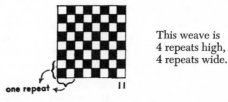

one repeat

11

This weave is
4 repeats high,
4 repeats wide.

About 80 per cent of all woven fabric is made with plain weave, which affords the tightest possible interlacing between the warp and the filling yarns.

TESTING

1. Define the following terms: raiser, sinker, repeat.
2. What is the name given to the vertical yarns in woven fabric? The horizontal yarns?
3. Are the raisers or the sinkers plotted on paper when making a weave?
4. What weave is used for the greatest production of woven goods?

Part 1—Unit 21

TOPIC: FABRICS MADE WITH VARIATIONS OF THE PLAIN WEAVE

A plain-weave fabric is made with two warp ends and two filling picks, painted two blocks high and two blocks wide for the single repeat. By the use of color, or by variations in the yarns used, a plain weave may be varied and improved in appearance in certain materials. A white or solid-color plain-weave fabric has the simplest construction of any woven cloth. A comparison between regulation plain-weave fabric such as voile, organdy, sheeting, muslin, lawn, batiste, and longcloth with chambray, crepe, gingham, and taffeta, all made from plain-weave variations, will reveal that there is a difference in surface effect and coloring arrangement. These latter fabrics because of the variation used will have different effects as to draping, durability, finish, and luster.

Below is a list of the major fabrics made from plain-weave variations:

CHAMBRAY: The entire warp is one color while the filling is another color, e.g., blue warp and white filling. The fabric is made with an all-white selvage. This dyed warp and unbleached or white filling material is made of carded or combed yarn. Texture is about 80 x 76.

CREPE: There are many types of crepes, one of the most popular staple fabrics to be found in the textile trade. The fabrics are made from all the major textile fibers. A crepe weave is nothing more than a plain weave with certain raisers in the construction left out according to a plan. Thus, instead of having a float of one yarn over or under the opposite system of yarn, the float of yarn will be at least for three threads in the fabric. This provides the crepe effect which is further supplemented by crepe or high twist in the yarns used in the fabric.

Crepe is a broad term given to various materials generally recognized by a crinkled, puckered, or pebble-effect surface.

DIMITY: The warp yarn is arranged in such a way that a white stripe is made. It may be accomplished by the manner in which the warp is reeded or by the introduction of cord threads which run in the direction of the warp, or by both warp and filling. Whether or not the check effects are used in this material, the textures range from 76 x 64 to 130 x 94.

GINGHAM: This variation has dyed yarns introduced at given intervals in both warp and filling to achieve check or block effects. The warp and filling may often be the same, even-sided, and balanced. Color schemes range from conservative to gaudy, wild effects. Textures are around 64 x 56.

MADRAS: One of the oldest staples in the cotton trade, it is made on plain-weave background which is usually white; stripes, cords, or minute checks may be used to form the pattern. Fancy effects are often of satin or basket weave, or small twill repeat. White filling is used. Yarn counts range from 40s to 60s in warp and filling while textures approximate 110 warp ends and 88 picks.

SEERSUCKER: This is a cotton, rayon, or nylon crepe-stripe cloth made on plain-weave variation, and it has a crepe or crinkled appearance. The effect is obtained in the weaving, wherein one warp used is woven under high tension in the loom while the other warp beam feeds the yarn in at a looser tension, thereby producing the crinkled effect. Woven seersucker is more expensive than the simulations obtained by chemical means. This fabric needs no ironing, and when made of rayon the content must be declared.

TAFFETA: This cloth is made from a tabby weave, another name for plain weave. One of the oldest fabrics on the market today, it is characterized by its cylindrical filling. Taffeta is closely allied with another popular staple, faille. The terms, at times, are used in an interchangeable way. The term means "twisted-woven," and examination of the yarns used will reveal the amount of twist and its effect in the finished state. Textures range from 70 up to around 130 for the pickage while the number of warp ends per inch is around 90. Taffeta may be plain, printed, changeable, striped, checked, plaided, or of the "antique" type in which uneven threads are used to advantage. Fabric weight runs from heavy to the "paper" or "tissue" types.

TESTING

1. State some reasons for the use of materials made from variations of the plain weave.
2. Give the characteristics of any four of the following fabrics made on plain-weave variation: chambray, crepe, dimity, gingham, madras, seersucker, taffeta, faille.
3. How do various cloths made from plain-weave variations compare with plain-weave fabrics as to durability and appeal?
4. Why would taffeta be known as a form-concealing material, while satin would be classed as a form-revealing fabric?

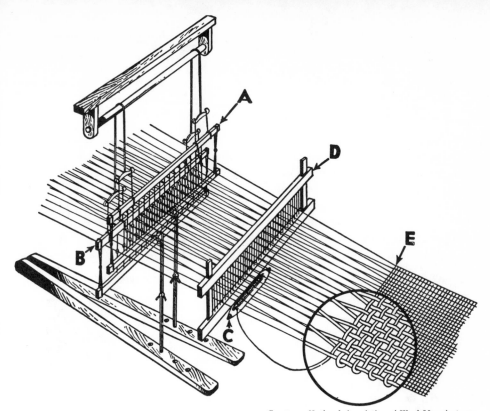

Courtesy: National Association of Wool Manufacturers

SIMPLIFIED SKETCH OF THE PLAIN WEAVE

1. Harness frame (A) controls odd warp ends. 2. Harness frame (B) controls even warp ends. 3. Harness (A) raises the odd warp ends while Harness (B) lowers the even warp ends. 4. Shuttle is shot through the warp shed and leaves filling pick in its wake. 5. Harnesses (A) and (B) return to center point and Reed (D) swings forward to beat loose pick into its component place in fabric or at the Fell of the Cloth (E). 6. For the next pick in cloth (A) and (B) reverse their action.

Part 1—Unit 22

TOPIC: TWILL WEAVES

Twill Weaves: The three basic weaves are plain, twill, and satin. All other weaves are a development of these weaves, directly or indirectly. There is no limit as to the number of twill weaves possible. The simplest and smallest twill that can be made is on three warp ends and three filling picks. The weave may be a two-up and one-down or a one-up and two-down, right-hand twill or left-hand twill.

Twill weaves produce diagonal lines on the face of the goods. In the great majority of cases the lines run to the right on the material. That is, they run from the lower left-hand corner of the goods to the upper right-hand corner of the material. Some few cloths made on this type of construction have a left-hand twill effect on the face of the fabric; from the upper left-hand corner of the material to the lower right-hand corner of the goods.

2-up, 2-down;
right-hand twill,
2 x 2.

12

2-up, 2-down;
left-hand twill,
2 x 2.

13

There will be no set rule that specifies as to whether or not a cloth must have a right-hand twill or a left-hand twill construction. Custom, deep-rooted tradition, local circumstances, usage of the material, and the appearance are all basic factors that usually determine the weave direction. Some twill fabrics may be either right hand or left hand in the diagonal twill line effect. Drill and certain small twill-effect construction may be right hand or left hand in twill line direction.

Effect: This term is used to sum up weaves as to appearance and effect noted on the actual cloth. There are three types of effect:

1. WARP EFFECT: When there is more warp than filling on the face of the cloth.

14

Example— a $\dfrac{4 \quad 2}{1 \quad 1}$ weave, a total of 6 ends up and 2 ends down.

15

2. FILLING EFFECT: When there is more filling on the face of the cloth. Example—

a $\dfrac{1 \quad 2}{2 \quad 3}$ weave, a total of 3 ends up and 5 ends down.

3. EVEN-SIDED EFFECT: When there is the same amount of warp and filling on the face of the goods. Example— a $\dfrac{3 \quad 1}{1 \quad 3}$ weave, a total of 4 ends up and 4 ends down.

16

These three terms apply to other types of weaves when designing for woven fabric—satins, steep twills, basket weaves, broken twills, herringbones, spot weaves, granites, etc.

SOME REPRESENTATIVE PLAIN WEAVE AND TWILL WEAVE MATERIALS

MADE OF	PLAIN WEAVE	RIGHT-HAND TWILL	LEFT-HAND TWILL
Cotton	Batiste, broadcloth, cambric, chambray, lawn, muslin, nainsook, organdy, voile, sheeting.	Drill, twillcloth, gabardine, lining fabric, some awning goods.	Galatea, denim, jean cloth, uniform goods, institution fabric, some drill goods.
Linen	Crash, canvas, dress linen, handkerchief linen; butcher, art, and pillowcase linens.	Bird's-eye, ticking, toweling.	Some novelty linen materials.

MADE OF	PLAIN WEAVE	RIGHT-HAND TWILL	LEFT-HAND TWILL
Woolen and Worsted	Albatross, balmacaan, broadcloth, challis, Donegal, flannel, homespun.	Covert, elastique, gabardine, cavalry twill, tweed, whipcord, novelty outerwear cloth.	Some few novelty dress-goods, most British outerwear goods.
Silk, Acetate, Rayon, Nylon, etc.	Chiffon, poplin, broadcloth, China silk cloth, habutai, shantung, taffeta, plaids, and novelties.	Foulard, gabardine, some plaid cloths, silk serge, tartan silk, seerah.	Gabardine and some novelty goods.

Degree Twill Weaves

The usual common twill weaves are forty-five degrees in angle. For example, a 2-up and 2-down twill weave will show that one repeat requires the use of four ends and four picks. The rule is to "go-up" one pick for each successive warp end in a forty-five degree twill weave. To make the second repeat of the 2-up and 2-down twill, the following arrangement should be followed:

1. The 5th end and the 5th pick weave the same as the 1st end and the 1st pick, respectively.
2. The 6th end and the 6th pick weave the same as the 2nd end and the 2nd pick, respectively.
3. The 7th end and the 7th pick weave the same as the 3rd end and the 3rd pick, respectively.
4. The 8th end and the 8th pick weave the same as the 4th end and the 4th pick, respectively.

In a 45-degree twill, right-hand effect, the raiser moves up one pick for each successive warp end. The diagonal line goes to the right.

In a 45-degree twill, left-hand effect, the raiser moves down one pick for each successive warp end. The diagonal lines go to the left.

See Drawings 12 and 13, p. 148.

63-Degree Twill Weaves: In the right-hand effect the raiser moves up two picks. In the left-hand effect the raiser moves down two picks.

70-Degree Twill Weaves: In the right-hand effect the raiser moves up three picks. In the left-hand effect the raiser moves down three picks.

75-Degree Twill Weaves: In the right-hand effect the raiser moves up four picks. In the left-hand effect the raiser moves down four picks.

Reclining Twill Weaves: Twill weaves in which the angle and the diagonal line are less than the usual forty-five degrees.

27-Degree Twill: Hold over for two ends and then go to the next pick.

20-Degree Twill: Hold over for three ends and then go to the next pick.

15-Degree Twill: Hold over for four ends and then go to the next pick.

Some steep twills are made with the left-hand direction on the face of the goods; however, this is rare.

Broken Twills: Weaves made from a regular twill weave by running the twill in one direction for a desired number of threads and then reversing the direction of the twill from running to the right by causing it to run to the left and by making as clear a break as possible at the "break" or "break-line."

A clear break in a weave is made by the placing of the raisers on the one thread opposite the sinkers of the adjoining thread; this is possible only in the case of certain even-sided twills.

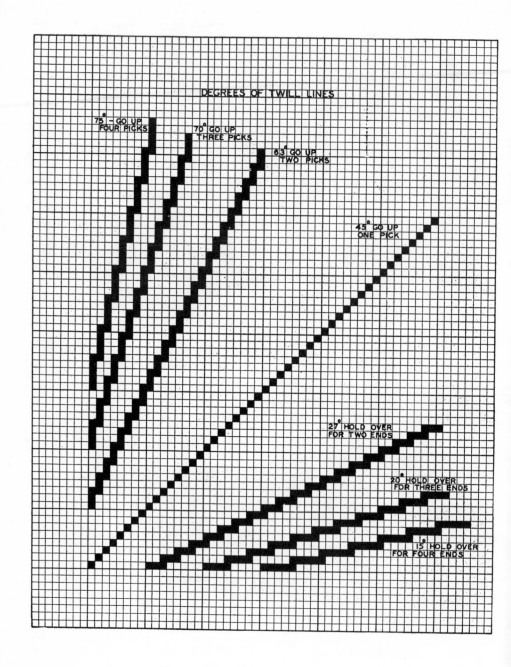

An example of this would be to have the sinkers of the first thread of the left-hand twill come opposite the raisers of the last thread of the right-hand twill at the break-line.

Incidentally, all herringbones are broken twills, but all broken twills are not necessarily herringbone weaves.

 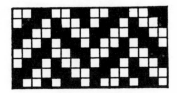

2-up and 2-down twill,
eight ends to the right, and
eight ends to the left.
2 repeats high x 1 repeat wide.

2-up and 2-down twill,
four ends to the right, and
four ends to the left.
2 repeats high x 2 repeats wide.

TESTING

1. Give the data for two of the smallest twill weaves, out of the total of four, that it is possible to make.
2. Define the following effects in twill weaves: even-sided twill, warp-effect twill, filling-effect twill.
3. Give an example of each of the three weave effects in the previous question.
4. What rule would have to be followed if you were to construct a reclining twill of 20 degrees?
5. What is meant by the "break" or "break-line" in a broken twill weave?

TOPIC: Satin Weaves

Satin weaves constitute the third group of the basic weave construction. The plain weave has no characteristic or distinguishable diagonal or twill line. There is a more or less prominent diagonal line in right-hand and left-hand twill weaves and in broken twill weaves.

Satin weaves do not have a distinguishable twill line despite the fact that it is actually present in cloth made of these weaves. The naked eye, however, does not discern these lines on the face of the cloth. For this reason, one speaks of a satin weave as devoid of any characteristic twill line. The absence of the twill lines in a satin weave is brought about by the way in which the interlacing of the threads is arranged. Because of this fact, practically the entire surface of the face of the goods is covered with either warp yarn or filling yarn, depending on the weaves having a warp or a filling construction. The fine diagonal lines do not show and to find them one must look carefully and closely at the material.

Regular satin weaves repeat on as low as five ends or threads. The following terms used with regard to satin construction are synonymous:

1. Base or counter.
2. End, shaft, or harness.
3. Satin, in silk, and sateen, in cotton, are the same when referring to the cloth construction.

Base or Counter

This is the key that is used in the distribution of the interlacings when plotting a satin weave on design paper. By means of the counter the correct warp end and filling pick interlacing are determined.

The base cannot be divided evenly into the number of ends or threads in the repeat of the weave: a 9-end satin weave, for example, can be made with a base of 2 or 4, but not with a counter of 3.

WARP ENDS

The weave above is an 8-shaft satin, filling-effect weave with a base of 3. The weave is begun in the lower left-hand corner where warp end #1 interlaces with filing pick #1. Since this is a painted block it means that the first warp end is over the first filling pick at the point of interlacing. For the completion of the repeat of the weave, count three blocks to the right of the raiser to determine the number of the warp yarn that is to interlace with the second pick. This action continues until the weave repeat is completed. In counting, if the numbers go beyond the limits of the original repeat, they are placed on corresponding blocks within the limits or confines of the original weave.

18

5-end satin,
counter of 3,
filling effect,
2 x 2

19

5-end satin,
base of 3,
warp effect,
2 x 2

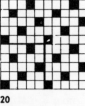

20

5-end satin,
counter of 2,
filling effect,
2 x 2

21

5-end satin,
base of 2,
warp effect,
2 x 2

22

8-shaft satin,
counter of 3,
filling effect,
1 x 1

23

8-harness satin,
base of 3,
warp effect,
1 x 1

[152]

In plain satin weaves there is only one interlacing between the individual warp end and the individual filling pick: the length, therefore, of the yarn float would be one number less than the total of the threads in the one repeat of the weave. In this weave, the float would be for seven threads.

When completed, the weave will show that every warp end in the construction interlaces at some point with some individual pick. There can never be two interlacings at any point on any warp end or filling pick within the limits of the original weave.

The following satin weaves, the 5-end and the 8-end constructions, are shown above with the accompanying data for each of the weaves.

Satin weaves are used to make brocade, brocatelle, cape or cloak fabric, cotton-back sateen, coverings, curtain material, damask, dress silk, evening gowns and wraps, fancies and novelties, furniture fabric, Jacquard fabrics of many types, runners, slipper satin, sport fabrics made of silk or manmade, striping effect in some materials, tablecloth and napkin material, tapestry, tie fabric, etc.

The word "satin" in construction, implies a silk or manmade cloth made with a satin weave; the term "sateen" implies a cotton material made with a satin weave.

Satin weave gives a more solid and glossier appearance on the face of the goods than any other type of weave—hence its great use in the above-mentioned materials. The types of yarn used have great effect on the brilliant luster noted in fabrics made with the satin weave. Satin-weave cloths do not possess nearly the tensile strength of plain- and twill-woven cloths because of the manner of construction. The loose plan in interlacing and the length of the floats in the weave cause this condition. Plain woven cloths have more tensile strength than twill woven fabrics, comparatively speaking.

The six-harness irregular satin weave, often used in satin constructions, has the following arrangement of the warp ends: 1, 3, 5, 2, 6, 4. The weave below is a filling effect, 2 repeats high by 2 repeats wide.

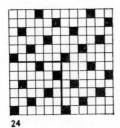

24

TESTING

1. Explain why it may be said that satin weaves are a development of the twill weave.
2. Give a synonym for the term "base"; the term "shaft."
3. What would be the length of the float in a 9-end satin weave?
4. What is the warp arrangement in a 6-shaft irregular satin weave?
5. Why is it not possible to make an 8-harness satin weave with a base or counter of 2 or 4?

TOPIC: Basket Weaves—A Development of the Plain Weave

Basket weaves are classed as a variation of the plain weave because a simple basket weave can be made on two harnesses in the loom.

In the simplest basket weave the warp is divided into two parts, as in the case of the plain weave, but with this difference: the simplest basket weave is called a "two-by-two basket" because the ends are arranged in groups of two. The ends in each group weave alike. They are arranged on two harnesses as follows:

Harness #1—controls ends   1&2   5&6   9&10   etc.
Harness #2—controls ends   3&4   7&8   11&12 etc.

When one harness is up and the other down, a warp shed is formed. In a simple basket weave the shuttle passes twice through the same shed, except for the selvages. Consequently, there would be two picks in the same shed.

When the harnesses reverse their positions, another shed is formed. Two picks are thrown through this shed. This completes the cycle, which is repeated as weaving continues.

A basket weave does give a good appearance to certain types of cloth. Hopsacking, a popular staple suiting and coating fabric, is made from a 2-2 basket weave. Monk's cloth, a staple curtain or drapery fabric, is usually made from a 4-4 basket weave, although a 3-3, 5-5, or a 6-6 basket arrangement may be used.

In writing the data for a basket weave, the numbers used do not refer to raisers and sinkers in the weave as in the case of twill weave. Rather the numbers refer to the groups of threads or yarns that weave alike. Thus, a 4-4 basket weave would have the first 4 threads in the repeat weaving alike, while the second set of 4 threads would weave alike but opposite the first set of 4 yarns. By adding the two sets of 4 threads it will be seen that one repeat of the weave would require a total of 8 ends and 8 picks. Even-series basket weaves will repeat on the number of ends noted in the data. For example, a 2-2-2-4 basket weave would repeat on 10 threads, because four, the number of series of threads in the weave, is an even number.

Uneven-series basket weaves will be twice the size ordinarily expected when adding the total number of ends in the repeat. Thus, a 4-1-4 basket weave (series of three groups of threads) would require 18 blocks in each direction to obtain a full repeat.

On the following page are examples of basket weaves made with even-series data and with uneven-series data.

It should be noted that the yarns in some basket weaves, where there may be rather long floats of yarn each way in the cloth, may have the tendency to shift or move about, thereby possibly making cloth that is rather difficult to sew upon. The tensile strength and abrasion-resistance of basket weaves do not compare with those of plain-woven materials which have the tightest interlacing possible in the finished goods, a float of only one over the opposite system of yarn.

With the exception of hopsacking fabric, a basket-weave fabric is not desirable for dress fabrics, which have to withstand chafing, friction, abrasion, and wear. The weaves do find, however, rather wide use in decorative materials such as hangings, portieres, and curtains.

EVEN-SERIES	EVEN-SERIES	UNEVEN-SERIES BASKET
A 2-4 basket weave, 2 repeats high and 2 repeats wide; total of 12 threads for the 2 repeats.	A 2-2-2-4 basket weave, 1 repeat high and 1 repeat wide; total of 10 threads each way for the 1 repeat.	A 4-1-4 basket weave, 1 repeat high and 1 repeat wide, total of 18 threads each way.

TESTING

1. What are the essential differences between a plain weave and a basket weave?
2. Why may difficulty be encountered in manipulating a basket-weave fabric into a garment?
3. How many blocks would there be in one repeat of a 1-2-3-4 basket weave? In a 2-3-4 basket weave?

Part 1—Unit 25

TOPIC: RIB WEAVES—A DEVELOPMENT OF THE PLAIN WEAVE

Rib weaves are derived from the plain weave, having two or more consecutive or successive ends or picks weave alike. A group of yarns that weave alike are used to form the cord or rib effect in the goods. Sometimes, however, a very bulky yarn may be used by itself to obtain the rib effect; this is more the exception than the rule, however. These "cord yarns" are said to "weave as one yarn" in the material. It is the rib yarns that indicate the direction of the rib, cord, or wale. The rib effect may be in the warp or the filling direction. These rib yarns are usually heavier or bulkier than the rest of the yarn used in the fabric.

Warp-rib weaves have the cord effect in the opposite or filling direction. Filling-rib weaves have the wale effect in the opposite or warp direction.

Common or simple warp-rib weaves repeat on two warp ends only; all even-numbered ends will weave alike while all odd-numbered ends will weave alike. Simple filling-rib weaves will repeat on two picks only; all even-numbered picks will weave alike while all odd-numbered picks will weave alike.

Rib weaves, incidentally, afford an opportunity for the use of waste or relatively poor yarn since the rib yarn does not actually show on the face or the back of the goods. The rib yarns are covered by the close texture of the yarns used as the base of the fabric and because of the fact that these yarns go over and under the cord threads.

It should be borne in mind that in these weaves the threads that are used to give the effect actually do not interlace or weave with the opposite system of yarn. Rather they are laid in the fabric and are held in place by the compactness of the other system of yarn as it goes over and under these cord yarns. In most rib weaves it is a relatively easy matter to remove the rib yarns from the cloth because they have not actually interlaced with the opposite system of yarn, which does have to interlace with the foundation yarns used in the goods.

A hatband is a warp-rib weave since it is woven on the loom with the rib running in the filling direction. Examination of the selvages will show this clearly. When the band, however, is worn on a hat the effect is that of a filling rib since the cords run vertically, or up and down.

Examples of rib weaves include ribbon of many types, bengaline, grosgrain (bengaline cut to ribbon width), Ottoman, transportation fabric, Russian cord shirting, some types of webbing, and some novelty effects in dressgoods.

The weave data and the plan followed for rib weaves of an even or an uneven series of groups of threads is the same as that noted under basket weaves.

On this page and the next are some typical warp-rib and filling-rib weaves with the necessary data for each weave.

Warp-Rib Weaves

All warp-rib weaves repeat on two warp ends with the rib runs in the filling direction.

 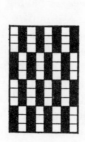  

		Even Series	Uneven Series
2-2 warp rib,	3-3 warp rib,	1-2-1-4 warp rib,	3-1-3 warp rib,
4 repeats high,	2 repeats high,	2 repeats high,	2 repeats high,
4 repeats wide,	4 repeats wide,	4 repeats wide,	4 repeats wide,
16 x 8 blocks.	12 x 8 blocks.	16 x 8 blocks.	28 x 8 blocks.

Filling-Rib Weaves

All repeat on two filling picks and the rib runs in the warp direction.

2-2 filling rib,
4 repeats high,
4 repeats wide,
8 x 16 blocks.

3-3 filling rib,
4 repeats high,
2 repeats wide,
8 x 12 blocks.

EVEN SERIES
2-2-2-4 filling rib,
4 repeats high,
2 repeats wide,
8 x 20 blocks.

UNEVEN SERIES
3-1-3 filling rib,
4 repeats high,
2 repeats wide,
8 x 28 blocks.

TESTING

1. Name the two types of rib weaves.
2. In what direction does the rib or cord run in a warp-rib weave?
3. From which basic weave is the rib weave derived? Explain your answer.
4. Name three cloths made from rib weaves.
5. How many blocks high and how many wide would there be in a single repeat of a 1-2-3-4 warp-rib weave? In a 4-1-4 filling-rib weave, for one repeat?

Part 1—Unit 26

TOPIC: PIQUE AND BEDFORD CORD WEAVES

These two types of construction are developments of the rib weave. A true pique weave and fabric has the rib effect running in the filling direction. Pique is worn, however, with the cord effect running in the warp or vertical direction. In common parlance the term "pique" is applied loosely to many cotton fabrics in which the ribs may run in either the warp or the filling direction. An ordinary filling-wise rib is formed by grouping several warp ends together in weaving to give the corded effect in the warp direction. The weave is plotted in the direction of the filling. (The word is pronounced pe-kay', and may be written piqué.)

An ordinary warp-wise rib is formed by grouping several filling picks in the same shed of the loom to give the ribbed effect in the direction of the filling. The weave is plotted in the direction of the warp.

In a pique weave the shrinkage of certain warp threads that float on the back causes the face of the goods to bulge and to form the rounded or peaked effect on the face only.

A feature of the pique weave is that it is made with two warps: a face warp and a binder warp. Each warp has its respective warp beam. The face warp is woven without too much tension, to allow the ribs to give the raised effect on the face.

The binder warp is woven under tight tension so as to produce a flat back and to aid in raising the cord effect on the face.

Pique is a weave that can also use stuffer picks. These lie under the face of each rib and are held in place by warp ends that float on the back of the rib. Stuffer yarns do not show on the face of the goods because the plain-weave threads on the face of the rib spread and cover the space left by the binder threads when these binder yarns float on the back of the goods.

Pique and Bedford cord are practically the same weave, and the latter is made on the loom with the cord running lengthwise. The word "pique" is the commoner because it is a short word, is pronounced with two letters of the alphabet —P-K—has a French spelling, and a stronger hold on the buying public. Pique in French means peaked or rounded at the top, an effect noted in the material. Either fabric may have rather narrow to wide wale effects. The true pique, like a warp-rib weave, has its wales in the filling direction; the Bedford cord, like a filling-rib weave, has its wales running in the warp direction.

The name Bedford cord is given to fabrics of this type made of woolen or worsted yarn, or when either of these yarns serve as a base and manmade fibers are blended with them. The name pique is given fabrics of this type when the yarns used are cotton, acetate, rayon, etc.

Pique is used for collar and cuff sets, infants' coats and bonnets, neckwear, shirts, vests, and is very popular in women's wear and children's wear. The popular types are fine, medium, and heavy wale fabric, honeycomb, waffle, diamond, and bird's-eye. Pique is very durable, launders easily and well, and is a "smart" fabric.

Bedford cord is usually an excellent fabric for wear, is easy to manipulate, tailors very well, and is very durable. Uses of this cloth include coatings, some suitings, uniforms, riding-habit cloth, and sport coating.

A typical construction for each weave follows:

Warp-Rib Weave	Filling-Rib Weave
3-3, two repeats high and four repeats wide. The cord runs in the filling direction. All simple warb-rib weaves repeat on *two warp ends*.	3-3, four repeats high and two repeats wide. Cord runs in the direction of the warp. All simple filling-rib weaves repeat on *two filling picks*.

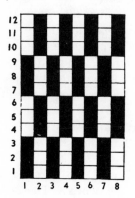

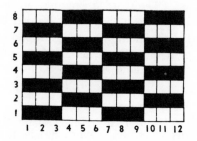

[158]

In both weave constructions, painted blocks signify raisers in the cloth—**warp** ends over the filling picks at the point of interlacing.

Bedford Cord Weave

The cord is composed of four ends which weave in a plain-weave order on alternate pairs of picks. The cords are separated by two ends in a continuous plain weave. One repeat wide and *two repeats high.*

Pique Weave

The cord is composed of four picks plus a stuffer filling pick. The cords are separated by an additional pick that weaves with an extra binder warp. Four repeats wide and *two repeats high.*

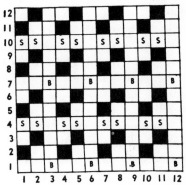

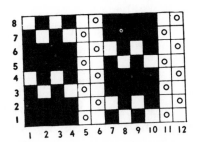

Painted blocks signify warp raisers over filling picks.
O signifies plain-weave raisers that produce a sharper groove between the threads that go in the warp direction. Plain weave prevents the cloth from slipping.

Painted blocks signify warp raisers over filling picks.
B signifies binder warp ends raised over filling picks.
The binder warp passes under each crosswise rib.
S signifies stuffer pick. This is usually a bulky yarn.

TESTING

1. In what direction do the cords run in a true pique fabric?
2. Give some reasons why the word "pique" is more popular than Bedford cord.
3. Define the term "wale."
4. Name three types of pique fabric.
5. Explain how pique and Bedford cord are considered as developments of rib weaves.

True-False Questions

1. _____ A plain weave is not generally used as a base weave in Bedford cord construction.
2. _____ In its best and original form, a pique is made with two warps and three fillings.
3. _____ Stuffer yarns add body and substance to a pique fabric.
4. _____ Pique is classed as a four-season fabric.
5. _____ Stuffer yarns in pique are tightly woven into the fabric.
6. _____ Stuffer yarns in pique never appear on the face of the goods but occupy a position between the face and back systems of yarn.
7. _____ The two successive ends of plain weave used in a Bedford cord actually hold the cord effect in place and help to show the cord plainly.
8. _____ Bedford cord is an ideal riding-habit fabric.
9. _____ Honeycomb, waffle, and bird's-eye should remind you of Bedford cord.
10. _____ Stuffer picks used in pique are often a rather bulky yarn.

TOPIC: DOUBLE-CLOTH CONSTRUCTION

Double-cloth construction can be made on a plain or a twill weave or in combinations of weaves. Two cloths are woven in the loom at the same time; one fabric is actually on top of the other. Binder threads hold the two fabrics together, one cloth forming the face of the double fabric, and the other the back of the goods. The binder yarns may be made to weave according to a plain, twill, or satin arrangement. A cloth of this type may have a plain-weave face, a twill-weave back, and a satin-weave stitching arrangement.

When a double cloth is separated, the face from the back, the binder threads which have held the two fabrics together may be seen. Without the use of binder threads there would not be a true double cloth made; hence, their importance in fabrics of this type.

Five sets of yarns, at least, must be used to produce double cloth: the face warp and the face filling for the face fabric, the back warp and the back filling for the back fabric, and the binder yarns which hold the two cloths together.

Double cloths make a thick fabric without using thick yarns, which would tend to give the fabric a bulky, unappealing appearance. The face of the goods is generally better in quality when compared with the back of the material. Some fabric of this type is made with a woolen-yarn face and a cotton-yarn backing. The use of lower-priced yarns tends to keep down the price per yard of the cloth.

Advantages of double cloth are that the spaces between the interlacings of the warps and the fillings are covered up, weight is added, and greater warmth afforded to the wearer. This fabric is very strong, durable, and rather heavy in weight—ideal for winter wear. Much double cloth is made with a plain side and a fancy side. In the case of overcoating the face is plain while the back is often elaborated with a plaid design to add color to an otherwise drab material.

Double-cloth fabrics may include melton, kersey, beaver, broadcloth coating fabric, bouclé, Saxony, Whitney, Montagnac, webbing, and belting.

TESTING

1. Describe the construction of a double-cloth fabric.
2. Of what value are binder threads in weaving the material?
3. What is meant by "a plaid-back overcoating"?
4. Why might the face of a double-cloth fabric be superior in quality when compared with the back fabric?
5. Name five double-cloth materials.

TOPIC: BACKED FABRICS OR FRENCHBACKS

A double cloth has at least five sets of yarn used in the construction, one of these a binder yarn arrangement to hold the fabric together. In backed fabric only three sets of yarn are required and a binder warp or a binder filling arrangement is not necessary. The cloth is made with two warps and one filling, or one warp and two fillings. The face and the back of the goods may be entirely different in appearance and in texture.

Any of the common basic weaves may be used to make the goods according to the arrangement of warp and filling yarns set up for the weaving. A twill weave may be used for the face, and a plain-, twill-, or satin-weave for the back. Both sides of the cloth may differ in the weave, yarns used, finish, and color. The face is usually superior in quality when compared with the back of the goods. Some of the fabric may have the same type of yarn for both sides; for example, the face with yarn dyed red, and back with similar yarn but dyed blue, and for the third system of yarn a filling dyed red or blue or some other suitably colored yarn.

The back construction in material of this type is used for the following purposes—to make the material stronger, to support the face construction, to add weight to the goods, to cover up the spaces in between the interlacings of the yarns, and to give added warmth to the wearer. The extra warp or filling adds to the wearing quality of the cloth.

A backed cloth cannot be torn apart as can a double cloth where two independent cloths are bound or stitched together by the binding yarn.

Usually the back of the goods has a lower and looser texture than the face. The arrangement is usually two face ends or picks and one back end or pick, commonly called a "two-and-one arrangement." A cloth of this formation, if it had 60 ends for the face per inch, would have 30 ends for the back structure.

Frenchbacks have a wide range of design, and the face is usually made with worsted yarn while the back is of cotton yarn; worsted filling is used. Uses include coatings, suitings, vestings, trouserings for formal wear, novelties, blankets, decorative materials, ski cloth, and mackinac cloth for cold-weather wear. Fabric ranges from 12 to 20 ounces per yard; it has a clear finish on the face and tailors well. Clothes of this type are in the lower quality and price ranges.

TESTING

1. Explain the differences in the construction of a Frenchback and a double-cloth fabric.
2. Why is it not necessary to use binder yarns in a backed fabric?
3. Name five backed materials.
4. Name four advantages of cloth of this type.
5. Could a backed fabric possibly be used as a reversible cloth? Explain.

TOPIC: PILE FABRICS

Many types of pile fabrics are seen today, some having the warp cut to give a pile effect, others having the filling cut for the effect, while some pile cloths are uncut. A general definition of a pile is that the material at times may resemble fur, may be cut or uncut, may have a nap on the face of the goods, or it can be made so that there will be long loops of uncut yarns which give the pile effect. Pile fabric may be soft or harsh in feel, have considerable body, and an appealing appearance.

Some of the commoner pile cloths include terry toweling, furniture covering, corduroy, velvet, velveteen, panne velvet; rugs, carpets, and runners; mohair plush, car seat plush, straight plush, transportation fabric, imitation fur fabric, powder-puff cloth, and automobile upholstery material.

In a pile fabric, cut or uncut, an extra set of warp or filling yarns, at least, is brought to the face of the goods in the form of loops. These loops are formed by the extra set of yarns being woven over a wire, which, for the time being, forms an integral part of the fabric. The wires used in the set may have a razor-like edge or tip, or they may be bladeless or plain at the one end.

The wires are drawn out of the fabric as the weaving progresses. The plain wires, when drawn out of the material, leave uncut loops. The tipped blades cut the loops of pile yarn and leave a cut-pile surface.

Uncut pile fabric

Cut pile fabric

Pile fabric weaving to show the "V" interlacing to hold pile yarn in place

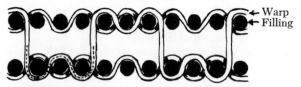

Pile fabric weaving to show the "W" interlacing to hold pile yarn in place. This formation is firmer than the "V" formation.

Some of the major pile fabrics are discussed below:

VELVET FABRIC is a cut-pile warp material; the warp-pile threads are cut by the tipped wires. CORDUROY and VELVETEEN are filling-pile cloths, the filling yarn in each instance is cut. However, these fabrics are cut after leaving the loom, by special cutting treatment. PLUSH, a warp-pile cloth, is cut in the horizontal direction by the blades, in the loom while being woven. On the other hand, VELVET, a warp-pile cloth, has its threads cut vertically by the blades. WILTON CARPETING, a warp-pile fabric, has its warp ends cut to form the pile effect in the vertical direction.

Another way of making pile fabric is to have two cloths woven face to face. To form the pile, an extra set of yarn is woven into both fabrics. This is interlaced with each cloth alternately as often as it is necessary and possible to do so. The two fabrics are cut apart before they reach the breast beam of the loom. The shearing is accomplished by a single traversing knife or by a set of blades which sever the yarn. Thus, two fabrics are produced, each with a cut-pile face, the pile-warp yarn having been cut by this blade or by the set of wires that may have been used.

Uncut-pile cloth does not necessarily have to be made this way. An example of this could be TERRY CLOTH or TURKISH TOWELING, for which no blades at all are used. The effect is produced by a receding or "trick" reed. The pendulumlike movement of the reed causes recession for two loose picks that are not, at the time, actually driven into the fell of the goods. The third pick beats the two loose picks into the fabric causing these picks to make the pile-warp yarn spring above and below the base fabric to form the pile. This fast pick produces an accordionlike action with the two loose picks and the pile warp yarn.

DOUBLE CLOTH PLUSH WEAVING
(Cross Section)

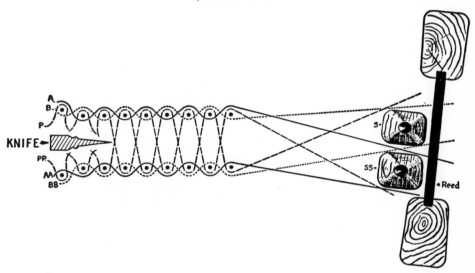

Courtesy: National Association of Wool Manufacturers

Lines A and B represent the ground warp threads of the upper base cloth and AA and BB are those of the lower base cloth. Lines P and PP are the pile-forming warp threads that weave into both base cloths and which are cut by the knife to form the pile. S and SS are the two shuttles which are thrown through the sheds together and the black dots represent picks of filling threads.

Some of the leading types of VELVET include:

a) BAGHEERA: A fine uncut-pile cloth with a roughish surface that helps make it crush-resistant.

b) CHIFFON VELVET: A lightweight soft fabric with the pile pressed flat. Used in dresses, suits, evening clothes.

c) CISELÉ VELVET: The motif on this fabric is formed by contrast of cut and uncut loops in the material.

[163]

d) FACONNÉ: A patterned velvet made by the "burnt-out method," which gives a motif showing both the ground and the pile.

e) LYONS VELVET: A rather stiff thick-pile fabric used for headgear and dresses when the so-called heavy velvets are in vogue.

f) NACRÉ: The pile or surface effect is one color, while the back is another color or shade, providing a changeable, pearly effect.

g) TRANSPARENT: Lightweight, soft, draping velvet using silk, rayon, acetate, or nylon for the pile effect; back is rayon, silk, or nylon.

SOME PROPERTIES AND CHARACTERISTICS OF PILE FABRICS

1. A pile fabric is attractive, since it may have a soft, rich depth, and it will provide comfort and warmth to the wearer.
2. Some pile cloths may have the tendency to press down and show wear or disturbed areas; the original appearance may be restored for the time being by steaming, as in the case of velvet, for example.
3. A good pile effect is thick and firmly fastened while a low-quality type does not hold its construction too well. The pile effect in some fabrics reveals that the pile yarn is held in place by a "V" or single- or base-binder thread, or by a "W" formation, stronger than the "V" formation. Three threads are better than one of plain weave to hold the cut-pile thread in place, thereby providing a firmer hold on this yarn.
4. A pile fabric may have a plain-weave or a twill-weave back.
5. Pile fabric with the pile more than one-eighth of an inch in height is called a PLUSH.
6. Corduroy and velveteen are both filling-pile fabrics. The former is made with one warp and two fillings. The latter material is made entirely of cotton, and simulates velvet.
7. Velvet is a warp-pile fabric with a short, thick face and a plain or twill backing. The face is acetate, rayon, silk, or nylon. The back may be any of these fibers or it may have what is known as a "cotton back." When pressed flat the cloth is called PANNE VELVET.
8. Mirror velvet is a fabric in which the pile is ironed down.
9. Frieze is an uncut-pile fabric in which the loops appear in a sort of rib formation or in some comparable plan. Also spelled "frisé."
10. Turkish toweling or terry cloth is very absorptive and is made without the use of wires in the loom. Made with two warps and one filling. One warp is tight and is the foundation warp; the other is a loose-tension pile warp which forms the loops on both sides of the cloth. It takes about six inches of this pile warp to weave about two inches of finished material, a take-up in the yarn of about 300 per cent. The pile warp in terry springs into final position in the "accordionized action" caused by the fast filling pick beating the two loose picks and the loose pile warp yarn into place by the loom action.

TESTING

1. Define pile fabric.
2. Name three types of pile fabric.
3. Name two filling-pile cloths; one warp-pile material.
4. Describe the two types of knives or blades used in weaving pile cloths.
5. Since terry cloth is made without the use of blades to obtain its effect, explain the manner of weaving the goods to provide the uncut-pile effect.
6. Define the term "plush."
7. Explain double-plush weaving.
8. What is meant by the "V" and the "W" formations in weaving—for example, of velvet fabric in the loom?
9. Describe briefly three types of velvet.
10. What is meant by a "cotton-back velvet"?

TOPIC: Dobby Weaves and Doup or Leno Weaves

DOBBY WEAVES OR DOBBY DESIGNS

They are woven on a dobby loom, harness frames and heddles being used. These fabrics have small patterns, which may be geometric, diamond-shaped, dotted, or of other small shapes woven into the goods. Small floral motifs can also be woven into the cloth. Uses for dobbies include shirting fabric, huck toweling, diaper fabric, certain dressgoods, blouse fabric, drapery and upholstery fabrics. Dobbies can be dyed, bleached, or woven with yarn-dyed effects in many colors to give a solid background with a design of another color as against less variegated piece-dyed cloths. Dobby effects are appealing, interesting, and intricate. Dobby is used in men's shirting fabrics, and it is considered a very popular cloth in this field.

Many harnesses must be used to produce dobbies on looms provided with the dobby head motion. From 16 to as many as 32 harnesses may be used in weaving the goods. Most dobbies, however, rarely require over 24 harnesses. This type of cloth is rather expensive to weave, it requires an experienced weaver, and the timing of the loom in all its actions is most important. Dobbies are often imitated, at a lower cost, with printed designs and by flock-dotting.

Dobby weaves are often referred to as "miniature Jacquards," and often there is a marked resemblance between the two. Close examination, however, will reveal whether the fabric has actually been woven on a dobby loom or a Jacquard loom.

LENO OR DOUP CONSTRUCTIONS

Also known as "gauze weaves." The purpose of these constructions is to give an open-mesh effect in fabrics, the filling threads being kept apart by the crossing of the warp yarns between each pick of filling. Doup was first used in the manufacture of mosquito netting in order to combine good ventilation with sturdy construction.

Uses include marquisette, gauze fabric, novelty dressgoods, webbing, shirting of the better quality, and material for containers of citrus fruits. Apparel made with the leno weave is durable, long-wearing, and easy to launder. The weave is ideal for laundry nets, as the open mesh permits the free flow of water through the sides of the bag.

Two sets of harnesses are used in leno weaving—standard and skeleton. The base fabric weaving is controlled by the standard harness frames while the crossing threads are controlled by the skeleton harness. The warp yarns are used in pairs, the entire warp consisting of this pair arrangement of ends.

One leno warp end is always over each filling pick, while the other end is always under the pick. Thus, the ends do not actually interlace with the filling picks in this full-leno-weave construction, but do interlace with each other between the respective filling-yarn picks. The fabric would be of little or no value if this crossing of the warp yarns were not possible.

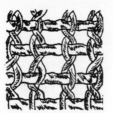

Full Leno or Doup
Weave

Half Leno or Doup
Weave

Lappet Weave
from loom

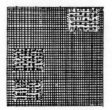

Lappet Fabric after
clipping

Clipspot from loom

Clipspot after
clipping

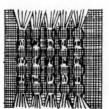

Warp Float from
loom

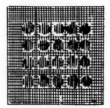

Warp Float after
clipping floating
ends

The skeleton harness carrying the one leno thread is always underneath, moving first on one side of the other leno thread, and then on the other side of the same thread, to form the interlacing. This crossing of the single thread from the one side to the other side of the other doup thread is called "douping," and the action occurs through the throw of the shuttle which shoots the filling pick through the open shed of the loom to actually weave all the warp and the filling threads in the construction.

It should be noted that a 24-by-36 leno texture would not have the same number of warp ends and filling picks as a 24-by-36 plain-weave net. The difference in the appearance is due to the leno's being woven in pairs tightly wrapped around each other, whereas in a plain weave the same texture is spread evenly throughout the fabric.

There are two types of leno weaves and they are:

a) FULL-LENO WEAVE: In what is known as a "one-pick" marquisette, for example, the leno is known as a full leno because both warp ends actually work in the leno heddles. The two types of harnesses have to be used—standard and skeleton. The latter controls the crisscrossing of the warp ends that weave the leno effect. This type of weave can also be made in a two-pick and a three-pick full leno or doup, using heavy yarns.

b) HALF-LENO WEAVE: The one warp end, as would be noted under pick-glass inspection, weaves plain weave with the filling yarn. The other warp end is the one that works in the skeleton harness. It is this end that weaves on each side of the plain-weave end and also interlaces with the filling yarn.

The nature of the leno weave is such that a firm fabric may be obtained with a smaller number of ends and picks per inch than in ordinary fabrics where the threads are not crossed. When only a few crossings are used, open stripes are produced, and these give the gauze effect. For these leno or lace-stripe fabrics the usual method is to use a thick end for the crossing, in order to give a zigzag effect to the ground or work body of the material.

TESTING

1. Compare a dobby-design fabric with a small Jacquard-loom motif.
2. Name three cloths that can be made on a dobby weave.
3. The names given to a doup harness frame are standard and skeleton. Which one makes it possible in the weaving of the material to produce the crossed effect of the doup ends?
4. What is gained by twisting the warp yarns in weaving leno goods?
5. Distinguish between a full-leno and a half-leno construction.

TOPIC: LAPPET, SWIVEL, CLIP-SPOT, AND WARP-FLOAT WEAVES AND EFFECTS

All of these weaves and effects are of a somewhat fancy type, embellishing a fabric with decorative motifs. Colored dots, spots, and similar small effects are woven or "embroidered" into the base fabric, usually by special loom attachments, or by cutting and shearing certain floating yarns to produce the finished novelty effect.

These effects are obtained in the following ways:

LAPPET WEAVE: This method of weaving entails the use of an extra warp; only one color is introduced in the lappet effect. The lappet ends work in the following way:

One or more needle bars are fitted with "depending needles" to carry a series of floating yarns (lappet yarns) in front of the reed. The action is such that the pattern is woven or "laid" on the surface of the woven cloth.

[167]

The needle bar (or bars) is raised, moved to the right, then to the left, and then lowered into position, which means that the pattern warp ends are threaded through the needles in a line with the shed of the loom. The needles, after doing this work, are then raised and kept stationary until the loom pattern chain indicates and activates the needle bar for the next effect to be woven into the material in the well-known zigzag formation. The filling yarn binds the lappet yarns into their component places in the cloth.

The long floats of warp yarn between the woven-in spots of lappet effect are cut away so that the effect will show to advantage. Lappets at the present time are not very popular, since there are other methods and ways to obtain elaborate effects in fabrics, at a much lower cost. These effects have use in some dressgoods, curtainings, and hangings.

SWIVEL WEAVING: The idea for this type of weaving was initiated on a Dutch loom in the early eighteenth century. It threw its shuttle through the open warp shed by means of a cog wheel. Although the loom was not a success, it did provide food for thought to several British weavers and inventors. By mid-century, some rather crude swivel looms were in action. It took many years to bring this method of weaving to perfection. As far as is known there is no acknowledged inventor for swivel weaving.

Swivel-plan weaving today calls for the use of an extra filling. The design necessitates the use of small shuttles or swivels. Each swivel, in a group set along the width of the goods, operates in a circular motion through a small area in a section of the warp. Weaving actually occurs only with the lowered threads in order to properly interlace to give the cluster, sprig, or "snowball" effect. As the loom is in action, the swivel work is done after the base or regular filling has been woven into the material; this serves as a base for each swivel to place its filling into the fabric simultaneously with the other swivels, sometimes referred to as "spoils." Several colors may be used in swivel weaving. This type of weaving has declined much in recent years because the effects seem to be obtained more advantageously on Jacquard looms.

It has been estimated that about fifteen hundred attempts have been made in textile history to propel or throw shuttles in a loom from one side of the race-plate to the other side of the loom. Uses for swivels include some dressgoods, chiefly cottons of a better quality, curtains, hangings, etc.

CLIP-SPOT EFFECTS: These have much the same appearance as straight swivel weaving, but a regular shuttle is used so that the fancy or novelty yarns may have their own shed when the fabric is being woven. The long floats are cut automatically or may be sheared off from the cloth, and the finished fabric shows small effects snugly woven into the basic warp and filling. Usually only one color is used in clip-spot weaving.

WARP CLIP-SPOTS OR WARP-FLOAT FABRICS: These effects are closely related to filling-effect clip-spots except that in the former, the fancy warp yarns provide the float effect. The long floats in each repeat of pattern in the fabric are cut or sheared in the finishing of the cloth. The base fabric is woven in the conventional manner. The yarn for decoration enters the base cloth from a separate warp beam or beams usually mounted on a stand above the whip roll of the loom. The beam or beams of yarn are called top beams. The fancy yarn does not add or detract from the wearing strength of the goods. If it were completely removed it would not leave a gap or even a flaw in the base fabric. The fact that both ground and decoration are woven from separate beams permits the use of either yarn system independently of the other.

Between the spots or areas, the extra yarn is carried loosely without interlacing on the clip-side of the cloth. This may be the face or the back of the goods, depending upon the nature of the motif. There are few mills equipped to make this fabric in this country, and those plants having the equipment do a good business in cotton fabrics, especially in the higher-priced range for dressgoods. One or more colors in a series of warp-float yarns may be used to advantage in the patterns.

Incidentally, these four types of textile materials have suffered much with regard to production because flock-dot or flocked motifs have superseded them. Flock-dot designs·are made by "hammering" ground-up wool, cotton, or other fibers onto the cloth—a form of printing. The designs and the color effects are unlimited, and the cost of this work is much less than that incurred in producing any of the woven-effect goods. Flock-printing or flock-stenciling is very inexpensive, and a very popular method of setting small patterns on fabrics. Flock-dotting may be applied to any type of fabric—one of the reasons for its rapid progress in the textile trade.

TESTING

1. Discuss any two of the following methods of weaving: lappet, swivel, filling clip-spot effect, warp clip-spot effect.
2. Name three uses for fabrics of these types.
3. Discuss flock-dotting or flocking.

Part 1—Unit 32

TOPIC: JACQUARD DESIGNS, MOTIFS, OR PATTERNS

The so-called "Jacquard weave" is a misnomer; it does not exist. A Jacquard pattern is a design which consists of two or more contrasting weaves in some form of combination. Basic weaves are used, such as plain, twill, satin, basket, rib, etc. Warp satins, filling-effect satins, shaded satins, bright- and dim-effects, right-hand and left-hand twills, and the use of float threads are also important in designing for a Jacquard.

Furthermore, Jacquard patterns are woven designs that are too elaborate and complex to be made on harness looms. A Jacquard head motion must be used in the loom to control the warp yarn at all times so that the yarn may become a raiser or a sinker at any time in the weaving operation. The warp yarn may be raised or lowered at will, over or under the filling on any pick of filling, as it goes through the shed of the loom to become a component part of the woven fabric. The fabric, to save wear and tear on the loom, is usually woven "face-down." A mirror arrangement at the front of the loom allows the weaver to examine the face of the woven goods at all times.

Harnesses are not used in Jacquard, except in rare instances. Very often, however, two harnesses with a few heddles on each frame are used to take care of the selvage ends of the warp.

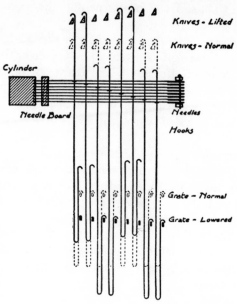

Knives - Lifted

Knives - Normal

Cylinder

Needle Board

Needles

Hooks

Grate - Normal

Grate - Lowered

Courtesy: Philadelphia College of Textiles & Science

A rise and fall, 416 machine.

Every warp end is controlled individually and may be raised or lowered at any time, in accordance with the instructions of the designer who laid out the pattern.

One repeat of a Jacquard motif may be used to cover the entire width of the cloth, and may be several feet, or even yards, long. Smaller repeats are used more frequently. A 9-inch by 12-inch size is used very often in many types of motifs. In fact, there is really no limit with regard to a pattern repeat, however large or small, if kept within reason.

Joseph Jean Marie Jacquard, 1759–1834, the inventor of the machine or loom which carries his name, was born in Lyons, France, and did most of his work there during his fruitful career. He was a soldier in Napoleon's armies, a personal friend of the Emperor, and received the Medal of the Legion of Honor, as well as a small pension for life at the specific request of Napoleon.

One Jacquard loom does the work that formerly required the efforts of about one hundred workers. His loom has done much to keep Paris and Lyons in the lead in beautiful fabrics that are and have been in fashion and in demand, and this loom combines the art and science necessary for engineering the best in textile fabrics. A Jacquard loom is an excellent example of a fully automated machine; it is the basis for the present-day punch-card systems.

PRINCIPLES OF JACQUARD WEAVING

1. A cloth-sized sketch of the motif desired is made: the repeat of the pattern.
2. The motif is then painted on the blocked design paper in proper ratio of blocks.
3. Instead of the harness frames used on other types of looms, which control all the warp ends, a set of oblong punched cards, not unlike the roll used on a player piano, controls each warp end in the entire warp. It is the punched holes in the cards

NATIONAL EXPORT EXPOSITION
1899
PHILADELPHIA

Made by the Sauquoit Silk Mfg. Co.,
BETHLEHEM,
PHILADELPHIA,
SCRANTON.

J. J. JORDAN.
designer.

Picture taken from woven silk fabric made on a Jacquard loom—by Sauquoit Silk Manufacturing Co., Philadelphia.

Jacquard label, front and back.

Picture of William Tell taken from silk-Jacquard woven fabric—by Maschinenfabrik Rüti, Zürich, Switzerland.

[171]

Courtesy: Philadelphia Textile Institute, Germantown, Pa.

THE JACQUARD LOOM

Note cards at top of loom control which govern weaving of intricate motif.

Maschinenfabrik Rüti, Zürich, Switzerland

JOSEPH J. M. JACQUARD

From woven silk fabric.

Courtesy: Nye-Wait Co., Auburn, New York

JACQUARD WEAVING OF NYLON CARPETING

Requires expert craftsmanship, two sets of cards.

Courtesy: Mohawk Carpet Mills, Amsterdam, New York

TAPESTRY VELVET CARPET SETTING

Yarns threaded in accordance with design on the drum-printing scale guide.

which actually control the ends. Usually a punched hole will cause the particular warp end to rise in the shed of the loom and form a raiser in the fabric, as the filling pick passes under it in its passage from the shuttle box on the one side of the loom to the shuttle box at the other side of the loom. Where there has been no hole made, the particular warp end will remain down while the filling pick passes over it, making a sinker in the goods.

4. A set of cards, dependent upon the size of the repeat, may run from a hundred or so cards up to several thousand cards. There will be as many cards in the set as there are filling picks for the one repeat of pattern. Much time, labor, and expense is involved in setting up the cards, and Jacquard weaving therefore is usually rather expensive. Costs depend on the type of fabric being made, and as to whether or not it is a fabric for volume production.

5. The cards, after the punching, are then laced together to form an endless chain. They are mounted at the top of the loom and made ready for action.

6. The head motion at the top of the loom where the cards have been set also has what is known as the Jacquard tie-up. From the frame hang long linen cords which hold fine steel wires. Each wire has an eye or hole in it through which a warp yarn is drawn or threaded. If the machine is running a 2,400 Jacquard (2,400 ends in the warp), there would be 2,400 wires and cords used so that each warp end could be controlled.

   At the top of the frame, each linen cord used is threaded through the eye of a needle. These needles, which are arranged in horizontal position, are controlled by a spring, the needle-board needles pressing forward against each card as it comes into position for loom action. Thus, when a needle goes through a punched hole in the card, it causes the particular warp end to rise and make a raiser in the cloth. The needles which cannot go through the card because there is not a hole at the point of contact cannot make the warp end rise. It remains lowered, forming the bottom part of the shed, and making a sinker in the material. In this action the filling pick goes over the lowered ends.

7. The action continues thus, repeat after repeat, for the length of warp in the loom. There has to be simultaneous activity of each warp end in each repeat of the motif in the width of the fabric, and in the interlacing with the filling picks when weaving, for accuracy in executing the design.

There is no limit as to the elaborateness or simplicity in a Jacquard motif. Damask, brocade, and brocatelle may have elaborate designs in them, while other fabrics may be rather simple in their pattern effect. Jacquard-woven labels, although not very wide, may have very intricate designs in them and may be made in multiple formation—up to 144 in a loom at one time—by the use of multiple shuttles or battens, circular or straight.

SOME COMMENTS ON JACQUARD WORK

1. The combinations of weaves and patterns are practically limitless.
2. It is possible to weave any scene or pattern on this type of loom—a photograph can be reproduced as well as flowers, pastoral scenes, buildings, calendars, store labels, historical scenes, etc.
3. Jacquard motifs are beautiful, intricate, and appealing in form and color.
4. It is the most expensive type of weaving since it entails pattern sketching, pattern layout and design work, card cutting, assembling and lacing the cards into a continuous set, mounting the cards in the head motion of the loom, setting up and timing the loom. Sometimes it takes several weeks from the time the cloth-size sketch is made until the loom is actually weaving fabric. Utmost accuracy and care are important at all times.
5. High textures feature many fabrics and the weaving is slow.
6. Jacquard weavers are the highest-paid weavers in the world and it takes years of experience on other looms to qualify as an acceptable weaver on Jacquard fabrics.

7. Jacquards can be durable and can give good wear, especially those with small motifs. Large designs are not as durable, since the long floats of yarn which feature many of these fabrics may be weak in actual interlacing with the opposite system of threads. Many Jacquards are not suitable for apparel, automobile upholstery, or transportation fabric, as they could not stand up under friction, chafing, or abrasion during wearing. Shirting, neckwear, and dressgoods are made purposely so that they will be able to undergo abrasion and wear in order to compete with comparable fabrics not made on a Jacquard loom.

8. Good judgment in the choice of the basic weaves used in the construction of cloth is very important. The length of the yarn floats has to be given considerable attention by the designer.

TESTING

1. Why is the term "Jacquard weave" a misnomer?
2. List five weaves that can be used in Jacquard patterns.
3. Why is most Jacquard fabric woven "face-down"?
4. Why is it not necessary to use harnesses for the body of the fabric?
5. Discuss the setting up of a Jacquard loom from the card cutting to loom operation.
6. Of what value are the holes punched in the cards as to their integration with the warp ends that each card controls?
7. Why is Jacquard weaving the most expensive method of weaving cloth?
8. Name five materials made with a Jacquard motif.
9. Define the term "float."
10. Why are floats used rather freely in Jacquard designs?

TOPIC: Résumé of the Major Types of Weave Construction

The following résumé covers briefly and concisely the recognition and the working properties of the twelve major types of weave constructions:

NAME OF CLOTH	HOW RECOGNIZED	WORKING PROPERTIES
PLAIN WEAVE	One warp over and one warp under the filling throughout cloth construction, checkerboard effect.	Used most; durable and strong, easily seen, firmest method of interlacing warp and filling. No diagonal lines.
TWILL WEAVE	Diagonal lines on face of cloth —to the right, to the left, or to right and left in same cloth, which gives a broken twill.	Durable, and tailors well; firm fabric, usually holds shape and crease; very popular for outerwear apparel.
SATIN WEAVE	Smooth, shiny surface caused by floats of warp over the filling or vice versa. Diagonal lines on the face of the cloth not readily observed by the naked eye; only distinct when seen through a pick glass.	Rich appearance; rather low tensile strength; high texture; cannot withstand friction because of the nature of the weave; gives a full, solid color on face; ideal for evening wear; reflects the rays of light very well.
BASKET WEAVE	Two or more warp ends over and two or more warp ends under in parallel arrangement, interlacing with the filling yarn.	Rather loose construction; does not have high tensile strength; difficult to sew on; not suitable for general wear; attractive surface; interesting effects.

NAME OF CLOTH	HOW RECOGNIZED	WORKING PROPERTIES
RIB WEAVE	Made by cords that run in the warp or filling direction. The corded yarn is covered up by the tight interlacing of the yarn system that shows on the face and back of the cloth.	Wearing quality varies with closeness of texture and type of yarn used; ideal for hat bands, grosgrain, faille, bengaline. Cord threads easily removed.
PIQUE WEAVE	Cloth has a corded effect, usually in the warp, but may have cord in filling or both ways. Cords usually held in place by a few ends of plain weave construction.	Gives good wear, attractive; cord is visible, since texture is not as compact as in the case of rib weaves. Popular material for summer wear. Has ease of care; "smart" appearance.
DOUBLE-CLOTH WEAVE	Two cloths woven together and held in place by binder warp or filling; not pasted; back is usually different from face of cloth.	Heavy; warm; durable; face better than back in stock, construction, and finish; used in overcoatings and other heavy cloths.
BACKED CLOTH WEAVE	Cloth of one warp and two fillings or two warps and one filling. The face is much more presentable than back of cloth. Back is usually dull in appearance. No binder yarns used.	Adds weight to cloth; durable face much better than back; many cheap cloths, to imitate better materials, are backed fabrics; back is thready to the touch and in appearance.
PILE WEAVE	Extra yarns form the pile on the face of the cloth. Pile effect may be cut or uncut on the surface. Basic construction holds cloth in place. Very wide fabric range.	Attractive; may be soft or harsh; pile of over one-eighth of an inch is known as a plush; cloth may press down and reveal construction, but may be restored by steaming; usually gives good wear.
JACQUARD CONSTRUCTION	Pattern or design is woven into cloth reproductions of persons, places or objects, wide range of beautiful designs; used in silks, brocades, etc. Made from basic weaves in combinations.	Beautiful effects; may be very expensive; durable; small patterns with minimum of long floats give best wear; many colors may be interspersed throughout the cloth pattern.
LENO OR DOUP WEAVE	Warp yarns are paired and half- or full-twisted about one another; porosity high in some of the cloth designs; two sets of harness used—standard and skeleton.	Gauze effects, used for curtains and draperies; launders fairly well; gives good effects in prints; tensile strength varies much depending on texture.
LAPPET, SWIVEL, AND CLIP-SPOT WEAVES	Dots or small figures are woven or embroidered into cloth by use of an extra filling in the case of swivel weave, and by extra warp in the lappet or clip-spot weaves. Effects are based on plain-weave background.	Similar to those of a plain weave or variations of that construction; dots are usually lasting and durable, but there are some cheap varieties of the cloth where the dots may not remain fixed.

BASIC WEAVE CONSTRUCTIONS
Variations of the Plain Weave in Staple Fabrics

Chambray; colored warp, always white filling

Crepe; plain weave with certain raisers omitted

Check, gingham, or plaid

Dimity; warp-cord dimity

Madras shirting; novelty stripe effects

Seersucker; pucker in warp direction

Taffeta; "cylindrical" filling

Moiré taffeta; bright and dim

Variations on Standard Twills, Checks, and Stripes

Homespun; plain weave, checkerboard effect

Tweed—heather; diagonal lines on face of goods

Plain or straight check; square/balanced

Shepherd's check

Hound's tooth; tooth surrounded by another color

Color effect on a 2x2 twill weave

Chalk strike in a twill woven fabric

TOPIC: DATA FOR WEAVE CONSTRUCTIONS AND WEAVES

WEAVE:

	REPEATS HIGH	REPEATS WIDE	BLOCKS
PLAIN WEAVE:			
1. $\dfrac{1}{1}$	4	4	8 x 8
RIGHT-HAND TWILLS:			
2. $\dfrac{2}{2}$	4	4	16 x 16
3. $\dfrac{3}{3}$	2	2	12 x 12
4. $\dfrac{4}{4}$	2	2	16 x 16
5. $\dfrac{2}{1}$	3	3	9 x 9
6. $\dfrac{1}{2}$	3	3	9 x 9
7. $\dfrac{3}{2}$	3	3	15 x 15
8. $\dfrac{3\ 1}{1\ 3}$ even-sided twill	2	2	16 x 16
9. $\dfrac{2\ 1}{1\ 2}$ even-sided twill	2	2	12 x 12
10. $\dfrac{4\ 1}{2\ 1}$ warp-effect twill	2	2	16 x 16
11. $\dfrac{1\ 1}{1\ 5}$ filling-effect twill	2	2	16 x 16
12. $\dfrac{3\ 1}{1\ 1}$ warp-effect twill	2	2	12 x 12
LEFT-HAND TWILLS:			
13. $\dfrac{2}{2}$	2	2	8 x 8
14. $\dfrac{2}{1}$	3	3	9 x 9
15. $\dfrac{1}{2}$	3	3	9 x 9
16. $\dfrac{3}{2}$	3	3	15 x 15
17. $\dfrac{2}{3}$	3	3	15 x 15
18. $\dfrac{2\ 1}{1\ 2}$ even-sided twill	2	2	12 x 12
19. $\dfrac{3\ 1}{1\ 3}$ even-sided twill	2	2	16 x 16
20. $\dfrac{1\ 1}{1\ 5}$ filling-effect twill	2	2	16 x 16
21. $\dfrac{4}{2}$ warp-effect twill	2	2	12 x 12
SATIN WEAVES—FILLING-EFFECT:			
22. 8-end satin, base of 3	2	2	16 x 16
23. 8-end satin, base of 5	2	2	16 x 16
24. 5-end satin, base of 3	3	3	15 x 15
25. 5-end satin, base of 2	3	3	15 x 15
26. 7-end satin, base of 4	2	2	14 x 14
27. 12-end satin, base of 5	1	1	12 x 12
28. 9-end satin, base of 4	2	2	18 x 18

WEAVE:

	REPEATS HIGH	REPEATS WIDE	BLOCKS
Satin Weaves—Warp-Effect:			
29. 8-end satin, base of 3	2	2	16 x 16
30. 8-end satin, base of 5	2	2	16 x 16
31. 5-end satin, base of 3	3	3	15 x 15
32. 5-end satin, base of 2	3	3	15 x 15
33. 12-end satin, base of 5	1	1	12 x 12
Broken Twill Weaves:			
34. $\frac{2}{2}$ twill; 8 right hand, 8 left hand:	4	1	16 x 16
35. $\frac{2}{2}$ twill; 4 right hand, 4 left hand:	4	2	16 x 16
36. $\frac{2}{2}$ twill; 2 right hand, 2 left hand:	4	4	16 x 16
37. $\frac{1}{5}$ twill; 3 right hand, 3 left hand:	2	2	12 x 12
Basket Weaves:			
38. 2-2	2	2	8 x 8
39. 3-3	2	2	12 x 12
40. 1-2	3	3	9 x 9
41. 4-4	2	2	16 x 16
42. 2-4	2	2	12 x 12
43. 2-2-2-4 even-series	1	1	10 x 10
44. 1-2-3-4 even-series	2	2	20 x 20
45. 4-1-4 uneven-series	1	1	18 x 18
Pointed Twill Weaves:			
46. $\frac{2}{2}$ twill, 8 right hand, 8 left hand:	4	1	16 x 16
47. Fancy-spot weave made on principle of pointed twill weaves:	2	2	16 x 16
Warp-Rib Weaves—Rib Runs in Filling Direction:			
48. 2-2 repeats on two warp ends	4	4	16 x 8
49. 3-3	2	4	12 x 8
50. 4-4	2	4	16 x 8
51. 2-4	2	4	12 x 8
52. 1-3	3	4	12 x 8
53. 1-2-1-4 even series	2	4	16 x 8
54. 3-1-3 uneven series	2	4	28 x 8
Filling-Rib Weaves—Rib Runs in Warp Direction:			
55. 2-2 repeats on two filling picks	4	4	8 x 16
56. 3-3	4	2	8 x 12
57. 4-4	4	2	8 x 16
58. 2-4	4	2	8 x 12
59. 3-1-3 uneven series	4	2	8 x 28
60. 2-2-2-4 even series	4	2	8 x 20
63-Degree Twill Weaves:			
61. $\frac{7}{8}$ go up two picks on each successive warp end	1	1	15 x 15
62. $\frac{3}{2}$ covert weave	3	3	15 x 15

WEAVE:

	REPEATS HIGH	REPEATS WIDE	BLOCKS
63. $\frac{3\ 3\ 1\ 1}{1\ 1\ 2\ 1}$ TRICOTINE WEAVE	1	1	13 x 13
64. $\frac{5\ 1\ 1}{1\ 2\ 1}$ WHIPCORD WEAVE	1	1	11 x 11
65. $\frac{4\ 1\ 4\ 1}{1\ 1\ 2\ 2}$ CAVALRY TWILL OR ELASTIQUE WEAVE; 18-19 oz. cloth.	1	1	16 x 8

NOTE: Weave begins with a sinker in lower left-hand corner.

70-DEGREE TWILL WEAVE:

	REPEATS HIGH	REPEATS WIDE	BLOCKS
66. $\frac{7\ 2\ 6\ 2}{1\ 1\ 3\ 2}$ CAVALRY TWILL OR ELASTIQUE; 24 oz. cloth:	1	1	24 x 8

NOTE: Weave begins with a sinker in lower left-hand corner. Go up three picks for each successive warp end:

63-DEGREE TWILL WEAVE:

	REPEATS HIGH	REPEATS WIDE	BLOCKS
67. $\frac{3\ 3\ 1}{1\ 1\ 3}$ CAVALRY TWILL but NOT USED FOR ELASTIQUE;	1	1	12 x 6

NOTE: Weave begins with a sinker in lower left-hand corner. Go up three picks for each successive warp end:

	REPEATS HIGH	REPEATS WIDE	BLOCKS
68. $\frac{2\ 3\ 1\ 1}{1\ 3\ 1\ 2}$ CAVALRY TWILL but NOT USED FOR ELASTIQUE;	1	1	14 x 7

NOTE: Weave begins with a sinker in lower left-hand corner. Go up three picks for each successive warp end:

70-DEGREE TWILL WEAVE:

	REPEATS HIGH	REPEATS WIDE	BLOCKS
69. $\frac{8}{7}$ go up three picks on each successive warp end:	1	3	15 x 15

75-DEGREE TWILL WEAVE:

	REPEATS HIGH	REPEATS WIDE	BLOCKS
70. $\frac{8}{7}$ go up four picks on each successive warp end:	1	1	15 x 15

FANCY SPOT WEAVE:

	REPEATS HIGH	REPEATS WIDE	BLOCKS
71. Novelty spot effect weave made on combination of $\frac{3}{1}$ and $\frac{1}{3}$ twill weaves:	1	1	8 x 8

PIQUE—BEDFORD CORD WEAVES:

72. This weave begins at the left with one end of plain weave followed by the first and second movements of a 3-up and 1-down twill, repeated. Two ends of plain weave, indicated by the dots, are next in order, followed by the third and fourth movements of the twill effect, repeated.

One end of plain weave completes the action. In this weave, attention is called to the alternate binding of plain weave opposing the twill.

Weave is 2 x 2 in size and requires 8 x 12 in blocks.

73. This formation is easier to weave when compared with the previous construction, and it also gives better appearance to the fabric. This weave begins at the left with one plain end followed by the first and third movements of the 3-up and 1-down twill, repeated; two ends

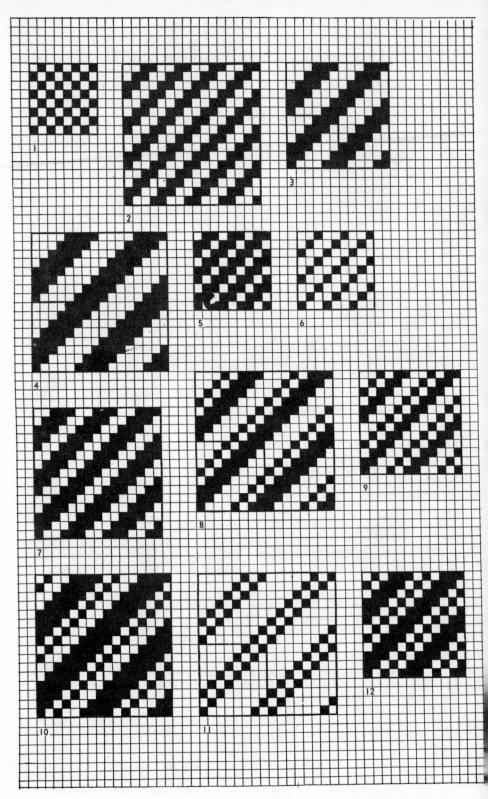

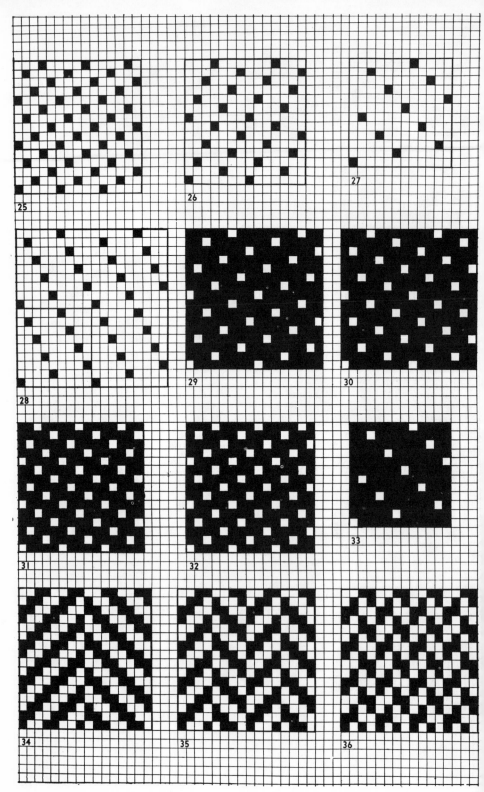

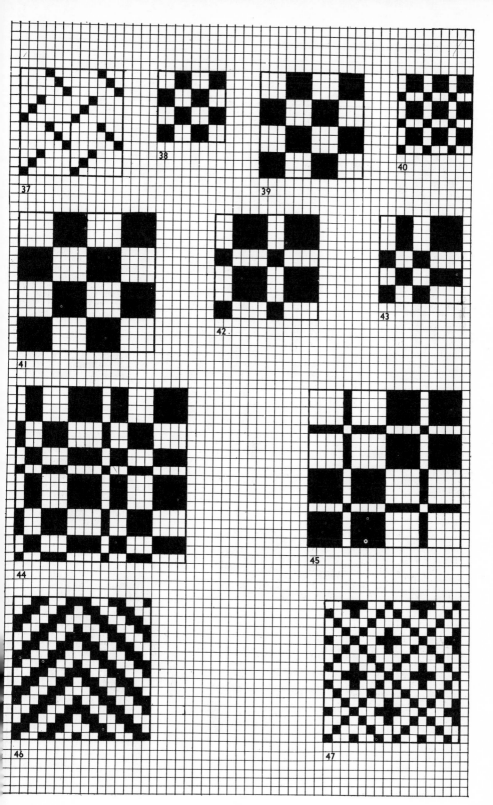

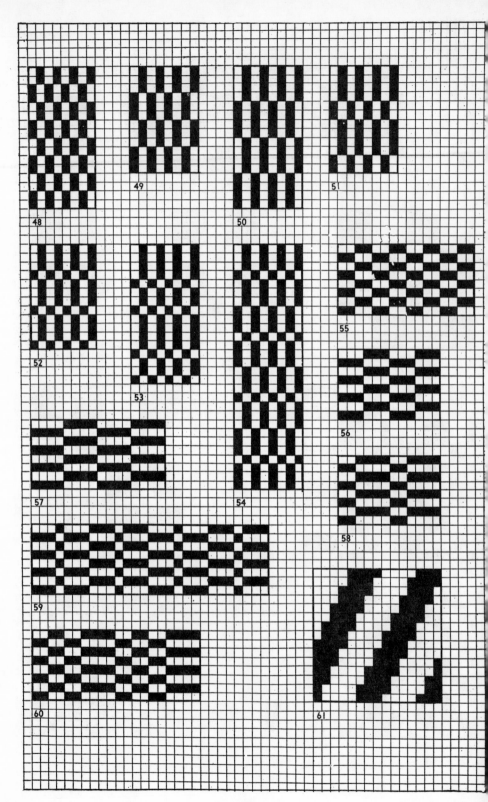

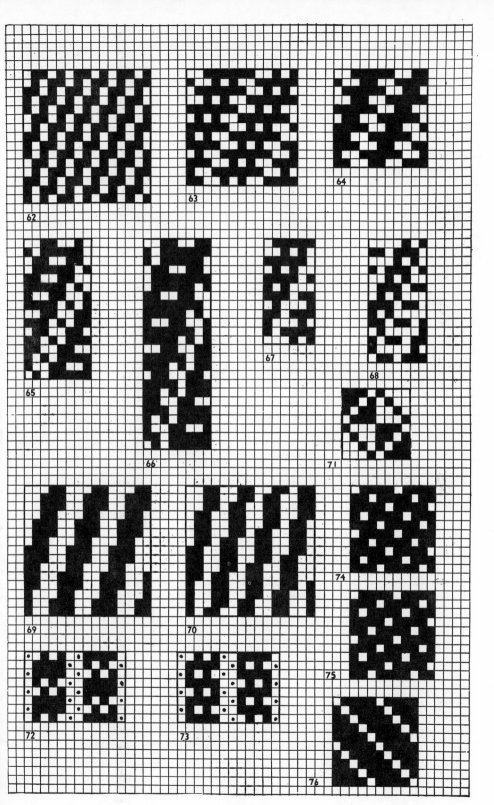

of plain weave are followed by the second and fourth movements of the twill, repeated; finally, one end of plain weave completes the construction.

As previously stated, attention should be given to the alternate binding of the plain weave opposing the twill.

Stuffer ends, which are usually heavier than face ends, are often used, as in the case of pique, to give roundness to the cord or rib effect and to add weight to the fabric. In weaving, they follow to some extent the twill movements in the respective wales; they must be "down" for all face picks, and "up" over all back picks when being woven.

Weave is 2 x 2 in size and requires 8 x 12 in blocks.

WEAVE:

Right-hand Steep Twill Weaves for Tackle Twill Fabrics:	REPEATS HIGH	REPEATS WIDE	BLOCKS
74. $\frac{4}{1}$ 63-degree twill	2	2	10 x 10

Although a twill weave, the effect is a 5-end, warp-effect satin weave with a base or counter of three. The weave does not begin with the customary sinker (filling over warp) in the lower left-hand corner in a construction of this type to provide a regular satin weave.

| 75. $\frac{4}{1}$ 70-degree twill | 2 | 2 | 10 x 10 |

Although a twill weave, the effect is a 5-shaft warp-effect satin weave with a base or counter of two. The weave does not begin with the customary sinker (filling over warp) in the lower left-hand corner in a construction of this type to provide a regular satin weave.

| 76. $\frac{4}{1}$ 75-degree twill | 2 | 2 | 10 x 10 |

Although painted in the right hand direction, the completed repeat of the weave reveals a $\frac{4}{1}$ left-hand twill effect.

These, and comparable weaves, provide a very high, compact, and strong texture in fabrics. Nylon is used the most in the manufacture of goods of this type where resistance to abrasion and chafing are necessary. The cloths have very high breakage strength and withstand rough, rugged wear. Tough fabrics, such as football pants, are made from these weaves.

TOPIC: Fabric Development and Its Functions

Fabric development, with all its implications, ramifications, and engineering factors, is a definite long-planning and long-term matter. It includes research, comparison, analysis, testing, and a definite build-up of fabric for its ultimate use by the consuming public. The successful fabric is not built upon inspiration alone. It is built or engineered after considerable thought and planning, and the specifications laid down must be followed to the letter in order to produce an acceptable product.

Research cannot be hurried, and the creation of a new material is real research with a dash of more or less daring inspiration plus a goodly measure of knowledge and experience on the part of the designer—who at best is also a textile technologist.

A fabric development department of a plant should be divorced from current business problems. Time is of the essence, for all findings must be accumulated, defined, sorted, collated, and then finally decided upon so as to achieve the desired finished fabric.

Unless the department is organized with utmost care, profitable results will not be forthcoming. The department should be operated as an "outside agency," and set up to create:

1. New fabrics.
2. New finishes on old and new fabrics.
3. Continued experimentation with fibers, yarns, blended yarns, combination yarns, twists, and the testing of the yarns used.
4. Use of the results obtained from the foregoing for experimentation in the many types of weave constructions and combinations, as well as in the textures.

The above information should produce definite results and facts in the completed fabric construction. The research should move from the raw material fibers, to the actual construction, to the color, and then to the finish on the material. At all times, the end use or terminal use of the cloth should be kept in mind. The availability of information on market trends and raw materials, as well as a keen insight into the productive equipment are very important to the designer or stylist. The future potentials of these points should be constantly considered. Close touch with the market trends will enable the department to gear its functions to the current needs in the market.

Perception and apperception should be used continuously when developing a fabric. It has been said that ideas "spring from everywhere." Space should be allowed for the department to show its results. Customers and suppliers should be able to see at first hand the work accomplished by the staff. Discretion, of course, should be used in the issuance of invitations to prospective buyers and viewers of the newly developed fabrics. Stimulation for viewers and buyers will be aroused if an adequate and pleasing atmosphere is provided.

There should always be close integration between this department and the sales department of the concern; interests should integrate and coordinate, or become divergent at any time.

An ideal setup for the department would include a director, a secretary, and whatever other technical personnel would be necessary for the smooth functioning of the department.

A *textile testing laboratory* should be installed so that firsthand information on all problems may be obtained in the least possible time. Experiments and testings can be run off easily and well if the department is run as a cooperative enterprise at all times. Only essential testing machines for both physical and chemical testing should be installed.

TOPIC:
MAJOR TYPES OF
TEXTILE FABRICS,
ILLUSTRATED

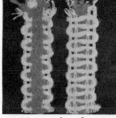

Woven fabric; yarns interlace at right angles

Knit fabric; yarn interlooping, a loop within a loop

Woven braid; yarn interlacings

Narrow braiding; woven with yarn interlacings

Lace fabric; yarns interlace at any angle

Felt; no yarn at all; made from mass of fibers

Felted fabric; woven cloth with weave covered

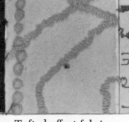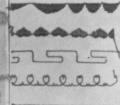

Nonwoven fabric; no yarn in fabric, made from fibers

Stretch fabric; stretch in one or both ways; corduroy

Laminated fabric; face of the goods is a twill weave

Laminated fabric; urethane foam is used as backing

Flocked fabric; full-surface flock applied

Flocked fabric; partial-surface flock applied

Tufted-effect fabric; produced by needle-work

Sewing machine stitch effect; many effects

Plain weave fabric	Right-hand twill weave	Left-hand twill weave	Broken twill (herringbone)
Satin weave	Sateen; always cotton, satin weave	Pointed twill	Basket weave
Filling-rib weave; rib is vertical	Warp-rib weave; rib is horizontal	Transportation cloth; novelty-rib weave	Bengaline; not a rib weave, bulky filling used
Taffeta; slight rib effect in filling, "rounded"	Shantung; not a rib weave, slub filling yarn used	True pique; rib is in filling	Pique "in the trade"; rib is warpwise

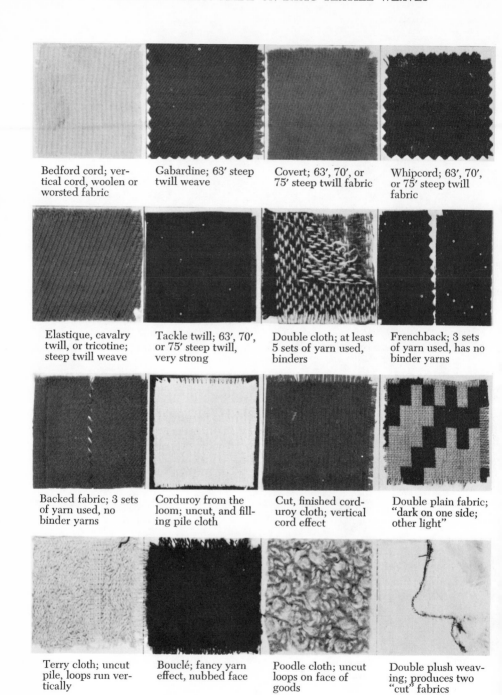

Bedford cord; vertical cord, woolen or worsted fabric

Gabardine; 63′ steep twill weave

Covert; 63′, 70′, or 75′ steep twill fabric

Whipcord; 63′, 70′, or 75′ steep twill fabric

Elastique, cavalry twill, or tricotine; steep twill weave

Tackle twill; 63′, 70′, or 75′ steep twill, very strong

Double cloth; at least 5 sets of yarn used, binders

Frenchback; 3 sets of yarn used, has no binder yarns

Backed fabric; 3 sets of yarn used, no binder yarns

Corduroy from the loom; uncut, and filling pile cloth

Cut, finished corduroy cloth; vertical cord effect

Double plain fabric; "dark on one side; other light"

Terry cloth; uncut pile, loops run vertically

Bouclé; fancy yarn effect, nubbed face

Poodle cloth; uncut loops on face of goods

Double plush weaving; produces two "cut" fabrics

Suede; soft finish on a twill woven cloth

Powder puff cloth; a type of plush fabric

Finished plush; nap always top to bottom

Pile fabric carpeting; has a cut pile finish

Velvet; warp cut pile fabric, cotton not used

Velveteen; filling cut pile cloth, is usually cotton

Dobby motif; made on power loom— "miniature Jacquard"

Jacquard fabric; each warp yarn is always controlled

Jacquard woven label—face of the label

Jacquard woven label—back construction of the label

Leno or doupe weave; warp ends cross each other

Another type of leno or doupe weave

Lappet; face as woven in loom, fancy zig-zag

Lappet with floating ends clipped off; shows face

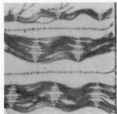

Clipspot as woven in loom; extra filling on top

Finished clipspot; either side may be finished as face

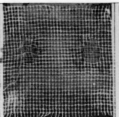

Swivel weaving; as woven in loom

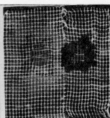

Swivel cloth; either side may be used as face

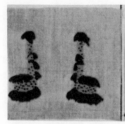

Warp floats, cut in warp direction; also may be uncut

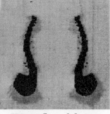

Warp float fabric; face of goods

SOME STANDARD JACQUARD LOOM WOVEN FABRICS

Matelassé; may provide a puckered effect

Jacquard brocade fabric

Another Jacquard brocade

Jacquard woven damask

Jacquard woven brocatelle

Jacquard woven tie fabric

Jacquard woven foundation fabric

One of the most important functions of the director is to work with the plant on the serviceability and marketability of the fabrics created. Another function is to examine well the finished garments made from the fabric, and to advise the various department heads on those fabrics that seem to be suitable for production in the several segments of the apparel trades.

The director should observe well and be familiar with competitive fabrics on the market, and be able to evaluate their possibilities versus the mill's own fabrics. Obviously this makes for keen competition and observation at all times.

The department should act as a clearinghouse for the fabrics for all mill affiliates and the converters, and should be able to distribute information as to fabric construction, widths, weights, textures, dyeing, printing, finishing, and all pertinent data that might be required.

Lastly, it is suggested that fabric and fabric constructions submitted by customers and other outside agencies or sources be studied with utmost care and frankness. Fair, ethical decisions should be made on the findings from the analysis of the fabric, its possibilities, and on the comparisons gleaned from the findings.

TESTING

1. Give in proper sequence the high points in the engineering of a cloth from the raw material to the finished fabric. Discuss the types of raw materials used, the weave, pick count or fabric texture, method of coloring, and the finishing of the material. A specific fabric could be used by the one or more persons discussing the cloth.
2. Define end use or terminal use of a cloth; texture, in both of its meanings in the textile industry.
3. List five factors essential in operation of a fabric development department.
4. Define perception, apperception. How could they be used in the development of a new cloth?
5. What does the term "textile technologist" mean to you? What particular background and abilities should he possess?
6. If you were the director of a fabric development department for a mill, how would you coordinate your department with the apparel industry? Your answer may be general or specific as to details.

Part 1—Unit 37

EXAMINATION ON UNIT 20 THROUGH UNIT 36
WEAVE DATA AND INTERPRETATION AND MAJOR TYPES OF FABRICS

True-False Questions   50 points

1. _____ The three basic weaves are plain, twill, and basket.
2. _____ The terms "end," "shaft," and "counter" are synonymous.
3. _____ A painted block on design paper signifies a raiser in the cloth.
4. _____ Five ends and five picks are required to make the lowest possible satin-weave construction.
5. _____ It is possible to make four different weave constructions on the smallest twill weave that can be made.
6. _____ Raiser, float, and riser are synonymous terms.
7. _____ The length of the yarn float in a 9-end satin weave would be eight.
8. _____ It may be said that a satin weave is a derivation of the twill weave.
9. _____ Generally speaking, all ends that weave alike in a fabric should go on the same harness frame.
10. _____ Reclining twills are less than 45 degrees in twill angle.

11. _____ A left-hand plain weave repeats on the same number of threads as a right-hand plain weave.
12. _____ Monk's cloth and hopsacking are made on basket weaves.
13. _____ The cords or ribs in a warp-rib weave run in the vertical direction.
14. _____ The warp numbering in a 6-end irregular satin weave is 1-3-5-2-4-6.
15. _____ Sateen is a fabric made of cotton and constructed with a satin weave.
16. _____ Covert is an example of a 45-degree twill weave.
17. _____ Tricotine is recognized by its double diagonal line on the face.
18. _____ Elastique and cavalry twill are closely related to tricotine fabric.
19. _____ Filling-effect satins should begin with a raiser in the lower left-hand corner of the weave.
20. _____ An 8-end satin can be made from a base of 2, 3, and 5.
21. _____ Twill-woven fabrics usually have more tensile strength than plain-weave materials.
22. _____ Ordinary warp-rib weaves should repeat on two warp ends.
23. _____ Stuffer yarns can be used in pique fabric.
24. _____ The yarns used to form the rib in a rib weave actually weave with the opposite system of yarn.
25. _____ Corduroy fabric is cut to give the pile effect after the gray goods have been taken from the loom.

Interpretation of Weave-Data Questions   20 points

1. _____ How many blocks in two repeats of a 9-end satin weave, base of 4?
2. _____ In a 4-1-4 basket weave, painted two repeats high and two repeats wide?
3. _____ In one repeat of a 12-end satin with a base of 6?
4. _____ How many blocks would there be in a warp-rib weave with the following data—a 1-2-3-4 weave, one repeat in height?
5. _____ How many blocks each way in a 2-2-2-4 basket weave, one repeat?
6. _____ What is the angle of a steep twill weave when 4 picks are held over?
7. _____ What is the angle in a reclining weave when 3 ends are held over?
8. _____ What is the height of 4 repeats of a filling-rib weave with the following data—2-3-4 filling-rib weave?
9. _____ How many ends and picks in one repeat of the following twill weave—$\frac{5\ 1\ 1}{1\ 2\ 1}$?
10. _____ How many blocks high and wide in 6 repeats of a plain weave?

Matching Questions: Place the number before the second column of terms or words on the blank lines provided to the left where there is a definite link or association:

                                                              30 points

1. _____ In warp-float fabric	1.	Should remind you of Jacquard loom
2. _____ Ottoman, taffeta, poplin	2.	Similar to Bedford cord weave
3. _____ Cannot be made	3.	Hopsacking, Monk's cloth
4. _____ Basket weave	4.	Uses two loom sheds and two shuttles
5. _____ Break line is used	5.	Must use at least five sets of yarn
6. _____ Pique construction	6.	Wilton carpeting when in the loom
7. _____ Lingoes, mail, cords	7.	In painting broken twills
8. _____ Does not actually exist	8.	Uses extra filling; one or more colors
9. _____ Point thread is used	9.	Ends may or may not be sheared off
10. _____ Plush fabric weaving	10.	Cylindrical filling
11. _____ Plaid-back overcoating	11.	A Jacquard weave
12. _____ Cut vertically	12.	10-end satin weave, base of 5
13. _____ Terry cloth	13.	Uses standard and skeleton harness frames
14. _____ Swivel-effect cloth	14.	When constructing pointed twills
15. _____ Leno or doup fabric	15.	Pile fabric made without use of wires or blades

TOPIC: THE LANGUAGE OF COLOR

COLOR: A visual attribute of bodies or substances distinct from their special characteristics; specifically, any one of the hues of the rainbow or the spectrum, or a tint produced by the blending of such hues. Loosely, any hue including black and white.

Color results from the light which illuminates an object, and from the brain which interprets the visual sensation. Basic theories of how the eye perceives color indicate that three colors of light rays (corresponding to red, violet-blue, and green) are primary and that our perception of other colors is the result of an additive process as these sensations are combined.

Thus, if a window display spotlight covered with a red gelatin filter, forming a ray of red light, and another spotlight filtered to provide a ray of green light, are focused on a single point (a point which in itself is white, thereby creating no additional factor of color reflection) lemon-yellow results. The primary red and the primary blue would result in a magenta or purple-red, if similarly focused. And the primary blue and the primary green would form a peacock blue.

When all three primaries of light are focused on a single point, white results.

These are also described as the "additive" primaries; when you begin with darkness, and add lighting in the primary colors focused onto a surface, all colors can be produced.

The three pigment primaries are those colors which cannot be produced by mixture of other pigments. The three "pigment primaries" are magenta, peacock-blue, and lemon-yellow, which are the secondary colors of light; that is, these three colors result when the three pairings of the three "light primaries" are blended.

When two of the pigment primaries are combined, they in turn form the so-called light primaries. For example, lemon-yellow and magenta mix to red; lemon-yellow and peacock-blue mix to green; peacock-blue and magenta mix and make violet-blue. When all these pigment primaries are combined, black is produced.

Color is reflected light. The sun, or artificial illuminants, radiate many light rays of different wave lengths, and the human eye can detect those wave lengths which range in size from 360/millionths of a meter (violet) to 700/billionths of a meter (red). In other words, each wave length of light waves represents a different color.

The observation of color is entirely a matter of light absorption and reflection. A red fabric is red, for instance, because it absorbs all visible light rays except those which are of the wave length which the human eye perceives as red; these red wave lengths are reflectd.

Some Major Terms Used in the Study of Color

ACHROMATIC COLORANT: Hueless, such as black, white, or gray.

ANALOGOUS COLORS: These are related closely and possess a common property such as bluish-green and greenish-blue. The tendency when used in striped materials is to separate and increase the color difference between them. Since these colors are one step removed from each other, it is important in striped effects to have them related.

CHROMATIC COLORANT: Having hue, such as red-yellow, blue-yellow, etc.

COLOR ACCENT: A bright or vivid color or colors used sometimes to dress up or improve dark, otherwise unattractive clothing ensembles.

COLORIMETRY: The testing of a color or dyeing compound by comparison with color solutions.

COLOR SCHEMES: These are:
   a) MONOCHROMATIC OR ONE-COLOR HARMONY: The use of one color in varying degrees of intensity and value: light blue, medium blue, dark blue.
   b) HARMONY: An agreeable combination of colors, all related to one another.
   c) COMPLEMENTARY HARMONY: A pleasing combination of complementary colors. One of the two could be used in larger areas than the other; the colors might show a difference in value and intensity; and there should be no clashing.

COMPLEMENTARY COLOR: The opposite color to a given color; it is found in several ways: If the given color is a primary, the complementary is obtained by mixing the other two primaries. The complement of any secondary color would be the remaining primary.

All colors have the property of calling upon their complementaries, in whatever colors are placed next to them. This is the property which causes many colors and color schemes to become hazy or mottled. Complementary colors, in brief, are those which, when mixed, produce a neutral gray.

COOL COLOR: Any color related to foliage, ice, sky, or snow, such as blue, green, violet.

HUE: The attribute of color, determined by the dominant wave length or predominant wave lengths of the stimulus, which distinguishes one color from another—red, yellow, blue, green, et al.

INTENSITY: Refers to the brightness or the dullness of a color; corresponds to saturation, or the purity of hue that a surface can reflect. When red is all red it is said to be in full intensity. When black, white, or gray is used in the color, there is a neutralization or a reduction in the intensity.

NEUTRAL COLOR: One in which there is no decided hue but in which gray or some shade of blue predominates, as in sand color, taupe, gunmetal, putty, beige, and some others.

PRIMARY COLORS: Red, yellow, and blue; pigments of these colors may be mixed to make many other colors.

SATURATION: Also known as chroma, intensity, purity. It is the strength or purity of a color, intense or bright, subdued or grayed. If the color is as brilliant as possible, it is known as one of saturation or strength; if subdued or grayed, it is dull, weak, and low in intensity.

SECONDARY COLORS: Green, orange, and violet, each of which is obtained by the mixing of two primaries.

SHADE: The dark tone of a color. Adding black will produce a shade. Adding the complement of the color to any standard color will produce a shade.

STANDARD COLORS: These are the six colors of the rainbow.

TERTIARY COLORS: Olive, citron, and russet, each of which is obtained by the mixing of two secondary colors.

TINT: A hue plus white.

TONE: A hue plus black.

VALUE: Also known as "lightness" or "darkness." Proportions of colorants, or variations of lightness or darkness with reference to a gray scale. Value encompasses shades, tints, and tones.

WARM COLOR: One that is related to heat, sunlight, and fire: red, orange, yellow.

Some Comments on the Uses of Color

DISGUISE: Observed in "allover motifs" or in patterns on fabrics which conceal or cover up possible flaws or defects in the fabric used. All fabrics should be examined very closely. Note the hand or feel, hold it up to the light and study the texture well.

IDENTIFICATION: Symbols of color apply to many holidays during the year, such as red and green at Christmas, purple and yellow at Easter, orange and black for Hallowe'en.

INTEREST: Certain colors affect us in varied and different ways, either pleasing or displeasing, satisfactory or annoying. Color interest is often intriguing and requires much attention in appraising its values and effects.

DECORATION: Color schemes, casts, shades, tones, tints, and hues, as well as full colors, all have their place in our daily lives—at business, in travel, in the home, in apparel.
   Some homes have a soothing, calm, serene color scheme; others may be such that the color scheme and decor are annoying, even very disturbing, or very uninteresting. Contrast and harmony in color or colors should be truly effective and developed in a sane, thoughtful manner. Color variety should always be "in good taste." The word "taste," however, may be somewhat difficult to understand or to define. Thus, sound judgment should prevail at all times in dealing with color.

VARIETY: Color, or colors, do make us "look different." Color can be the spice of life in many instances. A change of color, so to speak, often helps all of us. And color variety should be in good taste and well balanced as to details.

COLOR SELLS FABRICS AND GARMENTS: If the color or color scheme is one that is not satisfying or desirable, we will, psychologically, become annoyed and discard its use. An ensemble can often be very attractive except for one item—often an accessory—which may spoil the entire attire and comeliness of the wearer. Contrast and harmony should be in good balance and taste to be really worthwhile and appealing.

WE LIVE WITH, AND IN, COLOR: Color is always with us, around us, and it has much effect upon our feelings, whims, desires, satisfactions, and even our annoyances. Color can make or break any mode, dress, or garment. It may be refined, conservative, inviting, bizarre, wild, outlandish, serene. And, of course, color does much or can do much for the complexion, since both are closely correlated to each other, also for the profile, form, or silhouette. Color can also do very little for us, and in fact, might do us harm.

TESTING

1. Define color, color accent, color scheme, colorimetry.
2. Define hue, shade, tone, tint.
3. What is the result when all three primaries of light are focused on a single point?
4. Name the three primary colors of light rays.
5. Explain the three types of color schemes.
6. Name the secondary colors; the tertiary colors.
7. What is the difference between a tint and tone?
8. Comment on four uses of color in textile materials.

Some Psychological Connotations of Color

RED, DARK PURE	Love, amiability, strength.
RED, MEDIUM	Health and vitality, strength.
RED, BRIGHT	Passion, heat, warmth, vigor, strength.
RED, DARK GRAYED	Evil, slinking, cunning, slyness.
PINK, STRONG LIGHT	Femininity, festiveness.
PINK, PURE MEDIUM	Delicacy, innocence.
PINK, GRAYED LIGHT	Daintiness, lightheartedness.
PINK, GRAYED MEDIUM	Frivolity.

ORANGE, STRONG DARK	Ambition, glowing warmth, strength, flame.
ORANGE, STRONG MEDIUM	Enthusiasm, zeal, determination, interest.
ORANGE, STRONG LIGHT	Intensity, seriousness, excitement, vigor.
BROWN, DARK MEDIUM	Utility.
BROWN, LIGHT MEDIUM	Maturity, full-grown development.
YELLOW, STRONG LIGHT	Inspiration, thoughtfulness.
YELLOW, MEDIUM	Prudence, goodness, joyousness, clarity.
YELLOW, LIGHT MEDIUM	Wisdom, attention, sagacity, gaiety, lightness.
YELLOW, DARK MEDIUM	Love of humanity.
GOLD, STRONG LIGHT	Glamour, distinction.
GOLD, MEDIUM	Luxury, glory.
YELLOW-GREEN, LIGHT STRONG	Freshness, cheerfulness, smiling.
YELLOW-GREEN, LIGHT MEDIUM	Youth, youthfulness.
GREEN, LIGHT STRONG	Vitality, vigor, activity.
GREEN, STRONG MEDIUM	Sociability, friendliness, peacefulness.
GREEN, MEDIUM	Frankness, practicality, serenity, coolness.
GREEN, GRAYED MEDIUM	Innocence, naïveté, serenity, restraint.
BLUE-GREEN, STRONG LIGHT	Restlessness, instability, wandering.
BLUE-GREEN, STRONG DARK	Longing, nostalgia, memories, sedateness, quiet.
BLUE-GREEN, MEDIUM LIGHT	Calmness, repose, tranquillity.
BLUE-GREEN, GRAYED LIGHT	Placidity, stillness, soothingness.
BLUE, STRONG MEDIUM	Idealism.
BLUE, DARK MEDIUM	Sincerity, devotion, honesty.
BLUE, GRAYED MEDIUM	Kindness, gratefulness.
BLUE, LIGHT MEDIUM	Tranquillity, quietude.
BLUE-PURPLE, STRONG LIGHT	Sternness, frigidity, formality.
PURPLE, STRONG LIGHT	Magnificence, greatness.
PURPLE, LIGHT MEDIUM	Fragility, softness.
PURPLE, DARK GRAYED	Royalty, seriousness.
PURPLE, MEDIUM	Poise, individualism, distinctiveness.
WHITE	Purity, cleanliness, virginity, spotlessness.
BLACK	Mourning without hope, dignity, formality, sadness, melancholy.

List of Commercial Colors in Four Languages

ENGLISH	FRENCH	GERMAN	SPANISH
ANGLAIS	FRANÇAIS	ALLEMAND	ESPAGNOL
ENGLISCH	FRANZÖSISCH	DEUTSCH	SPANISCH
INGLÉS	FRANCÉS	ALEMÁN	ESPAÑOL
Amber	Ambre	Bernstein	Ambar
Apricot	Abricot	Aprikose	Albaricoque
Ashes	Cendreux	Aschgrau	Ceniciento
Bamboo	Bambon	Bambus	Bambú
Brick-red	Brique	Ziegelrot	Ladrillo
Black	Noir	Schwarz	Negro
Blue	Bleu	Blau	Azul
Brown	Brun	Braun	Café
Buttercup	Bouton d'or	Butterblume	Amargón
Canary	Canari	Kanariengelb	Canario
Cherry	Cerise	Kirschfarbig	Cereza
Chestnut	Chataigne	Kastanienbraun	Castaña

ENGLISH	FRENCH	GERMAN	SPANISH
ANGLAIS	FRANÇAIS	ALLEMAND	ESPAGNOL
ENGLISCH	FRANZÖSISCH	DEUTSCH	SPANISCH
INGLÉS	FRANCÉS	ALEMÁN	ESPAÑOL
Chocolate	Chocolat	Schokolade	Chocolate
Chamois	Chamois	Gemse	Gamuza
Coffee	Café	Kaffee	Café
Copper	Cuivre	Kupferfarbig	Cobre
Coral	Corail	Koralle	Coral
Corn	Mais	Korn, Mais	Maiz
Cream	Crème	Rahmfarbig	Crema
Dust	Poudre	Staubfarbig	Polvo
Emerald	Émeraude	Smaragd	Esmeralda
Fawn	Faon	Rehfarbig	Cervatillo
Flesh (color)	Couleur Chair	Fleischfarben	Color carne
Garnet	Grenat	Granat	Granate
Gold	Or	Gold	Oro
Gray	Gris	Grau	Gris
Grass (color)	Vert d'herbe	Grassgrün	Hierba
Green	Vert	Grün	Verde
Indigo	Indigo	Indigoblau	Añil
Ivory	Ivoire	Elfenbein	Marfil
Ivy (color)	Vert-de-lierre	Efeugrün	Hiedra
Lavender	Lavande	Lavender	Espliego
Leather	Cordoue	Leder	Córdoba
Lemon	Citron	Zitronengelb	Limon
Lichen	Lechen	Moosgrün	Liquen
Lilac	Lilas	Lila	Lila
Maroon	Marron	Maron	Castaña Marrón
Mole	Taupe	Taupe	Topo
Natural	Naturel	Natürlich	Natural
Navy (blue)	Bleu marin	Marineblau	Marino
Oak-green	Chêne	Eichengrün	Verde-roble
Olive-green	Olive	Olivengrün	Verde-olivo
Orange	Orange	Orangegelb	Anaranjado
Orchid	Lila-clair	Orchidee	Lila
Peacock-blue	Bleu-paon	Pfau	Pavón
Peach	Pêche	Pfirsichfarbe	Melocotón
Pea Green	Vert-clair	Erbsengrün	Verde-claro
Pearl	Perle	Perle	Perla
Pine Green	Pin-vert-foncé	Föhrengrün	Verde pino
Pink	Rose-clair	Rosa	Rosado
Plum	Prune	Pflaume	Ciruela
Purple	Pourpre	Purpurfarbig	Morado
Red	Rouge	Rot	Rojo
Rose	Rose	Rosenfarbe	Rosa
Ruby	Rubis	Rubinfarben	Rubi
Saffron	Safran	Safrangelb	Azafràn
Sand	Sable	Sandfarben	Arena
Salmon	Saumon	Lachsrot	Salmón
Silver	Argent	Silber	Plata

ENGLISH	FRENCH	GERMAN	SPANISH
ANGLAIS	FRANÇAIS	ALLEMAND	ESPAGNOL
ENGLISCH	FRANZÖSISCH	DEUTSCH	SPANISCH
INGLÉS	FRANCÉS	ALEMÁN	ESPAÑOL
Sky-blue	Ciel-bleu	Himmelblau	Azul-celeste
Smoke, Smoky	Fumeux	Rauchig	Humo-plumo
Straw	Paille	Strohfarbig	Bagatela
Strawberry	Fraise	Erdbeerfarbig	Fresa
Sunflower	Tournesol	Sonnenblume	Girasol
Sulfur	Soufre	Schwefelfarbig	Azufre
Tobacco	Tabac	Tabak	Tabaco
Tomato (red)	Tomate	Tomate	Tomate
Topaz	Topaze	Topaz	Topacio
Turquoise	Turquoise	Türkis	Azul-turqui
Violet	Violette	Veilchenblau	Violeta
White	Blanc	Weiss	Blanco
Wine	Vin	Wein	Vino
Yellow	Jaune	Gelb	Amarillo

TOPIC: TYPES OF DYES USED TO COLOR TEXTILES

The value of color is known to all. It can "make or break" the appearance of the individual. Examination of the clothes one is wearing reveals that many colors and color combinations are present, in full color, shade, cast, tone, or tint. The application of color to textile materials may be compared with the application of cosmetics to the face of an individual, or the dyeing or tinting of hair on the human head. Dyes today come from two sources, natural and synthetic. At present over 90 per cent of the dyes used commercially are made from synthetic base. Natural sources have been used for many centuries and are still used to some extent by handcrafters such as handweavers, hobbyists in various fields, cottage industries in some of the more remote areas of the world, and tribal groups.

Natural dyes come from plant or animal substances—barks, berries, flowers, insects, kelp or seaweed, lichens, stems, and shellfish. Some vegetable sources are brazilwood, butternut, cudbear, cutch, fustic, indigo, litmus, logwood (excellent on acetate, rayon, and nylon for fast shades), madder, quercitron, saffron, sumac, and turmeric-henna.

The matter of dyeing fabrics is not easy, since the setting of color on materials, by the dyer or printer, presents many complex problems, and what will apply in one case will be totally foreign in another instance. Some dyes, for example, will color only animal fibers and have no effect at all on vegetable fibers, yarns, or fabrics. Some dyes may be able to color many of the major fibers in use today. There are many variables in the dyeing of textiles, and the dyer must be aware of all facets involved in coloring in order to present a dyed or printed material that will be suitable for some particular end use. And his results have to withstand the physical and chemical testing given to his efforts—action of acids and alkalies, crocking, colorfastness to a particular fabric from sunlight, gases in the atmosphere, perspiration, drycleaning, washing, etc.

AFFINITY of a dye is its readiness to be assimilated by the fiber. The lack of affinity of a dyestuff may be caused by improper chemical combination between the dyestuff and the fiber. A dye can have great affinity for a woolen or silk fiber and none at all for a cotton or nylon fiber. FUGITIVITY is a term used when dyed materials are not durable, such as in fading from sunlight, bleeding from washing, or fading from perspiration. Fugitivity is the opposite of fastness.

There are today between 7,500 and 8,000 different dyestuffs used in the United States, and generally speaking, in all other major countries. Each of these dyestuffs has its own affinity for one or more fibers. To make some order from what would be a rather chaotic listing of so many dyes, they have been classified into groups or classes that have similar fiber affinities. Moreover, most of the dyes within each class have similar fastness characteristics. Each class of dyes may have several hundred different dyestuffs of as many colors, casts, shades, tones, and hues. By properly mixing these dyes in the dyeing operation, the dyer can produce an infinite range of colors and shades.

The matter of dyestuffs and the coloring of textiles are constantly being improved, and the strides made have been phenomenal, particularly since World War I. Much further improvement has come as an aftermath of World War II. The industry is a well-welded one, in which research, experimentation, pilot plant work, time and labor, and constant efforts for better dyes and methods are all definitely apparent.

Much is known about color today, but there is still much to be learned in this day and age of experimentation and research, and the dyeing profession is always alert to future possibilities in color, color blending, and their applications to textiles. The newer manmade fibers really compel the dyeing groups to be keenly aware of "What is new?" or "How can this be dyed better?" Give the dyer the implements to work with and the proper amount of time for research, and he is sure to come up with the answer to any of the myriad problems with which he is confronted. (See the important definitions which follow.)

THE TYPES OF DYES USED TO COLOR TEXTILES

ACID DYES: These are among the first synthetic dyes to be developed. Primarily for use on wool and other animal fibers, they are water soluble and applied directly with the aid of an acid, such as sulfuric acid. These dyes produce bright colors but do not provide outstanding colorfastness to wet treatment. Rated poor to fair in washing, but good in drycleaning; many of the dyes in this group, however, rate very good in fastness to light.

ACID-MILLING DYES: Like acid dyes, from similar chemical origin, they are much used in stock dyeing of wool and in the top dyeing of worsted tops to be ultimately used in worsted yarn. Milling dyes are good to excellent in fastness to light, good in drycleaning, and better than acid dyes in washing. In addition to their use on animal fibers, both acid and acid-milling dyes will dye nylon, acrylic, modacrylic, and spandex fibers. They can be used to print nylon, chlorinated wool, and silk. The manufacturing considerations and the end use of the fabric determine the type of dye to use—acid or acid-milling.

ACID-PREMETALIZED DYES: Like the acid and the acid-milling dyes, these are used mostly on wool. They also find use on nylon and acrylic fibers. They usually possess excellent fastness to washing, perspiration, sunlight and drycleaning. Much used in carpeting, upholstery, and suiting fabrics.

ALIZARINE DYES: The vegetable dye alizarin was originally obtained from the madder root, but it is now made synthetically. It finds much use on wool and, in some instances, dyes cotton very well. The once popular turkey red on cotton is produced with alizarine dye. Resistance to sunlight and washing are features of these dyes. Used to color apparel of obvious types.

AZOIC OR NAPHTHOL DYES: Known also as ice colors, insoluble azos, or ingrain colors, they are really components rather than dyes, and are used in two separate operations—combinations of coupling components and diazo compounds:

a) The fiber is treated with one component, which does not actually dye when used alone.
b) The first component reacts with the second one to form the dye color on the yarn or fabric. This process is called "coupling," and it is much resorted to in printing motifs or designs on fabrics. They find much use in fabric printing, since they afford good to excellent results in laundering and washing. Used on cotton draperies, sportswear, decorative fabrics, tablecloths, dressgoods, and comparable materials.

BASIC DYES: The first of these synthetic dyes, derived from coal tar, was mauve or mauveine, a bright but fugitive violet dye, aniline purple. Its discoverer, Sir William Henry Perkin, synthesized the dye by accident in 1856, in England. He established the first synthetic dyestuff plant in the world. Basic dyes color animal and many of the manmade fibers directly but do require a mordant on vegetable fibers, such as tartar emetic with tannic acid. Brilliant shades result, but lightfastness and washfastness rate from fair to poor.

Basic dyes have an organic base (carbon content in the structure) solubilized with an organic acid (one in which there is no carbon element). Thus they are capable of reaction with anionic substances in a dyebath.

Newer types of basic dyes have been developed specifically for acrylic, modacrylic, and some of the polyester fibers by direct application. Bright shades result which have excellent fastness properties. Acrylic fibers colored with basic dyes are much used in knitwear, woven goods, and in carpeting.

CHROME DYES: (See Mordant Dyes.)

DEVELOPED DYES: These are "direct dyes" or "disperse dyes," but, because of the presence of a digest amino group in the molecule, they can be developed by after-treating to provide improved wetfastness. After the application as a direct dye or a disperse dye, the dyeing is diazotized and then coupled with a suitable compound such as beta naphthol. In lightfastness the rating is poor to good, depending on the particular dye used; washing is rated fairly good to good. These dyes are used on rayon and cotton when derived from a direct dye, and on manmade fibers for use in knit and woven goods when developed from disperse dye bases. (See Direct Dyes.)

DIRECT DYES: These find much application on the cellulosic fibers such as cotton and rayon. Sometimes known as "application dyes" or "commercial dyes," the lightfastness rating is from poor to excellent, but because of their solubility they are not rated very highly in washfastness.

Aftertreatments are resorted to to improve lightfastness and washfastness. Ingredients used include copper salts, copperas or bluestone, copper-resin compounds, and comparable substances.

DISPERSE DYES: These were developed specifically for cellulose acetate in the 1920's. Chemically, these dyes are mainly azo or anthraquinone types. There are not any solubilizing groups in this set of dyes; the coloring matter is made into a paste or finely milled powder form. They are used on nylon, acrylic, modacrylic, and polyester fibers and are ideal for printing, as well. They are much used to color apparel, hosiery, linings, dressgoods, outerwear of several types, and decorative fabrics. Colorfastness rates from poor to very good for light and washing, depend-

[202]

ing upon the fiber to which the particular dye has been applied. Some disperse dyes, especially blues and purples, will fade from exposure to imperfections in the atmosphere, commonly referred to as gas fading.

INGRAIN COLORS: (See Azoic or Naphthol Dyes.)

MINERAL COLORS: These, in reality, are not true dyes but are precipitated oxides or insoluble salts of chromium, iron, lead, or manganese. They are applied in a soluble form and the precipitates are formed in the dye bath by double decomposition or by oxidation. These colors are dull in appearance and are used much in color effects in awnings.

MORDANT DYES: A mordant is a substance used in dyeing to apply or fix coloring matter to a fiber, yarn, or fabric, especially a metallic compound such as an oxide which combines with the fiber and organic dye and forms an insoluble color compound or lake in the fiber.

Also known as "mordant-acid dyes," or "chrome dyes," they are related closely to acid dyes. The chrome required is usually derived from sodium bichromate at some stage in the dyeing procedure. Results from the use of these dyes are rather dull when compared with those obtained from acid dyes but they are among the fastest colors used to dye wool.

Mordant-acid dyes are used to color wool, wool carpeting, nylon, silk. Silks and woolens may be printed by these dyes on the cylinder or roller method and worsted top by the Vigoureux Printing Method.

NEUTRAL DYEING—PREMETALIZED ACID DYES: Related to acid dyes except that they are produced on the basis of two molecules of dye bound to one of metal, usually chromium. The metal content improves the fastness so that they approach the fastness of mordant dyes. These dyes are usually azo compounds suitable for the coloring of woolen-union fabrics with cellulosic content in them. While good shades result from this type of dyeing, they are not as bright as regular acid dyeing colors.

They will dye all forms of wool and other protein fibers, nylon, acrylic, and modacrylic fibers. They are ideal for blends provided dye-bath additives are used. These dyes are much used in coloring apparel fabrics. They rate fair to excellent to light, good to excellent to washing, and excellent in drycleaning.

OXIDATION BASES: One of these bases is aniline dye, which is formed in the fiber by oxidation. For example, the base known as "aniline black" has been used for well over one hundred years, one of the fastest blacks known to man. Oxidation bases are ideal for dyeing fur, sheepskins, and pile fabrics, as well as for coloring cotton for a wide range of uses. Much printed fabric uses these bases in coloring.

PIGMENT COLORS: These are based on organic coloring matter—azo compounds, metal chelates, etc. None in the group has any affinity for any fiber. They are insoluble in water and have to be fixed onto the fiber by the use of resinous binders insolubilized by a curing treatment at high temperatures. Pigment colors give very bright shades. Acetate, cotton, rayon, and other manmade fibers can be pigment-colored or -printed. These colors have a very wide range of uses—awnings, decorative fabrics, dressgoods, outerwear, shirtings, and light and medium shades of sailcloth. Rated good to excellent in lightfastness but apt to be poor in crocking or rubbing.

Pigment printing has many advantages over other methods of coloring. Practically all types of fibers and blends can be printed; there are fewer "seconds," chiefly because it is an easy matter to observe the printing results, and if flaws are found they may be remedied at once. Compatibility of colors is assured if the pigments are of the same type and have been used in the processing, thereby increasing the range of colors available.

Fixing of the color is done by a simple process of curing. Much lighter engravings, as in photo engravings, can be used with moderate pressure in the machine, affording a saving in paste consumption. No aftertreatments, other than washing or soaping, are necessary—thus a saving in steam, time, and work.

[203]

REACTIVE DYES: These made their debut in 1957 and the chemical combination with the fiber sets these dyes apart from all other colorants. Reactives actually bond in the color into the fiber. They give very bright shades on cottons, and can dye acrylics, nylon, silk, wool, and blends of these fibers in cross-dyeing and union-dyeing. They are much used on printgoods, and also on stock, yarn, and piecegoods, and widely used on cottons; the light and washing tests are rated from good to very good. They are fugitive to chlorine-base bleaching agents.

SULFUR DYES: Coming into the market in 1879, they were originally made from sulfur, sodium sulfide, and sawdust. They are now made from indophenols, indamines, and other intermediates. They are insoluble in water but are solubilized with sodium sulfide and soda ash. They do not provide bright shades and their fastness properties are developed in the chemical inertness and insolubility in water. Soluble forms of sulfur dyes have been developed within recent years.

They are used to color heavy cottons, and knitwear in full and medium shades, and can also be applied to stock, yarn, and piecegoods work. They also find use in printing when chrome-plated rollers are used on the printing machine. Sulfur dyes are not as fast when compared with vat dyes but the costs are lower. They are weak in sunlight except for deep shades where the fastness is rated as good. Sulfur dyes tend to be fugitive to chlorine such as that found to exist in hypochlorite bleaches.

VAT AND VAT-SOLUBLE DYES: Natural dyeing with indigo has been known for centuries with its distinctive shades of blue. Synthetic indigo dyes came into the market in 1879. The anthraquinone groups were introduced in 1901, the water-soluble leuco esters in 1921. These dyes have been modified, but, chemically speaking, all give about the same end results as to effects and properties. Vat dyes are the fastest dyes known to man. Insoluble in water, they can be made soluble by chemical reduction. Applied to textiles, they can be returned in an insoluble form by oxidation, thereby firmly fixing the color within the fibers, a bonding-in of the colorant. They are the most resistant of any type of colorant to light, drycleaning, sunlight, washing, etc.

It should be borne in mind that vat dyeing, as such, does not exist. The dyeing is done by the conventional methods—yarn, piece, direct printing, etc. These dyes are used on cotton, and to some degree on wool. They are popular colors in workclothes, outerwear, sportswear, decorative fabrics of many types, awnings, towelings, bed linens, etc. Light shades can also be obtained from soluble vat dyes.

NOTE: The following notations should be kept in mind on certain dyes.

ACID DYES: Level dyeing is achieved with the use of the proper amount of sulfuric acid.

ACID-MILLING DYES: Usually applied with a weakly acidic bath.

"STRONG" ACID DYEING: Done with a 1:1 premetalized dye.

NEUTRAL DYEING: Done with a 2:1 premetalized acid dye which contains two dye molecules chelated with one metal ion.

AZOIC DYES: Three points should be observed:
1. The use of an azoic component.
2. The use of an azoic coupling component.
3. The use of azoic compositions.

Courtesy of Mr. Ludwig Fusser, General Aniline & Film Corporation, 140 West 51st Street, New York City.

SOME BASIC DEFINITIONS USED IN THE TYPES OF DYES, AND IN THE METHODS OF DYEING AND PRINTING TEXTILES

This group of terms, in some respects, is technical. The inclusion of technical terms attempts to give the full scope of the "language of dyeing and printing" to serve the textile technologist, students in textile colleges, dyers and printers, and those scientists interested in the types of dyes used to color textile yarns and fabrics.

Most of the terms, however, should be understood and digested by students in textile courses, textile instructors, and those interested in the chemistry of textiles especially with regard to the "how" and the "why" in color application. Most of the terms will be readily recalled by students who have had science subjects in high school and college.

Attention is also drawn to "Definitions and Terms Used in the Manufacture of Manmade Filaments and Fibers" in Part Two, Unit 13, of *Natural and Manmade Fibers*, by the author of this book. This unit is a brief history of the newer manmade fibers and should be of utmost interest to the diligent student interested in the study of textiles.

The definitions for this unit follow:

ALIZARINE: Originally obtained from the madder root, but now made from anthraquinone. The word *alizarine* means "to extract."

AMINE: Any of a class of compounds prepared from ammonia by replacing one, two, or all hydrogen atoms with organic radicals.

AMINO: A prefix denoting the amino group, a combination form of amine.

ANHYDRIDE: A compound formed by the abstraction of water, an oxide of a nonmetal (acid anhydride) or a metal (basic anhydride) which forms an acid or a base, respectively, when united with water. A compound from which water has been extracted.

ANION: A negatively charged ion which is attracted to the anode in electrolysis. Any negatively charged atom, molecule, or radical. From the Greek, it means "going up."

ANODE: The positive pole of a battery or other source of current.

ANTHRACENE: A hydrocarbon found in coal tar; of importance as a source for aniline. Formula is $C_{14}H_{10}$.

ANTHRAQUINONE: A crystalline substance from anthracene or phthalic anhydride; used in the preparation of alizarine or other dyes. Formula is $C_{14}H_8C_2$.

ASSISTANT: A dyeing assistant includes surface active agents, synthetic detergents, etc., which aid dyestuff to become fixed on or into the fiber by causing it to bloat or swell, thereby bringing about better color penetration and color leveling. The assistant may be a hastening agent to "speed up" the dyeing or a retarding agent to "slow up" the action.

ATOM: The smallest particle of any chemical element that can exist by itself and retain the qualities that characterize it as that element.

AZO: A term applied to a numerous group of dyes prepared by the modifications of one general reaction—the diazo. Most direct cotton colors are of this type. Insoluble azo colors (paranitraniline red) are developed directly onto the cotton and yield very fast colors.

BATH OR LIQUOR: The solution in which dyeing, bleaching, washing, scouring, etc., takes place.

BECK, KIER, VESSEL, WINCH: A machine used to dye piece goods. There are several types of machines and they are sometimes known by other, more or less closely-allied, names.

CHELATION: A chemical reaction where a metallic ion combines with an organic substance which contains hydroxyl and carboxyl groups in suitable portions in order to form a ring structure through ionic and coordinate bonding.

COAL TAR: A black, thick, viscid liquid formed during the distillation of coal and which, upon further distillation, yields anthracene, benzene, phenol, etc. A large number of dyes and synthetic compounds are made from these basic compounds.

COLORFASTNESS: Also known as fast color, it describes fabrics of sufficient color retention so that no noticeable change in the shade occurs during the normal life of the garment. Strictly speaking, there is not any fabric that is absolutely "colorfast," but many fabrics have remarkable durability in retaining the color.

COMPONENT: A composition, constituent or ingredient which aids to make the whole compound or article.

CURING: The setting of a chemical, plastic, or resin in or on textile materials, usually obtained by heating. A curing chamber is any type of drying equipment in which 300° F. and over can be obtained. The chamber may be of the loop, roller, or enclosed-frame type.

DEPTH OF DYE: The relative lightness or darkness of dyed woven or knit fabrics when compared with a control fabric.

DIAZOTIZING: Treatment of dyed material with a solution of nitrous acid obtained by adding sulfuric acid to sodium nitrite. (See Developed Dyes.)

DISPERSE: To drive, force, or scatter as in the case of a dyestuff dispersing throughout a liquid volume when it is placed in the liquor.

ELECTRON: A minute, negatively electrified particle charged with the smallest-known quantity of electricity and having a mass approximately 1/1550 of that of a hydrogen atom, the atom of negative electricity.

FIXING AGENT: An agent capable of reacting with a dye on a fiber to improve fastness to water or washing. It is usually applied as an aftertreatment to dyes which already possess some affinity for the textile substrate and is so distinguished from mordants. (See Substrate.)

INERT: Having no inherent power of action, motion, or resistance; a form of inaction. Some chemicals will remain inert during a reaction, method, or process.

INTERMEDIATE: Being situated or acting between two points or stages. It is a derivative of the initial material formed before the desired product of a chemical process. Examples of intermediates used to make dyes include benzene, naphthalene, ethyl alcohol, chlorine, lime, and ammonia.

ION: An important term in chemistry and physics when an electrically charged atom, radical, or molecule is formed by the gain or loss of one or more electrons. Positive ions, created by electron loss, are called "cations." Negative ions created by electron gain are known as "anions." The term also implies a fusing, or making a union, such as is often found in dyeing, between a fiber and the dyestuff used to dye it.

ISOMERIC: The word iso, from the Greek, means "equal," a prefix. Isomeric, in speaking of chemical compounds, means that the compound is composed of the same kinds and number of atoms, which differ from each other in the arrangement of the atoms and, therefore, in one or more properties.

JIG: The machine used to dye piece goods. Full-width material is passed from a roller through the dye bath in an open vat and then proceeds to another roller. The treatment is repeated until the desired shade is assured. Also referred to as jig-dyeing.

LEUCO: A colorless or nearly colorless soluble compound obtained in the reduction of a vat dye. Leuco means "colorless."

METALIZE: A reaction in chemistry, as in the dyeing procedures, wherein it is possible to obtain the characteristics of metal. (See Neutral Dyeing—Premetalized Acid Dyes.)

MILLING: (1) Subjecting something to the operation of a mill or milling. For example, a dyestuff that has been made into very fine granules prior to its use to dye a textile fiber or yarn. (2) Milling colors or "fast-to-milling" refers to dyes which will not bleed or fade in the wool-finishing operation on fabric known as "fulling" or "milling."

MORDANT: Much used in coloring textiles, it has the property of fixing or setting colors onto a fiber, yarn, or fabric. Especially used as a metallic compound, an oxide or hydroxide, which combines with the organic dye and forms an insoluble colored compound or color lake in the fiber. From the Latin *mordere*, and means "to bite, or to bite into."

NAPHTHOL: Either of two isomeric derivatives of naphthalene, having the formula of $C_{10}H_7OH$, and occurring in coal tar; much used in the manufacture of dyes. Betanaphthol is a crystalline antiseptic that has the same formula as naphthol and implies any of certain hydroxyl derivatives of naphthalene.

ORTHO: From the Greek, it means "straight, right, correct, upright" and is used in combination with other words. Chemically speaking, it is a prefix indicating that acid of a series which contains the most water. The expression "ortho-position," used in dyeing, means the correct position.

OXIDATION: A chemical union of oxygen with some other element or group of elements. Rusting of iron is an example. This involves the combination of iron with oxygen. Heat is released during an oxidation reaction. Burning is a form of rapid oxidation where the heat is quickly observed.

In the instance where oxygen is removed from a compound, the compound is said to have been reduced. If a compound of mercury and oxygen, for example, is heated, the oxygen is driven off, leaving the mercury in its elemental form. The compound, therefore, has been reduced.

Vat dyes, for example, are oxygen compounds which are insoluble in water. By reduction they are changed into a soluble, leuco, or colorless form, and are reconverted by oxidation into the colored insoluble state.

OXIDE: A compound of oxygen with other elements. Iron rust is an iron oxide.

OXIDIZE: To add oxygen to any material by chemical combination. Chlorine bleaching is an oxidizing action.

OXIDIZED COLOR: A dyestuff that is developed by a chemical combination to its full strength by application of certain chemicals to oxidize it.

OXIDIZER: Creates oxygen. "Rinso," for example, has sodium perborate in it, and it is the oxygen that serves as the bleach.

OXIDIZING AGENT: Any substance which can furnish oxygen to which another substance may unite. Hydrogen peroxide, for example, will bleach silk and wool because it liberates or furnishes oxygen which will combine with the dye to form a colorless product.

PAD: To impregnate fabric with dyestuff, mordant, etc.

PADDING, PADDING MACHINE: The application of dyestuff to fabric by a padding machine. It is equipped with a set of wringers that actually force the dyestuff through the material while passing through the wringers at full open width. The steam box will then develop the final color in the fabric.

This method of coloring is economical and only one application is necessary. Production is very good. Fast colors, the vat colors, are used to a great degree in pad- or vat-dyeing when large volume is wanted and production is an incentive. Some goods dyed this way include summer-wear fabric, solid-color sheeting, some curtain and upholstery cloth, and pastel-color material.

PIGMENT: The color of human hair is coloring matter and it can be bleached, dyed, or tinted. As a coloring matter in the skin, pigment cannot be removed like the color in human hair. Freckles are an example of pigment in the skin—irremovable. Applied to chemistry, it is a dry substance, usually pulverized, and when mixed with a liquid vehicle it remains insoluble.

Pigments used in textile coloring or printing are mechanically held to the fabric by a resin-binder and the goods are cured at high temperatures.

PRECIPITATE: To separate a substance out into a solid form from a solution. Curdled milk is an example.

RADICAL: An atom or group of atoms regarded as an important constituent of a molecule which remains unchanged and behaves as a unit in many reactions. Specifically, a group of atoms which act as a unit in a compound and may either pass unchanged through a series of reactions, or be replaced as though it were a single atom. Radical comes from the Latin *radix*, and means "root."

REDUCE: To take oxygen from a certain material or substance.

REDUCED COLOR: A dyestuff which has its formulation changed or reduced by chemical agents.

REDUCER: Vanished oxygen or its equivalent. Coke, for example, removes oxygen from iron ore and leaves the iron.

REDUCING AGENT: Any substance which will remove oxygen from another substance; the opposite of oxidizing agent.

REDUCTION: The process of depriving a chemical compound of its oxygen. Also, the process of decreasing the positive valence of an element by the addition of electrons; distinguished from oxidation.

SCOUR, SCOURING: In general, the cleansing of raw stock, yarn, cloth, etc., of dirt, granules, grime, grease, and a host of other possible impurities by dissolving, rubbing, scrubbing, etc., usually in some liquid which contains a detergent, soap, powder, or the like. Other suitable chemicals used in scouring, washing, and cleansing are alkalies, acids, bleaches, etc.

SIZING: The application of starch or other stiffening agent to yarn, cloth, and garments to provide a better and improved product when completely finished. For example, a size or starch applied to warp yarn increases the strength and smoothness and adds weight to the gray goods from the loom. Sizing may be applied to yarn in hank or ball form, or in the slashing or dressing frame when the warp is being made by the dressing tender. Sizes or stiffeners are much used on fabrics to enhance durability and eye-appeal to the consumer.

There are basically three main types of sizes or gums used in sizing:

1. BINDING AND STIFFENING: Sizes of casava, corn, flour, potato, rice, sago, tapioca, wheat, etc. Also, gum arabic, gum tragacanth, glucose, dextrine, Irish moss, and certain types of glues.
2. FILLING MATERIALS: China clay, talc, alum, blanc fixe, etc.
3. SOFTENING OR CONDITIONING MATERIALS: Coconut oil and some other soluble oils, glycerine, soap, tallow, waxes, etc.

STOCK REDUCTION PASTE: A printing paste used in vat dyeing that contains everything but the color. The paste and the color are mixed later on, in varying proportions, to give the desired printing paste for use.

SUBSTRATE: A substance that is acted upon by an enzyme or ferment. The term comes from the Greek and means "a stratum or layer spread or laid under another stratum or layer."

TANNIN: A natural vegetable substance much used in the preparation of dyestuffs and inks. Tannins find much use in making mordants for use in dyeing textiles. Tannic acid, for example, is soluble in water; so is tartar emetic, a white crystalline, poisonous tartrate of antimony and potassium. Both, however, will combine in a bath or liquor to form an insoluble mordant for use in dyeing textiles.

VALENCE: The property possessed by an element or radical of combining with or replacing other elements or radicals in definite and constant proportion. The degree of this property is commonly indicated by the number of atoms of hydrogen (or their equivalent) taken as a unit with which the atom or radical can combine, or which it can replace. It varies with different elements and with certain elements in different compounds. Thus, hydrogen has a valence of one, and is called univalent; oxygen has a valence of two, and is called bivalent. Carbon has a valence of four and is classed as a quadrivalent. Manganese, for example, may have a valence of two, three, or seven, etc. The word "valence" comes from the Latin *valentia,* which means "strength," or *valeo,* which means "strong."

TESTING

1. Define dyeing.
2. What is the difference between a natural dye and a synthetic dye?
3. Explain what is meant, in a general way, by the fastness of a dye.
4. Define affinity; fugitivity.
5. What type of dye has the greatest colorfastness on textile fabrics?
6. Name a dyestuff that will dye both animal and vegetable fibers.
7. Discuss basic dyes; pigment colors; vat and vat-soluble colors.
8. What is the difference between oxidation and reduction in dyeing?
9. Discuss sizing or starching of textile yarns, fabrics, and garments.
10. Define a mordant; tannin.
11. Discuss mordant colors.
12. Define the term "coupling."

Courtesy of Professor Arthur Price, Coordinator of Textile Department, Fashion Institute of Technology, New York City.

TOPIC: MAJOR AND MINOR METHODS OF DYEING STOCK, YARN, AND FABRIC

Textiles come in many forms with regard to color or lack of color. A fabric may be in the natural color, printed, dyed, bleached to white, mercerized as in the case of many cotton materials. In addition, fabrics may receive one or more of a host of finishing treatments such as napping, shearing, felting, smoothing, moiré or watermarking, starching, sizing, glazing, calendering. Finishes may be harsh, soft, stiff, limp, mosslike, silklike, surface-finished. Coloring and finish seem to go hand-in-hand to produce some definite texture on a fabric for consumption. There are several methods used to color textiles, and each of these depends usually on the so-called local conditions.

MAJOR METHODS OF COLORING TEXTILES

STOCK-DYEING: This method is extremely popular for dyeing woolen fabrics since the range of color and shade is very wide. The dyeing is done after the stock used has been scoured and dried but before the spinning of the yarn and the weaving of the cloth.

The actual dyeing is done in large vats or kiers, either in small or large lots. The final color effect is obtained when the newly dyed stock is blended, oiled, and mixed and ultimately spun into yarn.

Examples of stock-dyeing include plain colors, heathers, mixes, and shades as noted in homespun, tweed, cheviot, Shetland, covert, Venetian, and other comparable suitings and coatings.

YARN- OR SKEIN-DYEING: This is done after the yarn has been spun but before fabric has been made from the yarn. The yarn skeins are dyed by being placed on crossbars or rollers to support the skeins. Usually from 24 to 40 skeins can be accommodated on each bar. Several roller bars can be cared for in the machine. There may or may not be total immersion of the yarn while it is being dyed in the bath.

Examples include gingham, striped chambray, striped denim; checks, stripes, plaids, overplaids, tartans, Glen plaids, dressgoods.

PIECE-DYEING: This is applied to fabric which is colored a single color, shade, cast, tone, hue, or tint. It occurs after the fabric has been woven in the loom and then made as nearly perfect as possible, free from all defects.

Piece-dyeing is a continuous or semi-continuous process which takes place in a dye-beck, box, kier, jig, or vessel. On jigs and continuous machines the cloth is handled in the open width while on the dye-beck it is in rope form. Piece-dyeing is very popular because of the inherent flexibility from an economic standpoint. It is far more economical to weave fabric with undyed yarns and subsequently to dye the material into popular shades than to yarn-dye with the hazard that the colors may not be popular when marketed.

Examples include blue serge, brown gabardine, green organdy, black crepe, navy-blue dressgoods, purple satin.

CROSS-DYEING: A union cloth is one made up of two or more different textile fibers or yarns in the same material. Union fabrics are among the most popular to be found on the market today. Animal, vegetable, and manmade yarns or fibers are used to produce the many fabrics that are to be dyed in this manner. Examples could be a cloth with a cotton warp and a worsted filling; a cotton warp and a nylon filling; rayon warp and acetate filling; acetate warp and "Dacron" filling; worsted warp and Arnel filling.

The dyeing may be done in one or two baths, dependent upon the local conditions and the equipment available. Special dyes are needed for each type of fiber or yarn. When the dyeing is taking place, the one yarn will take on one color or shade, while the other yarn or fiber will take on another color or shade. The resultant coloring in the goods may be harmonious or contrasting in shade or cast. Much dressgoods fabric is dyed in this manner, as well as some evening-wear fabric, etc.

DOPE-DYEING, SOLUTION-DYEING; SPUN-DYED FABRICS: The original name for this method was dope-dyeing. It is a development from World War I, when the term "dope" meant to cover or coat the wings of airplanes; this dope was a solution of cellulose acetate, the forerunner of present-day acetate, the cellulose-derivative fiber.

Today the term is applied to dyeing in the following sense: After the solution of cellulose acetate has been prepared and filtered for purification, dyes are introduced into the solution. This solution is then extruded through spinnerettes and dried in the usual manner. The color used has become a corporate part of the filament itself, by the bonding together of color and fiber.

Only a skilled dyer can work with dope dyes, since the amounts of dye needed to achieve the desired shade will vary and only experienced dyers can produce colors of commercial satisfaction.

The method has met with acclaim in the trade wherever used. Dope-dyed fabrics have splended fastness to light, the colors and cast are genuinely good and attractive, and they will not wash out in laundering. This manner of dyeing is ideal for plaids, checks, stripes, and solid colors. Fabrics dyed with these dyes are such that it is practically impossible to remove the color should it be desired to redye the material.

UNION-DYEING: This is a one-bath process as a result of which the same color or shade can be imparted to two or more textile fibers or yarns in the same piece of material.

Both cross-dyeing and union-dyeing are forms of piece-dyeing in processing. Piece-dyeing is done on fabric made of only one type of yarn as to content. Union-dyeing differs from cross-dyeing in that in the former there is a single color or shade in the finished goods. It is possible, for example, to union-dye a fabric which contains "Orlon," "Dacron," rayon, and acetate—four fibers in the one cloth and in which a decided single color cast may be obtained. Union-dyeing is very popular in many types of men's wear, women's wear, and children's wear.

TOP- OR SLUB-DYEING: This is the dyeing of fibers in a top form or slub form which is wound into a top, usually worsted, and resembles a commercial cheese in shape and size. The top has been previously carded and combed but has not as yet been spun into yarn. The dyeing is carried out in circular machines and the pressure in the machine is very great. The entire top is dyed from the core to the outside in the treatment. Following dyeing the various colored tops are then blended to obtain some definite color or shade. Top-dyeing is resorted to in coloring fibers that are to be spun into yarn for use in worsted fabrics. Some of the better qualities of women's wear and men's wear fall and winter suitings are colored by this method.

VIGOUREUX DYEING OR PRINTING: This method of coloring embodies both dyeing and printing. It is the dyeing or printing of worsted top fibers by passing the slivers or slubbings through a printing machine which has a roller with raised bars to carry the dyestuff. The sliver is impregnated with the dyestuff when it comes in contact with the revolving raised areas on the roller that is to afford the pressure for printing the sliver areas which are to be colored onto the actual color roller. A roller with 60 per cent of its surface gouged out or cut will produce a sliver with a 40-per-cent-colored area. This method is also known as Melange dyeing or printing.

Blacks, browns, blues, and greens seem to be the most popular shades done in Vigoureux printing. Following the coloring, the stock is gilled and drawn, and is then spun into yarn to be made ready for the weaving of the fabric. Vigoureux-printed fabric appears only in the better class of men's and women's wear in the trade. Ideal for suiting and coating for cold-weather wear.

MINOR METHODS OF DYEING

Hand Methods

Many people like to dye textiles by hand. It may be done as a hobby but there are professional hand-dyers of textiles in the trade. This art is remunerative to them, otherwise they would not be in business. There is a vast difference between machine-dyeing and hand-dyeing as to production, labor costs, and the time element. Hand methods permit a very wide range of motif and decorativeness, and the commercial value of some of the products may be considered good, with prices in some instances rather high. Handwork is practically always more expensive than machine work. The most popular methods in hand-dyeing are:

BATIK-DYEING: The design obtained in this method of coloring is not clear cut since a mottled effect is always noted. The dyer obtains a medley of coloring which presents an interesting motif. Batik originated in Java, where the genuine fabrics, even obtainable today, used four colors—indigo blue, brown, black, and yellow. Other colors are now used, along with the originals, wherever the work is done throughout the world. *Batik* means "to paint."

A motif is traced or outlined on both sides of the cloth. Melted wax is then applied to the areas where the coloring will be more or less repelled by the wax. The wax, however, will crack and allow fine vein lines of cloth to appear as the dye seeps through and penetrates into the material. After the full colored areas and the vein-line areas are completed, the fabric is then removed from the bath, rinsed, and the wax is removed by hot water or a solvent. The operation may be repeated a number of times until the full design has been achieved. Multicolored effects result from the work, and the colors in batik are usually from light to dark.

BURL- OR SPECK-DYEING: Many specks and other foreign particles noted in cloth during the finishing operations must be remedied; much of this matter is vegetable in origin. Some types of woolens and worsteds, because of their nature, show these specks to disadvantage, chiefly in piece-dyed materials. The percher or specker, as he examines the goods, covers these blemishes by "inking on" the spots with the correct matching ink. These inks come in all colors. In some cases they are of much benefit to a mill.

TIE-DYEING: Also known as tie-and-dye, or dip-dyeing, this method is a very old one; it was used by hand-loom weavers of ancient times. Before the yarn or fabric is placed in the dye liquor, it is tightly tied with string or knotted at intervals. The areas not covered by the string or knots will take on the color as the yarn or fabric is dipped into the dye bath. The operation may be repeated a number of times to obtain this random method of coloring.

The dyed material upon completion will show a blurred, rather "shot-about" or mottled effect of coloring, since the colors tend to run into each other and overlap, thereby producing many varied color shades in the finished article.

The general steps used in tie-dyeing a piece of cloth:

1. Rolling the fabric into a "pig-tail" formation, and then tying certain areas of the rolled cloth with tightly wound string. Some dyers tie the cloth into a knotted formation instead of using string.
2. Dipping the cloth into the dye liquor.
3. Removing the dyed fabric and cutting away the string or unknotting the material.
4. Rinsing and handling the material. The operation may be repeated two or more times, if desired.

In this method of coloring, the uncolored portions are tied wherever possible. If several dippings are to be made, however, it seems to make little difference whether the tied or knotted areas are dyed or undyed. The use of a number of colorings by dipping will present a blurred effect that often borders on the bizarre.

Batik and tie-dyed fabrics are used for decorative purposes, novelties, covers, and runners.

Machine Methods

BALE-DYEING: A very low-cost method of dyeing cotton cloth. The material, without any scouring or singeing, is sent through a cold-water dye bath, where the sized warp yarn will have affinity for the dye. The filling will not dye since the wax in it has not been removed to admit dye absorption. Imitation chambray and a few similar fabrics are dyed in this manner.

BEAM-DYEING: A method of dyeing warp yarn prior to weaving. The warp is wound on perforated beams and the dye is forced through the perforations, thereby saturating the yarn with color.

CHAIN-DYEING: Used to dye yarns and cloths of low tensile strength. The lengths of yarns or fabrics are tied or tacked end to end and then run through the dye bath in a continuous operation. Production in this method may run high.

RANDOM DYEING: A method of dyeing yarn in which only certain areas are colored. Three methods give the result:

1. Skeins may be tightly tied in two or more places and dyed at one side of the tie with one color and at the other side with some other color.
2. Color may be printed onto the skeins which are spread on the blanket of the printing machine.
3. Cones or packages of yarn on hollow spindles may be arranged to form channels through the yarn by means of an air-operated punch, and the dyestuff

drawn through these holes by suction. The yarn in the immediate area of the punch absorbs the dye and the random effects are thereby attained. (See Tie-Dyeing.)

RAW-STOCK DYEING: The process of dyeing fibers before the spinning of the yarn made from the fiber stock. Used chiefly in coloring wool fibers, the dyeing follows the degreasing or scouring of the fibers and drying. (See Stock Dyeing.)

SPECK-DYEING: Many medium- and low-grade woolens and worsteds have to be speck-dyed to obliterate the specks caused by vegetable matter that has remained in the cloth during the various operations from raw stock to fabric. Much of this matter is rather deeply embedded in the goods. The cut of cloth may be dyed in a cold-soap bath of direct dyes which will color the cotton very well but leave the animal fibers unscathed. (See Burl- or Speck-Dyeing.)

WILLIAMS UNIT: Invented by S. H. Williams of the General Aniline & Film Corporation, New York City, this is an extremely versatile and economical machine for carrying out many operations in textile processing. It is widely used for dyeing, washing, pre-treating, and aftertreating, in the many continuous processes of the textile industry.

Other advantages of the unit include insulation to prevent loss of heat, minimum need of maintenance because of the simple mechanical construction, and compactness in size.

Light and dark shades are produced easily by a continuous-process treatment. There is control and a governing of the even circulation of solutions at all times, thereby preventing preoxidation. Each unit is equipped with microset rolls. The machine is installed to specifications using five- or ten-ton pressures, and it comes in widths of 40, 50, 60, and 70 inches.

TESTING

1. Name five methods used to dye textile fabrics.
2. Give the name of a fabric dyed by each of the foregoing methods.
3. Define cross-dyed fabric. Name a construction of fibers that could be used in a cross-dyed material.
4. What is union-dyeing? How does it differ from cross-dyeing?
5. What are some of the advantages of piece-dyeing that are not found in other methods of coloring fabrics?
6. State some reasons for the great rise in popularity of cross-dyed and union-dyed fabrics.
7. Name five materials that could be yarn- or skein-dyed.
8. Give the names of five different finishes that may be applied to textile materials.
9. Name five materials that ordinarily require no dyeing.
10. In Vigoureux printing, what would be the percentage of printing on the fiber stock if 60 per cent of the print roller were gouged or cut?
11. Describe batik-dyeing, or tie-dyeing.
12. What is meant by the term "burl- or speck-dyeing"? "random dyeing"?
13. Discuss the rise of dope-dyeing and give some reasons for its popularity.

Part 1—Unit 41

TOPIC: MAJOR AND MINOR METHODS OF PRINTING TEXTILES

Basically, the printing of textile fabrics is a simulation of the designs, motifs, and patterns observed in woven fabrics made on a hand or power loom. Printed cloths are, generally speaking, much lower in price when a comparison is made with woven goods in which patterns appear. The former has become relatively inexpensive when consideration is made of the fewer skills and intricacies necessary in the preparation of a design, the processes involved to make printed fabrics commercially successful, and the setting up of the rollers and other parts in a

Piece dyeing; single color effect; volume

Yarn or skein dyeing; two or more colors in fabric

Stock dyeing; hue, cast, or shade of a single color; wool

Cross-dyeing; two different colors and yarns

Union dyeing; two or more stocks to give single shade

Dope, solution, or spun-dyeing; very bright, fast color

PRINTING OF TEXTILE FABRICS

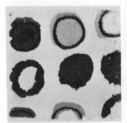
Direct, cylinder, roller, or calender printing; volume

Blotch printing; gives solid printed background

Discharge printing; some color areas removed, replaced

Resist printing; some areas resist color matter

Screen or stencil printing; hand or machine printing

Flock printing or flocking; any fabric may be flocked

Print-on-print or print-on-dyed

Duplex printing: both sides same or different; face

Duplex printing: different; back of cloth

printing machine. The improvements and advances in printed fabrics have been phenomenal, particularly since the close of World War I.

In work done by hand, such as handmade fabrics, clothes, cigars, or shoes, certain advantages are apparent such as better workmanship, closer individual attention, and more care in detail. Comparatively speaking, one pays more for products perfected by hand labor. When work is done by machine—taking a printing machine, for example—there are greater production, lower costs, progressive assembly, mass quantity, uniform sizes, and some job specialization. Printing of cloth is very economical from the commercial standpoint. To illustrate, at the present time an eight-hour shift in some printing plants can print as much as 15,000 yards of fabric on a single machine; this is at the rate of about 1,875 yards an hour or about 30 yards a minute. Some printing establishments prefer to print cloth in multiples of 5,000 yards; thus, a 16-hour run on two shifts would print about 30,000 yards of goods. Other plants are geared to take orders for any yardage within reason, "large or small."

Before taking up the printing of cloth on a printing machine, attention should be given to a device—the pantograph—used to set up the design that will be printed by one or more rollers on the machine.

THE PANTOGRAPH: All designs begin with the ideas of the designer. He outlines and produces his motif on paper, usually graph paper marked off in proper ratio lines. Following this, the design has to be developed and enlarged. The original pattern is enlarged by the pantograph magnifier. The motif is engraved by hand onto a zinc plate which is set on a flat table. A frame connects the table with the pantograph machine. The frame has an arm which is tipped with a diamond tracing-needle or point. The operator uses this pencil-like point to follow each line in the pattern. Every movement of the point is transferred to a series of diamond points controlled by a set of levers. These points are set so that they come in contact with the varnish-covered copper roller.

This special bituminous-base, acid-resistant varnish coating affords protection to the copper roller when it is placed in an acid bath. The needle points, controlled by the operator, cut through the varnish cleanly, leaving the copper in plain view. The points have been spaced in a predetermined accurate order dependent on the number of repeats of pattern cut into the roller. As mentioned, they are connected with the head point or master needle, which is guided by the machine operator; each needle point in the set will place its repeat of motif upon the one roller in simultaneous motions. The copper roller, which has been trimmed for smoothness and trueness prior to using it, may be used a great many times, since only a very small fraction of an inch is lost through complete engraving and printing procedures. Some rollers will last for many years.

After the pantographer has completed his work on the roller, it is then placed in a stone trough filled with iron sulfide. This chemical, by its oxidizing action on the copper, will widen the exposed design area. The roller is next placed in another trough which contains a solution of nitric acid. This acid will etch the pattern into the copper roller to a depth sufficient for the printing which follows. The roller is placed on a cylinder set upon axles, where the operator checks closely by optical inspection all gouged areas for correct depth and uniformity. He applies any finishing touches necessary to make the roller as nearly perfect as possible.

A third trough, served by a continuous flow of water, is used to wash away all traces of acid, and to prevent further oxidation of the copper roller. Finally, the roller is dried and the varnish is removed by benzine or some other suitable solvent. It is now ready for mounting in the printing machine.

PRINTING may be described as the decoration of the surface or surfaces of fabric by the application of insoluble pigments or fast dyes in definite repeated forms and colors. The earliest form of printing was probably done from carved blocks which were charged with a colored paste and pressed onto the fabric. The act is repeated in regular placement across the width and down the length of the goods. Block printing is necessarily slow.

The invention of roller printing speeded printing from a few hundred yards to thousands of yards per day. In this "print-on" method, a series of engraved copper rollers, up to 16, generally, are held in stands arranged through the front and bottom circumference of the platen or main drum. For each print roller, which represents one color, there is a color trough, color roller, and a "doctor" or excess-paste-removal blade. All colors, including the ground color, are successively applied at rapid speed. Depending on whether the applied color was direct or developed, the processed cloth then proceeds to the steaming, ageing, and other after-treatment operations.

A well-designed print roller will adequately color the surface and penetrate deep enough to give depth of shade, leaving the reverse side in an unfinished state. Certain thin fabrics can be "through-printed" so that the back of the goods is almost as well defined as the face. This is especially true in discharge printing.

Printing can be done on both sides of a fabric; this is known as duplex printing. The operation necessitates two independent operations and is expensive. Other types of printing include:

1. Spaced application print on white or dyed ground.
2. Allover print on white or dyed ground.
3. Resist print followed by dyeing.
4. Discharge print on dyed ground.

OPERATION OF THE PRINTING MACHINE

1. The color has to be thickened to the proper consistency so that it will not flow out of the engravings in the copper roller.
2. The color furnisher picks up the thick color paste from the color trough and covers the entire copper roller with color.
3. The color doctor is a long, sharp blade which scrapes off all color from the copper roller except that which is in the grooves or gougings of the design. The action simulates a man's removing face lather when shaving.
4. The roller then presses against the cloth to be printed, thereby leaving the design imprint on the cloth. It can be compared with the methods used in printing a newspaper, the comics, the making of wallpaper.
5. The lint doctor scrapes off any lint from the copper roller which may have been picked up from the cloth. Lint would interfere with the color pattern in the same manner as a hair caught on a pen point will smear writing.
6. The main cylinder holds the cloth to be printed so that the copper roller can press the design into the material.
7. The back gray cloth keeps the machine clean by absorbing any excess dye paste.
8. After printing, the cloth is sent to a steam chamber for setting. It is then dried, aged to fix the color, de-sized, and then finished.

Sketchmaking Department: Sketchmaker setting out design, checking proper repeat before setting out necessary zinc plates.

Sketchmaking Camera Room: Sketch seen in projection camera reflecting image onto set-out zinc plate. Sketchmaker follows full-color image to reproduce motif.

Plate Painting: Figures on sketched plate are being painted to distinguish one color from another before pantographing.

Plate Engraving: The design for each color is engraved on a flat plate.

Transfer of the Design by the Pantograph: Design is being transferred from zinc plate to wax-covered, copper roller by pantograph. Diamond needles are used.

Roller Painting: Cylinder being examined for defects before etching.

Etching Room: Print rollers are etched in various depths. Etching takes place only where pantograph diamond has penetrated acid-resisting coating.

Finish Polishing: Engraved cylinder is again examined, highly polished before chrome plating, and finally completed for printing.

Courtesy: Sanco Dye Works, Inc., Phillipsburg, N. J.

Courtesy: Textron, Inc.

SIDE VIEW OF DIRECT PRINTING MACHINE
(This method of printing is also called calender, cylinder or roller printing)

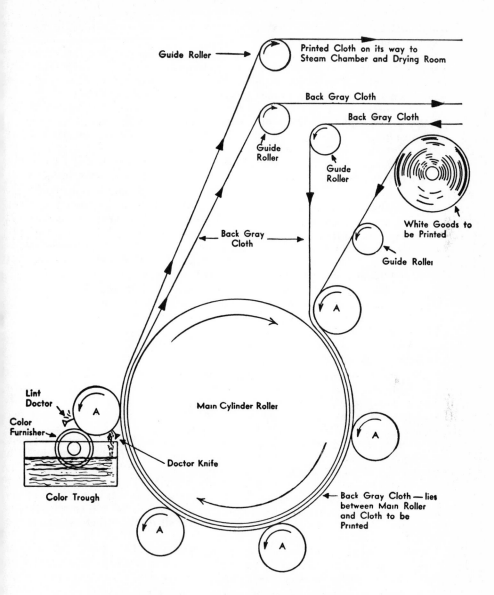

Guide Roller → Printed Cloth on its way to Steam Chamber and Drying Room

Back Gray Cloth

Back Gray Cloth

Guide Roller

Guide Roller

White Goods to be Printed

Back Gray Cloth

Guide Roller

A

Lint Doctor

A

Color Furnisher

Main Cylinder Roller

A

Doctor Knife

Color Trough

Back Gray Cloth — lies between Main Roller and Cloth to be Printed

A

A

A. The etched copper print rollers which make printing possible. There must be a roller for each color used in the pattern.

MAJOR METHODS OF PRINTING

BLOTCH PRINTING: This is printing material in order to give it a dyed ground effect. Blotch-printed cloth gives the impression that the cloth may have been colored in some particular manner, but close examination will readily show that the blotch method has been used. A material is printed, and as a result of this, the groundwork will be white if the blotch method has not been used. The large colored basic areas take the print because of the manner in which the dye paste is made to adhere to the goods. Very fine lines, from twenty to two hundred per inch, will hold the dyestuff for printing so that when the machine operation is given, the entire white surface is printed. Thus, a printed groundwork will appear on the cloth, with one or more small or spot designs in their proper places on the face of the goods.

Blotch printing differs from duplex printing in that in an examination of the former, the back of the fabric will not show the same as the face. There will be some absorption on the back but not nearly enough to give a duplex effect. Some blotch prints have white in their motif as a background, as well as some other basic color, depending upon the pattern. Little duplex cloth is seen today since the process is slow, the cost is high, and other methods of printing are more popular.

DIRECT PRINTING: This type of printing sets the patterns directly onto the material from rollers, usually made of copper engraved for printing the motif on the fabric when the rollers are set in motion. Other names for direct printing are CALENDER, CYLINDER, or ROLLER PRINTING. The bleached goods are fed into the machine, pass between the rollers which have the designs etched in them (one roller for each color to go onto the cloth), and take the printed motif directly. Direct printing is used for printed designs on cloth which has a white area for the background.

DISCHARGE PRINTING: Also called extract printing, this method is used for dark-colored materials which have white or colored designs. The fabric is piece-dyed, and certain areas of color are bleached or discharged, leaving white places in the goods. The cloth is then direct-printed and some or all of the white portions are colored according to the plan. It is also possible to add a basic color to the discharge paste to produce a colored pattern.

RESIST PRINTING: This method of printing is resorted to when it is desired to obtain a white figure on a colored background by dyeing the goods after they have been printed. The cloth to be treated is tannated according to some plan or motif. When the tannin acts upon the material at the designated places, it has the power to repel the action of the dyestuff that is to be used to dye the goods a solid color. The dyestuff will not become "fixed" on the material where it has been tannated.

After the goods have been dyed, they are treated in a correct chemical solution that will not affect the dyed areas, but will remove the tannin or mordant so as to produce a white effect on the colored cloth. Acetic acid may be used to remove the tannin. Thus a colored cloth with white effects will result. If it is further desired to have colored effects on the goods, they may be printed to give colored dots or designs on the colored background. Some or all of the white areas may be colored.

Basic colors are generally used for this method of printing, and if a color resist is wanted, then some color is added to the resist paste. Cloths which are often resist-printed include foulard, bandannas, polka-dot effects, bunting, dressgoods.

DISCHARGE AND RESIST PRINTING, SUMMARY OF: In discharge printing, the ground is dyed a solid shade or color. The design is then printed with a discharge paste, usually with some hydrosulfite since it will give a white discharge.

If color effects are desired, the color matter is used with the discharge paste, since it will not affect the color. Vat colors are often employed; they require hydrosulfites for their reduction and, at the same time, discharge the dyed background from the goods—an ideal plan used on rayons.

To obtain a white discharge print effect on a vat print, the material is essentially blotch-printed. Discharge printed goods will show pure white or color effects which go through to the back of the goods.

In reserve or resist printing, white effects on aniline black are very effective, since excellent results are obtained; the cost is relatively low and this fast black is exceptionally difficult to discharge. In this method of printing, the goods are printed with tin salts and a gum which acts as a resisting agent. The material is then dyed. The portions of the goods which are not treated with the resist substance will take on the dyestuff. Sometimes, however, colors are added to the resist paste. These are colors which are not affected by the dyeing treatment.

Resist-printed effects may show on only one side of the material; the other side of the fabric will present a more or less solid color, generally speaking. If the fabric is rather thin or sheer, the resist effect may be seen very clearly on both sides of the material.

OTHER METHODS OF PRINTING

APPLICATION PRINTING: The word "commercial" is synonymous with the word "application," and these two terms are used very loosely in the industry. Generally speaking, it is the printing onto white goods irrespective of the type of material involved; rather popular in printing of silk, acetate, and rayon. There is no discharge or resist-printing involved in this method of coloring, whether for dyed or for printed materials. It is sometimes referred to as direct printing but usually with the understanding that the colors applied to the goods in question, in most instances, are not fast to light and washing. The words "application" and "commercial" are loosely used with regard to dyes, dyed fabrics, or printed goods. Labels should always be carefully read whenever either of these terms appear on any fabric or garment.

BLOCK PRINTING: This is the oldest form of printing known to man. Some museum pieces are known to be over five thousand years old. Wooden, metallic, or linoleum blocks are carved with the motif or design, using one block for each color required.

The dye is applied in the form of a paste to the face of the block, which is then pressed and hammered onto the material. The operation is repeated as many times as necessary. Careful handling is essential.

Block printing is usually done to full-width goods on a strong supporting table. Compared with other methods of printing, block printing, as to production, is almost negligible; block-printed fabrics on the market today are considered expensive.

BURN-OUT PRINTING: Print which shows raised designs on sheer ground. Made by printing design with chemical on fabric woven of paired threads of different fibers, then burning out one of the fibers from the parts printed. Often used on velvet, scarf fabric, and soft goods for headgear, such as mantillas and veilings.

DUPLEX OR REGISTER PRINTING: This is the name given to fabric printed with the same or another motif on the reverse of the goods. Thus, both sides are colored and the material may be classed as a reversible. This print is used to simulate woven stripes and other basic designs in certain fabrics. Duplex prints at times command a good price since they find considerable use in hangings and curtains of medium and better grades.

FLOCK PRINTING: This method of printing has in recent years become very popular, chiefly because of the low cost involved and the types of motifs that are possible. The application of the dots to the cloth is accomplished by means of a gummy paste which consists of thoroughly ground powder-form fibers and an adhering agent. The effect on the goods is that of small embroidery such as dotted swiss, for example.

Metals are used to give gold, silver, or copper effects on some of the fabrics. The method is known as metallic printing. Any kind, grade, type, and quality of cloth may be flock-dotted. The dots and other effects, however, may not always be fast to washing and laundering. (See Flock, Flocking, Flock Printing, Unit 42.)

INDIA PRINT: Muslin printed with design typical in form and color of those used in India. Genuine India prints are hand-blocked with nature patterns in glowing oriental colors. Imitations must be declared as such.

OVERPRINTING: Colors or designs that are printed over other colors and motifs. Overprint is used when it is desired to alter the shades and to tone down certain vivid colors or effects. It is much used to give floral and splash-print effects to certain types of cloth.

PHOTOGRAPHIC PRINTING: This method of printing makes it possible to do very fine work on textiles which otherwise would be most difficult to do by the roller method. Dark ground and solid effects, as well as fine detail work, can be executed on cloth colored in this manner in one continuous etching operation.

The design is photographed and the negative is then covered with a screen plate. In this way it is possible to break up the solid areas of the design so that the dark portions of the negative will then be shown by fine lines.

A contact print is made by projecting a light through the screen plate onto another film. As many exposures are made as are necessary to produce a complete film covering the entire copper roller.

The film is then placed around a roller which has been previously treated with a sensitizing solution. A powerful arc light is then focused upon it. Whenever the light passes through the film it affects the sensitized roller, baking the chemical coating and causing it to harden.

Warm water is then used to wash the roller to take away the sensitizing solution areas which were not exposed to light. The copper roller is then placed in a bath of iron perchloride for several minutes. The solution etches the bare portions of the roller. These gougings form the engraved pattern that is to be printed. Afterwards the roller is washed to rid it of the portions covered with the baked sensitized solution which have resisted the action of the cutting or etching bath. Dressgoods of many types are printed in this novel, popular manner.

PIGMENT PRINTING: Pigment is a coloring matter or substance, a dry substance, usually pulverized, which, when mixed with a liquid vehicle in which it is insoluble becomes a dye, paint, ink, etc. Pigment printing has many advantages over other classes of colors. Practically all types of fibers and blends can be printed; there are fewer "seconds," chiefly because it is an easy matter to observe the printing results and if flaws are found they may be remedied at once. Compatibility of colors is assured if pigments of the same type have been used in the processing, thereby increasing the range of colors available. There are, for example, certain colors in the vat range for which there is not any match possible.

Printed goods may be stored for any length of time, within reason, prior to curing. Fixing of color is done by a simple process of curing. Much lighter engravings, as in photo engravings, can be used with moderate pressure on the machine, affording a saving in paste consumption. No aftertreatments, such as washing, oxidation, or soaping are necessary; thus, a saving in time, steam, and work.

PRINT-ON-PRINT: Self-explanatory, since the motifs are printed onto the material. It is fast becoming a conventional method of coloring textiles where the discharge or resist methods are not required. Each color used must have its individual roller, and each color must fit to the exact, minute part of the pattern required in the finished material. At present, it is estimated to be the cheapest form of printing with regard to price. Ideal for general printing purposes, it is particularly effective where high production and long runs of goods are required. (See Overprinting.)

SCREEN OR STENCIL PRINTING: A wooden frame resembling a window frame is constructed. One side of the frame is covered with silk bolting cloth. This cloth, high in texture and of very fine mesh, is rather expensive.

The design is traced on the silk cloth or screen. (Nylon is also a very popular base fabric.) A filler of enamel or varnish, sometimes called "tish," is applied to all parts of the screen except the design.

The prepared screen is placed on the material to be printed. The stencil must be in contact with the material. Dye paste is now placed on top of the stencil and stroked back and forth a few times with a squeegee. The dye paste is forced through the open meshes of the bolting cloth, but only in those places not previously covered with the filler.

To set the color in the design that has been transferred to the cloth, a steaming is necessary. Final treatments should be carefully done. Screen printing has considerable call in small production plants which specialize in intricate designs. The method is rather slow with regard to production since there must be a different screen used for each color to be placed upon the goods.

SHADOW PRINTING: Silk, ribbon, or cretonne, woven with printed warp yarn forming indistinct design. Reversible.

STIPPLE EFFECT IN PRINTING: This is merely the printing of small dotted effects in between the spaces or bare areas of a printed design. It is used chiefly for novelty effects on fabrics.

TJAP PRINTING: A very interesting type of block printing executed by dipping blocks into heated wax and then impressing them upon the material—usually a cotton, silk, or rayon fabric—after which it is dyed and the wax removed, leaving a permanent design. These blocks are made by the natives of Java and the other islands in the East Indies by bending small strips of copper into the desired curves for sections of the pattern and inserting them into the end grain of the blocks of wood, allowing them to project a little less than one-eighth inch from the surface.

The small copper ridges formed in this way are similar to the cloisons which are applied to keep the enamels separated in the decoration of the well-known cloisonné. Owing to the fact that it is a very difficult and painstaking task to make these blocks or tjaps, the results of this art often bring prices as high as direct handwork.

TOILE DE JOUY: Originally a set of cotton fabrics printed in imitation of the various imported oriental materials brought into France and executed in Jouy, by Oberkampf. In 1759, as the result of a governmental citation, Oberkampf established his plant in Jouy; his influence still prevails.

Prior to Oberkampf's methods, the printing process on cottons consisted of marking the outline of the design in black and filling in the colors by hand. Oberkampf introduced block and roller-print effects on his fabrics. His success soon became phenomenal, since his Jouy "canvases" became the rage in dressgoods and for general decorative purposes.

WARP PRINTING: The principles in this method of printing are like those in ordinary cloth printing, except that the mechanical operation is different. The yarn to be printed is wound onto a beam and the warp threads are passed through the printing machine. The dyestuff, which has been made into paste form, is applied to these parallel ends as they come in contact with the printing rollers.

The yarn is dyed prior to being rewound onto a second warp beam. This beam is ultimately set into sockets at the back of the loom, so that the weaving interlacing the warp ends and the filling picks may be done.

The pattern, motif, or design in warp-printed goods will not have the sharp cleavage lines noted in some other types of printed goods; the effect is mottled in appearance. Because of the white or single color filling used in the weaving, the spots of color on the warp that look brilliant before the weaving of the fabric will be subdued to considerable degree. Fabric printed by this method is said to have a quiet appearance.

So that the warp may be controlled while it is being treated, the following method is resorted to: every few inches a filling pick is inserted through the warp in order to give a loose construction controlled at all times. This method will hold the warp to be printed in a chain form when ready for treatment.

When the warp is spread out and placed in the loom, dominant and recessive effects of the color in the goods will be toned off. These prints are usually very attractive. Uses include counterpanes, spreads, dressgoods, covers, and hangings.

WEDGWOOD PRINT: Print of white design on colored ground similar to effect on Wedgwood china.

KNITTED FABRIC PRINTING

The utmost care and precaution have to be given knitgoods because of the nature of their construction. Four methods are in use today; these follow:

DIRECT PRINTING WITH COPPER ROLLERS: This method is ideal for warp knitgoods. The fabrics is gummed lightly to the back gray cloth to counteract possible slippage of the goods in processing. Printing is usually done on the reverse side of the material, since the back of the goods is smoother than the actual face of the cloth. (See page 218.)

SCREEN OR STENCIL HAND-PRINTING: Both warp and weft knit fabrics are colored by the method but compared with the other methods in use it is rather expensive since production is low and time-consuming.

AUTOMATIC PRINTING, FLAT-BED SCREEN: In one of the more recent developments in fabric printing of textiles, a heavy-gauge neoprene belt is used, and the screens are set to a specially designed set of lifting brackets, placed on each side of the belt. Cloth to be printed is run onto the belt and the brackets automatically lift and lower the screens onto the material thereby printing the motif onto the goods. production is low and time-consuming.

ROTARY SCREEN PRINTING: The "Aljaba" machine is set up comparably with the direct or cylinder method of printing, which is done by means of copper rollers. Phosphor-bronze gauze screens on the rotary method are used instead of the rollers to produce the pattern. The printing color paste is fed into the inside of the frame where a small metal roller forces it through the open areas (or interstices) onto the fabric. Both warp and weft knitgoods may be colored by this method.

TESTING

1. Explain the function of each of the following parts on a printing machine:

   a) Main cylinder.   d) Color trough.   g) Lint doctor.
   b) Back gray cloth.   e) Color furnisher.   h) Steam chamber and
   c) Color guide roller.   f) Color doctor.   drying room.

2. What is the difference between direct printing and blotch printing?
3. Why are resist-printed and discharge-printed fabrics so popular in the dressgoods trade?
4. How would you identify a dyed fabric from a printed material? Discuss some particular dyed cloth with a specific printed fabric.
5. Name three printed fabrics suitable for decorative purposes in the home; three suitable for evening wear; three for sportswear; three for at-home attire.
6. The same end results may be obtained by resist printing and by discharge printing. Explain how they differ from each other with regard to processing operations.
7. Define duplex or register printing.
8. Describe how flock printing is done; screen or stencil printing.
9. What are some advantages of photographic printing?
10. Discuss the work of Oberkampf and his famous Toile de Jouy prints of the eighteenth century.

TOPIC: FLOCK, FLOCKING, FLOCK PRINTING

Flocking, actually a form of printing, has become very popular in recent years for several reasons—the low cost involved to obtain an almost endless number of interesting motifs or designs, the appealing suede effect noted on a host of fabrics and apparel articles, brilliant color effects, and an allover flocking effect on a fabric such as velvet or velveteen, or designs that stand in relief effect on other types of cloth.

The word "flock" is derived from the Latin *floccus* and the German *Locke*, implying a lock or small portion of cotton, wool, flax, etc. In the seventeenth century Le François, a noted French designer, devised a method of attaching flock fibers to various types of paper to be used for decorative purposes. He also was successful in flocking textile materials. Up to that time, only the wealthier families on the Continent and the British Isles could afford to buy the expensive velvets, damasks, brocades, and brocatelles made in Florence, Genoa, and Milan in Italy; in Lyons, France; and in Seville and Barcelona, Spain. It was Le François who brought these simulated fabrics within the purchasing power of the middle classes.

Flock stock comes from many sources: from the short, uncontrolled-length fibers from the rollers of preparatory machines used in the manufacture of spun yarn, such as fibers from the licker-in, stripper, fancy, and doffer rollers on the carding frame; mill sweepings, "blizzard" fibers obtained in the manufacture of carpeting and other floor coverings, wastes of many and sundry types and origins, tailor's clippings; shoddy, mungo, and "findings" of many sorts. Metallic particles are also used in flocking to embellish fabrics with copper, gold, and silver effects for decorative purposes, evening wear, dressgoods, etc.

The fibers used in flocking may be natural fibers or manmade fibers. They may vary in quality from poor to excellent, with the so-called "waste fibers" being in the lower grades. Fibers used in flocking for the most part can be bleached and then dyed easily and well.

While practically all textile fibers provide flock stock, viscose rayon, nylon, and cotton are used the most often, especially since it is possible to obtain high-grade basic fibers from these sources. Viscose rayon and nylon come from tow fibers, which are straight, untwisted, uniform, and can be controlled as to length, denier size, and diameter. Cotton stock in the better grades is obtained in a full-bleach white fiber condition, while the poorer grades usually come from "findings"—cotton rag wastes, and discarded apparel and thread. Much cotton fiber is obtained from various mill wastes, and this is usually good to excellent in quality for use in flocking. Nylon flock is ideal for use in floor coverings because of its excellent resistance to abrasion and wear and its ability to withstand "foot traffic."

Flocks may be applied to practically any textile material, paper, leather, wood, etc. Textile uses include apparel, artwork, belts, decorative fabrics, curtains, drapes, floor covering, footwear, handbags, lamps, novelties of many types, pennants, commercial signs on fabric, jackets, jerseys, jumpers, linings of various types and uses, sweatshirts, toys, wall coverings, etc.

METHODS OF FLOCKING

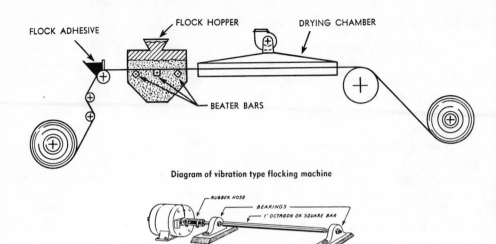

Diagram of vibration type flocking machine

Details of beater bars shown in diagram above

SCHEMATIC DIAGRAM OF
MECHANICAL FLOCKING

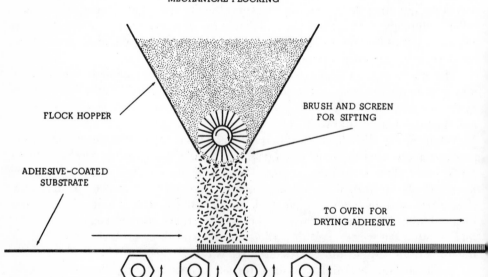

The principles of mechanical flocking are demonstrated by this diagram

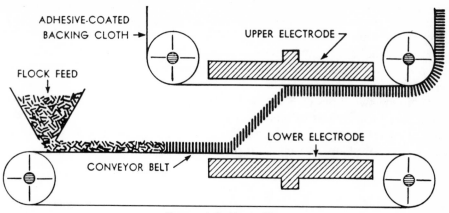

Electrostatic flocking machine

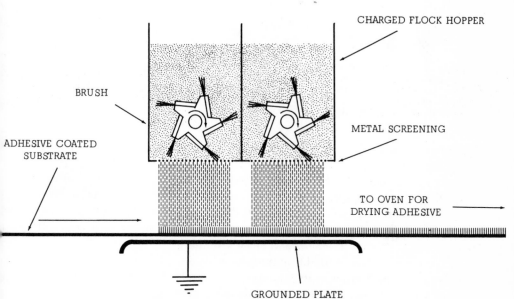

SCHEMATIC DIAGRAM OF
ELECTROSTATIC FLOCKING

This diagram illustrates the basic principles of electrostatic flocking

Courtesy: Cellusuede Products, Inc., Rockford, Illinois

[227]

The motifs can range from very large designs to miniature flock-dotted effects on dotted swiss, embroidery, curtains, dimity and some other types of summer dressgoods. While any grade, kind, quality, or type of material may be flocked, it should be borne in mind that not all flocked textiles are fast to washing and/or drycleaning. Thus, one should always heed the information on the label or labels attached to the article, and be guided accordingly. The type of fabric, quality, and price often determine as to whether or not the article is colorfast to light, perspiration, crocking, sea water, etc.

There are two types of flock used today—filler stock, which is used in plastic and rubber formulations to increase bulkiness or to add strength, and decorator stock, used for interesting surface effects, motifs, and textures, to absorb sound and cushion vibration, as well as to protect surfaces.

Pennant showing the famous badger of the University of Wisconsin. Shading, stripes, and detail were applied to the pennant by airbrushing transparent dye colors through stencils, including a very quick but very effective method of adding three-dimensional quality to the figure. Pennant made by Collegiate Manufacturing Company, Ames, Iowa, loaned by courtesy of Cellusuede Products, Inc., Rockford, Illinois.

It has been said "that any fiber so long as it has two tips or ends can be used in flocking." One type of fiber used in flocking is precision cut, thereby producing what is called controlled fiber stock. Viscose rayon, nylon, and some other man-made fibers are in this sphere. The term "random-cut" signifies natural fibers which cannot be controlled as to staple length, diameter, and size. In this category are wool, cotton, flax, etc., and the flock obtained is more or less of a conglomerate mass of stock, uneven in length and lacking uniformity.

Precision-cut stock with its uniformity may be used in short lengths up to long lengths, which provide, for example, a deep-pile effect on the finished article, such as a mat, carpet, rug, or a deep-pile-effect coating.

Random stock has to be graded, and a screening is used for this purpose. The treatment eliminates dust, chaff, dried particles and other foreign matters, as well as overlength fibers. A mesh screen is used which has anywhere from twelve to sixty interstices, meshes, or openings per linear inch.

Common flock ranges from a length of .015 inch in a 1.5-denier size with a diameter of .0005 inch to a length of .060 inch in a 9-denier size with a diameter of .0011 inch.

Application of Flock Stock: Three methods are used:

1. SPRAY METHOD: This is comparable with the spraying of paint onto wood, metal, paper, etc., with a spray gun. The opening, hole, or orifice of the gun is greater in diameter than that of the ordinary spray gun because the flock is a solid substance and cannot be atomized by a spray gun as in the case of adhesive or paint. An adhesive is defined as a compound which has the properties of sticking, clinging, or attaching itself to anything with which it comes in contact. Adhesives can be tenacious, viscous, and tacky.

Spraying of the fibers onto and into the adhesive should be done about eighteen inches from the adhesive surface of the base fabric to insure that the flock spears are driven into the adhesive in an upright position. This distance allows the air blast from the gun proper time for drying upon the adhesive. It also does away with possible high pressures which can cause improper drying and impede progress. The base fabric, incidentally, should always be of good construction and firmness, since low-textured fabrics are usually found to give trouble in manipulating and performance. Acrylic-base adhesives are the best to use since they will assure good, clean work and fulfill all the requirements of what a good adhesive should possess.

The adhesive coat should be applied over the entire surface and the flock will cover all this area when applied to it. It is also possible to spray the adhesive and the flock simultaneously to a material, the flock stream being directed into the adhesive stream in the operation. The adhesives coat the fibers and assure adherence to any object with which they come in contact. The action occurs about three inches from the object and the flock will strike it in a viscous, sticky, or tacky condition. The buildup of the flock coating can be secured to any reasonable thickness.

2. VIBRATION METHOD: Sometimes known as the "beater bar method," it is a mechanical operation which can treat a roll of material upon which the flock falls into a moving adhesive-coating backing to assume a random effect wherein the flock assumes horizontal, oblique, and vertical positions in the viscous adhesive bed. Incidentally, adhesives are used to stiffen, stabilize, and to give body and substance to the article and curb possible stretch, or to bond the flock used in a firm manner.

In the next step in the procedure, rotating beater bars strike the material on an endless belt which carries the fabric or paper. This action is done at a very high number of revolutions per minute. The action stands the fibers on end but the distribution of the vertically oriented fibers is not high in the finished item. The endless conveyor belt passes over the beaters in its functional work. The manipulation of adhesive in the processing may be done by the use of a silk or nylon screen, stencil, engraved rollers, printing press, etc. This results in a firm setting of the fibers into the adhesive.

The beater is actually a bar or a brush that rotates from a source of power. The vibration encountered in this method will likely cause varying degrees of static electricity which must be grounded by the use of an antistatic agent, since a fire hazard is caused by the static created. In addition, the fibers may firmly cling to various parts of the machine and resist removal unless some antistatic provision has been made during manipulation.

3. ELECTROSTATIC METHOD: This is the most practical, popular, and economical method for flocking. Since its conception about twenty years ago, it is based on the law in physics in which bodies of like electrical charge repel each other while bodies of unlike electrical charge attract each other. An electrostatic field is created between a positive and a negative electrode to give the power of attraction. The cut-filament flock is given a positive charge to draw it into an electrostatic field so that the fibers may align themselves in parallel position to the lines of force (flux). Thus, the fibers in the charged zone are attracted to the other electrode, and the ionized at-

mosphere around the one electrode causes the fibers to go to the other electrode where the adhesive or coating ingredient holds them securely in place.

In the action the fibers are impelled downward at high velocity to the adhesive film of the backing, which affords a high distribution of vertically oriented flock.

TESTING

1. Define flock; random flock; precision-cut flock; suede or suede finish.
2. List five sources from which flock stock may be obtained.
3. Define viscous; tacky; adhesive.
4. Name three textile fibers that are precision cut for flocking.
5. Name three textile fibers in the random flock category.
6. Name five articles or products that may be given a flock finish.
7. What are the three methods used today to flock materials?
8. Discuss the principle in the study of physics used in the electrostatic method for flocking materials.
9. Discuss in detail one of the three methods of flocking in use today.
10. Of what importance is the label or labels attached to an article or garment?

Courtesy of J. C. Sutton, President, Cellulose Products, Inc., 500 North Madison Street, Rockford, Illinois.

Part 1—Unit 43

TOPIC: Finishing of Textile Fabrics

Practically all fabric, with the exception of canvas, duck, and webbing, has to be given some type of finishing treatments. Loom fabric or greige (griege, gray, grey) goods as they come from the loom do not have any appeal. The cloth is usually soiled, unkempt, and contains varying amounts of foreign matter such as specks, motes, and a host of other impurities; blemishes and flaws are also noted. There has probably never been a perfect yard of cloth ever woven on a loom. Fabrics, it has been stated, are "made in the finishing," and "the fabric's the thing." Finished fabric must have "eye appeal to become buy appeal," along with other assets to make it salable. An unbleached cotton muslin, printcloth or sheeting, for example, from the loom is rather drab and uninteresting in appeal to the eye. When finished, however, they may have been bleached, dyed, or printed, or may come in some desirable shade or cast. They possess a very attractive appearance for surface effect, and are readily salable. The change from the greige state to finished condition wrought in fabrics is fantastic.

FINISH may be defined as the final, actual surface effect noted on fabric. A finish may be bright, dull, lustered, embossed, moiré or watermarked, napped, sheared, cropped, calendered, lacquered, soft, harsh, crisp, etc. The finish is a definite contributory point in the final "handle, hand, or feel" of a fabric.

FINISHING is an art and a science in making fabrics presentable to the consuming public. The resultant fabric may be fair, medium, good, or excellent in quality when made ready for the market. It is the converting of the unsightly greige goods into fabric with a definite appeal. Finishing instructions must be carried out to the letter, and discretion, judgment, and accuracy are paramount. Finishing may be compared with the application of cosmetics to the face to improve the attractiveness of the wearer. Some persons can use cosmetics to advantage; for others it does little or nothing at all. Some can apply cosmetics with a good technique, while others use them to a degree "where they seem to put it on with a spray, and a chisel is needed to remove them from the face." Hair on the head of a woman and some phases of finishing are comparable; hair and fabric can be bleached, dyed, tinted, washed, scoured, dried, etc. Thus with textile fabrics: finishing can usually do very much for materials, but there are some cloths that are truly not finished too well because of faulty applications, improper timing, incorrect temperatures and times, inferior ingredients, and so on. If anything in finishing cloth goes awry, the resultant fabric will not be salable and will likely become a "second."

Generally speaking, there are three types of finishes that fabric may have or be given:

1. MILL FINISH: The brand new fabric, well finished, as it comes from the textile mill or plant.
2. HOME LAUNDRY FINISH: Garments after laundering have to go through various and sundry treatments "to bring the fabric or garment back to as good as new."
3. COMMERCIAL LAUNDRY: Its function is "to bring soiled garments to the cleansed condition" so that further use and wear are possible.

In another sense there are two types of finishes applied to textiles. These are:

1. BASIC FINISH: The application of finishing ingredients to alter or improve the appearance, surface effect, or texture.
2. FUNCTIONAL FINISH: This is one which changes or improves the performance or wearability of a fabric.

Finishing is spoken of as being either physical or chemical. There is also a dry finishing method or process, as well as a wet process.

1. DRY FINISHING: These are operations or treatments given to cloth in which no water, bath, or moisture is applied to the goods. Examples would include perching, measuring, burling, specking, mending, sewing; shearing, napping or gigging, pressing, packing, etc.
2. WET FINISHING: The term signifies the various wet operations, chemical in nature, that may be given cloth so as to make it, in due time, presentable to the customer. Examples include soaping, scouring, washing, dyeing, fulling, milling, pounding, mercerizing, Sanforizing, etc.

Finished fabrics from the mill have either a temporary or a durable finish. Some fabrics are listed as having a permanent finish, but there are very few that can claim this distinction. The price paid for the cloths, the grade and quality of the ingredients with which they have been treated, and the end uses intended for the goods govern the type of finish to be given the material. The consumer pays for any product, and the "price must be right." The foregoing philosophy holds true at all times in buying finished articles or goods.

SELECTED LIST OF TYPES OF FINISHES

It has been estimated that there are around two hundred different types of finishes that may be given various textile fabrics. There are about fifty different finishes that can be applied to cotton alone. Below is a selected list of the more popular, major finishes given fabric today.

ABERDEEN: Slightly starched finish given to sheeting that has been dyed black for use as lining.

ABSORBENT: The result of treating fabric with chemicals to give the material greater and quicker water absorption properties.

ANTI-CREASE, CREASE-RESISTANT: Sometimes known as C.R.F. (Crease Resistant Finish) it is one in which the fabric is treated with chemicals to provide resistance, and then recovery, from wrinkling.

BACK-FILLING: Usually applied to low-grade, low-cost cloth to provide a better appearance. Only one side of the goods is affected by the process. The filling solution is composed of varying amounts of the following ingredients—corn starch, talc, China clay, and tallow. Other starches are often added to the solution when deemed necessary. The mixture is usually heavy and rather thick. Application is done by a starch mangle. In filling dyed goods, the compound is always colored to resemble closely the shade of the fabric itself. Care must be taken to see that this filling starch does not work to the surface of the goods. It is advantageous to calender the cloth heavily prior to the starching process since it presses the threads or yarns closer together and, at the same time, flattens them out, thereby preventing the starch from easily coming through to the face of the goods.

BEETLING: Provides a flattened appearance to the cloth by the use of beetlers or fallers. In the mechanical action of the fallers, the spaces or interstices among the warp and the filling are covered up and aid in obtaining the high gloss or sheen noted on the finished goods. As the cloth is wound slowly onto a roller, the hammers, which are heavy metal devices, strike the top layer of the goods with great force, causing the material to take on the "thready appearance." The process provides a sort of moiré or watermarked effect seen on the goods, caused by the heavy beating of the material in the layer formation. Several cotton fabrics are beetled; the finish, however, is not very durable when the fabric or garment is in use.

The term "beetling-out" or "beating-out" is often used in speaking of the surface effect on the cloth. Beetling provides a better linenlike finish on cotton than any other finishing method.

BLEACHED: Bleaching removes natural and other types of impurities and blemishes of various types from the goods, takes out coloring matter that might be present, and makes the cloth white, or very nearly white. It also provides for better and clearer dyeing or printing of the material. It aids in the affinity of the dyestuff in the dye bath to give better or improved color effect. It is possible to bleach practically any of the major textile fabrics seen today.

BLUE-WHITE: Used on cottons to give a distinctive finish. It is obtained by the use of a small amount of bluing on the bleached fabric so as to neutralize the yellowish effect which often occurs when running cloth through the various treatments in the Wet Finishing Department in the mill. Storage of cloth from time to time, on its way through the mill, will cause this yellowish cast or shade to appear. This is an undesirable cast; hence, the use of more of the desirable blue-white treatment or finish.

BRADESTA: An antistatic pilling-resistant finish used for "Dacron" polyester and cotton blends. Trademark of Bradford Dyeing Association (U.S.A.), New York City.

BRADLUSTRA: Durable finish which provides improved hand and a permanent ingrained luster to high-quality cottons. Trademark of Bradford Dyeing Association (U.S.A.), New York City.

BRADPERMA CMI: A chlorine-resistant wash-and-wear finish for fabrics made of cotton. Trademark of Bradford Dyeing Association (U.S.A.), New York City.

CAMBRIC: Gives a brighter and firmer finish to cottons than the muslin finish. The cloth has to be well singed and calendered, and may or may not be pure or back-filled.

CHASED: Beetled effects may be simulated on cottons with this finish, "an inexpensive treatment used on inexpensive fabrics." Many cloths receive this finish, which is not lasting in nature. Yarns and protruding fibers in the cloth are not all of the same "height," and this causes lines of bright and dim effects that are observed when the rays of light strike the goods. The fabric is "threaded" so that several layers of fabric can be passed through between the chasing rollers at the same time. From four to as many as sixteen layers of material may be manipulated at the one time. The effect is enhanced by the slightly excess speed of one roller over another.

CHLORINE-RETENTIVE: Resin finishes or treatments given cotton, rayon, nylon, and other fabrics may cause the goods to retain certain and varying amounts of chlorine. This is later removed by hot calendering or pressing, which will often cause degradation and/or discoloration. Chlorine in any fabric or garment is a detriment and its unsavory odor can usually be easily detected.

CRAVENETTE: This finishing process is about one hundred years old, a trademark of Bradford Dyers' Association, Ltd., England. The treatment makes fabrics spotproof, rainproof, and waterproof, and it can be applied to a garment more than one time. It is known the world over.

A solution is used which destroys the absorbent nature of the fiber and makes it water-repellent; the pores in the yarns or threads and the interstices in the fabric, however, do not become filled, so that the fabric remains porous.

CREASE-RETENTION: The ability of a cloth to retain a fold or pleat that has been created purposely, usually by a heat treatment. The heat-setting of the thermoplastic fibers used causes creases to become permanently set.

CROPPED: A staple finish given to woolen fabrics such as melton, kersey, beaver, and some broadcloth. Actually it is a closely sheared fabric in which the nap effect is quite subdued. Often given to good quality fabrics for use in rather expensive men's coatings.

DECATING, DECATIZING: Some woolen fabrics and practically all worsteds are given this steam treatment under heavy pressure "to set the yarns" in the goods, to prevent shrinkage in either direction, and to give an improved hand and finish.

DE LUXE: This affords cottons a high Schreiner, luster finish. The rollers used for this type of finish may have as many as 360 grooves or gouged lines to the inch. Venetians and other lining materials are often given this finish. Actually it is a "heavy" Schreiner finish. (See Schreinered, Schreinerized.)

DETERGENT: It is not a finish but is a cleaning agent or solvent, and much used in finishing fabrics. Originally it meant a soap, a water softener, or a "soap saver." The term now means a set of washing products known as "synthetic detergents" ideal for use in washing, cleansing, and placing the goods in a better, workable state. The term "detergent" is now disassociated from soap. (See Soaping.)

DRYCLEANING: Method used on garments which cannot be laundered. Organic solvents such as carbon tetrachloride or certain mineral compounds are used to remove dirt, soil, and most spots and stains. Unaffected stains, such as perspiration, have to be removed by other special agents.

DULL: Applied to cottons, the goods are sent directly to the frames to obtain the desired finished width, and then go to the "making-up room" for folding. The finish is produced on the goods with or without the tentering treatment, and is given a very slight heated calendering. This finish is often applied to cambric and comparable cloths that are to be used for linings. (See Tentering.)

DUPLEX: Name given to fabrics which have been printed on both sides with the same pattern on each side or with both sides in a different pattern. Some cottons are colored in this way, as well as cloths of other fibers.

DUVETYNE, SUEDE, FELTED: In a finish in this category, the cloth is napped on one or both sides, and it is then sheared and brushed carefully in order to obtain the necessary closely cropped nap that is characteristic of the finish.

DYEING: A method of coloring fibers, yarns, or fabrics with either natural or synthetic dyestuffs. The dye bath combines with water, heat, other chemicals, the bath strength, proper temperatures, etc. Dyes differ in their resistance to sunlight, perspiration, washing, alkali, acid, dust, colorfastness, etc. There is also much variation in their effectiveness on different fibers (affinity or fugitivity), their reaction to cleansing agents, their solubility and method of application.

ELASTIC DUCK: A very firm, starched finish applied to cotton sheeting, dyed black or some other dark shade for use in lining.

EMBOSSED: A popular effect made on cloth by passing it between a series of rollers, each set having one smooth and one embossed roller. These metallic rollers are heated so as to give better results. The embossed rollers have been engraved with suitable patterns, which will be reproduced on the fabric and give the appearance of a raised or embossed surface to the goods. Motifs may be birds, foliage, scrollwork, figures, pastoral scenes, etc.

Embossing is often applied to many fabrics, and can be used effectively on velvets and other pile fabrics to bring about the desired effects. The impressions seen on some embossed cloths more or less resemble genuine Jacquard woven effects.

FELTING: Woolen fabrics which have been scoured, soaped, fulled or milled, and shrunk to the extent that the yarns become so closely interlocked as to make it practically impossible to separate them. The weave construction is not discernible to the naked eye. Also known as WOVEN FELT FINISH, fabrics so treated are called face-finished cloths. Examples include kersey, melton, beaver, some broadcloth, paper-maker's felt, Service Academy uniform cloth, and fabrics used in coatings for firemen, policemen, etc.

FIREPROOF: Fireproof fabrics must be 100 per cent fireproof. If treated to prevent the spread of flame, they should be called fire-resistant. Some materials are treated with a chemical which melts at a low point and covers them with a nonflammable film.

FIRE-RETARDANT: Fabrics are chemically treated with special agents to make them re-tardant or resistant to fire. There is a wide range of fire-retardants on the market today.

FLANNEL: Mostly cotton and rayon fabrics, although the treatment may be given to other types of fabrics. They are slightly napped on both sides to resemble woolen goods used for some dressgoods, blanketing, coating, shirting, etc. Plain or twill weaves, with soft-spun filling to take a good napping treatment, are used in the material. Flannel fabric is a staple woolen cloth.

FRAMED: The cloth is "framed" or held out to full width in a taut manner so that the goods will meet the desired finished width. Fabrics finished in this way include organdy, voile, cambric, dimity, batiste, lawn, nainsook, longcloth, pajama checks, et al.

FRENCH: Similar to the dull finish, it gives a slightly starched appearance on some cottons. Little or no luster is seen on the goods.

FRICTION CALENDER: A very bright, shiny finish used on lining twills, sateen, silesia, messaline, and binding finish cloths. Brought about by the one calender roller going at a slightly increased speed over the other roller in the set. Rollers may or may not be heated.

FROSTING: A slight luster is given to fabric by the Schreiner method at low temperature. Used solely on cottons. (See Schreinered, Schreinerized.)

FULL-BLEACHED: This implies that the material has received at least one boiling in the alkali bath or baths, and that bleaching has taken place in the bleaching powder bath.

FULL- OR DOUBLE-MERCERIZED FINISH: This signifies that the fabric has received full-strength mercerizing immersion—25 to 55 degrees, Twaddle Thermometer, bath of caustic soda, cold. There is no marked increase in mercerization above the 55-degree mark on the thermometer. (See Mercerized.)

FULLING, MILLING, "POUNDING": This treatment is given to many woolen fabrics. The fabric is heavily wetted in a soap bath in which it circulates for a considerable length of time—from one hour to as many as twenty or more hours, depending on the fabric itself as to raw stock used, weave construction, compactness, fabric weight, etc. The cloth is also "beaten" by a set of heavy hammers set at the top of the vat in which the work is done. The weave cannot be seen when the operation has been completed and the goods removed from the bath. Weight of the cloth has been increased, and the cloth shrunk to considerable degree.

GASSING: The process of burning off protruding fibers from cotton yarns and cloths by passing them over a gas flame or heated copper plates. This gives the fabric a smooth surface which is very necessary for fabrics to be printed, and for those where a very smooth, inviting hand is desired. Also called "singeing."

GLAZED: This finish provides luster, sheen, shine, or polish to some fabrics. It is done by friction calendering and the depth and the life of the finish on fabric or garment depends on ingredients used. Some glazed fabrics have durable finish while others will not withstand laundering.

GREIGE (GRIEGE, GRAY, GREY) GOODS: Cloths, irrespective of color, that have been woven on a loom, but have received no dry—or wet—finishing treatments. Gray goods are taken to a perch for chalk-marking of all defects and blemishes, no matter how small. These blemishes must be remedied in the finishing of the goods. Fabric is converted from the gray-goods state to the finished fabric ready for the market.

HEAT-SETTING: Heat application will usually stabilize manmade fiber fabrics so that they will not be altered in shape or size. Resins and heavy pressures are often resorted to in this work; a resin will be applied to the material and the heat and pressure will then insure that the fabric will have the correct shape and width.

IMPREGNATED: A fabric in which the interstices (openings in it) are filled completely with an impregnating compound throughout the thickness of the material, as distinguished from sized or coated materials where the material is applied to the surface and these interstices are not completely filled. (Definition as decreed by A.S.T.M., Philadelphia, Pennsylvania.)

LACQUER: Cloth that has been treated chemically to produce a thin film on its surface; may be applied in the design. Not durable against drycleaning unless so stated.

LAUNDRY-PROOF: Laboratory-tested fabrics and garments which will withstand laundering without the loss of color or shrinking under ordinary washing conditions. The term can be applied only to materials so tested.

LONDON-SHRUNK: A treatment given to wool fabrics to shrink them and remove superfluous finish. Essentially it consists of placing the cloth between wet "blanketing" and then allowing it to dry without any tension and pressing. It relaxes stresses and strains left in the goods after manufacture. It provides a soft and supple hand, and improves appearance. The shrunken cloth is refinished in an aftertreatment in accordance with the wishes of the purchaser. A trademark name, over 250 years old, owned by Perrott & Perrott (Holdings) Ltd., England.

MERCERIZED: Extensively used on cotton yarn and cloth, the material is immersed in a cold, strong, sodium-hydroxide (caustic-soda) solution, at room temperature. The strength of the bath is from 25°–55° F., based on the use of a Twaddle (Twaddel) thermometer. The goods are run through a tentering frame at high velocity speed in the operation.

Results of mercerizing increases the strength and affinity for dyes; only seven-tenths as much dyestuff is needed to dye mercerized yarn or cloth. The treatment may be done under tension or without it. Tension mercerization increases the luster to a great degree, as well as giving a more cylindrical yarn. Discovered in 1844, by John Mercer, English scientist and chemist. Mercer's experiments, at the time, were to learn how to increase the affinity of dyes to cotton cloth. His accidental findings are considered to be one of the greatest phenomena in textile science. The process increases yarn strength about 30 per cent and decreases the weight about

5 per cent. The silklike luster on the goods lasts for the life of the yarn, fabric, or garment. (See Full- or Double-Mercerized Finish.)

MILDEW-RESISTANT: Treating textiles to make them impervious to mildew and mold; it is possible now to determine the degree or amount of degradation or damage done by mildew or mold.

MOIRÉ, WATERMARKED: A finish given cotton, silk, acetate, rayon, nylon, etc., where bright-and-dim effects are observed. This popular finish is achieved by passing the fabric between engraved rollers which press the particular motif into the goods, causing the crushed and the uncrushed parts to reflect light differently.

MOTH REPELLENT: Chemical treatment of wool to make it impervious to moth attack. There are several processes used and they seem to differ in resistance to dry-cleaning and laundering treatments.

NAPPING: The raising of the fibers on the face of the goods by means of teasels or rollers covered with card clothing (steel wires) that are about one inch in height. Action by either method raises the protruding fibers and causes the finished fabric to give more warmth to the wearer, makes the cloth more compact, causes the fabric to become softer or smoother in feel, increases durability, covers up the minute areas between the interlacing of the warp and the filling, and adds to the selling points of the articles made from these fabrics. Napped cloths include flannel, doeskin, molleton, silence cloth, unfinished worsted, blankets, bathrobing, dress-goods, and coating.

A napped fabric can be sheared to an even-height napped effect and is known as sheared fabric. When very closely sheared it becomes a cropped cloth. Other names for napping are genapping, gigging, raised, brushed, teaseled.

PERMANENT FINISH: A much used term given to a host of materials for which some particular claim is made. Examples may include moiré or watermarked on faille and taffeta, crispness on organdy or dimity, smoothness on broadcloth, embossed fabrics, crepe effects, glazed materials.

The term, as well, implies cloths which are crease-resistant, shrinkage-resistant, and wear-resistant. In reality, the better and safer term to use is "durable finish." Actually, very few finishes are permanent for the life of a fabric or garment.

PERSPIRATION-RESISTANT: Said of fabrics or garments that resist acid or alkaline perspiration. Laboratory test results should be consulted prior to selling any fabric or garment as perspiration-resistant.

PLISSÉ: Also known as caustic soda crepe, a puckered or crepe effect is made in the finishing by the shrinking action of caustic soda on cotton. Caustic may be printed directly onto the cloth, or else a resisting agent is applied and then the caustic. The treated areas in the goods will shrink and cause the untreated portions to pucker. Pattern is usually in stripes, termed plissé, but other motifs may be used in this blister-effect material. The fabric will, after a very few washings, lose its effect. Plissé actually simulates seersucker, in which the puckered effect is lasting and requires no ironing. The base or ground ends in seersucker are held under ordinary weaving tension in the loom, while the crinkle ends are woven slack; this gives seersucker a puckered effect lasting for the life of the fabric or garment.

PRE-SHRUNK: Fabrics or garments which have received a pre-shrinking treatment. Often done on cottons to remove the tendency for the cloth to shrink when washed or laundered. Worsteds and woolens are also shrunk before cutting the fabric for use in a garment to prevent further shrinkage. The percentage of residual shrinkage must be indicated on the label of the goods or garments thus treated.

RIGMEL, RIGMEL-SHRUNK: Trademark of the Bradford Dyeing Association (U.S.A.) for a stabilization process which also affords luster and a soft, mellow hand to fabrics such as cotton shirting and dress fabrics. The method controls shrinkage to within one per cent of the length or the width of the material; in fact it can be controlled to within one-quarter inch per yard in both directions.

SANFORIZED: A checked measure for shrinkage. The trademark is applied to fabrics that have been shrunk by the compressive shrinkage method, and indicates that the residual shrinkage of the cloth is less than one per cent and that the tests have been made by the trademark owner to insure that the shrinkage conforms to the one-per cent standard. Trademark owner is The Sanforized Company, a Division of Cluett, Peabody & Company, Inc., New York City. The company has licensees all over the world.

SANFORIZED PLUS: A Cluett, Peabody & Company, Inc., trademark which signifies a regularly checked standard of wash-and-wear performance. Fabrics so labeled have met the rigid test requirements for shrinkage, smoothness after washing, crease recovery, tensile strength, and tear strength as prescribed by The Sanforized Company of the parent company.

SANITIZED: A bacteriostatic type of finish which protects fabrics from deteriorating and having odor-causing effects of bacteria, mildew, and mold. Sold to licensee-manufacturers by the owner, Sanitized Sales Company, Inc., New York City.

SCHREINERED, SCHREINERIZED: A physical finish that improves natural luster of lining, muslin, sateen, silesia, etc., by means of embossing. Under heavy pressure, the cloth is subjected to the action of a steel roller, which has from 180 to 360 fine lines per inch. The roller flattens the threads in the cloth and imprints onto the surface a series of very fine ridges, so fine that a pickglass must be used to discern them.

The finish increases the surface for reflecting the rays of light and greatly enhances the luster effect. Some of the finishes allied with it are frost-schreinerization, imitation shreinered, imitation mercerization, and bloom finish, none of which will withstand washing and are non-durable.

SCOURING: (1) To cleanse a fabric in totality or its surface by washing and a rubbing or abrasion treatment; (2) the use of detergents and soaps, as well as other cleansers, to remove dirt, grime, soil, and other foreign particles or matter; (3) to remove the sizing and tint used on warp yarn in weaving, and, in general, cleaning a fabric or yarn prior to dyeing; (4) the freeing of wool from yolk, suint, dirt, and all foreign matter. It may be done by the washing of the stock with soap, alkali, by treating with chemicals or solvents, or by naphthalating at below-freezing temperatures.

SHEARED: The operation of leveling the napped effect on cloth to give an even, "same height" to the fibers on the face of the goods. Done on woolens and worsteds, as well as on some cottons. The shearing regulates the height of the nap or protruding fibers by a machine which has two or more shearing blades. Comparable with the blades on a lawn mower, the nap can be regulated to $\frac{1}{32}$ of an inch.

SHOWER-PROOF: Some materials are treated chemically and by the addition of a wax coating can be made to repel water. Cloth thus treated is more hygienic than nonporous rubber fabric, since air cannot circulate through the latter.

SHOWER-REPELLENT: Sometimes known as splash-resistant, the term implies cloth which is resistant to light rains and showers. The process is such that washing or drycleaning gradually removes the finish-coating, thereby diminishing its effectiveness.

SHRINKAGE: The contraction and increase of the density of fibers and yarns causing a change in the shape and size of the textile fabrics. Moisture, mechanical, and chemical actions are the main causes of shrinkage in washing and laundering. Shrunk fabrics show a loss in length, width, area, weight, etc. Textile testing is resorted to in order to assure the residual results, which will be satisfactory to the buyer of the goods in question. Woolens and worsteds are "pre-shrunk" before they are sent to the cutting-up house for "cut-fit-trim." Done with steam or cold water.

SILICONE: Generic term for one of a class of organic compounds, based on the partial substitution of silicon for carbon. Obtained from silicon, a component of sand, it is used to protect fabrics against spotting, soiling, and wetting, and also finds much use as a softening agent in finishing fabrics.

SINGEING: (See Gassing.)

SIZED, STARCHED: These two terms are used interchangeably. A size or starch is applied to warp yarn to increase strength, afford smoothness, and add weight to the gray goods from the loom. Sizes or starches are also applied to fabrics and garments. Many fabrics and garments are starched before they are sold over the counter in the department store, or sent to the cutting-up house to be made into the finished article. Corn, wheat, rice, and blended sizes are used most often, whether in the finishing plant, laundry, or in the home.

SOAPING: A most important item in the finishing of fabrics. Four types of soap find use in the finishing of fabrics: (1) HARD SOAP contains sodium compounds of fatty acids which harden under exposure to air. Used mainly in hard-water washing. (2) SOFT SOAP contains potassium compounds which will absorb water and have the tendency to liquefy. (3) NEUTRAL SOAP contains compounds of olive oil or lard oil with potash, freely soluble and free from alkalies. (4) ALL-PURPOSE SOAP is one in which mild alkaline-builders are added to improve cleansing and to soften water, and which often contains a brightener. Used mainly in "the family wash."

SOIL-RETARDANT: Fabrics are treated with various chemical compounds to enable them to resist the effect of soil on materials. Applied to many materials and also much resorted to by textile companies to ascertain the results on fabrics and yarns actually buried in the ground, either for a short time or for a year or more.

SPONGING: A partial-shrinkage by dampening with a sponge, by rolling in moist muslin, or by steaming, given to woolens and worsteds by the clothing maker before cutting to insure against a contraction of the material in the garment. The very popular sponging treatment is "London-shrunk," which is a cold-water treatment, originating abroad, and is frequently applied and guaranteed by the cloth manufacturers themselves. (See London-shrunk.)

SPOT- AND STAIN-RESISTANT: Applied to materials to resist spots and stains. Many ingredients can be used for the purpose, depending on the fiber or fibers used to make the fabric or garment. A fabric should be laboratory-approved before any such claim is made.

STARCHLESS: A cotton fabric, for example, is finished and "starchless," since there is not any starch to wash out or replace. Features of the finish include absence of lint, non-sleazy appearance and no fuzzy fiber surface after washing, laundering, or being exposed to moisture.

SYNTHETIC DETERGENT: Abbreviated form is SYNDET. It is a cleaning agent made from chemicals, usually hydrocarbons, sulfuric acid, and sodium carbonate. It comes in various forms—paste, powder, liquid, etc. Much used when quick and thorough wetting of fabrics is desired. Varied concentrations are available for the many different processes used in finishing textiles.

TARNISH PREVENTION: Chemical treatment applied to some cloths wherein there is an inhibiting of the action of atmospheric gases and body reagents which would cause tarnishing. The type of treatment decides how effective it will be. Any claim to tarnish prevention should describe its effectiveness.

TENTERING: A machine that dries and stretches cloth to its finished width, and straightens the weave by the action of two diverging endless chains. Each chain is equipped with a series of clips that hold an edge of the cloth as they convey it over gas flames or through a hot-air drying compartment.

UNBLEACHED: Many fabrics, especially cottons, in the trade come in an unbleached or natural condition. Materials of this type have a sort of "creamy" or somewhat "dirty" white color cast and much foreign matter is often seen in them—burs, nips, nebs, specks, et al. These cloths are stronger than full-bleached fabrics. Examples of unbleached goods include canvas, duck, unbleached muslin, Osnaburg, cretonne, sheeting, some toweling (cotton and linen), and some moleskin and comparable fabric used for pocket lining.

UNFINISHED: This term usually applies to "unfinished worsteds." This type of finish applied to worsted is the only one in which the cloth is given a napping or raising treatment on the face of the goods. The weave construction is obscured to considerable degree. The term, however, seems to be a misrepresentation because this nap is actually a finish on the goods which are ordinarily left with a smooth surface after the cloth is woven in the loom.

WASHABLE: Fabrics which will not fade or shrink when they are washed. The term should always be qualified by careful directions in methods of handling based on laboratory tests. Not to be confused with "wash-and-wear."

WASH-AND-WEAR: This type of garment is one that can be washed by hand or in a washing machine at the warm-water setting. When drip-dried it retains creases or pleats, and recovers sufficiently from wrinkles to need little, if any, ironing. Washing temperature should range between 95°–110° F.

WASH-FASTNESS: A term that seems to cause considerable confusion, especially among consumers. The term is applied, rather loosely at times, to fabrics or garments which can be washed and laundered. Much depends on the actual item or article before the term should be applied.

WATER-REPELLENT: Ability of a fabric to resist penetration by water, under certain conditions. Various types of tests are used and these are conducted on samples before and after subjection to standard washing and drycleaning tests. Immersion, spray, spot, and hydrostatic methods may be used. Shower-resistant, rain-resistant, and waterproof factors are interpreted from the results of the testing.

WEIGHTING: When applied to silk it is also known as DYNAMITING or LOADING. Sometimes metallic salts are used in the dyeing and finishing of silk to increase weight and draping quality—thus making the cloth more expensive. Overweighting causes deterioration of the goods. In November, 1938, the Federal Trade Commission established trade practices for the silk industry in this country, since some fabrics were weighted more than 200 per cent. Poor performance of the fabrics overweighted had been apparent for years prior to this time. At the present time, in the United States a silk fabric dyed black may have up to 15 per cent weighting and can be sold as a "pure dyed silk." All other colors are allowed only a 10 per cent loading to be sold as a "pure dyed silk." Tin salts (stannic chloride) are used to add weighting.

"ZELAN": A durable repellent finish; it is a finish and not the fabric or the garment. Fabrics treated with "Zelan" shed rain, snow, water, resist spots and stains with the exception of grease, resist perspiration, and wrinkle less easily. The treatment goes into the fibers and does not coat the weave formation. Air circulates normally, body heat and moisture can escape, and clothes are always comfortable. Not used on all-wool and all-acetate fabric. Product of E. I. du Pont de Nemours & Co., Wilmington, Delaware.

"ZE PEL": A fabric fluoridizer of E. I. du Pont de Nemours & Co., Wilmington, Delaware. This compound contains fluorine, which aids in the formation of a shield or layer of film around textile fibers in a fabric to prevent spots and stains penetrating these fibers in a cloth, thereby making their removal an easy matter. Treatment with the product does not affect washfastness of dyes used in a material, nor does it affect the "breathability" or strength of the fabric. It provides excellent protection against water and stains on garments.

"ZESET": A textile finish that imparts durable wrinkle- and shrink-resistance to cotton and viscose rayon fabrics. Spun rayon materials, many of which at present are not washable, when treated with "Zeset" can be laundered and bleached under the usual home conditions without serious loss of strength and discoloration often encountered in the case of home-bleached fabrics. Product of E. I. du Pont de Nemours & Co., Wilmington, Delaware.

TESTING

1. Define the following terms: loom goods; greige or gray goods; finish; finishing.
2. Differentiate among a mill finish, a commercial laundry finish, and the home laundry finish.
3. Explain the following: beetling; chased finish; decating; duplex finish; embossed finish.
4. What is meant by calendering? Friction calendering?
5. Discuss mercerization.
6. What is meant by fulling fabrics in finishing?
7. Explain bleaching; dyeing; printing.
8. How does moiré or watermarking improve some fabrics in their finished state?
9. What is meant by the term permanent finish?
10. Discuss Sanforized; Sanforized Plus.
11. What is meant by sizing or starching on yarn or fabric?
12. How do soaps differ from detergents in their use at the present time?
13. What is the difference between washable and wash-and-wear?
14. Discuss the weighting of silk and the limits of weighting as permitted by the Federal Trade Commission at the present time.
15. What is meant by tentering?

Part 1—Unit 44

TOPIC: PERMANENT PRESS IN FABRICS

Wash-and-wear garments are those which can be washed by hand or in a washing machine at the warm-water setting. When drip-dried they retain creases and pleats and recover sufficiently from wrinkles to need little, if any, ironing. Washing temperatures should range between 95°–110° F. These garments made their debut in 1957. PERMANENT PRESS, durable for life, may be said to be the acme of perfection in wash-and-wear. For example, slacks or pants will keep their shape and crease, as well as a smooth surface, after repeated launderings. There is an absence of seam puckering and wrinkled areas.

A CREASE or PLEAT is added by some whim of fashion—for utility, or for ease of care. Ordinary creasing or pleating is done by pressing and removed by washing and wearing. A WRINKLE is an unintentional addition to a fabric or garment and will disappear altogether after washing and a good pressing.

Before the advent of Permanent Press, all wash-and-wear goods were cured in the finishing department of the textile mill. In Permanent Press procedure this operation is also called PRE-CURED PROCESS. The other process is known as the DEFERRED- or POST-CURE PROCESS and is synonymous with the term PERMANENT PRESS or DURABLE PRESS (see Durable Crease, page 245).

This newest phenomenon in the textile and apparel industries, Permanent Press, was first announced by Koret of California, the well-known and highly respected women's sportswear house in San Francisco. In 1961, Koret obtained U.S. Patent No. 2,974,432, and then the company created the Koratron Company to market the process, called the Deferred-Cure Process. The first Permanent Press wash-and-wear pants went on sale in February, 1964.

The National Cotton Council of America, Memphis, Tennessee, and the Southern Regional Laboratory of the Department of Commerce, Baton Rouge, Louisiana, were also pioneers in the research and development of what is now known as Permanent Press. The Graniteville Company, Inc., Graniteville, South Carolina (the oldest successful cotton mill in the United States, founded in 1845)

[240]

made the first commercial men's wear fabric in this category in January, 1963, processed by the Deferred-Cure Process. The well-known and long-established company of Levi Strauss, known for its range of work clothes of all types, joined forces with Graniteville and the technologists came out with the first commercial men's wear garment made by the Deferred-Cure Process in February, 1964.

PERMANENT PRESS is obtained in two ways. The regular wash-and-wear process is called the PRE-CURED PROCESS and is brought about as follows:

IN THE MILL   IN THE CUTTING-UP HOUSE

Impregnation, Drying, Curing, Washing   Cut, Fit, Trim, Press

The second method is called DEFERRED-CURE or POST-CURE PROCESS or DURABLE PRESS:

IN THE MILL   IN THE CUTTING-UP HOUSE

Impregnation, Drying   Cut, Fit, Trim, Press, Cure

It should be borne in mind, however, that in regular wash-and-wear procedure the fabric finisher in the textile plant cures the cloth by impregnating the chemical or chemicals into the goods, then dries the run and provides the actual cure. The material is then washed, and made ready for shipment to the apparel house. The garment manufacturer, when manipulating the goods, will then do the cut-fit-trim and pressing operations.

These treatments, contrasted with Permanent Press in the Deferred-Cure Process, reveal that the mill finisher does the impregnation and follows through with drying of the bolts or cuts of goods. The manufacturer does the cut-fit-and-trim, the pressing, and then the final operation—the actual curing of the garment in his own plant or through some other agency set up to do this type of work. It is important to note that there is no washing operation in this procedure.

Pre-Cure Process

A cross-link chemical or resin is used in the process, aided by the action of a catalyst, a substance that will alter the speed of a chemical action or reaction without permanently altering itself.

Following impregnation of the piece goods with proper ingredients, the material is dried at a low temperature so as *not to set the chemical*. Thus a "sensitized condition" is created, and the chemicals are held in a state of suspension, a sort of "hypnosis," so to speak. At this time, there is not any reaction between molecules of the fibers and those of the chemicals.

Before a union can be made there has to be a BAKING or CURING. This action may be compared with many foodstuffs used in the home today—a TV dinner, dinner roll, frozen fish, frozen pies, et al. When the curing is completed it has brought about the union necessary of all ingredients to the fabric from what may be called a "half-baked condition" to the finished condition by the application of the heat treatment necessary. The catalytic agent has completed its work. Creases, pleats, seams, and other possible configurations of the fabric have been provided for, and no matter how much the goods are wrinkled or distorted, they will return to the predetermined form when pressed. Thus the "memory" in the pressed-in shape. Likewise, the TV dinner, when heated, has left the "half-baked condition," and is now ready to be served at the table.

Deferred-Cure or Post-Cure Process

It can be readily seen that curing fabrics in the textile plant presented problems to the garment manufacturer: there would be a loss in creases; seams would lose some of their flat-folded neatness; puckering would develop because of irregular thread tensions, and there would be a displacement of the cloth during the sewing operations. It was apparent that all these impediments would have to be corrected, and as a result this process came into being. Deferred Curing or Fixing occurs after the garment has been made, and instead of the "memory" to the flat fabric there is now a "memory" to the shape of the garment in its made-up form. The shape is locked in and the wrinkles are locked out. There are flat seams, no puckering, and a smooth fabric without flaws becomes apparent. No ironing is necessary in this type of garment, a condition that is not fully possible, generally speaking, with even the best of wash-and-wear articles.

Before Permanent Press came into being, all wash-and-wear was cured in the piece length in the mill. The garment would take on its appearance and character from pressing, usually with equipment that involved higher temperatures than those used ordinarily, increased steam pressure, and automatic controls that had to be closely watched at all times.

Much progress has been made in the technological developments in Permanent Press since its advent to the present time, especially so in regard to the Deferred-Cure Process. It was learned that lightweight cotton fabrics could not produce good results, and it was necessary to use rugged constructions and a rather heavy fabric around the eleven-ounce mark. Lighter-weight cloths were reduced in durability and strength, since the high concentration of the chemical and a curing temperature of around 320° F., with a ten-minute treatment, caused a loss of 35–50 per cent in tensile strength. Heavier-weight cotton cloth is not affected to this degree, and shrinkage is held to a minimum. It was observed, however, that some improvement should be made as to fiber content in fabrics that could withstand the existing conditions.

It should be remembered that the chemical cross-linking which gives a Deferred-Cure fabric its so-called "memory" occurs only with cellulosic fibers such as cotton and HWM rayon (high wet modulus rayon). With the high losses in tensile strength the true wash-and-wear properties were not possible to obtain. Research and development produced the logical solution to these vexing problems.

a) A really strong, compact cotton fabric is able to offset the inevitable loss of strength in a satisfactory manner.

b) Research brought out the fact that blending acrylic, nylon, or polyester fibers with the cellulosic fibers was ideal in all respects. Increased strength and resistance to abrasion became apparent. In addition it was found that a blended cloth of around seven ounces, or even less, depending on the weave construction and ingredients in the fabric, could be manipulated to advantage. The manmade fibers in the construction, being thermoplastic in nature, respond so well to heating that with this turn of events Permanent Press was now rid of any barriers, thereby making possible its meteoric rise to success.

Blends used are from 50–65 per cent of manmade fiber content, with 50 per cent down to 35 per cent for cotton or HWM rayon to afford an excellent marriage of the fibers for best results.

What is known as SPONTANEOUS CURE was a serious barrier in developing satisfactory garments when the Deferred-Cure Process was used. A sensitized fabric, one that has been impregnated with the chemical compound, will have the tendency to cure itself spontaneously during storage and prior to the manipulation into garments. There are two outstanding products on the market that now take care of the problem. One is Permafresh 183, a patented compound of the Sun Chemical Company, Inc., New York City. It is a patented imidazolidone and is used in the Koratron process. The other is owned by J. P. Stevens & Company, Inc., New York City. It is a range of sulfone chemicals and used for the company's Super-Crease process.

Another problem is that of ODOR. There is, for example, the odor of formaldehyde, which comes from treatments made with thermosetting resins. If noisome odors prevail they are sure to bring complaints from all operatives who come in contact with the goods during manipulation of the cloth into some item of clothing or apparel. Washing carefully and well should remove odors that remain in the goods after curing; however, this is not always the case. The washing operation in PRE-CURE goods is usually entirely satisfactory, but to the manufacturer of apparel it is not, since he has to wash the fabric after curing in his plant. Permafresh 183 and the Sulfone Range of J. P. Stevens & Company have, however, overcome this problem.

The cost of a CURING OVEN is rather high and may go to as much as $50,000. One type takes care of a single-batch run of garments while another can be run continuously and is capable of curing as many as fifty dozen pair of pants in about one hour's time. While costs are thought to be high, the high rate of production causes the manufacturer to regard them as worthwhile and an important adjunct in his plant setup. Overcuring has to be guarded against, since some areas in the goods may become distorted and out of line.

The problem of SHRINKAGE has to be considered in Permanent Press in the Deferred-Cure Process. Manufacturers usually allow an oversizing of the particular garment to the extent of .5 per cent to assure good results when the article is completely finished. This tolerance has worked very well with manufacturers to obtain satisfactory end results.

Pressing equipment has to be given close attention. If wrinkles in the garment are pressed in, they will later on become cured, and it is then impossible to remove them. Steam, heat, and pressure must be exactly correct at all times in order to provide a neater and more appealing garment.

The Sanforized Company, a division of Cluett, Peabody & Company, Inc., New York City, has taken much interest in Permanent Press activities. Under its label there is certification which guarantees crease retention, wrinkle resistance, and quality wash-and-wear performance.

Advantages of Permanent Press include ease of care, wash-and-wear properties, thus doing away with drudgery and saving time for the person involved, while at the same time the treated fabric will retain its soft, pliable, resilient qualities to the satisfaction of the wearer.

Important uses for Permanent Press include men's and boys' dress and sport slacks, work pants, dungarees, overalls, and work coats. The fabrics used include broadcloth, denim, gabardine, oxford, poplin, and small-twill repeat cloths. These cloths, especially in a proper blend of cellulosic fiber and nylon, acrylic, or polyester fiber, give ideal results.

[243]

Durably Creased Woolens

A woolen cloth does not come in the category of Wash-and-Wear, nor does it qualify as a full-fledged Permanent Press fabric. The treatment given woolens may be compared to the waving and setting of hair on the female head. Human hair and wool are of the same chemical structure, and it is the keratin in them that is conducive to the waved effect. Human hair is set by the use of a spray treatment. Likewise, woolens are finally treated with a spray to set the crease; then they are pressed.

The permanent crease in woolens is brought about by the use of monoethala-mine sulfite, which breaks the "memory pattern." When heat is applied to form the crease or pleat, a "new memory pattern" for the creased state is set up and the fabric will then return to its newly creased condition. Rain or steam, under ordinary conditions, will not affect the creases to any marked degree, if at all.

SOME IMPORTANT BASIC TERMS USED IN PERMANENT PRESS

ABRASION RESISTANCE: The degree to which a fabric is able to withstand surface wear and rubbing. An abrasion test for Permanent Press indicates the degree to which wash-wear chemicals have weakened the fabric.

BATCH CURE: One of the two methods used in curing Permanent Press garments. This method takes care of a single batch of garments at a time in the oven. The other method is of the continuous-process type.

CATALYST: A substance which changes the speed of a chemical action without being altered permanently itself. Applicable to Deferred Cure, it is a chemical which helps to achieve cross-linking and is therefore added to the padding solution. (See Deferred or Post-Cure.)

CHLORINE-RESISTANT: Certain chemical finishes used in textiles retain some of the chlorine used in laundering. This is called CHLORINE RETENTION, and it causes a yellowing of white fabrics. When yellowing is not apparent, the finish is known as CHLORINE-RESISTANT.

COMPRESSIVE SHRINKING: Application of pressure and steam to a fabric to provide dimensional stability against further shrinkage. (See Dimensional Stability.)

CONTINUOUS CURE: One of the two methods used to cure Permanent Press garments. This method uses a moving conveyor system to process garments in a continuous line from the pressing machine into and out of the curing oven. (See Batch Cure.)

CREASES VERSUS WRINKLES: A crease is a line or mark produced in anything by folding; a fold, or furrow. A wrinkle is a ridge or furrow on a surface caused by contraction, folding, rumpling, etc. A crease is a deformation in a fabric intentionally formed by pressing. Washing and wearing a garment will remove it. A wrinkle is formed unintentionally by washing and wearing, and it can usually be removed by pressing. In Permanent Press, however, the crease is not removable and there is an absence of wrinkles.

CROSS-LINKING AGENT: A resin or chemical that reacts with the chemical structure of a fiber in order to form an indissoluble bond or link. The agent, when cured in the fabric, provides the latter with a "memory" of its cured form.

CURING: Application of heat in order to fix chemicals permanently in the goods so that there will be no further change; comparable with the curing of fish or meat.

DEFERRED OR POST-CURE: The process whereby fabrics are treated with chemical cross-linking agents that are not fixed or cured into the goods until after the garment has been made. The goods remain in a sensitized state until after the proper heat treatment has been given. Thus the curing procedure has been deferred or delayed.

DIMENSIONAL STABILITY: The quality which enables a fabric or a garment to resist any type of change in measurement through repeated launderings, actually an ability to resist shrinkage.

DURABLE CREASE: More or less interchangeable with the term "Permanent Press," it is really limited since it refers only to the property of crease retention. Permanent Press, on the other hand, points to the shape-retaining properties of the whole garment.

"FABRIC MEMORY": The characteristic or property of a fabric which causes it to have a "memory" of its original form and thereby always return to that form on release from tension, certain treatments, etc. Wool and some of the manmade fibers possess a native or inherent "memory"; rayon, for example, in returning to its original fabric length after washing, the resiliency of wool, et al. Deferred or Post-Cure fabrics have their "memory" provided by chemical finishes.

FIBRILLATION: This pertains to the lightening of shade in Deferred or Post-Cure garments after repeated washings. This is found along the crease lines and is rather pronounced at times in dark-colored fabrics or garments, caused by the fact that the crease line is more exposed to abrasion and wear, which brings some of the fibrils in the material to the surface.

FINDINGS: Auxiliary fabrics used in the manufacture of a garment-lining, pocketing, tape, waistbanding, zipper tape, et al. All findings should be treated chemically in the same manner as the shell fabric.

FLAT CURING: Curing a fabric at the mill level—in flat-piece condition.

HAND BUILDER: The use of any chemical or finish which improves the hand, feel, or surface-effect texture in a fabric.

HOT HEAD PRESS: A type of pressing machine especially designed for processing Permanent Press garments. It generates heat between 450° and 500° F., with pressure to six tons at the head, and is generally equipped with precision automatic controls.

IMIDAZOLIDONE: Prepared by the action of ammonia on glyoxal; imidazole formula is made up of carbon (52.92%), hydrogen (5.92%), and nitrogen (41.15%). Imidazolidone is a chemical compound of which one derivative finds use in the Deferred or Post-Cure Process used in Permanent Press. It is a product of Sun Chemical Company, New York City, and is trademarked as Permafresh 183. (See Deferred or Post-Cure.)

IMPREGNATION: One meaning is to fill interstices or openings with a substance; another is to charge with something infused or permeating throughout; to saturate. Treating a fabric with some finishing compound or solution can provide full impregnation of the goods in question.

PADDING SOLUTION: Any of a number of chemical solutions that can be applied by padding the goods to be treated. The solution in the case of the Deferred or Post-Cure for Permanent Press may be described by the one produced by the Sun Chemical Company, Inc., New York City. Its composition follows:

Permafresh 183	120.0 pounds
Catalyst X-4	21.5 pounds
Mykon SF (polyethylene softener)	16.0 pounds
Mykon WA (penetrant)	1.0 pound

This combination provides one hundred gallons of the solution.

PERMANENT PRESS OR DURABLE PRESS: This term is used to describe a garment that will retain its shape-retaining properties throughout its career. Features include sharp creases, flat seams, smooth surface texture and appearance on the goods, and seams which are free from puckering.

PROGRESSIVE CURING: Term used to describe the occasion when a sensitized fabric, treated for the Deferred or Post-Cure, will cure itself during storage. This method of curing means that the sensitized fabrics had to be "made up" very shortly after treatment so that the goods would not set or cure in the flat condition. Deferred-Cure fabrics can now be safely stored for several months to more than one year. (See Deferred or Post-Cure.)

PUCKERING: The furrowed or rippled appearance of seams in a conventional wash-wear garment following laundering. It is caused by sewing tension and a varied shrinkage of the fabric and the sewing thread. Quality Permanent Press garments avoid seam puckering because they are cured and fixed after careful pressing of the articles.

REACTANT: Merely a chemical finishing compound which reacts with the fiber to form a cross-linking bond.

RESIN: Any of several organic substances obtained chiefly, or exuding, from plants in a semisolid state. A resin is insoluble in water but soluble in alcohol and ether. Resins are much used on fabrics in finishing when they are to be used for wash-wear finished articles.

SENSITIZED: Refers to fabrics that have been impregnated with certain finishing chemicals, then dried but not cured. The fabric is then said to be in a sensitized condition until the proper degree of heat is applied such as that observed in the Deferred or Post-Cure Process for Permanent Press fabrics.

SOFTENER: Any of a large number of chemical compounds used in fabric finishing to give the cloth a mellow, soft, and appealing hand or handle.

SPONTANEOUS CURING: Practically synonymous with Progressive Curing. (See Progressive Curing.)

STORAGE STABILITY: The ability of a sensitized material to remain in this condition without curing itself spontaneously during storage.

TEAR STRENGTH: Allied with abrasion resistance, it is the degree to which a fabric will resist rupture or tearing. With regard to Permanent Press, a test for tear strength also aids to determine how much the fabric has been weakened by chemical treatment. The term "tenderized" describes a fabric that has been weakened by some treatment. Tear strength is related to tensile strength, which refers to the ability of a fabric to resist vertical or horizontal stress or strain. Notations are made of the point of rupture or breakage for warp and filling directions in the sample being tested for tensile strength, chiefly for the standard or comparative purposes relative to the particular fabric.

THERMOSETTING RESIN: One that can be set permanently through the application of heat; a resin that will permanently cure a fabric through heat application.

SOME PROMINENT TRADEMARKS OF PERMANENT PRESS

BURMI-CREASE (Pre-Cure): Developed by the Men's Wear Division of Burlington Industries, Inc., it is based on the inherent thermosetting properties of fabric blends of acrylic and polyester fibers. No resins or other chemicals are used and the durable crease is achieved on hot-head pressing machines.

CONEPREST (Pre-Cure and Spray): In this pre-cure method of Cone Mills, Inc., the fabrics are treated and then completely cured at the mill level. Prior to processing the garment, its crease or pleatline is sprayed with Coneprest Solution. This produces "amnesia" in the area sprayed so that the fabric loses completely the "memory" of its cured shape. "Memory" is restored by hot-head pressing.

DAN-PRESS (Post-Cure): In this process of Dan River Mills, Inc., the application to Fortrel polyester fiber and cotton blends has been very successful. Recommended curing temperatures and time duration are: 1. 370° F. and 2 minutes; 2. 340° F. and 4 minutes; 3. 320° F. and 4 minutes; and 4. 320° F. and 15 minutes.

KORATRON (Post-Cure): Patented process for Permanent Press or Durable Press of the Koratron Company, Inc., San Francisco, California. The idea for this type of press was conceived and developed by Koret of California, a noted women's sportswear house in San Francisco. In 1961, Koret received a patent for its Deferred-Cure

Process and from this development the Koratron Company was formed to market the process. The licensing arrangement calls for strict quality controls at both mill and garment manufacturing levels. The established industry standards of the American Association of Textile Chemists and Colorists, Inc., are used to measure and check performance of the end product.

NEVER-PRESS (Pre-Cure): Developed by the Men's Wear Division of Wamsutta Mills, Inc., Lyman, South Carolina, the treatment is based on fiber-blend engineering and a special resin finish. Hot-head pressing at 320° F. is used. Normal wear for one year is guaranteed by the company.

PENN-PREST: The private label trademark for garments made for the J. C. Penney Company. Garments that bear this label must maintain a just-pressed look after home machine washing and tumble drying and are tested for no noticeable loss in appearance after five cycles of home laundering. The garments may be manufactured by any of the several systems, oven curing, high-pressure steam pressing, or careful tailoring of pre-cured fabric. The only requirements are that they perform satisfactorily and that they meet the usual minimum standards for strength, endurance, and color fastness expected of any other garment in the same end-use category.

PRIMATIZED (Pre-Cure): The process developed and merchandised by Deering-Milliken, Inc., New York City.

REEVE-SET (Pre-Cure and Post-Cure): This process of Reeves Brothers, Inc., New York City, involves two curing treatments. The fabrics are cured at the mill level in the flat condition and then are additionally set through oven curing at the manufacturing level.

SHARP/SHAPE (Pre-Cure): This method of Everprest, Inc., Salt Lake City, Utah, is especially effective on stretch fabrics. It uses the special hot-head press equipment, also developed by the company.

SUPER-CREASE (Post-Cure): Trademark name for the process developed by J. P. Stevens & Co., Inc., New York City. It is based on the use of sulfone chemicals rather than on the use of resins, thereby eliminating chlorine retention and unpleasant odors. The company, in addition, has another post-cure process merchandised as SUPER-CREASE K.

TESTING

1. Discuss the link between wash-and-wear garments and Permanent Press garments.
2. Define the following terms: (1) crease; (2) wrinkle; (3) pleat; (4) Pre-Cure; (5) Deferred Cure or Post-Cure.
3. Trace the history of the rise of Permanent Press or Durable Press.
4. Why is it necessary in the Deferred Cure to cure garments in the plant of the garment manufacturer?
5. What is a cross-link chemical? A resin? A catalyst?
6. Define spontaneous cure. Explain how it may be curbed.
7. List three advantages of Permanent Press in some garments.
8. Name five items of clothing that may be given Permanent Press or Durable Press.
9. Why does a woolen fabric that has been durably creased not come in the category of wash-and-wear?
10. Explain the procedure used to produce durably creased woolen goods.

Courtesy of William E. Segal, President, *American Fabrics Magazine*, New York City.

TOPIC: FLOOR COVERINGS

Anything that is purchased should be considered as an investment. Tempting to the consumer in any purchase, or in something that might be purchased, are eye appeal and "buy" appeal. In addition, one has to consider utility, service, wearability, durability, and the satisfaction in the thought that what you have bought was a wise investment. Particularly should the foregoing be of value when it comes to the purchase of a carpet or a rug. There is a difference between a carpet and a rug. Their meanings follow:

CARPETING meant originally a type of covering, generally worked in a pattern, motif, or design of diverse colors, and used for spreading on the floor, the ground, a table, or a mantelpiece. At present, carpeting means some suitable heavy fabric used for covering a floor or stairway. Compared with the rug, a carpet is used to cover large areas of a room with floor covering, and includes the so-called wall-to-wall covering.

RUG is defined as a carpeting or piece of carpeting that covers small to large areas in rooms throughout the home. Rugs may be practically any size to fit some definite purpose in covering floors. They may be oblong, square, circular, or cut to some particular shape. The two terms today are more or less interchangeable. Generally speaking, a rug is sold as a whole and consists of a body and a border design. It is often more attractive than carpeting and is more sanitary.

FACTORS TO BE CONSIDERED IN THE CARE OF CARPETS AND RUGS, OR WHEN ABOUT TO PURCHASE A NEW FLOOR COVERING

1. Values of a carpet include decoration and color, a carpet being the largest single area of color in a room.
2. The carpet is the basis for harmony or contrast in the decor, and it increases the apparent room size.
3. Floor covering makes a room look orderly, balanced, and having a furnished appearance.
4. The functional values of floor covering include comfort, quiet, safety, warmth, and ease of care.
5. The decorative points in floor covering include the color scheme—such as monochromatic, related, contrasted—and design elements, including line, scale, and balance.
6. The basic qualities in carpeting include the type and grade of the fiber or fibers used, yarn construction, depth of the pile, and the density of the pile.
7. The major woven carpet constructions used are Axminster, Brussels, chenille, velvet, Wilton, and tufted.
8. The major fibers used include wool, cotton, carpet rayon, acetate, and the man-made fibers, such as Acrilan, Arnel, Dynel, Creslan, nylon, "Orlon" acrylic fiber, Verel, Zefran, et al.
9. In planning a new purchase, one should have a definite decorative plan in mind. Think of the size of the room and the amount of traffic the floor covering will have to withstand; the style of the furniture, lighting arrangements in the room, the predominant colors, and the balance in the design, motif, or pattern.
10. Purchase should be made from a reputable dealer; buy a dependable brand and the best quality rug you can afford. Arrange time payments, if need be, in accordance with the budget at hand, and take advantage of the "in-the-home selection" plan.
11. You can estimate the value of a rug or carpet by working on it. This means going over it daily with a sweeper or vacuum cleaner, with a thorough vacuum treatment once a week. In this way one will be able to tell in a short time whether the article was a good purchase.
12. Remove spots and stains as soon as possible, and use the services of a professional cleaner when the condition of the article warrants it.
13. A carpet is an important addition to any room. Provided it is a good one, it is, in a way, a mark of social standing, an evidence of comfort, a means of recognition. The possession of a fine rug and the prestige that goes along with it are important to everyone.

[248]

14. The closer the weave or the more compact the texture, the better will be the wearing quality of the rug or carpet.
15. Rugs are easier to clean than carpets, as well as easier to handle.
16. Rugs should lie on the floor without any curling at the edges.
17. Colors and designs should be in good taste—not be gaudy or outlandish.
18. A rug should harmonize well with the furnishings in the room and should be in keeping with the color of the walls. There should be no clash of color schemes.
19. Hall-room rugs or runners should be on the bright side, more than other coverings used in the home.
20. A smooth surface on an uncut rug is easier to care for than a cut-pile rug, or one with scalloped, sheathed, or other types of surfaces of varying heights of yarns.
21. A rug that is made with a short, closely cropped pile will give very good wear if it has a worsted or a linen backing.
22. Cut-pile rugs seem to show to better advantage because of the long, soft pile, which gives the rugs a velvetlike surface.

MAJOR TYPES OF FLOOR COVERING

AXMINSTER: Originally made in Axminster, England, this carpeting has not been made there for many years and is now made in other world carpet areas. Spools of various colored yarns are placed in a continuous sprocket chain, the ends of yarn being brought down by steel arms into a chain of cotton warp threads.

Jute binder threads hold the wool threads in place while the ends or tips of these yarns are clipped off by broad knives, and the spools are then returned to their position in the chain.

Axminster has woolen yarn only in the face construction. The pile varies from ⅛ inch to ⅜ inch. Moderate in price, Axminster presents a good appearance and is made in a width up to 12 feet. It has the appearance of a hand-knotted carpet. Standard texture is 7 tufts wide and 8 rows per inch. The carpeting may be rolled in the lengthwise direction. Axminsters have a long, soft nap that is gathered into small bunches or tufts. The construction is not durable, since the warp does not stand up too well under wear. Tufted carpeting has largely replaced Axminster.

BRUSSELS: This uncut-pile, machine-made rug is made with worsted yarn and woven on a Jacquard loom. It is made in two-shot construction only. Brussels does not seem to "catch the dirt" as quickly as some other type rugs because of the cotton and jute combination used in the construction. The Brussels is not rich in motif or effect when compared with other rugs of the same class, such as velvets and Wiltons. In recent years tufted carpeting has replaced Brussels.

CHENILLE: The name is the French word for caterpillar. Woven on a very wide loom, the pile ranges from ⅜ inch to 1½ inches in height. A filling fabric or blanket is woven and then cut into narrow strips. The chenille weft or rows of filling using surface yarn tufts making up the blanket are woven with a fine but strong cotton catcher warp, and a leno or doup weave is used. The blanket is then cut into strips so that they may be wound onto bobbins or set into shuttles for use as filling when weaving the carpet. Two weavers are required to weave the fabric on the loom—the actual weaver and the weft-comber who must check each pick as it is woven into the fabric. A catcher warp is used to aid the weaving-in of the ironed chenille weft pick. Four picks of filling follow each row of chenille. This custom-made, expensive rug provides excellent wear since the base construction holds the chenille picks in proper place in a very secure manner.

COTTON RUGS: These are popular because of the price. They tend to become shabby in a short time because of the fiber yarn content. Foot imprints show very readily and the rugs will soil easily because of the porous nature of the fibers.

GRASS RUGS: Plain weave is used in construction and grass twine is used for warp and filling. In the so-called grass-and-fiber-rug, the fiber is used for the warp, while grass is used for the weft. The warp has cotton mixed with it to hold the twist and aid in weaving. These rugs are reversible.

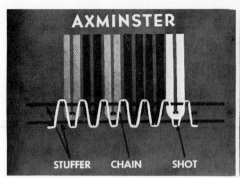

In the AXMINSTER weave each pile yarn is inserted independently, as in hand-tufted carpets of the Orient. This permits infinite variation of color and pattern. Patterned carpets using many colors in complex designs are Axminsters. Almost all of the yarn appears on the surface, and the pile is cut except in a few special weaves. The carpet is heavily ribbed as a result of the double shots that hold the tufts to the stuffer yarns with the chain bind.

Usually sizing or a latex compound is applied to the backing to lock the tufts. Varying pile heights are possible.

CHENILLE is made by two weaving processes. First the pile yarns are woven in a "chenille blanket" that is cut into long, furry, caterpillar-like strips. In the second weaving step, the strips of pile yarns are woven into the base of the carpet. The carpet base is made of heavy, thick wool yarn woven in the same operation that attaches the pile to it with the "catcher threads." Chenille carpet is thick and soft. It can be woven in a wide range of patterns and in any color. shape, or size up to thirty feet wide. It is usually custom-made.

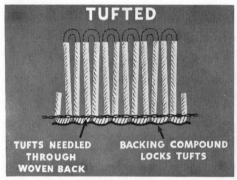

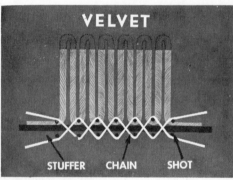

In the TUFTING construction, the pile yarn is needled through a prewoven backing fabric, usually made of jute, then firmly locked by a latex backing compound.

Hundreds of needles on the wide-width machines turn out rich, deep-pile carpets at high-speed production.

Though formerly limited to solid color or either cut or looped pile, tufted carpets can now be made in a variety of color combinations in varying heights for appealing and attractive motif and textural designs.

In the VELVET weave pile, yarns are seen on the surface at all times. As indicated by the dotted lines above the tufts, the pile may be cut or looped. New techniques make possible a wide range of textural effects, including tight frieze twists or pebbly surface and multilevel looped textures.

The "shot yarns" actually bind the pile yarns to the "stuffer yarns," which act as a structural foundation for the carpet. The entire construction is locked together by the "chain yarns."

[250]

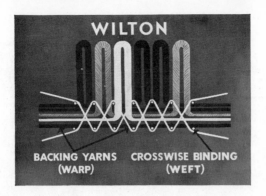

BACKING YARNS (WARP)   CROSSWISE BINDING (WEFT)

The WILTON uses up to six different sets of yarn to form the pile in this "rug of hidden values." When it is desired, each set of yarns can be a different color. The "hidden-value yarns," when not drawn to weave on the face of the carpet by the Jacquard loom upon which Wilton is made, are buried deep in the body of the carpet. This gives a cushion effect that provides luxurious feel and comfort.

Wilton weaving makes possible the modern carved effects of high and low pile constructions. The carpet pile may be cut to give a "plush effect," or looped as shown in the picture.

HOOKED RUGS: The foundation is burlap or monk's cloth, upon which the pattern is drawn. Yarns are made of cotton, silk, wool, acetate, rayon, or manipulated waste stocks. The yarns are about ½ inch in width. Prior to the American Revolution these rugs were very popular, but hand-loomed rugs, along with the later power-woven loomed fabrics, caused their decline. Handmade rugs, of course, vary considerably in price, but despite the inroads made by other types of floor coverings there is still a steady demand for this type of rug.

INGRAIN: The yarn is dyed before weaving; the warp is cotton, the weft or filling is wool. Ingrain has no pile effect. It is inexpensive; and 36 inches is the usual width. When this width is used the rug is called and sold as a Kidderminster. Ingrain gives good service, since it is without a pile effect. It does not, however, have the beauty or vividness of a pile-effect rug. Tufted carpets have largely replaced Ingram.

LINEN RUG: Plain weave is used in the linen warp and linen weft covering. The rug is durable, heavy, and will lie very well.

LINOLEUM: This floor covering is made from ground cork mixed with various gum ingredients, oxidized linseed oils, and dyes. The mixture is pressed into a burlap sack and then seasoned. There are four types of linoleum—plain, jaspé, inlaid, and printed.

Linoleum is made from 6 to 12 feet in width, and heavy linoleum is ⅛ inch in thickness. Medium type is .095 inches, while the standard type is .079 inches in thickness.

Low temperature will cause the fabric to become brittle and to crack. Plain, jaspé, and inlaid linoleum, when washed, should be waxed for the sake of preservation and wear. Printed linoleum should be lacquered and wiped with a mop or damp cloth.

ORIENTAL, AMERICAN: Commonly called domestic oriental, luster type, modern, sheen, and washed; Axminster or Wilton weaves are used in the construction. Woven on power looms, they have simulations of genuine oriental motifs. Some of the rugs are treated chemically to duplicate the patterns taken from true oriental rugs. For this reason most American orientals do not give good or satisfying service.

ORIENTAL, GENUINE: These are woven by hand and their names designate the district where they are made, or the tribes that made them. The value of these rugs de-

Face of fabric in loom   Back of fabric in loom

Fabric is cut vertically between the binder yarns thereby allowing the strips to be free to form their characteristic curled effect around these binder yarns and to simulate a caterpillar to give the chenille (caterpillar) effect.

CHENILLE WEAVING

Insertion of the single chenille weft or filling pick into the fabric after the two single chenille strands have been combined to weave as a single weft pick.

Single-cut chenille strand

The leno or doup-weave is used generally in weft weaving since it locks in the warp in the action.

Single-cut chenille strand

The two strands are combined in chenille weaving to form a single weft pick or filling pick in the fabric. Weaver number one does the actual weaving of the picks into the fabric. The "weft weaver" or weaver number two combs the pick immediately after it has been thrown through the shed of the loom to take its component place in the goods. The weft weaver combs this pick into correct position and its set-up in the fabric.

Picture of the famous Roxy Theatre chenille rug made by Mohasco Industries, Inc., Amsterdam, New York. Guaranteed for three years, the rug actually gave service for eight years. The Roxy Theatre, under the aegis of Samuel L. (Roxy) Rothafel, located at 135 West 50th Street, New York City, opened March 11, 1927, and closed March 29, 1960.

Individual weft or filling picks of chenille, to the left of the picture, have been "raised" to show a more pronounced effect of these picks.

pends on several factors, such as the age of the rug, the number of knots per inch, rarity and beauty, the results obtained in dyeing, composition and compactness of the weaving, color richness, intricacy of the motif, and the knotting technique. The six major groupings of oriental rugs are Caucasian, Chinese, Indian, Persian, Turkestan, and Turkish.

True orientals can be distinguished from domestic orientals by comparing the backs of both types of rugs. A true oriental will show the entire pattern or motif in detail on the underside of the rug.

TAPESTRY: This is a machine-made, uncut-pile fabric made with woolen or worsted yarn in the same manner as velvet rugs, which are made with a cut-pile effect. Inexpensive and rather durable, the rug does not have the softness of a velvet rug, and the motifs are often indistinct because of blending of the colors.

TUFTED CARPETS AND RUGS: These have had a great increase in popularity since the close of World War II, with price being a potent factor. The use of manmade fibers, negligible in 1949, has risen to about 70 per cent of the total fiber used at present. This product now accounts for more than 80 per cent of annual carpet yardage produced.

Tufting, a development of a technique used on bedspreads and small scatter rugs, is a process by which pile yarns are sewn into a broad fabric backing by wide multiple-needled machines. Backing fabric is jute (burlap) or cotton canvas. After tufting is completed, the yarn ends are secured by a coating of latex on the back of the rug. The use of tufting stimulated the production of broad cotton carpet on a wide scale, and in 1954 the first all-wool tufted carpet was produced. As previously noted, much of the product now employs manmade fibers.

Originally each tufted rug was made in a solid color, since dyeing followed construction. The nature of the process does not allow the flexibility of motif noted in Axminster and Wilton, for example. Developments, however, are constantly being made in color and texture variations.

Good quality tufted rugs have a thick, dense, luxurious pile and give good wear. Widths range from 9 to 15 feet. Some of the newer motifs, in one or more colors, consist of contrasting stripes on neutral ground, squares, striated or irregular crosswise stripes, random-rippled and other interesting designs.

The pile effect may be cut or uncut, and machines of more than sixteen hundred needles are now used in the broadloom types. One large machine can produce from ten to fifteen times the yardage produced on a regulation carpet loom, a tremendous advantage which is apparent when the respective price ranges are compared. (See Unit 46, Tufted Fabrics.)

VELVET: The simplest of all carpet constructions, this product is used chiefly for solid-color effects. When compact in texture, it is long wearing and rich looking; colors and texture variations are practically limitless. A plush effect results when the yarn is straight and the pile cut. Tightly twisted yarns in the cut pile provide a frieze surface effect. Uncut looped pile affords a pebbled texture. For sculptured effects, the pile is woven in different heights to form a pattern, a hit-and-miss, or a mottled effect. A combination of cut and uncut pile produces an appealing surface effect. The "shot yarns" bind the pile to the "stuffer yarns" which serve as the structural foundation of the carpet. "Chain yarns" lock the entire construction in a firm manner.

WILTON: Known as "the rug of hidden value" because of its excellent construction and compactness, this type of floor covering originated in Wilton, England. Wiltons are copies of Belgian, Flemish, and French tapestries. This machine-woven cut-pile fabric is made on a Jacquard loom. Woolen or worsted yarn is used. The pile is made by looping the warp yarns over a series of blade-tipped rods or wires, eighteen in number. The depth of the wire regulates the depth of the yarn. As each wire is withdrawn, the razor-blade tip cuts through the top of each loop, thereby forming the cut pile. The wires, in the loom action, actually weave for a predetermined length as picks in the fabric until each one is pulled out by an automatic finger at the fell of the cloth. As each wire is taken out of the fabric, it is automatically set back into the proper place in the rug-weaving structure, as a pick, to begin its work again.

This very desirable velvet-pile-effect rug gives better service when made of worsted yarn. Compared with woolen yarn, the worsted is a better grade of fiber, has more twist, has straighter fibers in the yarn, and produces a shorter pile effect and a stiffer back. Very often the yarn may be observed on the back of the fabric. While very serviceable, these rugs may be difficult to keep clean. Because of the nature of the construction and the number of warps used to give the soft, cushion-like effect, dirt and soil will gather rather quickly. With constant care, however, the rug will give many years of good to excellent service.

PUNCHED FELT: Felt is punched into burlap by means of a board which has an up-and-down motion. The board is set with a series of nicked pins which catch the felt fibers and carry them through the burlap on the upward motion. As the pins are on the way down, the burlap wipes off the felt fibers, thereby leaving the pins ready to pick up the next batch of stock to be punched into the burlap.

SOME IMPORTANT TERMS USED IN FLOOR-COVERING MANUFACTURE

BACKING: The back, foundation, or underside of a carpet or rug secures the pile yarns in position and affords a firm foundation. It is usually carpet rayon, cotton, jute, or Kraftcord.

In the weaving process, the backing is woven simultaneously with the pile yarn. In the tufting process, the carpet is tufted onto the broad woven fabric which serves as the backing.

All tufted carpets, as well as some types of woven carpet, are coated on the back with latex to seal in the tufts. With this type of finish individual tufts will not work loose and a clean edge can be cut in any direction. Binding is not necessary at all. Damaged or burned areas may be cut and replaced without showing a seam.

BEAM: Large horizontal cylinders or spools upon which the warp threads are wound. This warp beam is set at the back of the loom, and the warp yarn is fed off in a uniform, controlled manner as the fabric is being woven.

BINDING YARN: Filling or weft yarn carried across the loom by the shuttle. In Axminster weaving, this operation is done by a needle thrust. The binding yarn in carpet weaving alternates with the filling yarn, which is usually cotton or jute.

BROADLOOM: Carpeting that is more than three quarters (27 inches) or four quarters (36 inches) in width. A quarter is 9 inches; hence, a three-quarter carpet would be 27 inches wide. Broadloom is usually 6, 9, 12, 15, 18, up to 30 feet in width. Another meaning of the term is that of carpeting woven on a wide loom, usually 9 feet or more in width. Broadloom does not mean a type of carpeting, an actual fabric, nor a grade or quality of fabric.

CHAIN WARP: Two cotton yarns that run warpwise or vertically and are drawn by heddles over and under the weft binding and filling yarns as they are inserted, by shuttles in tapestry, chenille, velvet, and Wilton weaves, and by a needle thrust in Axminster fabric.

FILLING YARN: Weft yarn carried across most looms by a shuttle (in Axminster by a needle thrust) alternating with the binding weft yarn, which is usually cotton or jute.

FRAMES: Trays or creels holding spools of surface yarn in two to six levels at the back of a Wilton loom. One strand of yarn is lifted into position by the Jacquard mechanism to form the design on the pile surface, while the other yarns, one to five in number, are woven·dormant in the warp direction.

GROUND COLOR: The background color against which the surface colors create the pattern or motif in the design.

JASPÉ: In either plain fabric or fabric with a design, irregular warp stripes of two hues of one color in the surface yarn. The same effect may be obtained by using yarns of different twist.

KRAFTCORD: A tightly twisted, plasticized yarn made from cellulose fiber of a tiliaceous plant (lime or linden tree, etc.). Used in carpet weaves as an alternate backing yarn to cotton or jute.

PICK: A shot of weft binding or filling yarn to effect a weave by interlacing with the chain warp yarns. Use of the word indicates the quality; for example, 39 picks to the warp inch means that 13 wires would be used in a three-shot construction, or $3 \times 13 = 39$.

PITCH: The number of construction units per 27-inch width in a floor covering.

PLANTING: A method of spacing spools of different colored surface yarns in frames at the back of the Jacquard Wilton loom so that more colors will appear in the design than are supplied in the full range of solid colors used. These extra planted colors are usually arranged in groups of each shade to give added interest to the motif.

SHOT: The number of weft yarns to a row of surface yarn tufts; for example, a binding and filling shot for each row of tufts would be a 2-shot construction, while adding a second binding yarn would make it a 3-shot construction, costing more material and weaving time. Tapestry, wool velvet, and wool Wilton are two-shot, Axminster and worsted Wilton are three-shot, while chenille is a four-shot construction. (See Pick.)

STUFFER WARP: Jute, cotton, or Kraftcord yarns running dormant in the fabric to provide added weight and strength.

TOP COLORS: Colors of the yarn forming the motif, as distinguished from the ground color.

WEFT YARN: Cotton, jute, or Kraftcord running crosswise, weftwise, fillingwise, or horizontally in the fabric as binding or filling. In the "wire weaves" it is inserted through the chain and stuffer warp yarns with a shuttle, and in the case of Axminsters, with a needle thrust.

WIRES: Metal wires or strips which are inserted in the weaving shed of the loom under the surface yarns to form the loops as the yarns are bound by the weft shuttle, in tapestry-velvet and Brussels-Wilton weaves.

Round, untipped wires for tapestry and Brussels fabric are withdrawn from the fabric, leaving uncut pile loops; while flat, bladed-tip wires, in the velvet and the Wilton weaves, cut the loops to form a plushlike surface of tufts.

SOME RECENT DEVELOPMENTS IN AMERICAN CARPETS

1. Tendency to use strong colors instead of muted and pastel shades which have been in favor for several years.
2. High-pile textures with cut- and uncut-pile effects predominating.
3. The use of looped pile fabrics often styled in the multilevel construction to provide a more appealing and so-called softer look.
4. Twist textures are compact, dense, thick, and the velvetlike appearance is featured.
5. Motifs seem to emphasize the elegant or lush appearance to keep abreast of the constantly diverging trends in the home furnishing fields.
6. Wool styles are prominent in the higher-quality floor coverings, in both woven and tufted types.
7. Acrylic and continuous-filament nylon are very popular in the medium qualities in order to provide good value to budget-minded homemakers.
8. Polypropylene fibers are making themselves felt in the more brilliant colorings.
9. Tufted floor coverings continue their meteoric rise, the most popular type in use today.

TESTING

1. How does a rug differ from a carpet?
2. List five points that should be followed when buying a rug.
3. List three functional values of floor covering.
4. Name three decorative points that are important when buying a rug.
5. Name five textile fibers that may be used in carpet manufacture today.
6. Why is Wilton carpeting known as the "rug of hidden value"?
7. Give some reasons why chenille rugs are so expensive.
8. How does a true oriental rug differ from a domestic oriental?
9. How would you identify a true oriental rug?
10. Give some reasons for the great rise of tufted floor coverings.
11. How does the production of woven carpeting compare with that possible in tufted carpeting manufacture?
12. Define the following terms: backing, broadloom, binding yarn, weft or filling yarn, Jaspé, Kraftcord, pick, pitch, shot, stuffer warp, weft yarn, wires.
13. What is the difference between a tipped wire and a tipless wire used in the weaving of pile-fabric material?

Sources and courtesy of American Carpet Institute, 350 Fifth Ave., New York City; Mohasco Industries, Inc., Amsterdam, New York, and 295 Fifth Ave., New York City; Callaway Mills, Inc., 295 Fifth Ave., New York City, and LaGrange, Georgia.

NOTE: The American Carpet Institute provides excellent literature, charts, and other descriptive material upon request. Ideal for teachers, students, training departments in department stores. (See Unit 46, Tufted Fabrics.)

Part 1—Unit 46

TOPIC: Tufted Fabrics

Tufted bedspreads were first made in the New England colonies around 1650 and reached their highest development in the plantation South between 1725 and the beginning of the War Between the States in 1861. Following the war, the craft faded out and was practically forgotten. In 1896, however, Catherine Evans (the late Mrs. W. L. Whitener) of Dalton, Georgia, made a bedspread as a wedding gift, handicrafted, with each loop of the stitching neatly snipped off so that it looked like a "tuft of grass." When finished, it was washed and hung up to dry. A traveling man passing by saw it, purchased it, and the "tufted textile industry was on its way." Miss Evans continued to make the bedspreads and soon had more orders than she could handle. She sold them at $2.50 apiece. Soon she had the entire family working on the spreads and shortly thereafter she was hiring others to do the work.

The homely family groups in and around Dalton, Georgia, have long since given way to the huge batteries of specially designed "tufting" machinery. The former cottage industry has passed into oblivion, with many happy memories since it opened up what is now a vast textile industry still centered in and around Dalton, a very prosperous city about twenty miles southeast of Chattanooga, Tennessee.

The Evans family founded Evans Manufacturing Company in 1917, and it was operated by the family until 1963, when it was sold. Bath mats, bedspreads, housecoats, and robes were the important products in the early days of the industry and still hold a high-volume position in the industry.

Thus, in time, Miss Evans' phrase, "like a tuft of grass," gave way to the term "tufting." Electric needles, anywhere from one to one thousand five hundred or

[257]

more have replaced the laborious handwork once needed. Automation has taken over large segments of the industry. Now referred to as "TT" (tufted textiles), tufting now has the major portion of the floor-covering industry, especially so in the last fifteen years.

So rapid is the work of one machine in tufting that it can do the work formerly done by 300 or more operatives in hand tufting. The ideas developed on present-day tufting were all obtained from the sewing machine. Tufted fabric can be made much faster than carpet weaving on a conventional power loom. A tufting machine can turn out as much in three to five minutes as a loom can weave in eight hours. Actually the carpet-tufting machine is like an oversize sewing machine with hundreds of needles working simultaneously. There are at present about twelve hundred multiple-needle machines all located within a radius of three hundred miles of Dalton, Georgia.

Design motifs or patterns are printed on acetate film, passed under a bank of lights, and the photoelectric cells transmit the design directly to the chattering needles on the frames.

The fibers used include wool, wool blends, rayon, the most popular of the manmade fibers used, nylon in filament and staple form, cotton, and the acrylic and modacrylic fibers. The major company in the field of machinery is Singer-Cobble, Inc., a subsidiary of Singer Manufacturing Company, Inc., New York City. Sales of tufted products are around one billion dollars a year.

The construction principle of tufted fabrics is rather simple. A base fabric is mounted under tension beneath a row of coarse-eyed needles which carry the tufted yarn. For heavy rugs the base fabric is usually burlap made from jute, while lightweight rugs use cotton scrim or osnaburg. Jute backing seems to provide the best type of fabric to use for the insertion of the carpet yarn. The needles are driven into the backing fabric and then withdrawn. The backing fabric is advanced and the needles plunge back into it, leaving a loose loop of yarn on the surface of the article. Tensions are regulated with utmost precision to prevent the tufting yarn from being pulled out of the backing cloth on the upstroke or uptake of the needle. Although, generally speaking, the efficiency of a modern tufting machine is not rated as high, production is high when compared with that of the regulation weaving loom used to weave carpeting.

To hold the tufts in place permanently, the backing used is coated with a heavy layer of latex. Originally tufted carpeting was made with a single backing, with the latex applied to it. A great step forward has been the lamination of a second backing at the time the latex is applied in that this treatment provides a better finished product with an improved appearance and a more substantial hand because of the increased bulkiness to the product.

The quality of the backing is just as important as that of the base fabric and the tufting material. A good backing will not crack, become sticky or tacky, nor will it be affected by floor varnishes and waxes. It should not contain any substances that will eventually stain the rather expensive tufting yarns used on the face of the material.

Incidentally, the tufting industry has been a great boon to India, which annually produces a major part of the jute backing used in tufted goods. Woven in widths of more than one hundred inches, India furnishes about 80 per cent of the jute-burlap backing used in the United States at the present time.

Horizontal package which shows the tubes that guide the yarn all the way from the yarn package to the yarn feed into the machine. The creel is magazined so that there is one standby for each running end, and the end of the running cone of yarn is spliced into the leading end of the standby cone so that when one cone runs out the other takes over without any loss of time.

Horizontal creel yarn feeder. This creel is handling the largest cone package used at present, the 11-pound nylon 501 carpet yarn package.

Courtesy: Cobble Division of the Singer Company, Chattanooga, Tennessee

Yardage carpeting machine—208 DT. Tufting width is 208 inches maximum, 550 stitches per minute, pile height is $\frac{3}{16}$ inch to $\frac{7}{8}$ inch. Stitch length is 4 to 12 per inch. Weight of machine is 19,000 pounds.

TUFTED FLOOR COVERING

Face-effect pile is nylon yarn.   Back is coated with Latex to provide body and support.

There are about nine hundred looms in India used to weave this wide fabric and each loom costs around $25,000. There is some competition to this type of backing from paper backing, polypropylene fabric, and polyurethane foam supported by nylon scrim.

FINE-GAUGE TUFTING, a rather recent development, now accounts for about one-sixth of the apparel pile fabrics made in this country. This type of pile fabric competes with knitted and woven fabrics and has had a meteoric rise since its inception as to production and consumer acceptance. In contradistinction to the coarse gauge, the fine-gauge machine can show a distance of only $5/64$ inch between two tufting needles. Coarse-gauge machines have a needle space of $1/8$ inch, $5/32$ inch, and $3/16$ inch. Tufting producton line is composed of the yarn creels, which feed in the yarns used, the scrim, osnaburg or burlap backing cloth, and the device to take up the fabric as it is being created. Unlike other pile fabric producing methods, the tufting machines produce only the pile on the face of goods. Even the feeding in of the backing fabric has to be watched closely at all times.

A plain three- or four-ounce plain-weave cotton sheeting or printcloth is used in apparel pile fabric production. The $5/64$ inch fine-gauge machine contains two controlling rolls which apply the same tension on all the yarns fed into the frame from the creels. There may be several additional pairs of rolls on the machines, as warranted by the particular work and its details. The tension rolls control the height of the loop or pile. Tufting runs to ten or eleven stitches per inch, $1/8$ inch pile height, and if cotton yarn is used, the yarn count is around 1/5.5 with 4.5 to 5.5 turns of Z-twist per inch.

Fine-gauge machines can make as many as fourteen hundred stitches a minute. Production is from two to three yards a minute.

In purchasing tufted articles, especially floor covering, the price often determines the choice of the backing, since there is now a wide range in quality and the cost to the manufacturer of this backing. If the returns on an item go up, chances are that inferior backing has been used, and this is the chief cause of rejections by the public.

Tufting is now a major industry in the field of textiles and accounts for more than 75 per cent of the floor-covering industry. Broadloom tufteds are now available in widths from 12 feet to 15 feet, and are seamless. Sculptured effects, curved motifs, and other novel surface effects have done much to enhance the great rise of the industry. The industry is worldwide in scope.

SOME BASIC TERMS USED IN TUFTING

TUFTED FABRIC: A fabric decorated with fluffy tufts of soft twist, multiple-ply yarns. While some of the fabric is loom-woven, most of the work is now done on tufting machines. The tufts are inserted into a backing fabric by a set of needles working at a rapid pace, forming the pile-effect loops which are then cut by a machine to provide a cut-pile effect if desired.

The tufts may be intermittently spaced, giving the type known as candlewick, or arranged closely in continuous lines to give the type called chenille (French: "caterpillar"). Patterns vary from simple line effects to elaborate motifs. Tufted fabrics serve as carpets, rugs, bath mats, apparel coatings and robes, stuffed toys, fleece fabrics such as blanket oversleepers for infants and covers, liner fabrics, lounge wear.

TUFTING: The art and science of actually tufting yarns into a base fabric in order to form a pile effect on the face of the goods.

Chenille as woven in the loom for use as filling yarn in chenille.

Chenille or caterpillar effect in tufted fabrics.

Candlewick. Wicktip effect in tufting fabric.

TUFTING MACHINE: A machine that automatically compresses a spot in a mattress and inserts and stitches a tuft through a compressed area. Also a machine, based on the principle of a sewing machine, which inserts yarn into a base fabric in order to form loops in the material. These loops may be cut or uncut in the finished article.

TUFTING NEEDLE: The needle used to force tufting yarn or cord through the base or backing fabric used in the manufacture of tufted fabric. The needle may vary in size, shape (hooked or not) and length, all dependent on the work being done.

TESTING

1. Trace the origin and rise of tufted fabrics.
2. Name five textile fibers which serve as the base for the yarn used in tufting.
3. Define the following terms: (1) loop; (2) cut loop; (3) backing fabric; (4) tufted fabric.
4. How does a candlewick effect differ from a chenille effect in tufted fabrics?
5. Explain the differences between coarse-gauge tufting and fine-gauge tufting.

Courtesy of Tufted Textile Manufacturers Association, Dalton, Georgia; Paul Askew, Sale Department, The Singer Company, Cobble Division, Chattanooga, Tennessee.

Part 1—Unit 47

TOPIC: DOMESTICS

The generally accepted definition for the broad term "domestics" implies that they include any textile product, article, or object which has a practical use for decoration or service in the home. The term "linens and domestics" is a very old phrase, and somewhat of a misnomer at times. With regard to articles made of cotton or other fibers, and innocently or willfully sold as linen, the Federal Trade Commission on February 1, 1941, decreed the following rules as to how the term "linen," may or may not be used:

Rule 1

a) LINEN (AND FLAX) DEFINED: "Linen" is the generic term for textile fiber of the flax plant and for the thread, strands, yarn or fabric produced from such fiber. For the purpose of these rules, the terms "linen" or "flax" as applied to textile fiber shall mean the fiber of the flax plant.

b) DECEPTIVE PASSING OFF OF LINEN OR FLAX: It is an unfair trade practice to cause any linen or flax fiber, or any yarn, thread, strands, fabric, garment or other article composed of linen or flax, to be sold, offered for sale, distributed, advertised, described, branded, labeled, or otherwise represented:
1. As not being linen or flax;
2. As being somewhat other than linen or flax;
3. Without disclosure of the fact that such merchandise is linen or flax made clear unequivocally in the invoices, and in labels, tags, or marks attached to the merchandise, and in whatever advertising matter, sales promotional descriptions or representations thereof may be used, however disseminated or published, where such nondisclosure has the capacity and tendency or effect of misleading or deceiving the purchasing or consuming public.

c) OTHER MISREPRESENTATIONS: It is an unfair trade practice to cause any fiber, yarn, thread, strands, fabric, garment or other article containing, or purporting to contain, linen or flax, in whole or in part, to be offered for sale, sold or distributed under any conditions of deceptive concealment of the fiber content or under any other deceptive or misleading conditions or representations whatever.

Rule 2

PURE LINEN: It is an unfair trade practice to use the term "linen" or "flax" (not appropriately qualified) or the terms "pure linen," "pure flax," "all linen," or "all flax," or any other word, term, phrase, designation or representation of similar import, as descriptive of any fiber, yarn, thread, strands or fabric, or garment or other article containing the same, (1) the fiber content of which is not linen exclusively; or (2) which contains any other fiber; or (3) which contains any foreign or added non-fibrous substance or material except the necessary dyeing and finishing materials required to produce the color and finish of the product not exceeding 5 per cent by weight of the product in its finished state. Nothing in this rule shall be construed as permitting the use of dyeing or finishing materials, either within or in excess of such 5 per cent, for the purpose or with the result of thereby deceptively loading the product with excess or unnecessary dyeing or finishing materials.

Rule 3

"LIN," "LYN," ETC.: The use of the word or term or syllable such as "lin," "linn," "lyn," or "lynn," or other word, term, or syllable of similar import, alone or in part, cannot be used in any manner, capacity, tendency or effect of misleading or deceiving the purchasing or consuming public.

BATHROOM DOMESTICS
Towels

These are an important accessory in the bathroom, and there is a large variety from which to make your choice. Quality, size, and price are very important in the determination of the particular type or types that are to be used. Structure, compactness of the towel, the color scheme, and the weight should be given due consideration before making any purchase.

TERRY TOWELING: Also known as Turkish toweling, this type should be used for the bath and for face and hands. These towelings come in all sizes from the king size for the bath to the fingertip size for guest use. The latter is comparatively new and extremely popular. There is a very wide and exhaustive range of colors, but it is suggested that deep colors not be selected, as there is a good chance that these colors will "bleed" in washing and will stain other articles unless washed alone, which is not always practical. The use of metallic yarns for added interest is popular, and these yarns do seem to add to a towel, particularly when used in a border. All towels in this group should be vat-dyed.

LINEN: Linen towels come mostly in sizes for the hands and face, and in small sizes for use as guest towels. Practically all of this type of toweling is imported, chiefly from Ireland and Belgium. The surface is smooth, the weight is considered heavy, and plain or intricate motifs enhance the toweling. Absorbency is high in linen toweling.

COTTON: This toweling is made of the well-known huck construction and may come in bird's-eye, minute waffle effect, or some similar weave construction. Cotton toweling is used for the hands and face.

NONWOVEN: This toweling is new, novel, and popular. It comes in colorful prints in an allover or a border design. Nonwoven toweling serves chiefly as guest toweling.

Washcloths

These should be of terry cloth construction exclusively.

Shower Curtains

HEAVY COTTON: This type of curtain is used in many homes, and it is made of heavy fabric such as denim or sailcloth.

TREATED COTTON: This shower curtain material includes a variety of fabrics, all of them treated with a water-repellent finish, usually very durable in nature. They come in plain colors and in printed effects.

SUPPORTED VINYL PLASTIC OR VINYL FILM: These two curtain types are very popular and rather inexpensive; they too come in a wide range of designs, as well as in plain colors. It should be noted that both these film-type curtains should be further treated in order to make them fire-retardant.

Bathmats and Rugs

These come mostly in sets with a matching lid cover. There are four main types which are popular today:

1. HEAVY TERRY CLOTH.
2. COTTON CHENILLE.
3. DEEP-PILE COTTON OR RAYON, often in a sculptured effect.
4. BRAIDED COTTON.

Window Curtains

These are known as half-window or sill-length curtains.

COTTON OR RAYON: The leno weave is used to make the marquisette curtain fabric, which is very light in weight, porous, and neat. These curtains usually appear in tailored style.

VINYL FILM: This type has met with much favor, and it comes in sets with matching shower curtain.

BEDROOM DOMESTICS

Bedspreads

Many of these are made by manufacturers who specialize in spreads. They are usually thick, soft, flat-woven cotton; non-wrinkling; reversible; with stylized motifs or patterns; completely washable; vat-dyed; and they come in a very wide variety of colors and designs.

1. **SIZES:** Bedspreads are available in all sizes from cot to super-king-size. It is recommended that for size, measurement of the distance from one side to the other side of the bed be taken, with the addition of whatever width is needed for the drop to the top of the dust ruffle or to the floor. For the length, measure from top to bottom of the bed, and also take into consideration whether or not the spread will be tucked under at the bottom or will fall to the dust ruffle or floor, and whether or not at the top the pillow or bolster will be tucked in. Allow for shrinkage unless the material is guaranteed against shrinkage.

2. **MATERIALS:**
   SEERSUCKER: For summer use; should be Sanforized.
   FLOWERED CHINTZ: Ideal for the so-called cottage-type decor. Usually comes with some such matching as dust ruffles, draperies, valances, pillow shams, toss pillows, café curtains.
   QUILTED OR EMBOSSED: These bedspreads are usually made of polished cotton fabric. The polish may disappear in washing.
   CHENILLE: This includes the tufted and hobnail type of fabric or article, and is especially popular for use with American antique furniture.
   SATIN OR TAFFETA: Spreads of this type are grouped with period styles; that is, in rooms of foreign periods of furniture such as Louis XIV, Regency, Victorian antique, Empire, etc.
   DENIM: Lightweight cotton which is used for heavy duty, as in children's rooms. Should be Sanforized.

Blankets

There is a wide choice from which to make a selection—wool, Acrilan, rayon, rayon-"Orlon," rayon-Acrilan, etc. Electric blanket shells are made of the same fabrics. The binding is of nylon, acetate, or rayon.

Blanket Covers

The best type to use is made of percale, cotton challis, or similar fabric; a zipper closure should be used.

Closet Accessories

These include garment bags, shoe bags, odds-and-ends bags. They should be made of cotton twill fabric, supported vinyl, or plain plastic.

Glass Curtains

These are used to cover the glass portions of windows. The favored fabrics are cotton, rayon, or nylon marquisettes, sill-length and in tailored types. Ruffled organdy is good for the tie-backs or swags.

Mattresses

The cover should be made of good, sturdy cotton ticking or twill fabric. The stuffing may be of hair (horse and hog), cotton, cotton with layers of cotton felt on top; all foam rubber; cotton with foam rubber on top. Foam rubber should be used only in warm rooms since in cold rooms the air cells will be chilled and then transfer the chill to the sleeper.

Mattress and Box-Spring Covers

The best type to use is of Sanforized muslin with zipper closure.

Mattress Pads

Quilted, stuffed with cotton or fiber fill. Should be Sanforized or there will be considerable shrinkage. Some pads come with elastic bands at the corners to prevent sliding. A waterproof type is obtainable, made with a quilted plastic top, which makes it ideal for children's beds and cribs.

Pillows

The covering is made of cotton ticking or a closely woven twill fabric. The best stuffing is down, or it may be feathers, foam rubber, or fiber fill.

Pillowcases

These should be of the same fabric as the sheets.

Pillow Covers

These are fitted covers made of cotton muslin with zipper closure.

Rugs

Popular at present are washable cotton or rayon scatter rugs made with a deep pile effect, often sculptured. These rugs are given a rubber backing to prevent sliding. Wall-to-wall carpets or room-size rugs are of deep cotton pile effect, or of wool or nylon in the standard constructions. Coverings of hemp or sisal are recommended for summer use.

Rug Cushions

These are for use under rugs which do not have a rubber backing. They are made of rubberized hair or foam rubber.

Sheets

Cotton muslin or percale sheetings are the most popular. Textures range from 112, 128, 140, 160, 180 up to about 200 in pick count—the total number of threads in both warp and filling per square inch in the cloth. The lower textures are made of carded yarn, the higher textures of combed yarn. Fitted sheets of nylon tricot or of Sanforized cotton are popular. The "No-iron" cotton sheets are treated with a wrinkle-resistant agent to prevent rumpling or wrinkling. Napped cotton sheets have found favor for use in cold climates. Sheeting may be all white, or dyed a solid color, or printed with attractive prints and stripes, used either in an allover motif or only in the hems.

Slipcovers and Upholstery

These should not be of heavy weight or nubbed surface, or of violent or bizarre pattern. Choose smooth surfaces, delicate blending colors, and, if decorated, it is well to choose a restful or serene design.

DINING ROOM DOMESTICS

Table Covers

These come in a very wide range of sizes depending on the intended use, from full-size dinner cloths to small bridge-table size, including lunch cloths and dinette or breakfast nook tablecloths. The use of Lurex or other metallic yarns has occasionally been popular in informal fabric tablecloths.

PLAIN-WEAVE LINEN: This fabric comes in white or solid colors, often with a screen or stencil print motif. Hand-blocked borders are frequently used. The price range varies considerably depending on the quality. Plain-weave cotton or rayon table covering which simulates linen is also made.

DAMASK: This is made from several fiber groups—linen, cotton, rayon, cotton and rayon, etc. Linen damask is by far the most luxurious table covering. A single damask is made with a five-shaft satin weave while a double damask is made with an eight-shaft satin weave. The yarn floats in the single damask are four and in the double damask seven; therefore single damask is a stronger and better-wearing fabric. While the shorter yarn floats in single damask give greater strength to the goods, the longer floats in the double damask produce more luster. All damask is made on a Jacquard loom and the fabric is reversible. The higher the construction in damask the better will be the quality and resultant wear. This fabric launders well and retains its luster. Damask is also used for doilies, curtains, guest towels, napkins, and runners. A good table damask is rightfully called "the cloth of kings" and "the fabric of elegance."

NONWOVEN: This successful new table covering comes in printed designs and in a variety of sizes.

MACHINE-MADE LACE: This covering is made of all cotton, or of cotton and rayon. The lace is sometimes combined with fabric to produce novel effects.

COTTON: Cotton fabric is frequently used for table covering. Much of the fabric is coated on one side with vinyl to add body. The fabric is available in stripes, checks, screen prints, and other appealing motifs. It is well known for its ability to take punishment, and provides especially good service at all times.

VINYL: One type of table covering is a combination of vinyl plastic with a cotton-flannel back. Another type is the vinyl film covering. Both are inexpensive and provide good wear and service. Table coverings of nonwoven fabric coated with vinyl are all used extensively for outdoor eating.

Table Napkins

Matching napkins are often sold with a table covering as a set. Napkins, however, may also be bought in individual sets. They are made of linen, cotton, rayon, and nonwoven fabrics.

Table Pads

Three main types of table pads can be used—cotton felt, napped cotton (also known as molleton or silence cloth), and a thin foam rubber sheet pad.

Rugs

Wall-to-wall carpeting is not recommended for a dining room in a busy household because this type of floor covering must be cleaned frequently.

WOOL OR WORSTED RUGS: With respect to quality and cost, chenille, Wilton, and Brussels, in that order, are the best types of dining-room floor coverings. They have been standard for many years and are used in the more affluent homes. Their construction is designed to give good service; most rugs of this type will last for at least fifteen years if given proper care. Other types of woolen rugs are used, but their service does not begin to compare with the types mentioned before.

COTTON PILE: This fabric is made with a rubberized backing. The main point in its favor is its reasonable cost. The fabric, however, is not long-lasting. Crushing of the pile is a chief drawback because traffic marks are easily seen.

RUGS OF MANMADE OR MANUFACTURED FIBERS: Nylon floor covering has become popular in recent years because of its good service and ability to withstand very hard wear. It is made in plain or multiple colors and its surface may be even or sculptured.

Other manmade fibers are now being used to varying degrees in rugs. Included are the following:

ACRYLIC FIBERS: Acrilan, Creslan, "Orlon," Zefran.
MODACRYLIC FIBERS: Dynel, Verel.
POLYESTER FIBERS: "Dacron," Kodel, Fortrel, Vyrene, Blue "C."
REGENERATED CELLULOSIC FIBER: Rayon.
CELLULOSE-DERIVATIVE FIBER: Acetate.
TRIACETATE FIBER: Arnel.
POLYAMIDE FIBERS: Nylon, Caprolan.

They come in a wide price range and a variety of motifs and textures. Many of these rugs are tufted and give added appeal to the prospective purchaser.

SISAL: This fiber is also known as henequin or abaca. Rug mats of this product are used for summer wear and are easy to clean.

Curtains

These may be of the same type as the curtains used for the living room. Ruffled organdy and machine-made lace are quite popular.

Draperies

These may be the same as for the living room.

KITCHEN DOMESTICS

Dish Towels

LINEN: This is the best type of dish towel because of high absorbency and excellent wearing quality.

COTTON AND RAYON: This toweling comes in colorful prints. Absorbency, however, does not begin to compare with that of linen. The reasonable price is really the main reason for the popularity of this fabric.

COTTON: The absorbency of this toweling is poor and the fabric does not have the body and substance for dish toweling. Also, the fabric becomes very limp after usage.

TERRY CLOTH: The use of this fabric for dish towels is new. Many new uses are being found for terry cloth—beach wear, handbags, hats, coats. Terry has excellent absorbency when compared with ordinary plain-woven cottons for toweling. In addition, it does not have to be ironed after washing.

Hand Towels

The nonwoven type of hand towel is best since it is disposable after usage, and the cost is reasonable when compared with other types such as terry, plain cotton, or linen.

Pot Holders

Quilted cotton stuffed with cotton makes the most practical pot holders. Terry cloth and other fabrics are also used.

Dishcloths

COTTON: These dishcloths are loosely woven from yarn that is low in twist. The leno or doup weave is used to make a loose but strong fabric. Although the fabric is open and porous, the crossing of the warp ends over and under each other between the filling picks makes for strength and long wear.

NONWOVEN: These dishcloths can be used several times and then discarded. They are sanitary and inexpensive.

Wall Coverings

One widely-used type is the supported vinyl covering. Impregnated cotton is also used; this type has a coating applied to it. Both give good service and can be easily cleaned. There is a wide range of color choice with varied and interesting motifs. "Splash prints" are now very popular. Wall covering should be treated for fire-retardance.

Mops

Cotton mops are the most popular type. Wastes from acetate, rayon, nylon, etc., are now also being used. Nylon is rather expensive and because of its static electricity "may attract dust."

Ironing Board Covers

Cotton muslin, treated to resist scorching, is widely used. Much of the covering is also treated in various ways to improve service and wear. Some cover cloth is treated with aluminum or silicone.

Silver-Polishing Cloths

Napped cotton fabric such as flannel, molleton or silence cloth is used for this purpose. These cloths, as well as containers for silverware, are treated with tarnish-removing chemicals.

Glass Curtains

GLASS FIBER: Curtain fabrics such as Fiberglas have met with much acclaim because of ease of care, neatness, and intriguing color and motif. Most of the fabric, which is marquisette, is made with a leno or doup weave which provides porosity and excellent draping quality. Cotton, rayon, and "Dacron" are also used for curtaining, either in marquisette fabric or in weaves other than the leno construction.

GINGHAM: A great many color combinations are made possible by the use of gingham. It is used in half-window style and is popular. Price is a factor in curtaining of this type.

VINYL FILM: This material can also be used, since ease of care and cleaning, along with price, make it a good purchase for the housewife.

Rugs

Cotton scatter rugs, often with rubberized backing, are popular. These rugs or strips are good for use on cold floors or for placing in areas where there is a great deal of standing on the floor, such as before a sink.

LIVING ROOM DOMESTICS

Curtains

The most popular types include glass fiber, rayon and cotton, "Dacron," and nylon, all made with the leno or doup weave construction used for marquisette. Fabrics of other weaves are also used, sometimes having interesting motifs produced by the weave pattern. Machine-made lace and dotted swiss are also widely used.

Draperies

These may hang at the sides only or may be drawn over the whole window. Draw-draperies are pinch-pleated at the top. Draperies must either be thick enough to prevent penetration of light or lined with a backing. The lining is usually of cotton sateen fabric or casement cloth, and varies in weight depending upon the weight of the draperies. In all cases, draperies should be fast to light.

GLASS FIBER: Draperies of this type are translucent and cannot be lined successfully. They should not rub against rods, sills, or Venetian blinds because of the possibility of fabric splitting. Glass fiber drapery is rather heavy and is a textured construction as differentiated from the sheer type of glass fiber curtain fabrics.

LINEN OR COTTON: Draperies of this type are heavy in weight. They are usually of plain weave and they come in a host of designs. The price of cotton drapes is a governing factor since there is a wide range of quality, from low to high.

BLENDS: Fibers such as acetate, rayon, cotton, and nylon are used in many blended drapery fabrics. "Dacron" is also popular, in an all-"Dacron" fabric or in a blend. There is a very wide range of texture and color in these fabrics.

Upholstery

WOOL: Wool upholstery fabrics include tapestry, needlepoint, petit point, velvet, velour, and frieze. They are made in varying color ranges, motifs, and weights. Tapestry, needlepoint, and petit point give good service because of their compact structure. Velvet, velour, and frieze, depending on the raised-pile surface effect, may not give satisfactory wear because these fabrics tend to crush or lie down with usage. In addition, when rays of light strike this type of material, an undesirable "bright-and-dim" effect is created.

LINEN: Solid colors and plain-weave color effects are very popular. Basket weaves and variations in small weave repeats are also featured in modern decor.

COTTON: The use of cotton has increased considerably because it is easy to style and there are a great many varieties of fabrics. Some of the favorite materials include well-textured corduroy in pinwale construction, monk's cloth, usually in a 4-and-4 basket weave, and fine denim. Novelty-textured materials and nubbed-yarn fabrics are used frequently since there is wide range from which to make a selection. Fabric weights vary to suit particular needs, and the price factor also has a bearing on the purchase.

LEATHER AND PLASTIC LEATHER: Leather has always been used extensively in the upholstery trade. Plastic leather has been in demand because it so closely resembles genuine leather. The price factor must be considered when a purchase is to be made because of the wide range in quality.

COTTON AND ACETATE: This combination is found chiefly in novelty fabrics. The range of pattern is wide, and the price is a contributing factor.

RAYON: This fiber has been used chiefly in novelty fabrics and in frieze constructions.

DULL NYLON: Delustered or dull nylon, chiefly the semi-dull type, is ideal for smooth-surfaced upholstery.

METALLIC YARNS: Yarns such as Lurex are now used a great deal in upholstery fabrics to produce a novelty effect which enhances and adds pattern interest to the fabric.

Rugs

WOOL: Custom-made chenille can be ordered in a wide range of quality and price. It has been woven to simulate some of the finest and rarest oriental creations. Wilton is considered to be below chenille, which is easily the most expensive type of rug made on power looms. Worsted Wilton is superior to wool Wilton and is classed as a luxury fabric. Wool Wilton provides a luxury feeling under foot and has excellent design detail and a sturdy foundation construction. Axminster, velvet, Brussels, and tapestry floor coverings are in a lower classification and give good service commensurate with the cost. Hooked rugs, also made of wool, are popular with Colonial and Early American furniture.

NYLON: Plain or sculptured nylon carpeting in a deep-pile construction has become quite popular. The price has decreased considerably as the demand has increased. Nylon rugs are very long-wearing and can absorb considerable punishment in wear.

COTTON: Cotton rugs are usually made with a deep-pile or long-nap effect. Their sales have made some inroads on other types because of their reasonable price.

DRUGGETS: These are printed and felted fabrics made from any number of textile fibers. The fabrics, which are heavy, come in all sizes and in designs which run from the conservative and conventional to the brilliant and bizarre. Stencil-printed motifs are popular on these rugs, which originated in India.

ACRILAN (ACRYLIC FIBER) AND VEREL (MODACRYLIC FIBER): Durability is excellent and resistance to matting or resiliency good to excellent, as is soil-resistance. Rugs of this type can be readily spot-cleaned for stains, and they react well to professional cleaning; can be used in all general traffic areas in the home. Acrilan and Verel are mothproof and mildew-resistant. These fabrics compare well with wool floor covering.

SISAL: Floor coverings made from this rugged fiber are generally used for summer wear. This vegetable-fiber floor covering withstands hard, rugged wear very well.

Rug Cushions

The following materials are used for this purpose—foam rubber, cotton felt, and felted hair which has been treated for moth-resistance. Much work has been done in improving rug cushions, chiefly of the foam-rubber type, to provide "that sinking feeling of luxury" even when placed under a medium or low-priced carpet or rug.

Upholstery Stuffing

Cotton, foam rubber, hair with cotton felt on the surface, and vinyl foam, a new product, are all used for stuffing.

Window Shades

Impregnated cotton is the standard fabric used, although Velon is also popular for this purpose.

Dustcloths

Cheesecloth was generally used; nonwoven fabrics, however, have replaced cheesecloth to considerable degree. They are treated to pick up and hold dust, and they are lint-free and washable.

Slip Covers

These should be vat-dyed, fast to light, and Sanforized whenever possible.

COTTON: Several cotton fabrics, either plain or printed, serve as slip covers. Chintz, cretonne, denim, crash, rep, sateen, and monk's cloth are widely used. Nubbed and novelty-textured fabrics are also used to some degree. Sailcloth is a rugged cotton slip cover fabric.

KNITTED COTTON: This fabric is used to give a snug fit on the chair or couch. Elastic sections allow for good fitting of the covering. Price is a factor when buying this type of material.

BURLAP: The finer type of lightweight burlap, in plain colors or stencil prints, is frequently used to advantage.

TICKING: Cotton ticking is ideal for summer use; gives excellent wear.

CLEAR PLASTIC FILM: Heavy-gauge plastic is now being used for slip covers. It should be treated for fire-retardance. The seams of this material are electrically welded. It is especially useful for protecting upholstery since nothing can penetrate it.

RAYON: Nubbed and textured rayon fabrics are popular materials for slip covers. Price is a factor in this type of covering.

LINEN: Plain, screen-printed, or hand-blocked linens are used. Linen gives an impression of added serenity and a cool feeling when used for slip covering.

NYLON AND ACETATE: Blends of these two fibers produce fabrics which combine the beauty of acetate and the abrasion-resistance of nylon.

Part 1—Unit 48

TOPIC: FACTORING

In the early days, before textiles were manufactured in this country, the British mills were the main source of supply, and shipments were in transit for months. The mills did not have close connections with their sales representatives and lacked the facilities for checking credits and making collections. These serious problems and risks were reduced and handled by financially strong, enterprising specialists in the United States, known as "factors," who offered valuable services to the mills by:

1. Recommending local sales agents.
2. Checking the credits of customer orders and guaranteeing collection of the "credit-approved" receivables.
3. Handling all details of receiving import shipments, including customs and reshipping to customers.

4. Holding inventory here and making prompt shipment of "credit-approved" orders. Often the factor did the packing, shipping, and invoicing as "agent" for his client, the mill.
5. Making financial advances available to his clients. The security usually was the assigned accounts receivable and/or the inventory.

As the textile industry developed in the United States, the factors were a strong, constructive influence in the domestic field, having had long-time experience in checking credits and making collections. Their specialized services broadened to include sound financial guidance on management, policy matters including sales, general overall matters, as well as loans for modernization and expansion. The factoring expense to the client is in two categories:

1. A percentage on his sales volume for checking credits and the factor's guarantee on approved accounts receivable.
2. Interest is charged on funds advanced, but only until collected for the time outstanding, at a rate somewhat higher than the bank rate. This debit is revolving and/or self-liquidating by payments made by the customer of the accounts receivable.

   If no advance is required and the client's credit balance does not require advances from the factor, the credit balance may earn interest.

Factors are now serving many industries with the substantial growth of international trade since the close of World War II; the techniques of financing imports and exports have been adapted to meet the changing conditions. Close cooperation with the banks, here and abroad, and bank participation have become increasingly important in facilitating the necessary credit arrangements, and, if needed, handling foreign currency and exchange settlements.

COMMERCIAL FACTORING

This differs sharply from factoring, since the shipper checks his own credits and takes full risk on collecting the accounts receivable—the lender (commercial finance company) offers the short-term advances to the shipper secured by assigned accounts receivable. Generally, the customer is not notified of the assignment, and the shipper collects the accounts receivable and then repays the lender for the advance.

There are also other types of loans offered by commercial finance companies. The security required and the rates charged reflect the risks involved and the financial responsibility of the borrower.

TESTING

1. Why are factors important to the textile and other industries in the business world of today?
2. Discuss three functions performed by a factor.
3. Discuss the factoring expense to the client.
4. Differentiate between factoring and commercial factoring.

Courtesy of Albert O. Silverman, Textile Broker, New York City.

PART TWO

TABLE OF CONTENTS

Part 2—Unit 1

TOPIC: TEXTILE TESTING

Testing has many valuable functions, not only in the field of textiles, but in all other fields of manufacture, from the testing and inspection of the raw material's condition through to the testing of the finished product's performance. Whatever the product, testing does the following:

Protects the quality from the raw material stage to the finished product.
Prevents wasteful buying.
Discloses weaknesses and flaws that may appear in the structure.
Detects costly danger zones in processes.
Measures the efficiency of performance.

Points the way to better methods and better products.

Acts as a sales weapon and sales stimulus throughout the entire distributive system.

Establishes truth for advertising.

Testing is divided into three categories—physical, chemical, and optical. Textile testing is conducted for many reasons and at various stages in the production of fabrics. It may be divided into three major sections:

1. Testing within the textile plant.
2. Simple laboratory testing.
3. Advanced laboratory testing.

In general, textile testing is done to determine the answers to one or more of the following questions:

Are the goods satisfactory?

Are the goods better than or inferior to another lot?

What has been the effect of a certain process or treatment on the goods?

If the goods are unsatisfactory or unusual, what is the cause of the abnormality?

An analysis conducted to find the answer to the above questions will in some instances be based on specifications and standards; in other cases it may involve the comparison of two or more similar samples.

The various types of tests which are made for composition, construction, and performance of textile materials cover a very wide range. The following shows the major types of tests conducted in each category:

Physical Tests Include

Staple length, grade, and quality of fibers.

The size, strength, ply, twist, and the quality of the yarns.

Construction, weight, strength, abrasion, weave construction, shrinkage, and other important properties of textile fabrics.

Chemical Tests Include

Determination of sizings.

Quantitative analysis of the fiber content.

Identification and the analysis of special finishes.

Extraction analysis.

Various types of colorfastness tests.

Determination of the causes of defective materials.

Optical Tests Include

Qualitative and quantitative fiber analysis.

Grade of wool, worsted, cotton, etc.

Photomicrography.

Measurement determinations.

Inspection of defects.

Standard Atmospheric Tests

In the physical testing of textiles, the most important single factor is the amount of moisture in the air. This affects every phase of the physical properties of a fabric. Since the temperature and the relative humidity have an appreciable effect on the physical properties of textiles, it is necessary that the conditions under which the samples are tested be rigidly controlled. In standard atmospheric conditions for textiles the moisture equilibrium should be maintained at a standard atmosphere having a relative humidity of 65 per cent (±2%) at 70° (±2° F.). The relative humidity is set at a comparatively high value since it is much easier to humidify air than to dehumidify it.

Colorfastness

The capacity of a material for resisting any changing of shade from acids, atmospheric gases, alkalies, carbonizing, chlorine, drycleaning, wet cleaning, crocking, fulling, light, perspiration, dry-pressing, wet-pressing, salt water, washing, or weather.

Composition of Textiles

This refers to the kind and the amount of various fibers present in a textile material. It is determined chemically and microscopically and answers questions such as these:

Of what type rayon is the fabric composed—viscose rayon or cuprammonium rayon?
Is the fabric acetate or rayon, or a combination of the two?
Is the material 50 per cent nylon and 50 per cent cotton?

Construction of Fabrics

This refers to the thread count, threads-per-inch, or the texture in both warp and filling. It may also include the size or the count of the yarn or yarns used, as well as the determination of the twist used in the yarns.

Extraction Analysis

Finishes or other substances are removed from fabrics by means of solvents such as water—sometimes known as the universal solvent—carbon tetrachloride, or other organic solvents. The extracted substance is isolated by evaporating the solvent. It may then be identified or the percentage may be determined.

The Grade of Fiber: This is the class into which cotton, wool, and other fibers are classified to length, diameter, evenness, strength, and fiber color. For example, the grade of wool is designated by the fineness and the percentage distribution of the individual fibers. The average diameter and the distribution are then measured microscopically to determine the grade of the particular fiber.

Photomicrography: This is the art or the process of producing magnified photographs of small objects or surfaces.

Ply: In yarns, ply refers to the number of single yarns which are twisted together to make up the specific yarn under examination.

Sizing: Non-fibrous matter which is added during the weaving or during the finishing of fabric to impart a definite characteristic to the yarn or fabric.

Standards in Textile Testing: Specific standards and methods in testing set by certain agencies and societies are followed on all applicable materials. Included are:

American Association of Textile Chemists & Colorists.
American Standards Association.
Commercial Standards of U.S. Department of Commerce.
Federal Specifications.
Military Specifications for the Army, Navy, Air Force, Quartermaster Corps, Medical Corps, Ordnance, etc.
National Institute of Drycleaning.
The American Society for Testing and Materials (ASTM).

Yarn Size or Yarn Number: The size of a given yarn is expressed by a number based upon the relation between the length and the weight.

Finishes: Below is a list of the properties that a finish may impart to a particular fabric:

A FINISH FOR:

1. Abrasion-resistance	17. Lustrousness
2. Absorbency	18. Mildew-resistance
3. Antiseptic qualities	19. Moth-resistance
4. Antistatic qualities	20. Oil-resistance
5. Colorfastness	21. Perspiration-resistance
6. Crease-resistance	22. Renewability
7. Crispness	23. Scroopiness
8. Drapability	24. Shrinkage-resistance
9. Drycleanability	25. Slip-resistance
10. Dullness	26. Softness
11. Durability	27. Stain-resistance
12. Flame-resistance	28. Stretch-and-sag resistance
13. Gas-fading inhibited	29. Washfastness
14. Ironing (minimum)	30. Water-repellency
15. Lightfastness	31. Wilt-reduction
16. Lintlessness	

Courtesy of Cameron A. Baker, Director, Research and Development, Better Fabrics Testing Bureau, New York City.

L-22 AND L-24: MINIMUM STANDARDS OF THE AMERICAN STANDARDS ASSOCIATION

The standards of the American Standards Association of New York City were approved for rayon and acetate fabrics on December 31, 1952, and revised in 1960. Minimum standards are provided on these materials with regard to terminal uses of the goods. These cover a wide range, from the fiber producer to the finisher of the goods, the cutter and garment manufacturer, and the retailer and the consumer. Following World War II there was a maze of fabrics brought onto the market, which caused much chaos and confusion to all segments of the industry, let alone the public. The Association, keenly aware of the dilemma, undertook to do something about the bewildering conditions. It stated that "an American Standard is intended as a guide to aid the manufacturer, the consumer, and the general public. The existence of an American Standard does not in any respect preclude any party who has approved of the standard from manufacturing, selling, or using products, processes, or procedures not conforming to the standard."

Thus, it will be noted that acceptance of either or both standards is on a voluntary basis at all times. At the present time there are thirty-eight tests for women's and girls' apparel, twenty-three standards for men's and boys' apparel, and sixteen standards for the home-furnishings category.

In testing for setting the standards the use of the equipment in any well-established or well-setup laboratory for chemical and physical testing will suffice. Other organizations that perform tests for standards include the American Society for Testing and Materials, the American Association of Textile Colorists and Chemists, and the International Standards Association. In addition, through research, development, experience, and experimental work the following groups have also contributed to the setting up of standards, working in conjunction for the most part, with the foregoing textile associations: groups and organizations that represent the government, various segments of industry, some academic institutions, services, and consumer units.

Textile-testing projects, both chemical and physical, undertaken and accepted, for example, by A.S.T.M. and A.A.T.C.C., are accepted by the American Standards Association with regard to essential performance requirements. All accepted tests provide a minimum level in serviceability and performance after a consideration of all angles presented in the particular project or test.

L-24 provides Institutional Standards sponsored by the American Hotel Association. The latest revision of standards occurred in 1957 and it is still used at the present time. This set of tests and requirements does what L-22 does for the home furnishing field. Some standards are used by both groups.

One of the outstanding facets of the A.S.A. is that if a fabric meets with its approval as to a minimum standard, "it does not imply that it is the best fabric in its class that a consumer can purchase, or the best value for the money expended; it does imply, however, that its minimum standard for performance and serviceability has been approved after all positive and negative aspects have been given full consideration."

Part 2—Unit 2

TOPIC: The Microscope

As its name (from the Greek word *Micros,* meaning "small") implies, a microscope deals with the study of small objects. The lens, similar to a magnifying glass, bends the rays of light so that they appear to come from an object larger than the original source.

The closer an object is brought to the convex lens, the smaller will be the magnification; conversely, the farther away it is drawn, the larger it becomes, until it reaches the principal focus where it becomes obscure.

Beyond that, it appears upside down. Should this inverted image be magnified again and again, the principles of a compound microscope, which permits of an enlargement way beyond the normal 100-times enlargement of the ordinary magnifying glass, become apparent. Such microscopes, through the use of ultraviolet light, can enlarge objects as small as one two-hundred-thousandths of an inch in diameter.

When a specimen is examined through a powerful microscope, details are visible which the naked eye cannot see because the rays that would ordinarily give one impression when they strike the retina are spread into separate impressions by the lens.

Modern science, including the study of plants, insects, textile fibers, and filaments, fabric blemishes, cloth constructions, reactions of chemicals on textile materials, etc., is based on information gained through the microscope.

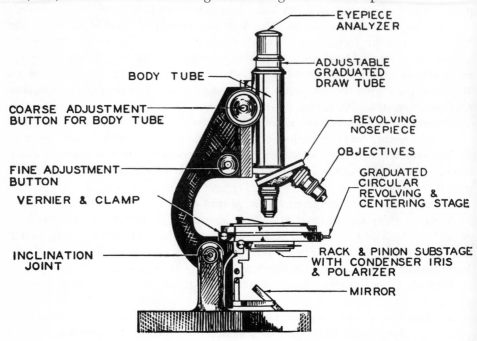

Courtesy: Bausch & Lomb, Inc., Rochester, New York

Textile laboratory microscope.

THE MICROSCOPE IN DETAIL

The microscope is of great importance to many phases of the textile industry. This expensive, delicate instrument can be easily damaged if not handled with utmost care. Work must be done with care, patience, and precision. A detailed study of the microscope and its parts follows:

Enlarging or magnification is done by two lens units: one, located near the eye, is known as the eyepiece or ocular; the other, near the object to be tested, is known as the objective.

The magnification of the microscope is found by multiplying the magnification of the eyepiece by the magnification of the objective.

If a 10× eyepiece is used with a 43× objective, anything seen through the microscope will be magnified 10 × 43, or 430 times.

The coarse adjustment is used to raise or lower the body tube to bring the object into focus so that it may be seen.

The fine adjustment is used for the final focusing and should be turned no more than a few turns in either direction.

If more turning is necessary, it implies that the coarse adjustment was not used enough.

The nosepiece holds more than one objective of different magnifying power and permits quick changing of objectives to obtain different magnifications.

The stage supports the glass slide on which the object to be magnified is placed.

The hole in the stage permits light to come through the objects so that it may be seen.

The clips on the stage hold the slide in place and keep it from slipping off when the microscope is tilted.

In carrying the microscope, it should always be held by the arm and in upright position.

The inclination joint permits tilting of the microscope to a comfortable angle.

The diaphragm controls the amount of light passing through the microscope.

The mirror reflects light up through the object. One side has a plane mirror, the other a concave mirror, which concentrates the light rays more than the plane mirror.

The horseshoe base supports the microscope.

Knowing the following parts of the microscope is important for anyone, either novice or technologist, who will be working with this instrument.

1. Eyepiece	5. Ocular	9. Coarse adjustment
2. Inclination joint	6. Nosepiece	10. Clips
3. Diaphragm	7. Objective	11. Mirror
4. Arm	8. Fine adjustment	12. Stage

Procedure in the Use of a Microscope

The how and the why of having a camera in focus to take pictures is known to most of us. A microscope has to be regulated similarly for the focus on the object under consideration. The following procedure in using the microscope explains in detail the steps to be taken in correct sequence:

1. Place the prepared slide on the stage of the microscope.
2. Move the slide until the object on it appears to be over the center of the hole in the stage.
3. Move the clips over the ends of the slide.
4. Turn the low-power objective into position.
5. Hold the base of the microscope with the left hand and with the right hand tilt it to a comfortable angle.
6. Open the diaphragm as far as possible.
7. Adjust the mirror to reflect maximum light through the microscope.
8. With the eye close to the stage, carefully lower the microscope tube by turning the coarse adjustment until the objective almost touches the slide or until the coarse adjustment cannot be turned any more.

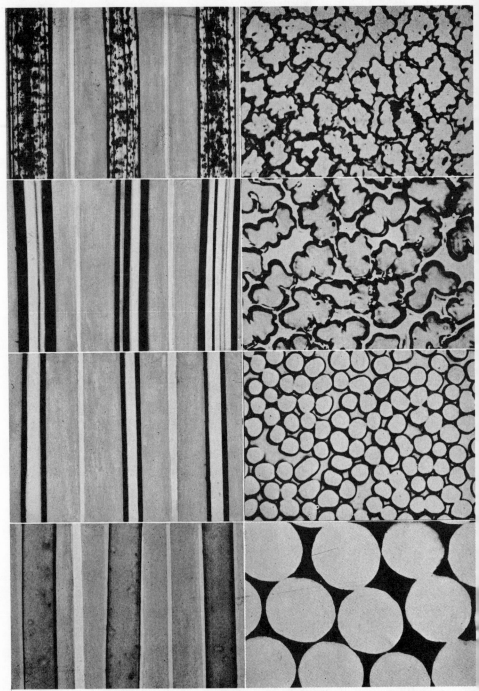

Courtesy: United States Testing Co., and Textile World

Viscose Rayon—longitudinal (Del.)—cross-section
Acetate—longitudinal—cross-section
Cuprammonium Rayon—longitudinal—cross-section
Nylon—longitudinal—cross-section

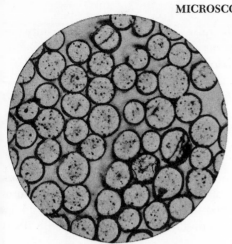

Dacron—cross-section with magnification
1000X

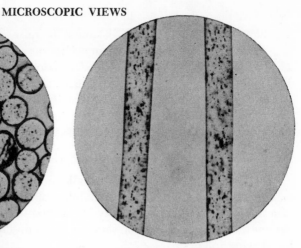

Dacron—longitudinal view

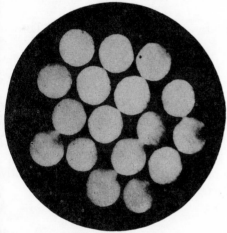

Nylon—cross-section with magnification at 660X

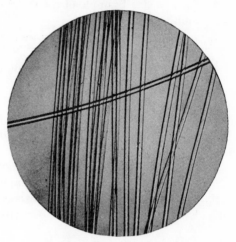

Nylon—longitudinal filament
magnification 160X

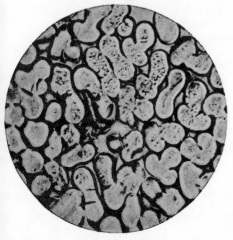

Orlon—continuous filament, cross-section

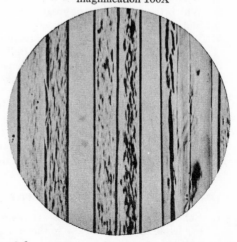

Orlon—continuous filament, longitudinal view

9. Look through the eyepiece with one eye but keep both eyes open.
10. Slowly turn the coarse adjustment to raise the microscope tube, until the object or the slide surface comes into view.
11. Move the slide to obtain a good view of the object.
12. Work the fine adjustment until the object appears sharp and clear.
13. Adjust the diaphragm for the best lighting conditions.
14. For higher magnification, turn the nosepiece to an objective of higher power.
15. Use the fine adjustment to bring the object into sharp focus again.

Preparation of Fibers for Microscopic Examination

The possibility of studying a small sample, the speed with which the work may be done, the accuracy and reliability of the results obtained are all features of a microscope's use. Fibers may be viewed in cross-section or the longitudinal structure of the specimens or samples studied. The preparation of textile fibers for viewing follows:

1. Clean a small sample of the fibers to be used with hot soap solution for a few minutes in a test tube.
2. If the fibers are white, stain them for a few minutes in a test tube of hot dye solution.
3. Fibers that are dyed too dark may be stripped in a test tube of hot hydrosulfite solution.
4. Rinse and dry the fibers.
5. Place a small drop of glycerine in the center of a clean glass slide.
6. Carefully cut about a quarter-inch length of fibers directly over the drop of glycerine.
7. Spread out the fibers in the glycerine with dissecting needles.
8. Lower a cover glass over the sample on the slide and press it down gently.
9. With a blotter, remove any excess glycerine beyond the cover glass.
10. Examine the fibers with the microscope.

TESTING   50 points

1. What are some functions of the microscope?
2. Why is the microscope of great value to the textile industry?
3. State some uses for the microscope in the testing of textiles.
4. Why are microscopic tests on textile fibers—longitudinal and in cross-section—of such great importance to a textile mill?
5. What must be done to place the microscope in proper focus?
6. Why should the microscope be looked through carefully while focusing upward but not while focusing downward?
7. Why should both eyes be kept open when looking through the lens?
8. Explain the reason why the low-power objective is used first and then the high-power objective.
9. What is the disadvantage of having too many fibers on the slide?
10. Why is the microscope considered the best means of distinguishing cotton from linen?

COMPLETION QUESTIONS ON THE MICROSCOPE   50 points

1. Enlarging on the microscope is done by two lens units; one is located near the eye while the other is close to the _____.
2. A 10× eyepiece and a _____ objective would give a magnification of 430.
3. The substage on a microscope is found above the _____.

4. The mirror used in a microscope has a plane and a _____ side.
5. The diaphragm controls the amount of _____ passing through the microscope.
6. The glass slide on which the object to be magnified is placed is supported by the _____.
7. The clips on the stage hold the _____ in place and prevent it from slipping off when the microscope is tilted.
8. Tilting of the microscope is regulated by the _____.
9. Another name for the eyepiece is _____.
10. Dark fibers to be examined with the microscope may be stripped in a test tube of hot _____ solution.

TOPIC: RELATIVE HUMIDITY

RELATIVE HUMIDITY is defined as the amount of water in saturated air as compared with the amount the air can hold at a given temperature. If the air is holding all the water it can at a given temperature, the relative humidity is 100 per cent; it is 50 per cent if it is holding only one-half of what it could hold at the given temperature. Hot air can hold more water than cold air. If air at 50° F. and 100 per cent relative humidity is heated to 70° F., the new relative humidity of the air will be about 50 per cent, since air at 70° F. holds twice as much water as air at 50° F. The amount of moisture in the air is important because it affects the weight and the strength of textile fibers: some fibers such as cotton and linen become stronger, while others like rayon, silk, and wool become weaker. Relative humidity is also defined as the ratio of the actual partial pressure of the water vapor in a given space to the saturation pressure of pure water at the same temperature.

Humidity may also be defined as the vaporous spray that is emitted in the several rooms of a textile plant. It is the percentage of water vapor in the air with relation to the total amount possible at the same temperature. At 32° F., a cubic foot of air contains two grams of water vapor; at 100° F., the cubic foot of air will hold a maximum of 20 grams, or ten times as much as at 32° F. A humidifier is the device used in mill rooms to vaporize water and to spray it into the atmosphere in order to increase the amount of moisture in the air. Absolute humidity is the weight of water vapor per unit volume, in pounds per cubic foot, grains per cubic foot, or grams per cubic centimeter.

In textile laboratories, standard conditions of 65 per cent R.H. and 70° F. are maintained so that the samples being tested acquire the normal amount of moisture. "Regain" is the amount of water or moisture in textiles based on their dry weight. If 10.0 grams of material, for example, is dried thoroughly and then found to weigh 9.0 grams, the regain is:

$$\frac{1 \times 100}{9} \text{ equals } 11\%$$

MOISTURE REGAIN OF SOME MAJOR TEXTILE FIBERS

Moisture is the water or some other liquid which renders anything moist. Absorbency means "to take up" or "receive in" by chemical or molecular action. Moisture regain is the percentage which the weight of moisture in a textile material represents of its bone-dry weight. It is sometimes referred to as content. Percentages of moisture regain in the fibers under standard conditions follow:

FIBER	PERCENTAGE OF MOISTURE REGAIN	FIBER	PERCENTAGE OF MOISTURE REGAIN
Acetate	6.00	Nytril	2.60
Acrilan	1.50–5.00	Olefins	0.00
Arnel	3.00	"Orlon"	2.50 at 95% R.H.
Cotton	6.00–7.00	Rayon—	
Creslan	1.50 at 70° F.	regular	12.00 at 95% R.H.
"Dacron"	0.50 at 95% R.H.	Rayon—high	
Dynel	0.40	wet modulus	12.20
Flax/Linen	6.00–10.00	Saran	.10 in 24-hour
Fortisan	10.70		immersion
Fortrel	0.40	Silk	10.00 and may reach
Kodel	0.40		28.00
Lycra	0.30	Verel	3.00–4.00
Mercerized		Vycron	0.40
Cotton	10.00–11.00	Wool	15.00–17.00
Nylon 6	8.00 at 95% R.H.	Worsted	10.00–12.00
Nylon 66	8.00 at 95% R.H.	Zefran	2.50 at 65% R.H.

The determination of the relative humidity is made by the use of a sling psychrometer which consists of two accurate thermometers. The bulb of one thermometer is covered with a wet, close-fitting, knit fabric of unsized, mercerized cotton yarn. The psychrometer is whirled in a vertical plane at a rate of 150 to 200 r.p.m. for 20 seconds.

The wet bulb thermometer is read quickly. The whirling is repeated until the wet bulb temperature reading remains constant. The relative humidity is read from special tables, based on the temperature readings of the wet and dry bulbs.

TESTING

1. What occurs in the tensile strength of wet rayon after it is dried?
2. Give a reason for the necessity of conditioning textiles before testing them.
3. Name two important effects of humidity on textile fabrics.
4. A fabric weighs 9.46 grams but only 8.40 grams when bone-dry. What would be the percentage of regain?
5. What would be the loss to a manufacturer if he bought 100 pounds of silk at $4.00 a pound with a regain of 16 per cent instead of 11 per cent?

Part 2—Unit 4

TOPIC: Texture in Woven Fabric

The first meaning of "texture" is the number of warp ends and filling picks per square inch in a woven cloth. Its second meaning concerns the finish, hand, or feel, and the surface effect noted on the face of the material—thus, a fabric may be soft, harsh, wiry, silklike, smooth, rough, wiry, boardy, limp, stiff etc.

Quality of a fabric may be determined by the number of warp ends and filling picks in the goods, particularly when compared with similar fabrics of competitors. Both systems of yarn should be counted carefully, since it is rare when both warp and filling have the same yarn count and the same texture or pick count. Texture, count, and pick count may be considered as synonymous. Texture, for example, is written as 60 x 48. This means there are 60 ends and 48 picks in one square inch of the cloth. In most materials there are more ends than picks per inch.

The yarns are usually counted by means of a pick-counter or pick-glass, sometimes referred to as a "linen-tester." This device is a magnifying glass supported on a small frame that has an opening of definite size in the base: one-quarter inch, one-half inch, one inch, two inches, or four inches. Usually the one-inch size is the best to use. All glasses are marked off in quarter-inch units.

The edge of the opening in the base of the glass is lined up carefully and evenly with a yarn in the cloth; all the yarns between two parallel edges of the base are then counted.

The pick count may also be determined by using a ruler to mark off a given distance; the counting of the yarns is then done between the marks. If the material is made of rather coarse yarns, counting should be done over a two-inch or a three-inch span; the result is then reduced to the number of warp ends and filling picks per inch in the cloth.

The count on a sample of fabric should be made by averaging the results from five separate countings made on various parts of the material. It often happens that textures may vary a little in the various areas of a cloth. Fabric close to the selvage should not be used since evenness of texture is not always exact in this area.

There are occasions when it is sometimes easier to count the repeats of a weave, motif, or pattern than to count the yarns on the individual yarn plan. If a five-end (shaft, harness) satin-weave fabric is being counted, the number of repeats plus the yarns of the incomplete repeat are counted. For example, if in one inch 24 repeats were counted, plus 2 yarns, the yarns or ends per inch would be 24 times 5 plus 2, or 122 ends per inch.

A suggested plan for texture follows:

Sample 1. _____x_____   Sample 4. _____x_____
Sample 2. _____x_____   Sample 5. _____x_____
Sample 3. _____x_____   Average counts: _____ ends; _____ picks.

TESTING QUESTIONS ON TEXTURE

1. Define "texture" in a woven fabric.
2. Explain the second meaning of texture.
3. List five ways to distinguish between the warp and the filling in a woven fabric.
4. Using the principle that texture is a means of determining the quality of a cloth, why would a 140 sheeting (76 x 64) be of better quality than a 128 sheeting (68 x 60)?

YARN TWIST USED IN SILK AND COMPARABLE MANMADE FIBER YARNS

The following chart shows the major types of twist used in silk and comparable manmade fiber yarns used in the textile industry.

TYPE	TURNS OF TWIST PER INCH	USE OF THE YARN
Singles	Hard twist or loose twist.	Ideal for filling in many fabrics. In the hard twist will work well in making sheer fabrics.
Tram	From 2 to 12.	Filling yarn and hosiery.
Organzine	From 12 to 20.	Warp yarn.
Crepe	No twist in singles; 65 to 85 in doubles, which are then doubled with 2½ to 5 turns per inch, opposite direction.	In all kinds of crepe fabrics—in warp or filling, or both.
Grenadine	20/18 to 60/60; a very hard twisted organzine thread.	In all kinds of sheer cloths such as voile, organdy, grenadine.

YARN TWIST AS APPLIED TO MOST MAJOR NATURAL AND MANMADE FIBER YARNS

S-TWIST: A yarn or cord has S-twist if, when held in a vertical position, the spirals conform in slope to the central portion of the letter S. Formerly called left-hand or clockwise twist.

Z-TWIST: If the spirals conform in slope to the central portion of the letter Z, the twist is then classed as Z-twist. Formerly known as right-hand or counterclockwise twist.

ZERO TWIST: Sometimes referred to as "no-twist." The thrower may request that cuprammonium yarns be supplied with no twist. This is rarely done, however; usually one to five turns are given the yarn. Viscose and acetate yarns with from three to five or six turns per inch are normally supplied to the thrower; this twist is known as "tram twist."

CABLE TWIST: A cord, rope, or twine construction in which each successive twist runs in the opposite direction from the preceding twist. This type is S-Z-S or Z-S-Z.

TESTING QUESTIONS ON TWIST IN YARNS

1. Define the following: 1. organzine; 2. tram; 3. crepe twist.
2. Explain the expression, "sixteen turns of right-hand twist followed by fourteen turns of left-hand twist." Discuss the use of this type of twist as applied to a silk yarn.
3. Define the following: 1. S-twist; 2. Z-twist; 3. zero twist; 4. cable twist.

TOPIC: TWIST IN YARN—THE TWIST COUNTER

The three essentials in the spinning of yarn are drawing, twisting, and winding. It is the twist in yarn that actually holds the fibers together and determines the strength, or lack of it, of the yarn in question. A yarn may be high, medium, or low in twist. The amount of twist necessary is determined by the end use of the yarn in a cloth. Both single and ply yarns are given twist.

Twist is defined as the number of turns about its axis, per unit of length, noted in a fiber, yarn, or cord. It is expressed in turns per inch, turns per meter, or by the helix angle in a structure of known diameter. Twist can be controlled mechanically.

S-twist is the direction of twist in yarn comparable with the spiral portion of the letter S. It was formerly known as left or reverse twist, and is clockwise in direction. Z-twist conforms with the spiral portion of the letter Z. It was formerly called right twist, and is counterclockwise in direction.

TWIST IN SILK YARNS AND THREADS

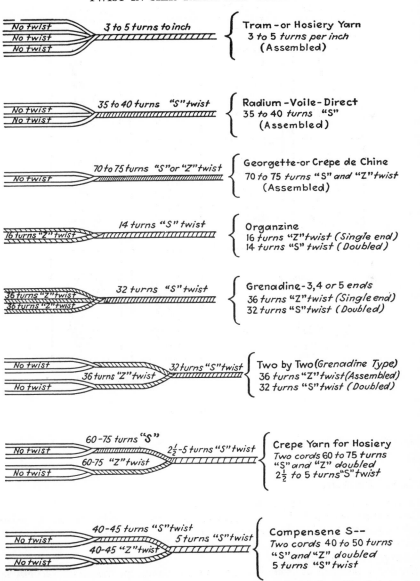

Courtesy: *Read & Lovatt Manufacturing Company*

The twist counter is an instrument that determines the number of turns of twist per inch in all types of yarn. It is also used to find the amount of take-up in yarns because of twist. The sample to be tested is inserted between two clamps, one of which is stationary while the other is free to be revolved in order to remove the twist from the yarn. The distance between the clamps is adjustable and can be set according to standard test requirements. The tension on the sample or specimen, as well, is adjustable, equipped with a device for recording the actual amount of twist in the yarn.

DIRECTIONS OF TWIST

TWIST TYPES FOR PLIED YARNS AND TWINES

"ZS" TWIST (Formerly Regular)   "SZ" TWIST (Formerly Reverse)   "ZSZ" TWIST (Formerly Cable)   "ZZS" TWIST (Formerly Hawser)

Examples:

Weaving Yarn	"ZS"	Twist
Wrapping Twine	"ZS"	"
Sail Twine	"ZS"	"
Seine Twine	"ZSZ"	"
Cable Cord	"ZSZ"	"
Twisted Rope	"ZSZ"	"

Officials of the Mt. Vernon-Woodberry Mills, Baltimore, Md., circulated the above chart among their employees to educate them on the new designations for direction of twist.

PROCEDURE

Determine the direction of the twist in the yarn. Then set and read the twist counter accordingly:

For Cotton Ply Yarn

Set the twist-counter clamps ten inches apart.

Clamp the yarn carefully in the machine without disturbing the twist, using just enough tension to straighten the yarn or thread.

Untwist the yarn until a dissecting needle may be run between the strands from the fixed clamp to the rotating clamp.

The twists per inch are found by dividing the twists for the 10-inch length sample by 10.

For Single Cotton Yarn

Set the counter at zero; place the clamps ten inches apart.

Clamp the end of the yarn in the rotating clamp and then draw it through the open fixed clamp.

Hang a 3-gram weight in the center of the yarn and adjust the tension of the yarn in the open fixed jaw to give a deflection of one-eighth inch from the line formed by the yarn if it were straight from clamp to clamp.

Tighten the fixed clamp and remove the 3-gram weight.

Untwist the yarn until all the twist is removed and continue turning the clamp in the same direction until enough twist is put back into the yarn to prevent the fibers from untwisting.

Hang the 3-gram weight at the center of the yarn and continue turning the clamp in the same direction until the yarn moves up enough to show a deflection of one-eighth inch.

The twists per inch in the yarn are found by dividing the dial reading by two and then by the distance between the clamps.

For Wool Ply Yarn

Same as given under cotton; tension is the weight of 100 yards of yarn.

For Single Wool Yarn

Set the clamps four inches apart; use enough tension to straighten the yarn.

Untwist the yarn until a needle can be run between the fibers from one clamp to the other.

TESTING

1. How does the test for twist in single-ply wool yarn differ from that for single-ply cotton yarn?
2. Why must the direction of twist in the yarn be determined at the beginning of a test?

Part 2—Unit 6

TOPIC: WEIGHT OF FABRIC FROM SMALL SAMPLE OF CLOTH

Knowledge of the weight of a fabric is important to the consumer as well as to the textile technologist and analyst. Knowing the correct fabric weight is important to the consumer since he should wear the proper-weight garment for the various seasons of the year. The technologist and the analyst are interested in fabric weight not only for its end use and for the season or seasons that the garment made from the cloth may be used, but so that the material may be reproduced in entirety, even from a sample as small as one square inch. From an analysis it is possible to reproduce one's own fabrics and also those from other companies and competitors, samples of which may be obtained from many sources. The quality of any fabric depends upon the quality of the raw materials used and on the techniques and skills of each and every worker who has anything at all to do with the manufacture of the cloth.

Weight Per Yard of Fabric from Sample

The determination of the weight per yard of fabric from a sample is the basis for proving all other results obtained in a complete fabric analysis. It is the means of checking on all figures found and compiled in the work.

Some fabric is sold as having "so many ounces per yard," while another method of sales measurement is on the basis of "so many yards per pound of fabric." A third method is to sell fabric on a "weight-per-square-yard-in-ounces" basis. The latter two methods find use in figuring lightweight cloths and sheers, in cotton, silk, manmade fibers. Some companies sell fabrics which weigh less than four, six, or eight ounces per yard, in this manner.

When speaking of the weight per yard of fabric, it is always necessary to state the width of the goods. This is because there is no absolute rule which governs all classes of material. Various fabrics are finished in different widths in order to best suit the purposes for which they are to be used.

The nearest approach there is to a standard is in men's wear and women's wear woolens and worsteds. In the majority of cases, the cloth is finished as near to 56-inch width as possible. In other instances the finished width is 28 inches, chiefly in hand-woven fabrics, some velvets, etc.

The term "quarter" is sometimes used and refers to the width of a fabric. A quarter is a 9-inch width, one-quarter of one yard (36 inches). Thus, a cloth in the 54- to 56-inch width would be a 6/4 (six-quarter) material. A 36-inch fabric would be a 4/4 fabric. Speaking in a general way, a yard means a lineal yard of 36 inches. Since, however, very few fabrics are finished at this width, it is therefore necessary to do something more than merely cut off one yard of the material and then weigh it to ascertain the weight.

Grain-Scale Procedure to Find Weight of Fabric

The first step in determining the weight per yard of a fabric is to measure dimensions very carefully. Naturally, a minor error in the preparation of the sample will upset all calculations throughout the analysis. The sample may be cut with sharp scissors or by means of a hammer and die. Dies come in ½ inch, 1 inch, 1½ inches, 2 inches and 4 inches in size.

The use of the die is the surest way to obtain accuracy. Never allow a fringe or raveled edge to remain on the sample. Make sure that the edges are parallel. There are 437.5 grains in one ounce; 7,000 grains in one pound.

In manipulating the scale, follow this plan:

a) Examine the various weights in the weight box.
b) To adjust the scale, turn the screw in the base until the scale is shown to be level.
c) Move the sliding piece or rider to the zero point on the bar. This should be done with a pick-needle or a sharp pencil.
d) When the scale is balanced, the small line on the right end of the beam will swing the same distance above and below the small line marked on the frame.
e) Note the highest reading possible on the scale and the value of each division.
f) If the sample weighs more than 20 grains, the set of slotted weights is used. Note how these fit onto the scale.
g) The weight of the sample is the sum of slotted weights used, plus the readings on the bar. For practice, weigh five samples of less than 20 grains, and five of more than 20 grains.
h) There are three reasons for finding the weight of cloth per yard:

   1. Assurance for the proper weight of the goods.
   2. For comfort to the wearer: a tropical suiting would not be ideal for winter wear, nor would a 16-ounce suiting satisfy for summer.
   3. To insure the proper value for the money expended by the consumer, who has to be satisfied, and as a check on specifications. The United States

Quartermaster Department, for example, has very rigid specifications for all fabrics made for the government. Weight and texture must be in accordance with all specifications set up in government contracts.

On Fabric Weights

The weight of fabric, as previously noted, is expressed in ounces per yard, yards per pound, and ounces per square yard. The width of the goods must be known so that calculations may be completed.

The sample to be used on the grain scale must be cleanly cut. The scale must be sufficiently fine and sensitive to record to the tenth part of a grain. In the instance of sheer and lightweight fabrics torsion balances should be used instead of the grain scale.

Having weighed the sample carefully, the following formula is used to obtain weight by the so-called "long method":

SAMPLE AREA : SAMPLE WEIGHT :: YARD AREA : YARD WEIGHT

Thus, a sample that is 3 by 3 inches, with a weight of 18 grains and a width of 56 inches, would be set up as follows:

SAMPLE AREA : SAMPLE WEIGHT :: YARD AREA : YARD WEIGHT

$$9 \quad : \quad 18 \quad :: \quad 2016 \quad : \quad x$$
$$9x \text{ equals } 36{,}288 \text{ grains}$$
$$x \text{ equals } 4{,}032 \text{ grains}$$
$$437.5\overline{)4{,}032}(9.22, \text{ ounces per yard of fabric (Answer)}$$

The One-Inch-Square Method to Find Ounces per Yard of Cloth

This method is used whenever approximate results are needed quickly.

FORMULA: $\dfrac{\text{Width in inches} \times 36, \text{length in inches} \times \text{sample weight:}}{437.5, \text{number of grains in one ounce}}$

$\dfrac{56 \text{ inches wide} \times 36, \text{lineal length} \times 3.2, \text{grain weight}}{437.7 \text{ grains in one ounce}}$ equals 14.74:

ounces per yard of fabric (Answer)

The Twenty-Square-Inch Method to Find the Yards per Pound of Fabric

This method may be used for lightweight fabrics such as cottons, rayons, acetates, nylons, instead of resorting to the torsion-balance method. The scale may be set with the rider weight on the 20-grain mark on the scale bar; the rider is moved to obtain the actual grain weight of the sample. This method is also called the "long method."

PROCEDURE

a) Divide the weight of the sample by the number of square inches to find the weight per square inch.
b) Multiply the width of the goods by 36 to obtain square inches in one yard.
c) Multiply the square inches per yard by the weight per square inch to obtain grains per square yard.
d) Divide the grains per yard by 437.5 to obtain ounces per yard.
e) Yards per pound are found by dividing 16 by ounces per yard.

[291]

a) A cloth is finished at 40 inches.
b) 20 square inches weigh 50 grains.
c) Weight per square inch is 50 divided by 20, or 2.50.
d) Square inches per yard is 40 × 36, or 1440 square inches.
e) Grains per yard are 1440 × 2.50, or 3600 grains.
f) Ounces per yard are 3600 diivded by 437.5, or 8.228 ounces.
g) Yards per pound are found by dividing 16 by 8.228, or 1.94, the yards per pound (Answer).

The Twenty-Square-Inch Method to Find Ounces per Yard of Fabric

This method is known as the "short method."

PROCEDURE

a) If a 20-square-inch sample is always used, with this method the weight per square yard can be determined quickly.

b) FORMULA A: $\dfrac{\text{Weight} \times 36 \times 36}{20 \times 437.5}$ for $\dfrac{\text{Weight} \times 1296}{8750}$ equals 0.148, the factor to be used in calculating.

c) FORMULA B: For a sample width of other than 36 inches, the weight in ounces per yard is equal to the width divided by 36, times the weight per square yard.

EXAMPLE

20 square inches weigh 27 grains
The weight in ounces per square yard is 27 × 0.148, or 4 ounces per yard on a square-yard basis. If the fabric is, say, 45 inches wide, the formula is then:

$\dfrac{45, \text{ width in inches} \times 4, \text{ square yard weight}}{36 \text{ inches in lineal yard}}$, gives 5, the ounces per yard at a 45-inch width of goods (Answer).

PROBLEMS ON THE FOREGOING METHODS OF FINDING OUNCES PER YARD OF CLOTH

1. PRACTICE EXAMPLES: Find the ounces per yard, the ounces per square yard, and the yards per pound of fabric from the following data:

   Width of fabric in inches: 56
   Square inches weighed: 16
   Weight of square inches taken in grains: 34
   Calculate by the long method, and then by the short method, for the following:
   a) Ounces per yard: _____.
   b) Ounces per square yard: _____.
   c) Yards per pound: _____.

2. EXAMPLES

   LONG METHOD ON THE SA : SW :: YA : YW EQUATION:
   a) Sample area is 4″ × 4″.   *b*) Sample weight is 30 grains.
   c) Finished width is 56 inches.   *d*) Find weight per yard of cloth.

   ON THE SQUARE-INCH METHOD:
   a) 56-inch-width finished goods.   *b*) Sample weight is 3.6 grains.
   c) Find the weight per yard of the goods.

[292]

ON THE TWENTY-SQUARE-INCH METHOD—FOR YARDS PER POUND OF FABRIC:

a) Cloth is 38 inches wide. *b*) 20 square inches weigh 44 grains.
c) Find the yards per pound of the fabric.

ON THE TWENTY-SQUARE-INCH METHOD—FOR OUNCES PER YARD OF FABRIC:

a) 20 square inches weigh 32.0 grains.
b) Find the ounces per square yard of the material.

Weight of Fabric on the Square-Yard Basis

Within the last few years this method for figuring fabric weight has become popular. The method began in France, spread to the rest of Europe and the British Isles, then to Canada, and finally has come into some use in the United States. The system is much used with regard to fabrics for import and export from and to other nations. A factor system using the number 576 is very popular. This number is found by multiplying 36 inches in a yard by 16, the ounces in one pound.

Example: 80 yards of a cloth weigh 60 pounds on the scale. The fabric is finished at 58 inches wide. Find the ounce-per-yard weight, and then the ounce-per-square-yard weight.

a) $\dfrac{60, \text{ the pound weight, } \times 16 \text{ ounces in one pound}}{80, \text{ the yardage in the cut of cloth}}$ gives 12 ounces per yard.

b) $\dfrac{60, \text{ weight in pounds, } \times 576 \text{ factor}}{80, \text{ yard length } \times 58\text{-inch width}}$ gives 7.45 ounces per square yard.

Another Method to Figure the Square-Yard Weight

This quick and sure method is illustrated by the following example: a fabric that is 50 inches wide weighs 26 ounces. Find the square-yard weight of the material:

$\dfrac{36 \text{ inches in one yard } \times 26, \text{ the ounce weight,}}{50, \text{ the finished width of the fabric}}$ equals 18.7 ounces (Answer).

A fabric is finished at 56 inches and weighs 20 ounces per yard. Find the square-yard weight.

$\dfrac{36 \text{ inches in one yard } \times 20, \text{ the ounce weight,}}{56, \text{ the finished width of the goods}}$ equals 12.9 ounces (Answer).

TESTING

1. Name the three methods used to find the weight per yard of textile fabrics.
2. Why is the width of the fabric important when figuring the weight per yard of the goods?
3. Define the term "quarter."
4. What would be the width of a 6/4 goods? a 4/4 fabric? a 7/4 fabric?
5. Explain the formula—SA : SW :: YA : YW.
6. Give the formula for the one-inch-square method of finding the ounces per yard of a fabric.
7. Why is the grain scale ideal for weighing small samples?
8. What is a disadvantage of weighing exactly one yard of a cloth?
9. Why should at least 20 square inches of a sample be used for weighing when the method is used for calculating fabric weight?
10. Give three good reasons for finding the weight of fabric per yard.

[293]

TOPIC: Yarn Standards, the Counts or Number of Yarn, and the Yards per Pound per Count of Yarn

There are hundreds of types of yarns and constructions used to make fabric, whether for apparel, decorative purposes, or industrial use. The texture of fabrics varies considerably, and the compactness or lack of it in the construction of a piece of cloth may be very marked. Apparel such as jackets, skirting, suiting, blouse, dress, or neckwear varies a great deal as to the size and type of yarn used in the fabrics. The twist in yarn runs from high to low depending upon the end use for which the yarn is intended. Thus there is much importance in trying to distinguish among all yarns used today.

In figuring yarn sizes of any type, the point to consider is that there is a direct relation between the length and the weight of a particular yarn. Yarns are sold according to a count, size, or number. There are two methods used to number textile yarns: one is for SPUN YARNS, the other for FILAMENT YARNS. In spun yarn, the higher the number of the yarn, the finer will be the diameter. In filament yarn, the higher the number of the yarn, the coarser or greater in diameter will be the yarn. A set of standards has been set up for the various types of yarns used today.

Yarn Standards

The standards for the major yarns are given below. It should be noted that yarn counts or numbers are written by number and this is followed by the letter "s." The apostrophe is not necessarily used between the number and the "s."

840 yards in one pound of a 1s cotton yarn.
560 yards in one pound of a 1s worsted yarn (two-thirds the number used for the cotton standard of 840 yards in one pound of 1s).
1,600 yards in one pound of a 1s run woolen yarn (Boston or New England).
300 yards in one pound of a 1st cut woolen yarn (Philadelphia system).
300 yards in one pound of a 1s linen yarn.
840 yards in one pound of a 1s spun silk yarn, in the single ply.
4,464,528 yards in one pound of a Number-One-denier filament yarn: used to figure silk and manmade or synthetic filament yarns.

Approximate Highest Counts of Yarn Spun for the Natural Fibers

Based on a per-pound basis, these approximations for commercial purposes follow:

Cotton: 140s × 840 standard, gives 117,600 yards.
Cut Wool: 30s × 300 standard, gives 9,000 yards.
Run Wool: 10s × 1,600 standard, gives 16,000 yards.
Worsted: 70s × 560 standard, gives 39,200 yards.

Incidentally, 8/10-denier silk is about the finest yarn used commercially. Thus, with a mean number of nine:
9)4,464,528(496,059 or 500,000 yards in the one-denier size or count.
34/36 denier is about the coarsest silk yarn size used in the commercial world today.

All yarns with the exception of glass yarns are numbered alike according to the system on which they have been spun irrespective of fiber content—cotton, run wool, cut wool, worsted, linen. This point is very important in the figuring of yarn sizes in all types of yarns made from blends, mixes, and combinations, such as a yarn of cotton, and acetate staple; one of worsted, and nylon staple; one of acetate, nylon, and cotton, the two first fibers being in staple form. The count of yarn would be expressed in terms of the natural fiber used.

Yarn Counts, Counts of Yarn

The best results are obtained in yarn counts by weighing a definite known length; the figures can be used to work out the relation between the known length and the known weight.

Incidentally, some yarn sizes are obtained by making a comparison with other known sizes. There may be, however, some inaccuracies that will become apparent in this method of figuring; it is not a scientific method to use and is only for comparison.

In the length-weight relation method, the yarns may have to be taken from a piece of fabric, possibly a small swatch of goods. It is then necessary to straighten out the yarns and eliminate the crimp or waviness caused by the take-up in the weaving of the cloth, "the warp ends over and under the filling, and vice versa."

Generally speaking, not less than one hundred inches should be used in the weighing of yarn.

The formula used in figuring yarn size from the natural fibers, with the exception of silk, follows:

Number of inches weighed: Weight in grains *as* x : 7,000. The 7,000 used is for the number of grains in one pound.

The result is then converted into yards by dividing by 36, the inches in one yard. This result is then divided by the standard for the yarn being weighed.

EXAMPLE: If 20 pieces of yarn, each 5 inches long, weigh 1.7 grains, find the count in terms of worsted yarn.

$$100 : 1.7 \text{ grains} :: x : 7,000 \quad \text{grains in one pound}$$
$$1.7\,x = 700,000 \quad \text{(inches)}.$$
$$x = 411,437 \quad \text{(inches)}.$$
$$36\overline{)411,437}(11,437 \quad \text{(yards)}$$
$$560\overline{)11,437}(20.4, \text{ or a 20's worsted yarn (Answer)}.$$

EXAMPLE: If 144 inches of yarn weigh 1.0 grain, find the count of yarn in terms of cotton.

$$144 : 1.0 \text{ grains} :: x : 7,000 \quad \text{grains in one pound}$$
$$x = 1,008,000 \quad \text{(inches)}$$
$$36\overline{)1,008,000}(28,000 \quad \text{(yards)}$$
$$840\overline{)28,000}(33.33, \text{ the count of this yarn (Answer)}.$$

Denier Methods for the Counts of Yarn for Silk and Manmade Filaments

A denier is a coin used as a unit of weight when speaking of the size of these yarns. Officially, one denier weighs 0.05 grams or .771618 grains. In actual value it was worth about one-twelfth of the old French sou. Originally, the denier coin was used in the time of Julius Caesar and several of the coins are still extant. From

Caesar's time the coin passed into oblivion until it was revived as the medium used for the size of silk yarns by Francis I, king of France (1515–1547), called "Father of the Silk Industry" there.

It was Francis who made France conscious of textile fabrics woven of silk and who founded the industry in Paris and Lyons well over four hundred years ago. Silk fabrics for apparel and decorative purposes made Paris the fashion and style center of the world in women's wear, a position it still holds.

The number of yarns in one pound of a 1-denier is 4,464,528. The equation follows:

$$\frac{492.2 \text{ yards, reeled length standard} \times 7,000 \text{ grains in 1 pound}}{.771618, \text{ the grains in one denier}} \text{ equals 4,464,528 yards.}$$

Thus, to find the number of yards in one pound of any size denier, silk excepted, divide the yarn size into this standard. Hence, in a 150-denier yarn, there would be the following computation:

$150\overline{)4,464,528(}$ equals 29,763.33 yards in the pound. Round-number yardage would be 30,000 yards to the pound. (Often called "the Rule of the Seven 4's.") Silk sizes in denier, for example, are written as a fraction, such as a 24/26-denier. The mean number is 25. Thus, $25\overline{)4,464,528(}$ equals 178,581.1 yards to the pound. Round-number yardage would be 180,000 yards to the pound.

Thousand Meters—Units-Per-Kilogram Method for Denier

This method is based on the weight of 1,000 meters—units per kilogram. Thus, there would be 60,000 meters of yarn in a 60-denier yarn, since 1,000 times 60 gives 60,000 meters of yarn per kilogram; the English equivalent is 2.2 pounds.

Gram Method for Denier

It became popular during World War II and is much used throughout the world today. As noted previously, one denier weighs .05 grams. Multiplying .05 by 20 gives a 1-gram weight. The standard length used is 450 meters (492.13 yards).

450 multiplied by 20 gives 9,000 meters. Thus, all that has to be done is to weigh a reeled skein of filament whose total length is 9,000 meters. If the weight, for example, is 200 grams, the denier size of the yarn is 200 and there is no further figuring to be done.

Factor in the Denier System

To figure the size of filament yarns, the yarn count is obtained by multiplying the weight of the 12 yards by the factor 53.15.

EXAMPLE: If 12 yards of rayon filament yarn weigh 2.82 grains, find the denier count of yarn.

2.82 × 53.15 equals 149.9, or a 150-denier yarn size.

Another Method Used to Find Denier Counts of Yarn

Multiply the weight of skein weighed, in grains, by 4,464,528. Divide the result by the product of the skein length multiplied by 7,000, the grains in one pound.

EXAMPLE: Find the denier size of a yarn in a skein length of 120 yards that weighed 47 grains.

$$\frac{47, \text{ weight} \times 4,464,528, \text{ standard}}{120, \text{ length} \times 7,000 \text{ grains in one pound}} \text{ equals 249.8, or 250, the denier}$$

size of the yarn (Answer).

Yarn Numbering by the Use of a Constant or Factor

The following factors and formulas are convenient in finding the counts of yarn readily for comparative purposes:

COTTON

1. $\dfrac{\text{7,000 grains in one pound}}{\text{Grain weight for 840 yards}}$ equals 8.33, factor.

2. $\dfrac{1000}{\text{Grain weight for 120 yards}}$ (using common factor 7) equals 8.33, factor.

3. $\dfrac{\text{Inches of yarn weighed} \times 0.2315}{\text{Grain weight of the yarn}}$ (840 cotton standard $\times$ 36 inches) in one yard
divided into 7,000 grains in one pound gives the factor 0.2315 as the cotton constant.

4. $\dfrac{\text{Inches of yarn} \times 0.015 \text{ gram constant}}{\text{Weight in grams}}$ equals the count of the yarn.

EXAMPLE

1. 144 inches of yarn weigh 2 grains. By use of the constant 0.2315, find the yarn count:
$\dfrac{144 \times 0.2315}{2 \text{ grain weight}}$ equals 16.668, the yarn count from grain constant (Answer).

2. $\dfrac{144 \times 0.015 \text{ gram constant}}{0.1296 \text{ gram weight}}$ equals 16.668 yarn count by gram constant (Answer).

3. The constant 0.1296 is found in the following manner—to change from grains to grams, multiply by 0.0648. The yarn weighed 2 grains. Thus 0.0648 $\times$ 2 equals 0.1296, the constant to use.

The Formulas for Other Major Yarn Systems

WORSTED

1. $\dfrac{\text{7,000 grains in one pound}}{560, \text{ worsted standard} \times 36 \text{ inches in 1 yard}}$ equals 0.3472, factor.

EXAMPLE: Find the worsted count of yarn if 160 inches weighed 1.4 grains.
$\dfrac{160 \times 0.3472}{1.4 \text{ grains}}$ equals 39.68 or a 40s worsted count.

CUT WOOL

1. $\dfrac{\text{7,000 in one pound}}{300, \text{ cut wool standard} \times 36 \text{ inches in 1 yard}}$ equals 0.648, factor.

EXAMPLE: Find the count of cut wool yarn if 90 inches weighed 5.8 grains.
$\dfrac{90 \times 0.648}{5.8 \text{ grains}}$ equals 10.06 or a 10s cut wool count.

RUN WOOL

1. $\dfrac{\text{7,000 grains in one pound}}{1,600, \text{ run wool standard} \times 36 \text{ inches in 1 yard}}$ equals 0.1215, factor.

EXAMPLE: Find the count of cut wool yarn if 80 inches weighed 3.3 grains.
$\dfrac{80 \times 0.1215}{3.8 \text{ grains}}$ equals 2.94 or a 3s run wool count.

1. Denier size of a 450-meter skein is found by multiplying weight of skein, in grams, by 20. Size in a 90-meter skein is found by multiplying skein weight, in grams, by 100.
2. Multiply skein weight, in grains, by 1.64 and divide product by .771618. On a gram scale, divide product by .05. See Denier.

DENIER: (Filaments other than silk)

1. $\dfrac{\text{Weight in grams} \times 9,000}{\text{Length in meters}}$ equals the denier count of the yarn.
2. Denier of one meter length equals the weight in milligrams $\times$ 9.
3. Consult the conversion tables at the end of this unit for ready references in factors, constants, and comparative yarn counts.

Another Factor System Used to Figure the Counts of Spun Yarns

The number or size of a spun yarn may be found by dividing a certain number by the weight, in grains, of 12 yards of the yarn in question. The number which is divided by the weight of 12 yards varies for the different fibers. These factors are:

1. Cotton   100.00   4. Linen   280.00
2. Cut wool   280.00   5. Worsted   150.00
3. Run wool   52.50

(These are all natural fiber yarns.)

EXAMPLE: Find the size of the cotton yarn if 12 yards of this yarn weigh 10 grains.

$\dfrac{100}{10}$ equals 10, the size of the cotton yarn.

EXAMPLE: What is the yarn count of a worsted yarn if 12 yards weigh 8.33 grains.

$\dfrac{150}{8.33}$ equals 18, the count or size of the worsted yarn.

Ply Count for Spun Yarn with Exception of Spun Silk Yarn

The yarn number in the ply-yarn gives the size of the single or equivalent yarn, and the ply used to obtain the particular yarn.

For example, if a two-ply yarn is found to be a single 20s, it is written as a 2/40s yarn. A three-ply yarn would be a 3/60s yarn. In some textile areas, and depending on the local conditions, the ply would follow the yarn number such as a 40/2 yarn or a 60/3 yarn.

Yards of Yarn per Pound, Natural Fiber Yarns in Single-Ply

To find the yards of yarn to the pound, multiply the count of the yarn by its standard.

Example: How many yards of yarn in one pound of a 40s cotton yarn?

40 × 840 cotton standard, equals 33,600 yards in one pound.

Yards of Yarn per Pound, Natural Fiber Yarns in Two-Ply

To find the counts, first of all in the two-ply, divide the ply into the yarn count to obtain the single equivalent count of yarn. Then multiply this single equivalent number by its standard for the yarn count.

[298]

1. How many yards in one pound of a 2/30s cotton yarn?
    2/30s cotton. 2)30(15. 15 × 840 standard gives 12,600 yards.
2. How many yards in one pound of a 3/48s worsted yarn?
    3/48s worsted. 3)48(16. 16 × 560 standard gives 8,960 yards.
3. How many yards in one pound of a 2/18s cut woolen yarn?
    2)18(9s cut wool. 9 × 300 standard gives 2,700 yards.

Yards of Yarn per Pound in the Denier System

The rule is to divide the size of the given yarn into the standard for the 1-denier, which is the constant factor number, 4,464,528.

EXAMPLES

1. How many yards in one pound of a 150-denier yarn?
    150)4,464,528(29,763.5 or 30,000 yards to the pound.
2. How many yards in one pound of a 30-denier yarn?
    30)4,464,528(148,817.6 or 150,000 yards to the pound.
3. How many yards in one pound of an 18/20-denier silk yarn?
    The mean number for the 18/20 yarn would be 19.
    19)4,464,528(234,973.5 or 235,000 yards to the pound.

Thus, as has been shown, the denier as a true length-weight measurement is specifically one gram per 9,000 meters of yarn. Thus, if 9,000 meters of yarn weigh 100 grams, the yarn is then known as a 100-denier yarn.

Consequently, the higher the number of the denier size, the coarser or larger will be the yarn in question. A 100-denier yarn will be finer in diameter when compared with a 150-denier yarn; there will be more yardage per pound in the 100-denier yarn.

A New Method in Figuring Denier Yarns

Devised a few years ago in France, this method has met with favor in many textile areas throughout the world. The yarn numbering is based on the weight of 1,000-meters unit per kilogram. Thus, a 60-denier yarn would have 60,000 meters per kilogram, which is 2.2 pounds.

TESTING

1. How many grains in one ounce? In one pound?
2. How many grains in one gram?
3. How many inches in one meter?
4. How many pounds in one kilogram?
5. List the yarn standards for the seven major types of yarn.
6. If 200 inches of yarn weigh 1.6 grains, find the yarn count in terms of cotton. What would be the count of yarn in 2-ply?
7. If 12 yards of acetate filament weigh 1.41 grains, find the denier yarn count.
8. Find the count of a cotton yarn if 12 yards weigh 9 grains.
9. What would have to be done to find the yarn count or number if only 3 yards of cotton yarn were available?
10. Write the equation for the denier standard of 4,464,528 yards in 1 pound of a 1-denier yarn.
11. What is the weight of 1 denier in grams? In grains?
12. What is about the finest denier size used in silk yarn? The coarsest?

13. How many yards in 1 pound of a 1/40s worsted yarn? In a 2/60s worsted yarn? In a 1/60s cotton yarn? a 2/100s cotton yarn?
14. How many yards in 1 pound of a 4/16s cotton yarn? In a 12-cut wool?
15. How many yards in 1 pound of a 22/24-denier silk yarn? In a 150-denier rayon filament yarn? an 1100-denier nylon filament yarn?
16. If 9,000 meters of a denier yarn weighed 150 grams, what would be the count of the yarn? 300 grams? 1,650 grams?

NOTE: The following tables should be of help to the student.

Conversion Table

The French *gramme* or English "gram" is a metric unit of weight. It equals 15.432 grains in troy and 1/30 of an ounce avoirdupois.
One grain equals 0.0648 gram.
To change grams to grains multiply by 15.432.
To change grams to grams multiply by 0.0648.
To change grams to ounces multiply by 0.0353.
To change ounces to grains multiply by 28.35.
There are 437.5 grains in 1 ounce and 7,000 grains in 1 pound.
There are $27\frac{11}{32}$ (27.343) grains in 1 dram; 16 drams in 1 ounce; 256 drams in 1 pound.

Table of Factors to Find the Equivalent Counts of Yarn

2776 divided by deniers	gives run wool count of yarn.
5289 divided by deniers	gives cotton count of yarn.
7932 divided by deniers	gives worsted count of yarn.
160 divided by drams	gives run wool count of yarn.
305 divided by drams	gives cotton count of yarn.
457 divided by deniers	gives worsted count of yarn.
2776 divided by runs	gives denier.
5289 divided by cotton	gives denier.
7932 divided by worsted	gives denier.
160 divided by runs	gives drams.
305 divided by cotton	gives drams.
457 divided by worsted	gives drams.
Denier times 0.0576	gives drams.
Drams times 17.352	gives denier.

Table for Comparative Equivalent Yarn Counts

FILAMENT YARNS—DENIER	COTTON SYSTEM COUNTS: SPUN YARNS	WORSTED SYSTEM COUNTS: SPUN YARNS
15	—	—
30	177.17	—
40	132.87	—
50	106.30	—
60	88.58	132.87
75	70.87	106.30
100	53.15	79.72
150	35.43	53.15
300	17.72	26.58
600	8.86	13.29
900	5.90	8.86
1100	4.83	7.24
1650	3.24	4.85
2200	2.41	3.62

Weights and Measures Table

   7000.000 grains equal 453.6000 grams equal 1 pound.
   437.500 grains equal 28.3500 grams equal 1 ounce.
   15.432 grains equal 1.0000 grams.
   1.000 grain equals 0.0648 gram.
   1.0000 meter equals 100.0000 cm. equal 39.37 inches.
                    2.5400 cm. equal 1 inch.
   0.9144 meter equals 1.0000 yard.
   1.0000 meter equals 1.0936 yards.
   768.0960 meters equal 840.0000 equal one hank.
   1.0000 square meter equals 1.196 square yards.
   0.8361 square meter equal 1.000 square yard.
   1.0000 square centimeter equals 0.155 square inches.
   6.4520 square centimeters equal 1.000 square inch.

Part 2—Unit 8

TOPIC: THE TEX SYSTEM FOR DESIGNATION OF YARN NUMBER OR COUNT *

The tex system is a plan for the orderly introduction of the single system of numbering yarns made from all types of fibers introduced to the textile industry in most of the countries of the world. United States participation has helped to keep our industry abreast of this significant development.

Yarn number represents the "size," "fineness," or, more accurately, the relationship between weight and length of a yarn. The tex system has been chosen to replace the many conflicting systems now used, after extended study by the Technical Committee on Textiles of the International Organization for Standardization (ISO/TC 38). Delegates representing the textile industries of twenty-one nations including the United States and four international textile associations participated in the study and unanimously adopted this proposal.

It is proposed to make the changeover in three easy stages over a period of years. The action to be taken in each stage will be given here. The first stage began in 1960 and will run until the trade is thoroughly familiar with the new system. Dates for the second and third stages will be set when the trade becomes ready for them.

THREE STAGES OF ACTION

First Stage

This stage is designed to familiarize everyone working in the textile industry with tex numbers. The existing yarn count systems will continue in use, but a corresponding rounded tex number will be given in parentheses after the traditional yarn count or yarn number, for example: 18 cotton count (32 tex), 48 worsted count (18 tex), 100 denier (11 tex).

During this stage the rounded tex numbers in parentheses are illustrative or explanatory and have no legal standing. They cannot be used as the basis of claims or other disputes, which must be based on the traditional yarn numbers. A note

---

* Sponsored by ASTM Committee D-13 on Textiles ASA Sectional Committee L-23 for ISO/TC38 on Textiles: AMERICAN SOCIETY FOR TESTING AND MATERIALS.

to this effect may be stamped on contracts or other documents where this is felt to be desirable or helpful.

Second Stage

Commercial transactions and manufacturing operations will be shifted to tex numbering. The equivalent traditional yarn number or count will be given in parentheses after the tex number—for example: 32 tex cotton yarn will be written 32 tex (18.5 cotton count); 18 tex worsted yarn will be written 18 tex (48 worsted count).

Third Stage

The traditional yarn number in parentheses will be deleted; only tex numbers will be given.

ACTION TO BE TAKEN NOW

In view of the benefits to be derived from the general use of a single yarn-numbering system throughout the industry, all textile trade associations are urged to endorse the plan for introduction of the tex system and to recommend participation in it by their members. Manufacturers, distributors, testing and research laboratories, and individuals throughout the industry are urged to give rounded equivalent tex numbers in parentheses following the traditional numbers or counts wherever they appear on orders, invoices, tags, reports, in trade literature, and in technical publications.

The rounded tex numbers can be obtained readily from short tables relating them to the numbers or counts in the system now used. Condensed tables are appended to this report for cottons, worsted, woolen, and denier numbers or counts, with directions for their use. The tex number of a yarn, fiber, or other strand is defined as the weight in grams of one kilometer of yarn. Constants have been calculated for converting yarn numbers or counts of all systems currently in use to tex numbers. For the present, however, only rounded equivalent numbers need be used.

The ISO Committee, developing plans for the introduction of the tex system, has suggested that as far as possible the rounded equivalent tex numbers listed in Table II of the Appendix should be used in preference to other intermediate numbers or to the exact tex numbers. The preferred numbers have been carefully selected to cover the entire range needed for commercial yarns in a series of steps that, in general, reflect variations observed in practical spinning operations. In the second stage, when yarns are numbered in the tex system, intermediate values can, of course, be used whenever tradition or customer's requirements indicates this to be desirable.

SCOPE AND BENEFITS OF THE TEX SYSTEM

Since the tex number is also applicable to yarn intermediates, it can be used for laps, slivers, and rovings as well as yarns. It can also be used for individual fibers; the millitex unit can be used to avoid low numbers.

The success of the analogous denier system gives assurance that the proposed tex system is workable. The tex system has already been used successfully in local installations, both in cotton-spinning laboratories and in manufacturing units, so that no one need have any hesitation about its suitability as a yarn-numbering system.

Adoption of a single universal system for numbering yarns made from any fiber has the following advantages:

1. The various yarn systems now in use with different fibers, for example, English cotton counts, French cotton counts, metric counts, Yorkshire woolen skeins, American woolen runs, English worsted counts—all will be replaced with the tex system, eliminating time spent in converting units from one system to the other and avoiding mistakes that occur when technicians are forced to think in unfamiliar units.

2. Efficiency in mills spinning yarns from any fiber will be increased. Picker laps, slivers, rovings, and yarns will all be numbered in the same units, thus facilitating the calculation of drafts at all stages of spinning and eliminating confusion due to changing systems between laps and slivers, slivers and rovings, tops and gills, rovings and yarns.

3. Operating procedures will be simplified in mills simultaneously spinning yarns from fibers numbered in different systems; for example, wool and manmade fibers on both the worsted and woolen systems. Sales of these products to different customers will also be simplified.

4. The buying and selling of yarns that must meet specifications given in different traditional numbering systems will be simplified by eliminating the time spent in converting and checking results.

5. Efficiency in cost accounting and inventory control will be increased, since all yarns, regardless of the fiber used, will be based on the same yarn-numbering system.

6. Fabric design work will be simplified, since the same amount of yarn, that is, the same length of yarn of a given number or count, will be needed to make the same weight of fabric, regardless of the fibers involved.

7. Calculation of the resultant count of all plied yarns that are numbered in indirect numbering systems will be much easier, since with tex numbers the equivalent single number can be calculated by simple addition.

8. Efficiency of quality control and cost comparisons will be improved, since all derived or calculated yarn properties such as breaking tenacity or lea product will be in the same units regardless of fiber used.

9. It will be easier to interpret and use the findings of textile research workers published anywhere in the world.

10. Any spinning or blend study involving the number of fibers in a yarn will be easier to make, since the yarn and the fibers used will both be numbered in the same or closely related systems.

11. The time spent in technical textile schools teaching and practicing the use of various yarn-numbering systems will be eventually eliminated. This time will be available for teaching other important subjects.

12. The United States textile industry will avoid being placed at a further disadvantage in production costs with respect to competition from foreign countries who are expected to adopt the tex yarn-numbering system fairly soon.

13. In addition to the ultimate lower costs resulting from all these increased efficiencies, each textile scientist or executive will have the personal satisfaction of promoting the use of the universal yarn-numbering system in his own company and trade association and of knowing that, at the cost of some relatively transient personal difficulty, he is contributing to the advancement of the textile industry for the benefit of all future generations.

CONCLUSION

Agreement on the tex system for yarn numbering is a notable achievement in international standardization in a field where standardization is long overdue. It merits the support of every person, organization, and company interested in the long-range good of the textile industry.

It is urged that everyone in the textile industry participate in the general educational program leading to the introduction of the tex yarn-numbering system in his part of the industry.

Discussions of the tex yarn-numbering system have appeared in textile journals in the United States and in foreign countries from time to time. Anyone desiring more information on this international development should consult his own technical experts, his ASTM representative, or should refer to the References listed below.

D. L. WHITTIER, chairman,
ASTM Committee D-13 on Textile Materials.

W. D. APPEL, chairman,
ASA Committee L23, U.S. representative on ISO/TC 38 on Textiles.

REFERENCES

Anon. letter to the editor reporting use of the tex system in the large Alpargartos Cotton Mills in Argentina and Uruguay, *Textile Age*, Vol. 8, p. 108 (1944).

Tentative Recommended Practice for Use of Tex System to Designate Linear Density of Fibers, Yarn Intermediates, Yarns, and Other Textile Materials, ASTM Designation: D 861 – 58 T, 1958 Book of ASTM Standards, Part 10, p. 347.

ASTM Yarn Numbering Conversion Table. This Table gives exact tex equivalents of normal yarn counts for all traditional yarn-numbering systems. Appendix III of Compilation of ASTM Standards on Textile Materials, published annually.

A. W. Bayes, "Tex Universal Yarn Numbering System," *Journal Textile Inst.*, Vol. 48, p. 225 (1957).

Canadian Advisory Committee on ISO/TC 38 "Textiles—Introduction of the Tex Yarn Numbering System," *Canadian Textile Journal*, Vol. 76, pp. 59–63 (Dec. 11, 1959).

J. Corbiére, "The International Numbering of Yarns and Threads," *Textile Research Journal*, Vol. 23, p. 946 (Dec., 1953).

Deutsche Normen, DIN 60905 (Official German Standard), "The Tex System for the Numbering of Textile Fibers, Yarns, and Fabrics," Melliand Textil-Berichte, Vol. 38, p. 642 (1957) (In German).

R. W. Forrester, "Yarn Counts—Proposed Universal System," *Journal Textile Inst.*, Vol. 40, S8-12 (1949).

J. W. S. Hearle, "Tex Universal Yarn Numbering System," *Journal Textile Inst.*, Vol. 48, pp. 416–17 (1957).

K. Henschel, "Simplification of Yarn Numbering, Preparation for the Introduction of the International Numbering of Yarns in Germany," *Textile Research Journal*, Vol. 25, p. 140 (1955).

International Cotton Federation, "Approval of the Tex Yarn Numbering System for Cotton and Allied Textile Industries," *Textile Mercury and Argus,* Vol. 139, p. 360 (1958).

H. L. Röder, "The Tex System Adopted as the Universal Numbering System for Yarns and Fibers," *Enka and Breda Rayon Review,* Vol. 10, p. 133 (1956).

L. Szponder, "Tex—A Universal Yarn Numbering System," *Textile Industries,* Vol. 122, p. 149 (1958).

A. G. Scroggie, "The Tex Universal Yarn Numbering System," *Textile Research Journal,* Vol. 28, p. 330 (1958).

Spanish Government, Promulgation of the Tex System for Numbering Yarns Made from All Fibers (1946) (In Spanish).

B. L. Whittier, "Tex—A New Yarn-Numbering System," *Textile World,* Vol. 107, p. 88 (Aug., 1957).

The Tex System of Yarn Counting, Recommendation to all members of the Federation of Master Cotton Spinners Associations Ltd., The Yarn Spinners Association, and the Cotton Yarn Doublers Association in the United Kingdom, to proceed with the adoption of the Tex System, pamphlet, Federation of Master Cotton Spinners Association Ltd., Manchester 2, England.

APPENDIX

CONVERSION TABLES

Conversion tables giving the rounded equivalent tex numbers for various ranges of English Cotton Count (Table III), English Worsted Count (Table IV), American Woolen Run (Table V), and Denier Number (Table VI), together with instructions for their use, are given in this Appendix.

Tables for other systems can be prepared by means of the factors, given in Table I. Factors for a number of other systems can be found in Draft ISO Recommendation (Document ISO/TC38 (Sc 4-1) 210).

To prepare a conversion table, use the appropriate factor from Table I to calculate the equivalent traditional value for the limiting range of the recommended rounded tex units listed in Table II. Each calculated value forms the upper limit of one range and the lower limit of the next range as shown in Tables III through VI.

TABLE I. CONVERSION FACTORS

DIVIDE	TO GET TEX NUMBER BY
Denier No.	9
Spyndle No.	0.02903
4960.5	Asbestos cut [a]
590.54	Cotton count (English) [b]
4960.5	Glass cut [c]
1653.5	Linen cut [d]
1000.0	Metric No. [e]
310.03	Woolen run (American) [f]
885.8	Worsted count (English) [g]

MULTIPLY	BY
Denier No.	0.1111
Spyndle No.	34.45

[a] Asbestos cut, NaA, equals 100-yd hanks per lb. [b] English cotton count, Nec, equals 840-yd hanks per lb. [c] Glass cut, NG, equals 100-yd hanks per lb. [d] Linen cut, NeL, equals 300-yd hanks per lb. [e] Metric number, Nm, equals kilometers per kilogram. [f] American woolen run, Nar, equals 1600-yd hanks per lb. [g] English worsted count, Ne, equals 560-yd hanks per lb.

TABLE II. RECOMMENDED ROUNDED TEX NUMBERS [a]

RANGE OF TEX NUMBER		RECOMMENDED ROUNDED TEX NUMBER	RANGE OF TEX NUMBER		RECOMMENDED ROUNDED TEX. NUMBER
ABOVE	UP TO AND INCLUDING		ABOVE	UP TO AND INCLUDING	
9.4	9.8	9.6	31	33	32
9.8	10.25	10	33	35	34
10.25	10.75	10.5	35	37	36
10.75	11.25	11	37	39	38
11.25	11.75	11.5	39	41	40
11.75	12.25	12	41	43	42
12.25	12.75	12.5	43	45	44
12.75	13.5	13	45	47	46
13.5	14.5	14	47	49	48
14.5	15.5	15	49	51	50
15.5	16.5	16	51	54	52
16.5	17.5	17	54	58	56
17.5	18.5	18	58	62	60
18.5	19.5	19	62	66	64
19.5	20.5	20	66	70	68
20.5	21.5	21	70	74	72
21.5	22.5	22	74	78	76
22.5	23.5	23	78	82	80
23.5	24.5	24	82	86	84
24.5	25	25	86	90	88
25.5	27	26	90	94	92
27	29	28	94	98	96
29	31	30	98	102.5	100

[a] Reproduced from the draft ISO Recommendation ISO/TC 38 (SC 4-1) 210, section 3.2. The decimal multiples and fractions of the rounded values indicated in this table are valid for the decimal multiples and fractions of the corresponding ranges.

The rounded tex number appropriate to any number in a traditional system can be obtained by following the procedure set forth in the draft ISO Recommendation, but it is more convenient to use a table in which the limits of the rounded tex numbers have been converted into those of a traditional system.

TABLE III. CONVERSION OF ENGLISH COTTON COUNT INTO ROUNDED TEX NUMBER

For Use During the First Stage of Introduction of the Tex System.
Tex = 590.5/Cotton Count.

COTTON COUNT [a]		RECOMMENDED ROUNDED TEX NUMBER
BEGINNING WITH	UP TO BUT NOT INCLUDING	
57.59	60.26	10
54.91	57.59	10.5
52.47	54.91	11
50.24	52.47	11.5
48.19	50.24	12
46.30	48.19	12.5
43.73	46.30	13
40.72	43.73	14
38.09	40.72	15
35.78	38.09	16
33.74	35.78	17
31.92	33.74	18
30.28	31.92	19
28.80	30.28	20
27.46	28.80	21
26.24	27.46	22
25.13	26.24	23
24.10	25.13	24
23.16	24.10	25
21.87	23.16	26
20.36	21.87	28
19.05	20.36	30
17.90	19.05	32
16.87	17.90	34
15.96	16.87	36
15.14	15.96	38
14.41	15.14	40
13.74	14.41	42
13.13	13.74	44
12.57	13.13	46
12.05	12.57	48
11.58	12.05	50
10.94	11.58	52
10.19	10.94	56
9.524	10.19	60
8.947	9.524	64
8.436	8.947	68
7.980	8.436	72
7.571	7.980	76
7.201	7.571	80
6.866	7.201	84
6.561	6.866	88
6.282	6.561	92
6.026	6.282	96
5.759	6.026	100
5.758	5.759	105

In the left-hand columns of this table, find the range that includes the cotton count under consideration. On the same line as the selected range and to the right of it, find the corresponding rounded tex number. This is the number to be placed in parentheses after the traditional number during the first stage of the introduction of the tex system.

EXAMPLE: Cotton count 21 falls in the range of 20.36 to 21.87. The corresponding rounded tex number is 28. The recommended notation for this yarn during the first stage of the introduction of tex yarn numbers is accordingly: cotton count 21 (28 tex), or, using the European abbreviation, Nec 21 (28 tex).

When required, the values below 10 tex and above 100 tex can be derived from the same table simply by multiplying the values by 10 or dividing them by 10. When doing this, it should be noted that the decimal point in the left columns moves in the opposite direction to that in the right column.

EXAMPLES:

COTTON COUNT		RECOMMENDED ROUNDED TEX NUMBER
BEGINNING WITH	UP TO BUT NOT INCLUDING	
20.36	21.87	28
2.036	2.187	280
203.6	218.7	2.8

[a] Cotton count (Nec) = 840-yd hanks per lb.

[307]

TABLE IV. CONVERSION OF ENGLISH WORSTED COUNT INTO ROUNDED TEX NUMBER

For Use During the First Stage of Introduction of the Tex System.
Tex = 885.8/Worsted Count.

In the left-hand columns of this table, find the range that includes the worsted number under consideration. On the same line as the selected range and to the right of it, find the corresponding rounded tex number. This is the number to be placed in parentheses after the traditional number during the first stage of the introduction of the tex system.

EXAMPLE: Worsted count 32 falls in the range of 30.54 to 32.80. The corresponding rounded tex number is 28. The recommended notation for this yarn during the first stage of the introduction of tex yarn numbers is accordingly: Worsted count 32 (28 tex), or, using the European abbreviation, Ne 32 (28 tex).

When required, the values below 10 tex and above 100 tex can be derived from the same table simply by multiplying the values by 10 or dividing them by 10. When doing this, it should be noted that the decimal point in the two left columns moves in the opposite direction to that in the right column.

EXAMPLES:

| WORSTED COUNT | | RECOMMENDED |
BEGINNING WITH	UP TO BUT NOT INCLUDING	ROUNDED TEX NUMBER
30.54	32.81	28
3.054	3.281	280
305.4	328.1	2.8

| ENGLISH WORSTED COUNT [a] | | RECOMMENDED |
BEGINNING WITH	UP TO BUT NOT INCLUDING	ROUNDED TEX NUMBER
82.400	86.419	10.5
78.737	82.400	11
75.387	78.737	11.5
72.310	75.387	12
69.474	72.310	12.5
65.614	69.474	13
61.089	65.614	14
57.148	61.089	15
53.684	57.148	16
50.617	53.684	17
47.881	50.617	18
45.425	47.881	19
43.209	45.425	20
41.200	43.209	21
39.368	41.200	22
37.693	39.368	23
36.155	37.693	24
34.737	36.155	25
32.807	34.737	26
30.544	32.807	28
28.574	30.544	30
26.842	28.574	32
25.308	26.842	34
23.940	25.308	36
22.712	23.940	38
21.604	22.712	40
20.600	21.604	42
19.684	20.600	44
18.846	19.684	46
18.077	18.846	48
17.368	18.077	50
16.403	17.368	52
15.272	16.403	56
14.287	15.272	60
13.421	14.287	64
12.654	13.421	68
11.970	12.654	72
11.356	11.970	76
10.802	11.356	80
10.300	10.802	84
9.842	10.300	88
9.423	9.842	92
9.038	9.423	96
8.641	9.038	100
8.240	8.641	105

[a] English worsted count (Ne) = 560-yd hanks per lb.

TABLE V. CONVERSION OF AMERICAN WOOLEN RUN INTO ROUNDED TEX NUMBER

For Use During the First Stage of Introduction of the Tex System.
Tex = 310.03/American Woolen Run.

AMERICAN WOOLEN RUN [a]		RECOMMENDED
BEGINNING WITH	UP TO BUT NOT INCLUDING	ROUNDED TEX NUMBER
30.247	31.633	10
28.840	30.247	10.5
27.558	28.840	11
26.386	27.558	11.5
25.309	26.386	12
24.316	25.309	12.5
22.965	24.316	13
21.381	22.965	14
20.002	21.381	15
18.790	20.002	16
17.716	18.790	17
16.758	17.716	18
15.899	16.758	19
15.123	15.899	20
14.420	15.123	21
13.779	14.420	22
13.193	13.779	23
12.654	13.193	24
12.158	12.654	25
11.483	12.158	26
10.691	11.483	28
10.001	10.691	30
9.395	10.001	32
8.858	9.395	34
8.379	8.858	36
7.949	8.379	38
7.562	7.949	40
7.210	7.562	42
6.890	7.210	44
6.596	6.890	46
6.327	6.596	48
6.079	6.327	50
5.741	6.079	52
5.345	5.741	56
5.000	5.345	60
4.697	5.000	64
4.429	4.697	68
4.190	4.429	72
3.975	4.190	76
3.781	3.975	80
3.605	3.781	84
3.445	3.605	88
3.298	3.445	92
3.164	3.298	96
3.024	3.164	100
2.884	3.024	105

[a] American woolen run (Nar) = 1600-yd hanks per lb.

In the left-hand columns of this table, find the range that includes the woolen run number under consideration. On the same line as the selected range and to the right of it, find the corresponding rounded tex number. This is the number to be placed in parentheses after the traditional number during the first stage of the introduction of the tex system.

EXAMPLE: American woolen run 11 falls in the range 10.691 to 11.483. The corresponding rounded tex number is 28. The recommended notation for this yarn during the first stage of the introduction of tex yarn numbers is accordingly: Woolen run 11 (28 tex), or, using the European abbreviation, Nar 11 (28 tex).

When required, the values below 10 tex and above 100 tex can be derived from the same table simply by multiplying the values by 10 or dividing them by 10. When doing this, it should be noted that the decimal point in the two left columns moves in the opposite direction to that in the right column.

EXAMPLES:

AMERICAN WOOLEN RUN		CORRESPONDING
BEGINNING WITH	UP TO BUT NOT INCLUDING	ROUNDED TEX VALUE
10.691	11.483	28
1.0691	1.1483	280
106.91	114.83	2.8

TABLE VI. CONVERSION OF DENIER NUMBER INTO ROUNDED TEX NUMBER

For Use During the First Stage of Introduction of the Tex System.

Tex = Denier Number/9.

In the left-hand columns of this table find the range that includes the denier number under consideration. On the same line as the selected range and to the right of it, find the corresponding rounded tex number. This is the number to be placed in parentheses after the traditional number during the first stage of the introduction of the tex system.

EXAMPLE: The denier number 250 falls in the range of 243 to 261. The corresponding rounded tex number is 28. The recommended notation for this yarn during the first stage of the introduction of tex yarn numbers is accordingly: 250 denier (28 tex), or, using the European abbreviation, Td 250 (28 tex).

When required, the values below 10 tex and above 100 tex can be derived from the same table simply by multiplying the values by 10 or dividing them by 10. When doing this it should be noted that the decimal point in the two left columns moves in the same direction as in the right column.

EXAMPLES:

DENIER NUMBER		CORRESPONDING
BEGINNING WITH	UP TO BUT NOT INCLUDING	ROUNDED TEX VALUE
24.3	26.1	2.8
243	261	28
2430	2610	280

DENIER NUMBER [a]		RECOMMENDED
BEGINNING WITH	UP TO BUT NOT INCLUDING	ROUNDED TEX NUMBER
88.2	92.25	10
92.25	96.75	10.5
96.75	101.2	11
101.2	105.7	11.5
105.7	110.2	12
110.2	114.7	12.5
114.7	121.5	13
121.5	130.5	14
130.5	139.5	15
139.5	148.5	16
148.5	157.5	17
157.5	166.5	18
166.5	175.5	19
175.5	184.5	20
184.5	193.5	21
193.5	202.5	22
202.5	211.5	23
211.5	220.5	24
220.5	229.5	25
229.5	243	26
243	261	28
261	279	30
279	297	32
297	315	34
315	333	36
333	351	38
351	369	40
369	387	42
387	405	44
405	423	46
423	441	48
441	459	50
459	486	52
486	522	56
522	558	60
558	594	64
594	630	68
630	666	72
666	702	76
702	738	80
738	774	84
774	810	88
810	846	92
846	882	96
882	922.5	100
922.5	967.5	105

[a] Denier number (Td) = grams per 9000 meters.

TOPIC: Takeup in Weaving; Width of the Warp in the Reed; Number of Ends in the Warp; Compound Counts of Yarn; Equivalent Counts of Yarn

PERCENTAGE OF TAKEUP IN WEAVING

Takeup in weaving fabric is caused by the bending of the warp yarns over and under the filling picks as the cloth is being woven in the loom. It is found in practically all types of goods; silk seems to be the lowest in weaving takeup with an average of around 1 per cent. It is evident that this bending of the warp yarns makes it necessary to have warp ends actually longer in the loom beam than there is length in the woven cloth ready to be taken from the loom for finishing. The bending depends on several conditions, such as the number of interlacings in the weave, relative size of the yarn as to its diameter and count of yarn, the number of picks per inch in the texture, and the tension at which the warp is maintained during weaving. Generally speaking, the more often the warp interlaces in the goods the more will be the takeup of the warp yarn.

CRIMP is the difference in the length of the yarn as it lies in the cloth, with its straightened length expressed as a percentage of the crimped length. Crimp length is always longer than takeup length.

TAKEUP or CONTRACTION is the difference between a length of yarn as it lies in the fabric and its straightened length, expressed as a percentage of the straight length of the yarn in question.

The method of calculating takeup is based on the fact that it is the warp which takes up and that the goods do not. For this reason, the original length or the stated length of the yarn or thread is considered as 100 per cent. Thus, if a sample of fabric is 4.5 inches long and a warp yarn taken from it and straightened out, with the waves or crimps caused by the bending over and under the filling picks removed, shows a total length of 5 inches, the calculation is as follows:

5.0 inches—straightened length of the yarn,
4.5 inches—original length of yarn in the woven goods,
$\overline{.5}$ inches—the takeup in the yarn.
.1 or 10 per cent, the percentage of takeup in weaving (Answer).

WIDTH OF THE WARP IN THE REED

In practically all instances, goods are narrower than the width at which the warp was set in the loom. The length of one pick may be considered, generally speaking, as equal to the reed width. Hence, in calculating the yards of filling necessary to make a yard of fabric, it is essential that you know the width of the goods in the reed.

RULE: Width of sample : Straight length of filling yarn :: Finished Width : Reed width.

EXAMPLE: Say that a piece of filling yarn in a fabric is 4 inches long. When the thread is straightened out, it measured 5 inches in length.
Thus: the equation would be   4 : 5 :: 56 inch width finished : x
4x equals 280, in inches,
x equals 70 inches, reed width.

NUMBER OF ENDS IN THE WARP

The number of ends in the warp in a piece of fabric is regulated by the width of the goods and the number of ends per inch in the fabric. The total number of ends is found by multiplying the finished width of the goods by the number of ends per inch in the texture of the material in the finished state.

EXAMPLE: A fabric finished at 56 inches wide contains 60 ends per inch. Find the number of warp ends in the fabric.
56 × 60 equals 3,360, the number of warp ends in cloth (Answer).

YARDS OF WARP YARN PER YARD OF GOODS AND INCLUDING THE TAKEUP IN WEAVING

The yards of warp yarn in a yard of goods depend upon the number of ends in the warp and the takeup in the warp during weaving. If there is no takeup in weaving, each warp yarn in a yard of the goods would be one yard long. In such a case, the number of ends in the warp would equal the number of yards of warp yarn per yard of goods. If there is, however, takeup, then each end in the warp will be more than one yard in length. The original or straightened length of a yarn is considered as 100 per cent. The length which it represents in the fabric is considered as 100 per cent minus the percentage of takeup durng the weaving.

EXAMPLE: How long would a warp yarn be in a yard of goods if there is a 10% takeup in the weaving?
100% minus 10% gives 90% or 36 inches, the one yard length.
1% equals $\frac{36}{90}$. 100% is $\frac{36 \times 100}{90}$ or 40 inches length of the yarn (Answer).

In this case each warp yarn will be 40 inches in length, and what is true of the one warp thread, is true, say, of 3,360 ends or yarns that make up the warp on the warp beam of the loom. Thus, the combined length of the warp yarn in a yard of goods can be found by multiplying 3,360 ends by 40 inches and then dividing by 36 to convert to yards of yarn.

Another method used in fabric analysis on the ends in the warp, and including the takeup in weaving, is to consider the total number of yarns in the warp as being equal to 100 per cent minus the percentage of the takeup in weaving. The so-called "short method" is to multiply the total number of ends by 100 and then to divide by 100 minus the percentage of takeup in the weaving.

EXAMPLE: How many yards of warp yarn in a fabric that is 36 inches wide and has 150 ends per inch with a 10% takeup?
150 ends times 36 inches in one yard equals 5,400, which is 90 per cent.
$\frac{5,400 \times 100}{90}$ equals 6,000, the number of yards of warp yarn per yard of goods including the takeup in weaving (Answer).

YARDS OF FILLING PER YARD OF GOODS

This yardage depends upon the number of picks per inch and the length of each pick. This length of a filling pick is usually considered as being equal to the reed width in the loom. Thus the yards of filling yarn per yard of goods is found by multiplying the picks per inch by the reed width, in inches.

EXAMPLE: How many yards of filling yarn in a yard of fabric that is 74 inches wide in the reed, with 46 picks per inch in the construction?
74 × 46 equals 3,404 yards of filling yarn per yard of goods (Answer).

COMPOUND YARN COUNTS

Fancy and novelty yarns of many types appear in a host of fabrics and garments. Often these yarns are made up of two or more threads of different colors and different sizes twisted or plied together. When yarn sizes or counts of compound yarns are of unequal count, the count of the compound yarn is determined in the following manner:

RULE: Divide the product of the two counts by their sums.

EXAMPLE: Find the yarn count produced by twisting a single 20s cotton and a single 30s cotton: $\dfrac{20 \text{ plus } 30}{20 \text{ times } 30}$ equals $\dfrac{600}{50}$ equals 12s (Answer).

EQUIVALENT COUNTS OF YARN

Because of the fact that different standards are used in figuring yarn counts, it often becomes necessary to calculate for the equivalent count of a yarn in another system. This is done by determining the yards in a pound of the yarn in question and then to divide by the standard of the desired system of yarn. In other words, multiply the count by its standard number and then divide it by the standard of the required system of yarn.

EXAMPLE: What size does a 40s cotton yarn equal in the worsted system of yarn?
$\dfrac{40 \times 840, \text{ cotton standard}}{560, \text{ worsted standard}}$ equals 60s in worsted count (Answer).

EXAMPLE: What size worsted yarn does a 2/48s cotton yarn equal?
A 2/48s cotton equals a 1/24s cotton yarn in diameter.
$\dfrac{24 \times 840}{560}$, cotton standard equals a 1/36s worsted. Since the yarn is two-ply worsted standard, the size would be a 2/72 worsted yarn (36 × 2 ply) (Answer).

TESTING

1. Define the following terms: takeup; crimp; contraction.
2. If the original length of a yarn is 6 inches and the straightened length is 7.25 inches, find the percentage of takeup in the yarn.
3. If a fabric is finished at 56 inches and it has 66 ends per inch, how many ends would there be in the warp?
4. How long will a warp yarn be in a yard of goods if there is a 6 per cent takeup in the weaving of the cloth?
5. How many yards of warp yarn would there be in a fabric that is 40 inches wide, has 92 ends per inch, with a 6 per-cent takeup in the weaving?
6. Find the yarn count produced by twisting a 1/24s worsted yarn with a 1/36s worsted yarn.
7. What does a 60s cotton yarn equal in the worsted system of yarn?

FABRIC ANALYSIS WORKSHEET   Fabric Sample # . . . .

Student's Name:

Name of Fabric:

Fabric Characteristics:

Paste

Even Numbered

Major
End Use:

Samples

Here

Reason for
Selecting Face as Shown:

Reason for
Selecting Warp as Shown:

YARN INFORMATION   *WARP*   *FILLING*

1) Filament
   or Spun:

2) Number
   of Ply:

3) Twist
   Direction:

Name of
Weave: Fabric
                              Count:

Method of
Coloring:

Special
Finishes:

BURNING TEST   *WARP*   *FILLING*

Flame:

Odor: Paste

                                              Odd Numbered
Ash:
                                              Samples
Other Tests for
Identification: Here

Fiber:

TOPIC: QUALITY CONTROL

This very important spoke in the great wheel of textiles necessitates a trained staff to carry on a continuous program of research, development, and testing in order to improve production efficiency and fabric quality. Exchanges for technical information, such as conventions, symposiums, panels, and textile organizations are very beneficial in that they offer initial and basic information on the new developments that are constantly coming to the fore. It is the work of the quality control division to investigate and learn as much as possible about new textile fibers, new types of yarns, new fabrics, new finishes, and new methods. The rapid rise of blended fabrics of many types is always given utmost attention by the quality control groups. The end use of a fabric in the apparel, decorative, or industrial businesses is of great value to quality experts.

The physical and chemical testing done by the quality group is of inestimable value to the textile concern. Some of the major testing aims follow:

RESIDUAL SHRINKAGE TESTING: Determines results in washing, laundering, and dry-cleaning; of much value in testing the so-called "wash-and-wear" garments.

COLOR-RESISTANCE TESTING: Results, for example, will show the effect of chlorine actions on yarns and fabrics, of drycleaning, sunlight or salt water, crocking, gas-fading, perspiration, washing, etc.

BASIC AND MISCELLANEOUS TESTING: The control staff can learn much about fabrics from the following tests—for abrasion, elasticity, twist in yarn, mildew-resistance, tensile strength of yarns and fabrics, seam slippage, water-repellency, crease-resistance, nonflammability, moth-resistance, pilling, etc.

During the finishing of the goods, samples are taken from the various cuts of cloth and given rigorous laboratory testing in accordance with the accepted standards that have been set up by the various agencies in the industry. Shrinkage control, for example, is one of the most important items that must be observed closely at all times. Fabrics must be closely watched and tested, measured, marked, washed in a standard washing machine, dried on a flat press, and then remeasured, in order to make absolute determinations. Residual shrinkage of less than 1 per cent is usually satisfactory in all cases.

Another major standard that must be followed to the letter is colorfastness. Tests are run continuously to ascertain the resistance of the goods to fading upon exposure to sunlight, to washing or drycleaning, to atmospheric fumes, and to crocking, or the rubbing-off of the color.

Flammability tests will show the resistance to burning, and porosity tests are essential in the controlled application of water-repellent finishes. Tensile-strength tests on yarns and fabrics are of utmost importance since they aid in establishing fabric wearing and serviceability qualities. The same is true of abrasion tests. The twist count is another important standard because the number of turns of twists per inch in yarn is a vital factor at all times. However, in fine, sheer fabrics it happens frequently that the importance of the twist in the yarn is subordinate to the fineness of the yarn used.

It is interesting to note that in the case of the so-called average or coarse cotton yarns, fiber strength consists of up to 37 per cent of the strength of the

INSTRUMENT DEVELOPMENTS OF THE BETTER FABRICS
TESTING BUREAU, INC.

BETTER FABRICS TESTING BUREAU, INC.

101 WEST 31ST STREET

NEW YORK 1, N. Y.

ORDER FOR TEST

TEST NO._____

CLIENT_____

STREET_____

CITY & STATE_____

ATT:_____

MATERIAL TO BE TESTED:_____

_____

TESTS TO BE MADE:_____   CHARGES
QUOTED:_____

_____   _____

_____   _____

_____   _____

_____   _____

_____   _____

_____   _____

TOTAL CHARGES:_____

ARE RESULTS TO BE PHONED?_____   TEL. NO. _____

ARE SAMPLES TO BE RETURNED? IF YES, WHERE?_____

BILL TO:_____   COPY OF REPORT TO:_____

_____   _____

TESTS AND CHARGES AUTHORIZED BY:_____

ORDER TAKEN BY: _____

IN PERSON ☐   BY TELEPHONE ☐   DATE_____19 _____

yarns. Fiber fineness is very important in yarn manufacturing; it contributes up to 16 per cent of the yarn strength in average counts of yarn and becomes increasingly more important the finer the yarn. When the cotton yarn sizes pass a 50s yarn count, the order is reversed and fineness becomes more important than fiber strength. The maturity of the cotton is also an important item for dyers and finishers. The nature of immature cotton fibers can change the strength and fineness readings.

The grade of the cotton indicates waste, staple limits, and yarn sizes. These points are under consideration by the control staff at all times. Incidentally, the upper half means the average length of the cotton fiber is in the upper half of the sample in question. The mean average is the length of all the fibers being tested. The uniformity ratio of the mean is compared with the upper-half mean. From this it has been established that the length of the fibers and their uniformity coincide to 47 per cent relative to yarn strength. Other textile fibers present problems similar to those in cotton.

The finishing of textile fabrics is an art and a science. It has been said often that "fabrics are made in the finishing," a very true statement. The control unit is responsible for the compounding of the many formulas for resins from raw chemical stocks, the effects when these formulas are used in dyeing the goods, and the development of new formulas.

Experimental work is done on model or miniature padders and jigs in dyeing fabric and perfecting the application of dyestuffs before a new formula is assigned for production. On the completion of dyeing and finishing, the material is measured and examined thoroughly, inch by inch, by experienced inspectors.

Fabrics which pass all the rigid requirements are then placed in production in the mill, and, when approved by the final inspection group, are given a seal of approval by the company. Quality control takes the close, undivided attention of every person in the department, and the synchronization of the work of all parties concerned is of paramount importance.

Part 2—Unit 11

TOPIC: The Conditioning Oven for Determination of Moisture in Textiles

Conditioning in textiles is the determination of the true or basic weight of fibers or fabrics by the standard percentages of moisture content. The term also implies the restoration to fibers and fabrics of moisture lost during manipulation or manufacture.

Conditioned weight is the oven-dry weight of fiber, yarn, or fabric taken directly from the conditioning oven, plus the standard commercial moisture regain added to this dry weight.

Fiber weight in conditioning is taken for fibers that contain oil, and there is the possibility that a particular oil may become volatile. This would impair the accuracy and the repeatability of the conditioning and boil-off tests. To offset this, the fiber test has been developed. This test is a combination of the conditioned weight and the boil-off tests. For example, a 200-gram sample of raw silk could be made up, tested, and reduced directly in one operation to clean, dry fiber. This fiber weight can be mathematically built up to any desired moisture and boil-off content for contractional buying and selling.

1. *Chemstrand Knit Fabric Stretch and Recovery Tester*—This apparatus is designed to provide means for measuring the stretch potential of knitted fabrics and to gauge recovery against time after specimens have been held at a predetermined stretch level. The unique feature of the method is the hourglass shape of the test specimen which prevents curling and roping of the specimen under tension.

The potential of a knitted stretch fabric is obtained on the front portion of the apparatus by hanging a weight proportioned to the weight of the fabric itself on the bottom stirrup. Fresh specimens are then placed in the rack as shown and held at an extension dictated by the end use of the fabric. Direct reading scales are hung on the specimen to determine stretch and recovery.

3. *Ozoniter*—Certain combinations of textile fibers and dyes are color sensitive to ozone in the atmosphere. These same combinations may be highly resistant to other destructive agents such as oxides of nitrogen, sunlight, or laundering agents.

The Ozoniter provides a generating system and exposure chamber for use in performing the test of American Association for Textile Chemists and Colorists for resistance to color change. Samples placed in the upper chamber are subjected to ozone generated in the lower chamber when the fumes are pumped through a fan and baffle system. A standard ribbon which changes color in ozone is used to regulate the length of cycle. Two cycles will usually produce a measurable color change in samples which are ozone sensitive.

4. *Cyclic Stretch Tester*—Certain woven and knitted stretch fabrics behave differently in repeated short-time load cycles than they do in the more popular static extension tests. Depending on end use and the style and cut of a garment for the particular end use, one or the other of these methods of evaluation gives the true answers on fabric performance.

The apparatus shown here provides repeated short time loadings (200 per minute) at any given extension in the range of 10 to 50 percent. The apparatus provides ten stations for multiple sample testing.

Distortion of the sample in terms of percent growth is used as the test criterion. Such distortion is obtained at various time intervals of rest after the sample has been cycled for a selected number of cycles.

2. *Precision Marking Device*—Shown here is a stamping device for the placement of indelible bench marks on specimens to be subjected to the dimensional change phenomenon. The unit consists of a set of stamping dies attached to a spacer bar which in turn is equipped with handles. A stamp pad is provided to ink the dies.

The obvious advantages of this marking system are cleanliness, clearly defined marks, and built-in precision. Five-, ten-, and eighteen-inch markers cover the usual range of dimensional change tests.

Procedure

1. The sample is placed in one of the baskets and hung on one of the hooks in the oven.
2. The sample is bone dry after about one hour in the oven at a temperature of 220° F.
3. A fan changes the air in the oven.
4. When ready for weighing, the basket holding the sample is placed on the rod connecting with the balance.
5. The fan is turned off during the weighing. Why is this done?
6. After about ten minutes the sample is reweighed.
7. This is continued until two weighings at ten-minute intervals do not vary more than .003 gram.
8. If the amount of moisture present is to be determined, the sample is weighed as received on an ordinary analytical balance and then placed in the conditioning oven.
9. If the dry weight alone is desired, the sample is placed directly in the oven.
10. The sample should be placed in the basket in such a way that the air may circulate easily through the sample.

Application of the Procedure

Find the percentage of moisture and the percentage of regain of a piece of woolen fabric, as follows:

a) Weigh about ten grams of woolen cloth on the analytical balance.
b) Place sample in the oven.
c) After one hour determine the weight of the sample.
d) Repeat the weighing after ten-minute intervals until a constant weight is obtained.
e) Weight of the sample as received _____ grams.
f) Bone-dry weight _____ grams.
g) Calculation:

Percentage of moisture equals $\dfrac{\text{weight of water} \times 100}{\text{sample weight as received}}$.

h) Percentage of regain equals $\dfrac{\text{weight of water} \times 100}{\text{bone-dry weight}}$.

TESTING

1. Give two advantages of combining balance and oven in the same unit.
2. How is compensation made for the weight of the basket and connecting rod?
3. Explain the use of a temperature of 220° F. for drying.
4. When is the sample considered to be bone dry?
5. What is the difference between regain and moisture percentage?

Part 2—Unit 12

TOPIC: TENSILE STRENGTH OF YARN AND FABRIC

Tensile strength is defined as the maximum load per unit of the original cross-section area obtained prior to rupture. It is the actual resistance in number of pounds that a fabric will give to a breaking machine before the sample is broken and no longer may be classed as a yarn of cloth. Bursting strengths are recorded on a dial on the machine. Tensile strength is one of the most important requisites of any fabric.

Tensile strength loss is usually reported as loss in pounds per inch. It is also commonly reported as percentage loss, based on the loss and the original strength, in pounds per inch. It varies with the different fabrics under a fixed set of conditions.

[319]

TENSILE STRENGTH OF YARN USING THE SINGLE STRAND YARN TESTER

All yarn and thread should undergo testing for strength, and there should be a minimum breaking strength requirement. In performing a yarn-breakage test, the following procedure is followed:

1. Grip the free end of a piece of yarn in the upper clamp without disturbing the twist.
2. Straighten the yarn and then grip it in the lower clamp. Check well for accuracy.
3. Raise the lever on the machine so that the lower jaw will, by gravity, move downward and break the yarn. Speed is 12½ inches a minute.
4. Reading the scale, record the strength and the stretch of the yarn broken. Stretch is expressed in terms of inches or percentage.
5. If a yarn breaks at or near a clamp, discard it.
6. Five tests should be made for each yarn tested. The average is then computed and this number is taken as the breaking strength.

TEST NUMBER	STRENGTH	STRETCH
1		
2		
3		
4		
5		
Total		
Average		

TENSILE STRENGTH OF CLOTH BY THE GRAB METHOD

This is the testing of cloth for strength by a controlled method on a fabric-breaking machine, the important features of which are two metal jaws which grip the material and pull the fabric until it is ruptured. The breaking strength is recorded on a dial on the scale disk.

Ten samples are required for this test, five for the warp and five for the filling. The sample size is 6 inches by 4 inches. Samples should not be cut within 3 inches of the selvage of the goods since the edges of the fabric may not always show the true pick count in the cloth.

A line is drawn lengthwise of each sample; the line should be on the yarn 1½ inches from the edge. This line indicates where the right edge of the clamps on the machine must grip the sample. The samples must be conditioned to standard regain prior to testing, to give standard, accurate, and comparative results. The clamps on the machine are three inches apart at the beginning of the test.

The front clamps of both upper and lower jaws measure 1 by 1 inch; the back clamps measure 1 by 2 inches with the 2-inch length horizontal.

Procedure

1. The sample is clamped into the machine with the long side vertical.
2. The application of power to drive the machine and the release of the recording nog will set the machine in motion to break the fabric between the jaws.
3. When the fabric is ruptured, the nog slips into the saw tooth of the quadrant and remains there until released.
4. The reading is taken and recorded, and the machine is then set up for the next test.

EFFECT OF OUTDOOR EXPOSURE ON YARN TENACITY

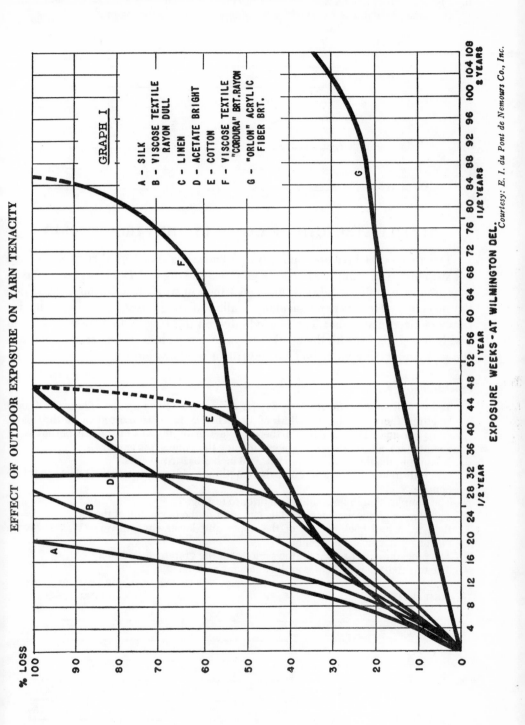

GRAPH I

A – SILK
B – VISCOSE TEXTILE
      RAYON DULL
C – LINEN
D – ACETATE BRIGHT
E – COTTON
F – VISCOSE TEXTILE
      "CORDURA" BRT. RAYON
G – "ORLON" ACRYLIC
      FIBER BRT.

% LOSS

EXPOSURE WEEKS – AT WILMINGTON DEL.

Courtesy: E. I. du Pont de Nemours Co., Inc.

5. Samples which break at the jaws should not be recorded in the testing, since a true breaking strength has not been determined.
6. The average of five tests in the warp direction is taken for the actual strength result; the same procedure is followed for the filling direction in the material:

TEST NUMBER	WARP	FILLING
1		
2		
3		
4		
5		
Total		
Average		

TENSILE STRENGTH OF CLOTH BY THE STRIP METHOD

This method of breaking fabric is also known as the raveled strip test or the cut strip test. The samples are cut about 6 inches long and 1½ inches wide. Ravelings are made until the fabric is an even 1 inch in width prior to inserting it into the machine. (However, no raveling is allowed in the test done especially for heavy or sized materials.) The raveled edge on the lengthwise side may vary in width in accordance with the number of yarns per inch in the material. The lower the pick count, the wider will be the fringe used, within reason.

Procedure

1. Ten samples are cut for the test; five for the warp and five for the filling. The 6-inch length of fabric will have a width of 1¼ inches if there are more than 50 threads or yarns per inch; 1½-inch width if there are less than 50 yarns or threads per inch.
2. Samples are cut so that no two pieces include the same yarns lengthwise.
3. No sample should be taken from within 3 inches of the selvages.
4. Carefully remove the yarns from the lengthwise sides until exactly 1 inch of fabric remains.
5. The samples should be conditioned prior to testing.
6. The clamps on the machine are 3 inches apart at the beginning of the test.
7. Both front and back clamps of the upper and lower jaws measure 1″ x 1½″ with the longer dimension horizontal.
8. The procedure for breaking is the same as for the grab-method testing.
9. The test chart may be set up in the following manner:

TEST NUMBER	WARP	FILLING
1		
2		
3		
4		
5		
Total		
Average		

TESTING

Single-Strand Tester

1. At what rate of speed does the lower jaw move in testing?
2. Why is the speed at which the lower jaw moves important?
3. Why would results have to be discarded if the yarn broke at or near the clamps on the machine?
4. In what two ways may stretch be expressed?

Grab Method

1. Why are five tests made in both the warp and the filling directions of the fabric?
2. Explain the value of the line drawn 1½ inches from the lengthwise edge of the sample to be tested.
3. Why should samples to be tested be conditioned before actual testing?

Strip Method

1. Why are warp samples for this test cut out side by side from the cloth, and the filling samples cut out one over the other?
2. What is the distance between the two jaws at the beginning of this test?

Part 2—Unit 13

TOPIC: Bursting Strength of Knitted Fabrics

Comparable with the tensile-strength tests for woven fabrics, there is a bursting-strength test for the host of knitted fabrics in use today. The Mullen Tester, of B. F. Perkins Company, Inc., Holyoke, Massachusetts, is used for these tests. The machine makes use of a hydraulic system, the pressure being exerted on the sample by means of a rubber diaphragm. The tester is comprised of a set of ring clamps to hold the sample which is arranged over a well of glycerine covered by the rubber diaphragm.

The fabrics should be conditioned prior to testing in order to insure accurate results for comparative purposes. The diameter of the opening of the diaphragm is 1¼ inches, and in cutting the fabric about 1 inch more should be added so that the circular-cut specimen, about 3¼ inches in diameter, is of adequate size for testing. With this allowance in the fabric the cloth will be held in a firm and uniform manner in the machine.

When the machine is in action, pressure is built up behind the diaphragm, and it distends into a dome shape and then forces its way through the test specimen. Readings are obtained of pressure in pounds per square inch. A correction should be made in this test to allow for the pressure necessary to distend the diaphragm itself to the point where it will rupture the sample.

When testing knit goods for bursting strength, always refer to the "Standard Methods of Testing and Tolerances for Knit Goods," American Society for Testing Materials, Philadelphia, Pennsylvania. The designation is D-231-46.

Procedure

1. Clamp the sample over the rubber diaphragm.
2. Bring the gauge needle to the zero point.
3. Turn on the motor switch.
4. Push the operating handle to the left, thereby causing the rubber diaphragm to press against the sample.

[323]

Pick counter

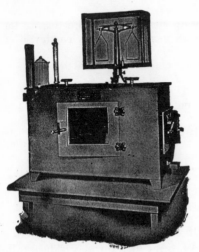

Conditioning oven

Yarn strength
tester

Yarn reel

Courtesy: Alfred Suter & Co., Inc.

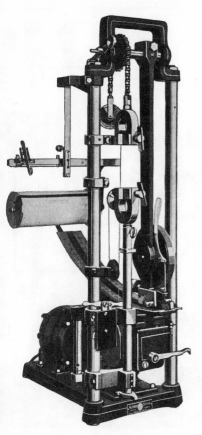

Fabric strength tester

Hydrostatic pressure
tester

Taber abraser

Courtesy: Alfred Suter & Co., Inc.

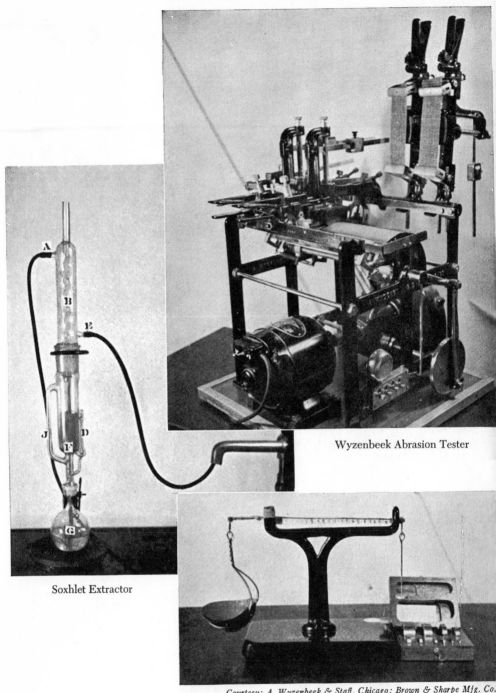

Wyzenbeek Abrasion Tester

Soxhlet Extractor

Grain Scale

Courtesy: A. Wyzenbeek & Staff, Chicago; Brown & Sharpe Mfg. Co.

Mullen Bursting Strength Tester

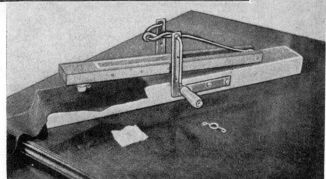

Courtesy: B. F. Perkins & Sons, Inc., A.A.T.C.C.

Crockmeter

Random Tumble Pilling Tester

Courtesy: Bradford Dyeing Association; American Viscose Corp.

Air permeability of fabrics

5″ rayon staple   3½″ to 6″ rayon staple

[329]

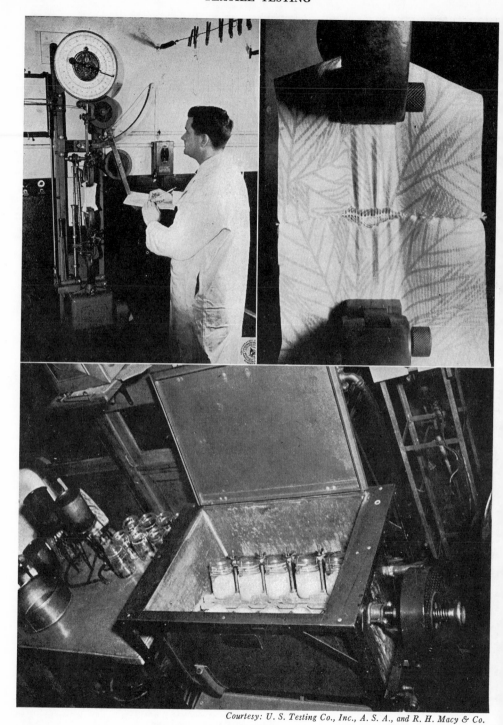

Courtesy: U. S. Testing Co., Inc., A. S. A., and R. H. Macy & Co.

Fabric tensile strength   Seam strength

Launder-Ometer for fastness of dyes to washing

Courtesy: Atlas Electric Devices Company, Inc., Chicago

Fade-Ometer tests fastness of dyes to light

Soxhlet extractors for grease, oil, etc. determination

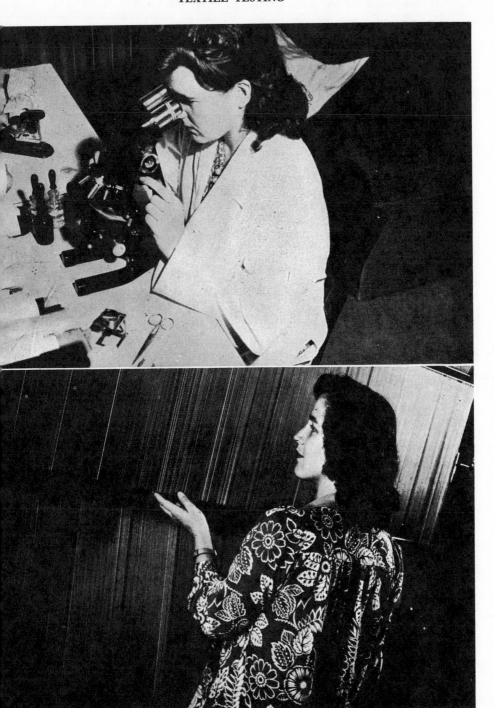

Courtesy: Bureau of Standards, R. H. Macy & Co.

Fiber identification

Yarn inspection

5. As soon as the sample bursts or ruptures, push the handle halfway to the neutral position.
6. Record the reading on the gauge.
7. Release the clamp.
8. Press the gauge button to bring the needle back to the zero mark.
9. Record the pressure required to expand the diaphragm.
10. Find the actual bursting strength by subtracting the first pressure from the second reading.

Five tests should be made on a conditioned knit fabric as per the following chart:

TEST NUMBER	TOTAL PRESSURE	DIAPHRAGM PRESSURE	SAMPLE PRESSURE
1			
2			
3			
4			
5			
Average			

TESTING

1. Why should samples to be tested be conditioned?
2. Discuss the advantages of a bursting-strength test for knit fabrics.
3. What provision is made so that the fabric to be tested will be held taut in the machine during testing?
4. In what terms are the readings recorded in this type of test?
5. What is meant by subtracting the first pressure from the second pressure in this test?

Part 2—Unit 14

TOPIC: ABRASION TESTING

This type of testing is used to measure the resistance to wear of fabric and other materials. There are two major types of machines used in abrasion testing—the Taber Abrasion Machine, and the Wyzenbeek Associates Abrasion Tester.

THE TABER ABRASER

The abrasive action on this machine is performed by wheels which come in different numbers. The toughness of the fabric to be tested determines the number of the wheel to be used on the machine. There is a range of pressure applicable to all types of samples, and this runs from 125 grams to 1,000 grams. The sample used is about six inches in diameter. The machine runs about 100 cycles per minute. The rate of wear may be increased by the use of a coarser wheel or by increased pressure on the specimen. The fibers from the abrading wheel which accumulate and become embedded in the weave structure of the sample must be removed periodically during the test, since they would affect the actual results of abrasion action on the fabric.

Procedure

1. Fold the sample in half, twice; then cut a small hole in the center of the folded cloth.
2. Mount the fabric in the sample holder and clamp down with the washer and nut.
3. The sample is made smooth by forcing the ring onto the edge of the holder.
4. The nut in the ring is tightened and the excess material then cut off.
5. The center nut is tightened and the sample is now ready for the action.
6. Prior to beginning the test, the wheels are refaced by running them against abrasive paper on the refacing holder.
7. The sample holder, with the prepared sample, is placed in the machine and the counter is set at zero.
8. A pressure of 500 grams and Number Ten wheels are used.
9. The test is run for the number of cycles necessary to impair the serviceability or appearance of the fabric.
10. Results should be obtained between 500 cycles and 5,000 cycles.

TESTING

1. What provides the abrasive action in this machine?
2. Why are various numbered wheels provided for the machine?
3. About how many cycles does the machine make per minute?
4. Name two ways whereby the rate of wear may be increased when testing.
5. If the waste fibers from abrading when testing are not removed, what would their effect be on the smooth running of the test?

THE WYZENBEEK ASSOCIATES ABRASION MACHINE

The function of wear-testing machines is to determine the durability of fabrics in their resistance to wear. The testing should be done in both warp and filling directions in order to ascertain if the fibers and yarns in the one direction vary from those in the opposite direction. Fabrics which may be tested for abrasion include melton, kersey, beaver, broadcloth, blanketing, carpets and rugs, bolivia, pile cloths, napped materials, overcoatings, etc. In fact, the test is applied to practically any fabric where the question of abrasion-resistance needs to be known.

The samples for the Wyzenbeek machine are from 9 to 10 inches in length and 2½ to 3 inches in width. In setting up the samples for testing, two sets are used. One is cut with the long dimension in the warp direction, the second set is cut with the long dimension in the filling direction. The reason for this is that the yarns running in one direction very often are different from those in the other direction; one set is usually weaker and has less twist and may vary in the number of plies used in the respective yarns. Thus it is an easy matter to determine which set of yarns stands up better in the test.

The pressure and the tension on the samples are controlled by a system of weights and levers.

Procedure

1. The samples are set into the holders and made fast so that they will not slip or creep during the testing.
2. The tension and pressure bars are set in horizontal positions from the beginning of the test until the test run has been completed. The fabrics are set in their respective places on the abrasion cylinder or drum.
3. Following this, the bars and the pressures are regulated so that each unit being tested will be in proper alignment with the other specimens. It is most important to

make a recheck on the machine setup prior to turning on the switch to start the machine. There must be uniform tension and pressure at all times on all samples being tested.

4. The abradant used is emery cloth No. 320.
5. The machine in its action has an automatic recorder for the number of rubs given the sample or samples.
6. As the materials are rubbed, small particles or pieces of fiber which have become loosened from the fabric must be brushed off the machine. If allowed to remain, they will impede and offset positive results in testing.
7. Some samples may be prepared with a lengthwise fold in them to correspond to the wearing action—for example, the cuff or the collar of a suit.
8. The operator of the machine must record the number of rubs before the pilling effect begins to show, the number of rubs before a lengthwise yarn breaks, and the number of rubs before a crosswise yarn breaks. On the completion of the test, computations and comparisons can be made with similar materials and with the standards that have been set up for the test. After running the machine for a few rubs, it is well to note the effects of abrasion by the oscillating cylinder upon which the abradant has been placed. The effect on the fabric might be checked after 15 or 30 rubs to see how the fabric seems to withstand the action.
9. This machine has a vacuum pick-up system which removes the rubbed-off particles of fibers.

TESTING

1. Define abrasion on a fabric.
2. Why is it necessary to test in both directions on a fabric?
3. Name five cloths that should be given abrasion testing.
4. What values result from abrasion testing?
5. Why is it necessary to test in both warp and filling directions of a cloth?

REFERENCES: Taber Abraser, North Tonawanda, N. Y.; Wyzenbeek Associates Abrasion Testing Machine, Atlas Electric Devices Company, Chicago, Ill.

Part 2—Unit 15

TOPIC: PILLING AND THE USE OF THE RANDOM TUMBLE PILLING TESTER MACHINE

Pilling is the formation of fuzzy fibers, entangled fibers, or "pills" on the surface of fabrics caused by rubbing, abrasion, friction, or chafing. It occurs in lightweight lofty materials made of wool, manmade fibers, and even cotton. The rise of knitwear made of loftier fabrics and looser construction, and using some of the manmade fibers has caused much attention to this matter, since customer complaints on wearing apparel on which pills formed have increased considerably within the last few years. Pills on manmade fibers particularly will cling to their fabric base because of abrasion-resistance, flexural resistance, and high tenacity, without rubbing off through continuous wear of the article.

This distressing effect on fabrics and apparel can be measured in the testing laboratory by means of the random pilling tester. It was developed by E. I. du Pont de Nemours & Co., Inc., for use on all types of woven and knitted fabrics regardless of whether made from one fiber or from a blend or mixture of several fibers.

[336]

Procedure

1. Prepare the fabric by hand-laundering, machine-laundering, or drycleaning.
2. Condition the fabric sample at 65 per cent relative humidity and 70° F.
3. Cut from the fabric six 4-inch-square specimens on a 45-degree bias.
4. Seal the edges of the specimens with rubber cement to prevent raveling.
5. Fit a freshly washed and conditioned standard neoprene liner into each chamber on the tester.
6. Insert three specimens into each chamber and add approximately 25 milligrams of 0.2-inch-long cotton fibers to aid in the formation of pills.
7. Place the end cover on each chamber and start the tester.

ON WOVEN FABRICS

a) Run the tester for 30 minutes, clean the excess lint specimens and chamber, and then rate the specimens by comparing with the standard rating charts.
b) Reverse the liner to obtain a clean surface, repeat the steps from item 6 under Procedure through a of On Woven Fabrics. Then obtain the rating of the specimens after a total of 60 minutes of testing. Discontinue the testing after a desired interval or whenever the rating exceeds 4.5.
c) If 90- or 120-minute ratings are desired, use the same general procedure, but insert a new liner after a 60-minute rating.

ON KNITTED FABRICS

a) Use the same procedure as for woven fabrics, but clean and rate the samples after 20 and 30 minutes of testing.
b) Add a new charge of cotton fibers after a 20-minute rating.
c) Use the same liner surface for a total of 30 minutes.

In the application of this test, compare the results of the pilling characteristics with the standard used for the particular type of fabric. Make a determination of the relative surface distortion due to wear, to fabrics that do not pill.

The way to control or decrease the possibility of pilling on fabrics is given below:

1. RAW MATERIAL: As the fiber denier increases, the possibility of pilling decreases; the higher the tenacity of the stock used, the greater will be the possibility of pilling. Fibers should be used that are not easily deformed or entangled.
2. YARN: The use of the finest-diameter yarn count possible will retard pilling effect. Single yarns have a greater tendency to pill than ply yarns. The amount of twist given to the yarns used is of utmost importance to the processor. Using straggly, hairy, protruding fibers in a material will increase the chance of pilling.
3. FABRIC CONSTRUCTION: The more compact the texture of the cloth, the less will be the possibility for pilling. Weaves with long yarn floats should be avoided.
4. FINISHING: Brushing, gigging, gassing, or genapping, and shearing will lessen the chance of pilling. Heat-set thermoplastic fibers will also lessen pilling tendencies. Care should be exercised in the use of certain resins in the finishing of fabrics since they may impair the hand of the goods.

TESTING

1. Define pilling. Recall experience you may have had with some article of apparel which pilled.
2. What is meant by the surface wear on a material?
3. Give three reasons why a sweater might show a pilling effect.
4. Define abrasion-resistance; flexural resistance; high tenacity.
5. Explain how the principle of twist in yarn will lessen the possibilities of pilling.

Courtesy of E. I. du Pont de Nemours & Co., Inc., Wilmington, Del.; and Atlas Electric Devices, 4114 Ravenswood Avenue, Chicago 13, Illinois.

TOPIC: WATER PERMEABILITY OF FABRICS

Permeability is the ability of air, gas, or water to pass or flow through the interstices or openings between the yarns or threads in a fabric. Water-repellency is the ability of a fabric to repel water. Various types of tests are used and these are conducted on the samples before and after subjection to standard washing and drycleaning tests. Immersion, spray, spot, and hydrostatic methods may be used. The classification of readings on the scale of the machine used follows:

1. Shower-resistant ..17 cm to 50 cm mark.
2. Water-repellent ...50 cm mark. (Sometimes referred to as rainproof.)
3. Waterproof ......50 cm mark and remaining there for one hour before seepage of three drops of water.

In the waterproofing of a fabric there are various methods used to coat a fabric so that it will repel water altogether. Rubber, oil, or lacquer compounds are often used. The use for which a fabric is intended determines whether it should be made waterproof, water-repellent-processed, or shower-resistant.

Waterproofing closes the pores of a fabric. Water-repellent finishes do not close the pores of the cloth against air; hence they are more comfortable to wear because the body can "breathe" through them.

The machine commonly used is of the static head type, and its purpose is to measure the resistance of a fabric to water under pressure.

Procedure

1. Set the indicator at zero on the vertical scale of the machine.
2. Switch on the light and then place the sample, 8 by 8 inches, over the opening in the metal ring.
3. Clamp sample securely by means of the clamp lever. Make sure that there is no distortion of the fabric to be tested.
4. Open the main water valve fully and adjust the valve on the machine until the water fills the glass overflow chamber and flows steadily out of the overflow pipe in the center. This maintains a constant level. The water chamber rises at rate of twelve inches a minute.
5. Turn on the motor and operate the clutch.
6. Observe the surface of the sample through the inclined mirror underneath.
7. As soon as three drops on three separate points have been observed, the clutch is immediately thrown into neutral. Disregard any drops which might occur at the circle of contact.
8. Read the scale and then record the height in centimeters.
9. Repeat the test twice and take the average of the three readings for the conclusion.
10. If the sample reaches the 50 cm head, maintain this height until three drops appear or until one hour has elapsed.

TESTING

1. Define permeability; shower-resistant, water-repellent, waterproof.
2. Why would a water-repellent raincoat be more comfortable to wear than one which has been made waterproof?
3. At what rate does the water chamber on the machine rise when the machine is in operation?
4. Name five materials or garments that might be made water-repellent.

TOPIC: AIR PERMEABILITY OF FABRICS

The three main factors which affect the passage of air through fabrics are the weave construction, the compactness in the weaving texture of the goods, and the thickness of the material. Through porosity air permeability affects the warmth provided by a fabric; the less the permeability of a cloth, the more warmth it will provide. The finish on a fabric will affect permeability because it may tend to close up the openings or interstices of the material.

A permeability testing machine comes equipped with orifices of various sizes and a chart which shows the possible results from the various orifices to record the permeability of cubic feet per minute per square foot of fabric. The chart records the orifice openings horizontally, and the permeability range runs vertically.

Procedure

1. Adjust the horizontal scale on the machine to make it level.
2. Turn the knob above the horizontal scale until the liquid reaches the zero reading of the scale.
3. Raise the clamp handle.
4. Remove the ring.
5. Place the smooth fabric over the opening.
6. Put the ring in place over the fabric.
7. Lower the clamp handle and lock it in place.
8. Turn on the switch.
9. Move the slider or rider on the coarse-rheostat until the horizontal scale reads close to 0.5.
10. Move the slider on the fine-rheostat until the horizontal scale reads 0.5 and then record the reading on the vertical scale.
11. For the test an orifice should be used which gives a reading between 3 and 13 on the vertical scale.
12. Find the cubic feet of air, per minute, per square foot of fabric; to do this use a chart for the orifice used and for the vertical scale reading. Charts come with the machine for this purpose.

Based on the foregoing procedure, the following form may be used to make recordings of five tests, after which the average may be found in terms of cubic feet per minute per square foot of fabric. This chart is set up for three sets of tests, five tests on each material:

SAMPLE NUMBER	VERTICAL SCALE READINGS		
	1	2	3
1.	———	———	———
2.	———	———	———
3.	———	———	———
4.	———	———	———
5.	———	———	———
TOTAL:	———	———	———
AVERAGE; the cubic feet, per minute, per square foot of fabric.	———	———	———

TESTING

1. Name three factors which affect the passage of air through a fabric.
2. Explain each of these factors.
3. Discuss the reading and interpretation of the chart that comes with the machine.
4. What effect does permeability of air have on the warmth provided by a fabric?

EXAMINATION ON UNIT 1 THROUGH UNIT 17

COMPLETION QUESTIONS   50 points

1. The number of warp ends and filling picks per inch in a woven fabric is known as _____.
2. A fabric with a texture of 64 by 64 is known as a _____ cloth.
3. Another name for count of cloth is _____.
4. The warp usually has _____ threads per inch than filling.
5. The three essentials in spinning yarn are: 1. _____. 2. _____. 3. _____.
6. S-twist yarn has diagonals running upward to the _____.
7. The weight of the gram weight used in determination of twist is _____ grams.
8. The amount of water in air compared with what it can hold at the given temperature is known as _____.
9. Standard conditions in mills and laboratories call for relative humidity of _____% and temperature of _____° Fahrenheit.
10. _____ is the amount of water in textile fabrics or yarns based on the dry weight.
11. Worsted has a standard regain of _____%.
12. Acetate has a regain of _____%.
13. Standard regain in cotton may vary between _____% and _____%.
14. The usual temperature for drying in conditioning ovens is _____° Fahrenheit.
15. There are _____ grains in one ounce.
16. There are _____ grains in one pound.
17. A woolen suiting fabric would be sold in terms of _____ per yard.
18. Lightweight cotton fabrics are sold in terms of _____ per pound.
19. In spun yarn, the higher the number of the yarn, the _____ will be the yarn with regard to diameter.
20. In filament yarn, the higher the number of the yarn, the _____ will be the yarn with regard to diameter.
21. The numbers on the flanges of a spool of thread indicate the _____ of thread.
22. The maximum load per unit of the original cross-section area obtained prior to rupture on a breaking machine is called _____.
23. If a 2-ply yarn is found to be a 20s in size, the yarn would be specified as a ___/___ yarn.
24. Samples to be tested for the strip or the grab method in breaking strength should not be taken from fabric that is near the _____.
25. _____ tests should be made on yarn-breaking or fabric-breaking tests in order to give a fair sampling of results.

TRUE-FALSE QUESTIONS   50 points

1. _____ Cotton has a higher percentage of standard regain than wool.
2. _____ Tussah silk has a higher regain than cotton.
3. _____ Z-twist is counterclockwise in direction.
4. _____ There are 840 yards in one pound of a 1s cotton yarn.
5. _____ The standard for cut or Philadelphia woolen yarn is 300 yards to the pound.
6. _____ A ¾-width fabric would be 54 inches wide.

7. _____ An 8/10-denier silk yarn is finer in diameter when compared with 22/24-denier silk yarn.
8. _____ There would be more yards in one pound of a 150-denier than there would be in a 100-denier yarn.
9. _____ The single equivalent of a 2/40s cotton yarn would be 1/80s.
10. _____ The weight of 492.2 yards is .05 grams for a 1-denier yarn.
11. _____ The higher the denier number of a yarn, the heavier will be the yarn.
12. _____ If 9,000 meters of filament yarn weigh 150 grams, the size of the yarn is a 150-denier yarn.
13. _____ In testing for abrasion on a fabric it is necessary only to test the warp yarn.
14. _____ Surface wear on a fabric is tested for pilling.
15. _____ "Rainproof" and "waterproof" are considered to be synonymous.
16. _____ Air permeability is figured in the cubic feet of air per minute per square foot of fabric.
17. _____ Orifices are essential in testing air permeability of a cloth.
18. _____ There are 22,400 yards in one pound of a 40s cotton yarn.
19. _____ The standard for cut wool and linen for a 1s yarn is the same.
20. _____ The fabric-breaking machine is worked on the principle of gravity.
21. _____ There are two gauges on the machine used to test knitted fabrics.
22. _____ The yarn-breaking machine is equipped with two sets of jaws.
23. _____ A torsion balance may be used to find the weight of a fabric.
24. _____ A thermostat regulates the speed of air flow in the air-porosity machine.
25. _____ In testing on the Taber abraser, the sample should always be placed flat.

Part 2—Unit 19

TOPIC: Shrinkage of Woolen Fabrics During Sponging

A test of this type is important because it will reveal how a fabric or garment will be affected by sponging, and whether or not the dimensions or size are affected. The determination is made by marking off a measurement of sufficient size in both directions. The article is then washed and allowed to dry; then it is pressed, and finally remeasured to determine the shrinkage, which is calculated as a percentage or in terms of inches per yard.

Procedure

1. In the setting-up of fabric for this test, a measurement of at least 20 inches square is made, and three 18-inch lengths are marked in the warp direction and three similar lengths in the filling direction. Indelible ink or sewing thread is used to mark off the distances, which should be at least 6 inches apart.
2. The sample is then immersed in water at 80° F. ($\pm 5°$), and then wrapped in a clean towel.
3. Following this, the sample is dried in a current of air on a flat perforated surface and, after dampening and standing for five minutes, is pressed dry. The original lengths of 18 inches are then measured and the shrinkage calculated.

The following form may be used to determine the shrinkage in the article:

TEST NUMBER	FINAL MEASUREMENTS	
	WARP	FILLING
1.	_____	_____
2.	_____	_____
3.	_____	_____
TOTAL:	_____	_____
AVERAGE:	_____	_____

1. Per cent shrinkage for the warp equals: $\dfrac{(18 - \text{warp average}) \times 100}{18}$

2. Per cent shrinkage for the filling equals: $\dfrac{(18 - \text{filling average}) \times 100}{18}$

3. Shrinkage in inches per yard:
4. In the warp equals $2 \times (18 - \text{warp average})$.
5. In the filling equals $2 \times (18 - \text{filling average})$.

TESTING

1. Define the term "shrinkage."
2. How may the shrinkage of fabrics be calculated?
3. Under ordinary conditions which would shrink more, woolen or worsted fabric? Explain your reasons.
4. Why should separate determinations be made for the warp and the filling directions in cloths used in this test?
5. Why should three warp measurements and three filling measurements be made when setting up the test?

TOPIC: Shrinkage of Cotton Fabrics During Laundering

Shrinkage is caused by a relaxing of the yarns in the fabric from the strained positions imposed on them during the weaving of the cloth in the loom. The shrinkage is figured in percentage or in inches per yard. Shrinkage of cotton is taken care of by the COMPRESSIVE METHOD OF SHRINKING, as shown in the Sanforized method.

Sanforized

A registered trademark applied to fabrics that have been shrunk by the compressive shrinkage method. The trademark is an indication that the residual shrinkage of the fabric is less than 1 per cent and that tests made to insure that the shrinkage conforms to the 1 per cent standard have been checked by the trademark owner.

A shrinkage of 1 per cent would never be noticed during the life of a garment that has been given the compressive shrinkage treatment. Thus, a Sanforized-labeled dress thirty inches long would shrink only three-tenths of one inch or less. The trademark appears on piece goods and garments made from cotton, linen, or mixed fabrics.

The trademark owners—Cluett, Peabody and Company, Inc.—permit the use of the "Sanforized" label on compressive preshrunk fabrics wherever the following conditions have been met:

1. The residual shrinkage in the fabric, that is, the amount of shrinkage left after shrinking, does not exceed 1 per cent by the United States test method CCC-T-191a.
2. Tests to determine residual shrinkage have been checked and approved by the trademark owner.

[342]

The amount of shrinkage in cotton fabrics is determined by the laboratory wash formula, CCC-T-191a, which predetermines the shrinkage of washable cotton and linen fabrics in accordance with federal specifications, which follow:

1. SAMPLES: 20 inches by full width of the cloth.

   Mark off three 18-inch measurements, in both the warp and the filling directions.

2. EQUIPMENT AND MATERIALS:

   Small reverse wheel, cylindrical (twenty-inch wheel).
   Use a standard load—three pounds dry samples.
   Water to be fifty times the weight of the goods.
   Soap—good grade laundry soap to running suds. (Add additional pieces of cloth to the samples if necessary to make a standard load.)
   Cloth should be well covered by water.

Procedure

1. Place samples in the wheel and start wheel.
2. Turn on water and steam.
3. Run water in to proper level, add soap.
4. Turn off steam when water boils—approximately 212° F.
5. Run wheel forty minutes from the time started.
6. Draw off water. Do not stop the wheel.
7. Fill wheel to proper level with water; bring the temperature to 140° F.
8. Run for five minutes.
9. Draw off water.
10. Fill to proper level—bring temperature to 140° F. Run ten minutes.
11. Remove samples from wheel—squeeze, do not wring. Spread out and dry on screen or ventilated surface.
12. Dampen with spray dampener—allow samples to condition for five minutes.
13. Press on press machine or by hand iron—by raising and lowering iron—do not slide the iron.

INFORMATION REGARDING THE WASH WHEEL

1. Speed of the wheel (when not running in one direction) almost 35 r.p.m.
2. Reversals of direction of rotation every eight or nine minutes.
3. Keep the belts tight in order to prevent slippage.
4. Water, steam, and drainage connections should be so arranged that the wheel can run continuously during the test.

In the application of this testing, a cotton fabric should be washed in the given procedure, and then the calculation of the percentage of shrinkage as well as the shrinkage per yard determined. The form below is based on original 18-inch lengths for final measurement:

TEST NUMBER	WARP	FILLING
1.	————	————
2.	————	————
3.	————	————
TOTAL	————	————
AVERAGE	————	————
Percentage of shrinkage in the warp	————	————
Percentage of shrinkage in the filling	————	————
Shrinkage per yard (inches)	————	————

TESTING

1. List five fabrics that can be compressively shrunk.
2. What company owns the "Sanforized" trademark and controls the use of the compressive shrinkage process?
3. What are two ways to express shrinkage?
4. If a material shrinks from 18 inches to 17.5 inches, find the percentage of shrinkage.
5. What is the guaranteed maximum shrinkage for a Sanforized fabric?

NOTE: Obtain a label from a Sanforized fabric, read it carefully, and note the great value of Sanforized fabrics for the textile and apparel trades.

Courtesy of Sanforized Division of Cluett, Peabody Co., 530 Fifth Ave., New York City.

Part 2—Unit 21

TOPIC: FASTNESS OF DYES TO LIGHT

The simplest method of testing a fabric for fastness to light is to place a sufficiently wide strip of the material, a foot or more in length, on a window sill, where it will come in contact with sunlight. This method can be used also for "all-weather testing." One end of the sample should be held in place by the closed window sash. Markings of from 1 to 4 inches are made crosswise on the cloth throughout the width, so that each successive section may be examined for results. Examining is done periodically according to a schedule; and the fadeability is noted by comparison with the other parts, beginning with the first length set under the closed window, in testing for the effect of sunlight. The degree or amount of fading and the length of time can be compared as long as the test lasts. Testing for fastness to light is always relative to some set standard for a particular color on a certain type of fabric. This supposed "old-fashioned method" is still used today, as it does give a true test. However, since this test does require a great deal of time, a machine called the Fade-Ometer is used in laboratories, insofar as it is usually necessary to obtain results as soon as possible. The machine tests the fading characteristics of dyed fabrics under standard conditions of light, humidity, and time; and weather does not interfere with the actual testing.

Some of the advantages of the Fade-Ometer over the use of the windowsill method include control of the time of the day, the time of the year, and weather conditions as well as measurements, for comparison with the standard requirements. The true sunlight method is better when dyes sensitive to sunlight have been used, and when a study of the behavior of fading is desired.

The following outline describes the setting-up of the Fade-Ometer before actual testing:

1. Light is produced in the Fade-Ometer by means of carbons and an arc. These carbon lengths or rods will burn out in time and must be replaced. The carbons may be cored or solid. The upper carbon in the machine is twelve inches long, the two lower carbons used are four inches in length.

   A combination of solid and cored carbons must be used to obtain the proper lighting. Either the upper or the lower carbons may be cored; the cored carbon must be opposite the solid carbon. Long carbons can be cut to a four-inch length after the one end has served its purpose as a long carbon, while the other end, which has not seen action, can be cut to the four-inch length for use as an opposite carbon.

[344]

2. A pyrex globe is used around the arc. This globe should be set in place, after checking, before the actual testing commences.
3. At least forty samples may be exposed at one time; each disc takes care of two samples. Some of the newer machines can hold several more specimens. Each sample is set in its holder, two to a holder. This is hung from a circular frame near the outer shell of the device. The frame in some cases is stationary while some machines have a revolving holder frame. The frame is set about ten inches from the arc of the device.
4. Under the arc there is a cone-shaped pan, and under this cone there is a fan. The pan aids both the arc and the fan in diffusion of light and air. The fan circulates air all the time the testing is taking place. The very high heat of the light and arc must be controlled at all times, hence the proper functioning of the pan and the fan is essential.
5. There is a circular water trough at the base of this circular machine. The trough is kept filled to the waterline at all times. Thus the atmosphere inside the machine is always moist and regulated.
6. A series of wicks is placed in the water trough. These wicks are set around wire frames and are almost totally immersed in the water. The open ends of the wicks, which help in the diffusion of moisture, are set facing the fan. In this way they aid the flow of moist air circulated by the fan evenly throughout the whole enclosure, when the machine is running.
7. The Fade-Ometer is equipped with a clock that can be set for any number of hours for testing. The machine can be set by the clock and can be made to run all night, if necessary.
8. The machine, as to action, is governed by means of a switch.

Procedure

CHANGING THE CARBONS

1. When the carbons have become spent, it is necessary to change them. Make sure that the power switch is turned off before changing.
2. Remove the cone-shaped copper fan and several of the wick frames, the latter so that there will be adequate space in which to work.
3. Hold the globe with one hand, and with the other hand slip off the wire globe-holder.
4. Remove the pyrex globe with care.
5. Loosen the screw which holds the upper carbon in place.
6. In the removal of the old upper carbon take notice of the manner in which it is inserted and hold in place.
7. Insert the new upper carbon and tighten it into place.
8. Either the upper or the lower carbon must be cored; check this, and if the upper is cored, then the bottom carbon must be solid.
9. Clamp the two four-inch carbons in place.
10. Carefully place the globe in position and hold it up with the wire clamp.
11. Make sure that the globe is firmly in place by rotating it slowly.

SETTING THE FADE-OMETER CLOCK

1. Loosen the dial knob by turning it to the right.
2. Turn the shut-off pointer to the time at which the Fade-Ometer must go off.
3. Tighten the knob by turning it to the left.
4. Turn the pointer to the actual time.
5. Push the "on" lever downward.

MAKING THE EXPOSURE

1. Remove the back of the sample-holder.
2. The samples should be cut to fit well in the holder.

3. Lock the back of the holder in place with the exposed portion of the sample un covered on both sides.
4. Hang the sample on the circular frame around the globe.
5. Turn on the power switch.
6. Expose the samples for the required number of hours.

TABLE TO FOLLOW WHEN TESTING

1. Five hours of Fade-Ometer action is equivalent to six hours of sunlight testing. The lower carbons in the machine do not exceed a four-inch length because beyond that length the effect of light intensity would be impaired.

L1 *	L2	L3	L4	L5	L6	L7	L8
			Hours of Sunlight				
1½	3	6	12	24	48	96	192
3	6	12	24	48	96	192	384
			Hours of Fade-Ometer				
—	—	5	10	20	40	80	160
—	—	10	20	40	80	160	320

* L is the symbol for Light.

TESTING

1. Describe the purpose, function, or value of each of the following:
   a) Pyrex globe.
   b) The cone-shaped copper pan.
   c) Function of the light produced in the machine.
   d) The value of the wicks in the circular trough which is filled with water.
   e) The value of the fan.
   f) The carbons, both solid and cored.
   g) The time clock.
2. Which causes fabrics to fade quicker, sunlight or Fade-Ometer light?
3. What is the ratio of Fade-Ometer light versus sunlight?
4. What would a lightfastness of L6 indicate as to the number of hours of exposure?
5. Why must the lower carbon not exceed a length of four inches?

Part 2—Unit 22

TOPIC: FASTNESS OF DYED COTTON TO WASHING

Dye-fastness tests are conducted in the Launder-Ometer. All fibers cannot be washed by the same procedure, because the structure varies. For example, cotton can be washed easily while woolen fabrics, generally speaking, are not washed. Wool is the weaker of these two fibers, and it would not be able to withstand friction in washing if it were washed as thoroughly as cotton. It also requires lower-temperature water because there is possibility of its felting or matting; the length of washing time is also a factor. Certain cotton materials can withstand more rigorous treatment than others because of their structure and end use. Fabrics used for work clothing would receive different treatment from a woman's summer dress, a man's shirting, or cotton fabric for children's wear.

It is better to use a test fabric made of different types of fibers rather than a cloth of white cotton alone. Not all the fibers in a test would be stained; if only cotton were used, it would not be possible to tell the reactions of other fibers, many of which are now blended with cotton. Launder-Ometer testing is important because it gives advance information on the material's reaction to grime, soil, color-retention, and whether it will be satisfactory in its terminal use. Some of the factors that have to be controlled in a washing test are the length of time, the strength of the soap solution, and temperatures.

An example of a dyed material which is likely to be bleached in washing might be a white towel with a blue edge or border; or a white madras shirting with colored stripes in it. The colors used in these two articles should be fast to washing and there should be no bleeding of the colors from the operation.

The test is given in accordance with the standards for the various fibers as set forth by the American Association of Textile Chemists and Colorists, Research Triangle, Durham, North Carolina. The table of standards is given below.

COTTON:

TEST NUMBER	TEMPERATURE DEGREES F.:	SOAP CONCEN- TRATION PERCENTAGE	SODA ASH PERCENTAGE	AVAILABLE CHLORINE PERCENTAGE	TIME IN MINUTES
1	105	0.5	none	none	30
2	120	0.5	none	none	30
3	160	0.5	0.2	none	45
4	182	0.5	0.2	0.01	45

RAYON:

1	105	0.5	none	none	30
2	120	0.5	none	none	30
3	160	0.5	none	none	30

WOOL: Samples are washed in the Launder-Ometer with 100 cubic centimeters of ½ per cent soap solution for ½ hour at a temperature of 100° F.
The samples are then removed, rinsed, air-dried, and then pressed with a damp cloth.

Procedure

1. Fill the Launder-Ometer to the water line. Turn on the switch and set the temperature at 120° F.
2. With the machine come twenty jars; hence twenty tests could be run at the same time, if need be. Whether running one test or full capacity, the dyed samples are cut 2 by 4 inches. The same dimensions may be used for a piece of unsized material.
3. Each jar being used in the test contains 100 cc of 0.5 per cent soap solution which has been previously heated to the test temperature of 120° F. The prepared sample, and ten small steel balls that come with the machine, are placed in the jar. The jar is then sealed, ready for the rotating action.
4. Clamp the jar or jars in the Launder-Ometer and then turn on the motor. Allow the machine to run for 30 minutes.
5. Empty the jars and then rinse the samples carefully and well. After wringing out, press each sample dry, placing the white cloth of the prepared sample over the dyed piece of fabric.
6. Compare the tested sample with the original sample. Observe whether the dye has run or bled, and also whether the white material has become stained, either lightly or heavily.

TESTING

1. Why should test fabric be used in this type of test?
2. What is the purpose of this test?
3. Why are steel balls placed in the jar with the solution and the sample?
4. List three factors that have to be considered and controlled in this washing test, in addition to the temperature.

TOPIC: Fastness of Dyed Material to Perspiration

Everyone more or less has the problem of perspiration stains on garments. Perspiration testing is the same for all fibers because it does not vary to any marked degree. Perspiration is acidic in nature, and then in due course of time becomes alkaline. The two common substances in perspiration are salt and water. In this test three objectives are kept in mind:

1. Change of color in the fabric.
2. The movement or migration of color which produces a grain-in-wood effect.
3. Possible staining of white material which may come in contact with perspiration.

Two solutions are used in the testing, one of acid, the other of alkali:

Acid Solution

>   10 grams salt.
>   1 gram 85% lactic acid, U.S.P.
>   1 gram di-sodium orthophosphate, anhydrous.
>   Make up to one liter with water.

Alkaline Solution

>   10 grams salt.
>   4 grams ammonium carbonate, U.S.P.
>   1 gram di-sodium orthophosphate, anhydrous.
>   Make up to one liter with water.

Some textile tests can be run off in a few minutes. This is not the case with perspiration testing, because proper time must be given to allow for natural drying, and it is the slow drying of the sample which really brings out the damage from perspiration on a fabric. Any fabric that comes in contact with the body when worn should be given this test, particularly those materials which come in contact with the underarms.

Procedure

1. The white test fabric to be used should be composed of strips of the major textile fibers, all woven into one piece of goods. Fabrics for this type of testing, and for some other types, can be obtained from Testfabrics, Inc., New York 13, N. Y.
2. Two strips of dyed fabric should be cut to a width of two inches. The same should be done with two strips of the white test fabric.
3. Wet a white and a dyed piece of cloth with the acid perspiration solution; then wind the two pieces into a roll with the dyed fabric inside.
4. The pieces should be long enough to make a roll which will fit reasonably tightly into a small glass bottle 120 by 22 mm.
5. A second roll is made with the other dyed and white samples. This roll is wetted with the alkaline solution, and then inserted into a second tube.
6. One third of each roll is allowed to protrude from the respective tubes.
7. The samples are then dried in an oven heated to 100° F. This approximately corresponds to body heat of 98.6° F.
8. The exposed part of the sample will dry more rapidly than the inserted portion of the roll.
9. The condition of the dyed material exposed to perspiration will show that the partially inserted roll duplicates the uneven drying of perspiration in clothes

[348]

actually worn by a person. There is also a chance of color migration, and this effect has to be closely checked. In loosely constructed fabrics there is likely to be no migration at all.

10. Determinations and ratings are then made at the conclusion of the testing, such as fast, fairly fast, poor, etc.

TESTING

1. Why is the perspiration-procedure test the same for all fibers?
2. What is meant by test fabric that is used as the white fabric in testing?
3. Name the two common substances one might expect to find in perspiration.
4. Why are samples not rinsed following a test?
5. What types of fabrics or garments should be given perspiration tests?
6. Why is drying done in an oven heated to 100° F.?
7. Of what value is the time element in the testing?
8. Define color or dye migration. What is its effect on fabrics?
9. Name five garments or fabrics that should be tested for perspiration.
10. Define grain-in-the-wood effect with regard to perspiration stains.

Part 2—Unit 24

TOPIC: FASTNESS OF DYES TO CROCKING

If a piece of bleached fabric is held over the finger and then rubbed ten times over a material known to be poor in crocking fastness, there will be a rubbing off of the color, and a smudge of color stain will appear on the white goods. This rubbing off of the dye is called crocking. This was the old method of testing for crocking, and it is still resorted to at times for comparative purposes. The pressure of the finger in this test is about two pounds. Obviously, there is a difference between hand-crocking and machine-crocking. Hand-crocking does have certain drawbacks, such as inconsistent pressure, speed, and possible slippage. A crock-meter has been devised to give some standardization to crocking tests.

Procedure

1. Samples used are cut 2 by 5 inches. They are cut on the bias so that both warp and filling yarns will be rubbed well and because the warp yarns might differ in color or colors from the filling yarns. By the color of the smudge it is possible to tell which colors are not fast to crocking and in which system of yarn they are used.
2. The white fabric used in the test should be around 2 by 2 inches. It should be of fine high texture so that the smooth, flat surface will afford easy manipulation.
3. Place the sample to be tested over the abrasive cloth located on the base of the crock-meter.
4. Place the white cotton fabric over the crock-meter finger, and fasten it by means of the spiral clip.
5. Turn the handle ten times to move the finger back and forth over the dyed fabric. The finger moves ten inches over the fabric.
6. Remove the white cloth from the finger and examine it closely for results. Observe whether or not the staining is apparent, as well as the depth or degree of the stain.
7. Two tests should be made on each material tested; one should be marked "dry-crocking," while the other is labeled "wet-crocking." The dry test should be done with dry white cloth; the wet test with a wet, but wrung out, white piece of material. Comparisons then can be made between the dry test and the wet test.
8. As to which test, dry or wet, causes more crocking, there are certain factors to be kept in mind—the type of dye used on the goods and its fastness, the fabric and the yarns used in it, as well as the method of dyeing.

TESTING

1. What is meant by a color being fast to crocking?
2. What is the finger pressure of the crock-meter against a dyed sample?
3. What is the distance the finger moves over the cloth in the machine?
4. Name some objections to hand-crocking.
5. How does dry-crocking differ from wet-crocking?

Part 2—Unit 25

TOPIC: FASTNESS OF DYES TO HOT PRESSING AND IRONING; CARE SYMBOLS

The ironing and pressing of garments is done to bring them back as nearly as possible to their original condition when new. Electric irons have graduated temperatures so that the proper heat will be used for a material dependent upon the fiber content of the goods. Scorching is the greatest hazard in ironing and pressing: it is defined as a decomposition of a fabric caused by overheating. Some scorches may be treated but most of them spoil a fabric so that repair is impossible.

There are several things to pay attention to when ironing and pressing:

1. Many colors will have a tendency to change color or shade while the fabric is hot; they may or may not return to the original cast on cooling.
2. Colored silks have a special tendency to change color under heat pressure. White silks will take on a yellowish cast under extreme heat—usually not removable.
3. Dry heat will change the shades of many colors but the original colors will return when the materials have cooled.
4. Do not press garments too often; it should be kept in mind that after every laundering and ironing the article does depreciate, and in time will outlive its usefulness. The results of overpressing are creases that split, over-lustering that may develop, and abrasion of the article from repeated rubbing may occur.
5. A "rosebud-sprigged dimity," for example, might be a poor purchase for a child's dress. A bunched, corded, or ribbed effect in a fabric usually requires much heat in ironing and great care, lest the effect be spoiled.
6. Keep in mind that if the heat is too high, cottons may scorch and then disintegrate; many manmade fabrics will melt and stick to the iron; silk, wool, and other animal fibers used in fabrics will scorch and then bead and readily deteriorate.
7. Irons today are well marked for the housewife. One marking used is "high-medium-low"; on the same iron the following words may be seen denoting correct ironing temperature—linen (the highest), cotton, wool, synthetics. Some irons use the word "rayon," which is the lowest rating for heat. Others have the term, "manmade," which includes rayon, acetate, nylon, and so on.
8. Dyes in fabrics where frequent launderings are necessary must be fast to washing and ironing. Articles in this group include aprons, denims, house dresses, pajamas, rompers, and shirtings and uniform fabrics.

Procedure

1. Moisten a sample of material. Place it on an ironing board and press it with a hot iron until completely dry.
2. Compare this sample at once with a material that has not been ironed. Note whether or not there is any change in the color on cooling.
3. Moisten a piece of white muslin and place it over the sample. Press until the muslin is dry. Note whether the color has suffered any alteration, and if there is any smudging of the color onto the muslin.
4. If there is no change, or if the original cast, color, or shade returns when the material has cooled, this particular color is said to be fast to ironing or hot pressing.

Laboratory wringer and padder; for extracting controlled amounts of liquids to produce test specimens as required by many textile testing programs.

Weather-Ometer; produces the deteriorating effects of years of outdoor exposure to rain, sunlight, and thermal shock in a short laboratory test (registered trademark).

Accelerator; developed by the A.A.T.C.C. for evaluating wet and dry abrasion-resistance of fabrics.

Courtesy: Atlas Electric Devices Company, Inc., Chicago

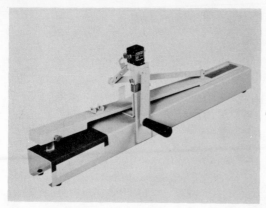

Crockmeter; used for the A.A.T.C.C. determination of color fastness to crocking.

Perspiration tester; used to test color-fastness to perspiration and water—A.A.T.C.C. test methods 15–1960 and 63–1957.

Scorch tester; standard A.A.T.C.C. tester for damage caused by retained chlorine in fabrics.

Courtesy: Atlas Electric Devices Company, Inc., Chicago

TESTING

1. How do you account for the fact that linen and cotton will stand a higher heat temperature than wool and silk when being ironed?
2. Why is the temperature when ironing the manmade fibers below that of wool?
3. Why is it poor policy to press fabrics too often?
4. What might happen to the color of a material from ironing that will not occur in washing?

TOPIC: DETERMINATION OF THE PERCENTAGE OF ACETATE IN A UNION FABRIC OF ACETATE AND RAYON

Different kinds of textile fibers may be combined in several ways in a union-type material. For example, a fabric may have an acetate warp and a rayon filling; the yarn may be a blend of acetate and rayon staple stocks, or there might be a ply yarn used of rayon and acetate filament; or there may be acetate yarn in both warp and filling along with other yarns, to obtain some desired fabric effect.

Acetate might be used in a fabric to improve the drape, the hand, the luster, or some other quality that would be of value in the cloth. To find the percentage of each type or kind of fiber present, the weight of each fiber must be determined in a sample of known weight. Acetone is used in such a test because it dissolves the acetate and leaves the rayon unscathed. In this test one should bear in mind that the acetone should be warmed or heated over water and not over a burner, as it is inflammable.

Procedure

1. A sample having a weight of about 5 grams, and previously freed of all fibrous matter, should be used.
2. The sample should be dried at 220° F., until the weight is constant.
3. Warm a beaker which contains 250 cc of acetone by floating it in a larger beaker of hot water. A 600-cc beaker and one of 800 cc are ideal for this test.
4. Work the sample for thirty minutes in the covered beaker of acetone.
5. Filter the solution without losing any of the undissolved fibers.
6. Wash the residue twice with 10-cc portions of acetone and then with water. Be sure to remove all traces of the acetate.
7. The residue should be dried in an oven at 220° F., until bone-dry.
8. Determination of the percentage of acetate in this union fabric follows:
   a) Bone-dry weight of clean original sample: _____ grams.
   b) Bone-dry weight after acetone treatment: _____ grams.
   c) Weight of acetate: _____ grams.
   d) Percentage of acetate equals $\dfrac{\text{weight of acetate} \times 100\%}{\text{weight original dry sample}}$.

TESTING

1. Why is acetone used in this test?
2. Why are two rinses with 10-cc acetone given the sample?
3. Why can acetone be warmed over water but not over a burner?
4. Define the term "bone-dry."

TOPIC: DETERMINATION OF THE AMOUNT OF OIL AND GREASE IN TEXTILES

Textiles in the production stages from raw material, yarn, through construction of the fabric, coloring, and finishing, go into and out of many machines and are handled by many workers. Obviously, considerable amounts of foreign matter will be picked up along the way. The handling of the ultimate product en route to finished fabric should be done with cleanliness in mind; however, since in some of the treatments avoidance of spots and stains as well as various foreign substances is not possible, cleanliness is often overlooked. One of the most irksome elements to contend with is oil or grease which may be picked up in many ways from practically any of the machines in which the yarn or fabric receives action and treatment. To remove oil or grease, the Soxhlet Extractor is used; and its function also includes testing for methods of removing these soiled areas.

It is possible to reclaim the used solvent—recovering it, purifying it, and then using it again. The samples to be treated should be conditioned all over before testing. Accurate weighing is very important in this type of test. For example, in a test to determine the percentage of oil absorbed in the fabric, the results are based on the weight of the oil instead of the final weight of the clean material; and it should be noted that a solvent which is taken from a specimen contains the grease or oil that was in the goods; if the solvent is evaporated, the amount of grease will still remain. This weighing is very important, since it is possible from the weight of the grease to calculate the amount as a percentage content in the cloth.

Procedure

1. About 5 grams of material are dried to a constant weight.
2. The sample is placed in "F."
3. The solvent, such as carbon tetrachloride, is heated to the boiling point in "G." This solvent, after the upper section of the extractor has been removed carefully, is poured into "F" until it flows through the siphon; half as much of the solvent is again added.
4. The sample is then inserted carefully in the tube. Care should be taken that none of the material extends above the bend in the siphon tube. If the sample does extend beyond the top of the tube bend, the liquid will come out and the specimen would not be properly wetted with the solvent.
5. The upper section marked "B" is removed so that the test setup may be completed. It is then set back into place when the test is about to begin.
6. When testing, cold water, which enters at "E" and leaves at "A," flows slowly into "B" in its course.
7. The burner under the water bath is lighted and adjusted so that the solvent will evaporate at a satisfactory rate. The liquefied solvent drops down into "F" on the sample and dissolves the oil or grease.
8. When the level of the solvent reaches the bend of the siphon tube, "D," the solvent and the dissolved grease are siphoned back into "G."
9. As the boiling continues, the solvent is evaporated but the grease remains behind.
10. The extraction is continued for two hours, and in that time the solvent siphons over about six times.
11. On removal the sample is first dried in air and then in the drying oven until the weight becomes constant.

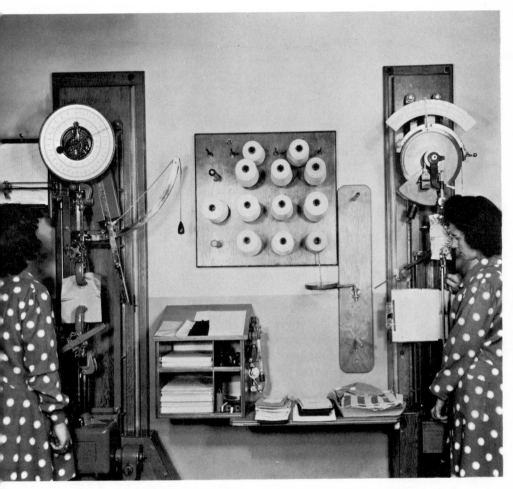

A corner of a textile testing laboratory showing two fabric-breaking machines.

12. The following form may be used for recording the test to determine the percentage of oil in a given piece of fabric:
   a) Dry weight of original sample _____ grams.
   b) Dry weight of extracted sample _____ grams.
   c) Weight of the oil _____ grams.
   d) Per cent of oil present equals $\dfrac{\text{weight of oil} \times 100}{\text{original weight}}$.

TESTING

1. Why should all of the sample to be tested be placed below the top bend of the siphon?
2. How can the solvent be purified and used over again?
3. Give some reasons for utmost accuracy in this type of testing.

TOPIC: MILDEW AND ITS PREVENTION

Generally speaking, mildew is a parasitic fungus or mold found on foodstuffs, textile fabrics, and garments—or, loosely, it is the mold found on walls, foodstuffs, and garments that is caused by dampness or staleness. Certain measures may be taken to prevent mildew, such as care to prevent dampness by proper circulation of air, properly lined closets that will not retain dampness or moisture, either heavy or light. Bacteria will cause molds to form on cotton, linen, rayon, wool, etc., under certain conditions. Proper storage of articles will prevent mildew formation.

Inhibitors may be used to prevent this scourge: these are agents which slow down, check, diminish, or prevent a physical or chemical change in fabrics. Starches used in the finishing of certain fabrics may cause mildew, but there are inhibitors on the market that will curb or prevent its forming.

There are three main organisms which cause the formation of rotted or stained areas in a garment:

   a) Aspergillus Niger, which produces a stain or rotted area.
   b) Metarrhizium Glutinosium, which produces rot and stain.
   c) Chaetomium Globossum, which produces rot and stain.

INHIBITION OR PREVENTION OF MILDEW ON FABRICS AND GARMENTS

There are three methods used to prevent or inhibit mold formation:

1. **Mercurials**

   a) These compounds will prevent the formation of mildew.
   b) They will inhibit the growth of ammonia-forming bacteria.
   c) They are corrosive in nature and may cause skin burns if not properly applied.

2. **Phenols**

   a) Pentachlorophenol is used extensively in the textile industry for mildew-proofing.
   b) Phenols are considered to be irritants at a strength of over 1 per cent following impregnation of the fabric.
   c) They are toxic when handled in the dry state, and great care must be used to prevent injury to the operator who prepares the solution.

[356]

d) Ultraviolet light may attack the fabric treated with pentachlorophenol because hydrochloric acid is released with the action, thereby causing tenderness to the material in question.

e) Orthophenylphenol is used when starch has been employed as a sizing agent; the addition of this compound to the stock solution will prevent souring of the solution during hot, humid weather.

3. **Quaternary Ammonium Salts**

   a) These are best for mildew-proofing since they are nontoxic, nonirritating, and noncorrosive.

   b) They are surface active agents.

   c) They belong in the cationic group, which possesses definite inhibitive properties on molds.

All of the foregoing are used to combat fungus growth in textile materials. Mercurials and phenols are toxic and can cause skin irritations unless used under proper control. In the laundry industry, mildew control is for the staining type of mildew fungus rather than for the rotting type.

TESTING

1. Define mildew; inhibitor.
2. Name two measures that could be resorted to in order to avoid mildew.
3. What are the three main organisms which cause mildew?
4. Name three inhibitors used to prevent mildew on fabrics or garments?
5. What finishing material often found on cottons is readily attacked by mildew?
6. What is the advantage of quaternary ammonium salts for mildew-proofing?
7. Name two types of mildew-proofing agents which may cause skin irritation.

Part 2—Unit 29

TOPIC: INTRODUCTION TO THE CARE OF CLOTHING—SPOT AND STAIN REMOVAL, THE SURE CARE SYMBOLS

GENERAL CONSIDERATIONS

A stain is a discoloration produced by the presence or action of some foreign matter on the material. For example, grease causes a stain by its presence. If the grease is dissolved out of the goods, the stain will disappear. However, acid causes a chemical action which may change the appearance of the material. The latter type of stain may be difficult to remove since the fiber itself is affected, or the color on the fiber is destroyed.

Stains should be treated as soon as possible. The longer they are allowed to remain on the goods, the more difficult it will be to remove them. If an acid stain is not cared for immediately, the chemical action will continue until the fiber is completely destroyed.

Ironing will set certain stains, such as those produced by inks or dyes. The action of soap in laundering will make an iron stain more pronounced.

There are three major types of materials used in the removal of stains: (1) absorbents, (2) solvents, (3) bleaches.

The action of absorbents is comparable with that which occurs in using a blotter to take up ink.

Solvents dissolve the staining substances and the solutions formed are removed from the goods by proper technique.

[357]

Bleaches are chemicals which change colored substances to white. Some of the commoner bleaching agents are sodium hypochlorite, hydrogen peroxide, sodium perborate and potassium permanganate. Care must be exercised in the use of bleaches on colored materials. The color, itself, may be affected.

Prior to beginning work on a stain, it is necessary to know what the stain is. The treatment depends upon the nature of the stain. The treatment given one stain may fix another. For example, an alkaline substance would be used to neutralize an acid, but the same treatment would make an iron stain more pronounced.

In the identification of stains such items are considered as appearance, odor, color, feel, etc.

For example, liquor, perfume, medicine, tar, etc., have characteristic odors. Tar, blood, iodine, lipstick, etc., have a distinct color. Gum, blood, nail polish, etc., may be identical by their feel. Mud and perspiration usually occur on certain parts of a garment.

After the nature of a stain is known, the fiber or fibers present must be determined. The different fibers cannot stand the same chemical action. The stain may be removed, but the fiber may be injured or damaged by the chemicals used. Although acetone is a good solvent for many substances, if it is used on acetate fiber, a hole will appear in the fabric because acetone dissolves this filament or fiber.

The kind of fiber or fibers present may be determined by igniting a few yarns taken from a seam in the garment. Both the warp and the filling yarns should be tested because many fabrics consist of more than one type or kind of fiber.

The fibers may be identified by a simple burning test. If necessary, a chemical or a microscopical test should be made, provided the essential materials are at hand.

After the treatment has been decided upon, from the nature of the stain and the fiber content, the effect of the stain remover should be tested on some unseen portion of the material. This will show whether or not the color of the material is altered.

The stain remover may cause more of a discoloration on the material than the staining substance itself.

SUMMARY

The longer a stain remains on a material, the more difficult it may be to remove it.

Stain removers are divided into three major groups:

1. Absorbents
2. Solvents
3. Bleaches

Each type of stain requires special treatment, so that the kind of stain present must be known before commencing work relative to the removal of the stain in question.

Certain stain-removing chemicals may injure the fiber. Thus it is often necessary that a test be made for the identification of the fiber or fibers present in the cloth or garment which contains the spot or stain.

ACTION OF CHEMICALS ON FIBERS

Acids

There are two classes of acids—the mineral and the organic. The first group includes such acids as sulfuric, hydrochloric, nitric, etc. The second group includes such acids as formic, acetic, tartaric, oxalic, etc.

Strong acids completely destroy all fibers and therefore should not be used full strength on textile materials. Under proper conditions the dilute mineral acids may be used. The organic acids are much milder in their action, and if possible should be used where an acid treatment is necessary. *Inorganic or mineral acids do not contain the element carbon.*

Animal fibers are more resistant to the action of acids than are the vegetable fibers, or viscose and acetate.

Dilute mineral acid may be dried on wool at a high temperature without any harmful effects. This is the action employed in the carbonizing process, whereby vegetable matter is reduced to carbon and removed from the wool.

Nitric acid is not used much on animal fibers because it stains them yellow.

Hydrochloric acid or sulfuric acid may be used on wool without harm if in dilute form and properly handled.

Since organic acids are milder than mineral acids, the former group is used a great deal on the animal fibers.

The vegetable fibers and rayon are readily attacked and destroyed by mineral acids. Even dilute solutions will cause damage, if they are allowed to dry on the material without neutralizing and rinsing. In the drying, the acid gradually becomes more concentrated because of the evaporation of water; finally, the acid becomes strong enough to disintegrate the fiber.

The organic acids, on the other hand, can be used on vegetable fibers even in fairly strong concentrations without any harmful action resulting. However, the non-volatile organic acids—oxalic acid for example—if allowed to dry on the vegetable fibers, at high temperatures, will cause tendering.

When acids are used, they should be rinsed off the material, then neutralized and rinsed three or four times. Acids are neutralized by the use of an alkaline or basic substance.

The reaction of animal fibers to the action of alkalies is just the opposite of what it is to acids. Wool and animal fibers, which are quite resistant, even to mineral acids, are completely decomposed by dilute solutions of alkalies; yet vegetable fibers will even withstand boiling in alkaline solutions.

Sodium hydroxide or lye is a strong base and should not be used even in dilute concentrations on the animal fibers. Other milder alkalies include ammonium hydroxide, sodium carbonate, trisodium phosphate, soap, etc. If vegetable fibers are boiled in alkaline solutions, the material must be kept below the surface of the liquid because the alkaline solution and the oxygen of the air cause a tendering of the fiber.

Bleaching Agents

These are chemical compounds which destroy color, leaving the material white. The important bleaching chemicals are sodium hypochlorite, hydrogen peroxide, sodium perborate, and potassium permanganate. All except the first one may be used on animal fibers. The other fibers may be treated with any of the given bleaches.

Sodium hypochlorite will turn animal fibers yellow, and if concentrated enough and used for a long enough time, will actually destroy these fibers.

In permanganate bleaching two distinct treatments are necessary. In the first step, immerse the fabric in the potassium permanganate solution being used. This will produce a brownish cast or color on the goods almost immediately. It is the use of this permanganate which causes the removal of the stain.

In the second step, and without rinsing the cloth, place the material in the solution of sodium bisulfite. The color will then come back to its original shade.

Permanganate bleaching is ideal for stain removal on white goods made of cotton, wool, blends, mixtures, etc.

There are two QUALITATIVE TESTS used for the presence of a chlorine bleach:

TEST ONE: This is the Potassium Iodide and Starch Test.

The sample to be tested is placed in 25 cc of water. Ten drops of a 20 per cent solution of potassium iodide, to which a few drops of starch have been added, are used.

If the resultant color is brown or black, a bleach is apparent.

TEST TWO: This is the Orthotolidene Test.

Five drops of orthotolidene reagent are placed in 25 cc of water.

If the resultant color is yellow, a bleach is apparent.

QUANTITATIVE TESTING for a bleach is usually done by the popular Sodium Hypochlorite Bleach, using the Sodium Thiosulfate Method. The materials needed are:
1. 50 cc burette with ring stand and clamps.
2. 250 cc Erlenmeyer Flask.
3. 25 cc graduate.
4. Pipette marked in cubic centimeters.
5. 25 cc glacial acetic acid.
6. 25 cc potassium iodide (20 per cent solution).

Procedure

1. Place 50 cc of tenth-normal (N/10) sodium thiosulfate in burette.
2. Draw off 5 cc to remove air bubbles and replace with 5 cc of the sodium thiosulfate solution.
3. Use the pipette and draw up exactly 1 cc of bleach solution to be tested and place this in the Erlenmeyer flask.
4. Fifty cc of water is added to the flask content.
5. Add 15 cc of potassium iodide (20 per cent solution), to the flask. At this point the solution will turn light brown.
6. Add 5 cc of glacial acetic acid to the flask and a dark-brown color will appear.
7. The solution is now ready for titration—the process of determining the strength or concentration of the solution by adding to it measured amounts of a standard solution until the desired chemical reaction has been effected.

    In this case a drop-by-drop procedure is used by taking the thiosulfate solution from the burette until the solution in the flask becomes light yellow in color.

    The number of drops needed will depend on the strength of the solution; a 1 per cent solution will need only a very few drops.

    Add, very carefully, one drop at a time until the solution in the flask becomes colorless. This ends the titration action.
8. Read the burette and use this formula in computation:

    Number of cc of thiosulfate used in the burette times .355 to obtain the percentage of available chlorine. Incidentally, the .355 used is the molecular weight of chlorine using a N/10 solution as previously noted.

Example: If 16 cc of thiosulfate were taken from the burette, find the percentage of available chlorine.

16 cc times .355 gives 5.68% available chlorine. (Answer)

Bleaches must be used with extreme care, since they may weaken fibers if used at too high a temperature or if they have too great a concentration. The chlorine action in bleaching should be arrested or retarded by the use of so-called antichlor compounds, an example of which is sodium bisulfite. The peroxide bleach is a safe one to use since it will decompose slower than the sodium hypochlorite bleach.

An alkali, such as sodium carbonate, is used with the peroxide bleach to liberate nascent oxygen. The alkali, however, must be controlled so that the pH of the solution does not go below 10.2 or exceed 10.6.

If the alkalinity is too high, the peroxide bleach will cause tendering of the goods; below 10.2 there is very little bleaching action.

TEST FOR CHEMICAL DAMAGE TO TEXTILE MATERIALS

Fehling's Solution Test is ideal in determining damage to textile fabrics and garments. It tests for damage done by oxycellulose but will also indicate the presence of hydrocellulose.

Hydrocellulose is caused by an acid reaction while oxycellulose is caused by an alkali reaction. Bleach usually will cause oxycellulose while mineral acids will bring about hydrocellulose action.

Fehling's Solution Test for Damage to Cloth; Oxycellulose Test

1. 5 cc of Fehling's Solution A are mixed with 5 cc of Fehling's Solution B.
2. This is placed in 10 cc of water.
3. The sample, 2 by 2 inches, is placed in the solution and boiled for five minutes.
4. Rinse under cold-water faucet.

   RESULTS:
   a) Brown color will show chemical damage indicated.
   b) Blue color will show that there is no chemical damage indicated.

TESTING FOR OXYCELLULOSE AND HYDROCELLULOSE

TEST ONE: To determine the difference between oxycellulose and hydrocellulose, immerse the fabric sample for ten minutes in a 1 per cent aqueous solution of ferrous sulfate.
Wash in warm water.
Immerse in a 1 per cent solution of potassium ferricyanide.
Wash in warm water.
If oxycellulose is present, a deep-blue stain will result because of the absorption of ferrous sulfate and conversion to Turnbull's Blue.
Under similar circumstances, hydrocellulose is stained only a faint bluish color and ordinary cotton will stain only slightly deeper than the hydrocellulose blue stain.

TEST TWO: Immerse the fabric for five minutes in a cold 1 per cent solution of lead acetate.
Rinse well.
Immerse the sample, for five minutes at room temperature, in a 1 per cent solution of sodium chromate.
Wash well.
Oxycellulose will show a deep yellow stain on the goods.
Hydrocellulose will show a cream color on the material.
Undamaged cotton will show a faint yellowish cast on cloth.

Optical bleaching is a term used to describe bleaching by the reflectance of light rather than by chemical action such as brought about by the use of peroxides and hypochlorites.

It is a known fact that substances absorb light at various wave lengths which are invisible to the naked eye. With the use, however, of certain types of dyes (colorless in nature), the light is reflected from the fabric in the form of visible blue light. This blue light will form a bluish haze over the material. There is an increased surface reflectance which neutralizes the yellowish cast that usually results from the laundering process.

In optical bleaching certain of these colorless dyes work. better in alkaline baths, while others will require acid baths. A "build-up" is an undesirable visible color which will appear if too much dye is used too frequently. Build-ups should be avoided altogether. Incidentally, all optical bleaching agents do not cause a build-up. The user should know well the type, properties, and characteristics of dyestuff to be used.

Organic Solvents

These are a very important group of chemicals used in spot and stain removal. Before using a solvent, its action on the fiber should be known or determined.

In attempting to remove dye or ink stains from textile materials, the following points should be kept in mind:

1. Dyes are fixed on animal fibers by high temperatures and an acid condition.
2. Acid will keep the dyestuff from impregnating vegetable fibers.
3. Acetate is dyed with a special class of dyestuffs.
4. In working on a dye stain on woolen goods, the treatment should be cold and on the alkaline side, with soap, for example.

Water is the solvent most used on textiles. Vegetable fibers become stronger when wet; animal fibers and rayons become weaker. The strength, however, returns on drying. If the rayons are treated in boiling water, their luster is affected. Acetate, if it is treated in hot alkaline solutions, becomes saponified, that is, it changes from cellulose acetate to cellulose. This change results in an alteration of the chemical properties, dyeing properties, and in a loss in weight of the fiber.

SUMMARY

Animal fibers can stand the action of dilute mineral acids but are destroyed by even dilute alkaline solutions.

Vegetable fibers will withstand alkaline treatment but not an acid treatment.

Organic acids, which are milder, should be used wherever possible.

All the common bleaching agents can be used on the vegetable fibers, but chlorine bleaches cannot be applied to the animal fibers.

Certain organic solvents, such as acetone, will dissolve acetate but will have no effect on the rayons or the natural fibers.

Water will weaken animal fibers and rayon but will add strength to the vegetable fibers.

It should be borne in mind, very definitely, that the presence of chlorine. can be detected by adding potassium iodide and starch in solution; if a dark blue color appears chlorine is present.

TOPIC: GENERAL METHODS USED IN SPOT AND STAIN REMOVAL

General Method of Removing Stains

Stains may be divided into two groups—the "build-up" and the "absorbed." A built-up stain is mostly on the surface, such as gum, food, blood, etc. The absorbed stain penetrates into the material between the interlacings or interloopings of the yarns as well as actually "getting into" the yarns of the goods.

The stains in the first group are easier to remove since simple methods are employed, such as brushing, scraping, etc.

The absorbed stain must first of all be loosened from the material by solvent action and then be taken out of the material by proper treatment. Some absorbed stains do not respond to solvent action directly. These are treated with chemicals which change the insoluble staining substances into soluble forms which are then removed by the use of a solvent. In the use of a bleach, the colored substances are converted to colorless compounds and in that way the stain is made invisible.

SOLVENT ACTION

Many stains are removed by solvent action. Water will dissolve more substances than any chemical. If this fact is remembered, the use of costly chemicals may be avoided, and the material may not have to be exposed to harmful chemical action. However, water cannot always be used, since it may not have the desired action on the stain, or it may harm the color or finish on the fabric.

In the use of a solvent, the material is placed on a flat surface with the stained side down. The reason for this position is that the stain should come out of the material from the same side it entered. A piece of absorbent cloth or a blotter should be placed under the stain. The stain is then sponged with a cloth wet with the solvent. Too much solvent should not be used since the stain may have the tendency to spread. The absorbent material should be changed as it becomes stained. If this is not done, the fabric will be stained again. The spot should be stroked toward its center with the solvent-saturated cloth so that the stain does not spread. When the stain is removed, the excess liquid in the fabric should be absorbed with a cloth or sponge. The same area is then dampened by using a cloth pad moistened with the solvent. The dampening should be done in such a way that the center of the stained area contains more solvent, with a gradual reduction of solvent toward the dry outside edges. This is done so that the material will not show rings around the cleaned spot when it is dry. The rings are caused by the migration of sizing and finishing materials to the parts of the goods which dry last.

If the area around the spot contains more liquid, it will dry last and the sizing will accumulate in that area; a ring is sure to result. Quick drying tends to prevent the formation of rings by not giving the sizing compound an opportunity to migrate.

To remove the rings, the material may be wetted once more and an attempt made to have the sizing distributed more evenly. If the dry ring is scraped gently, enough of the excess sizing may be removed to overcome the defect.

THE ACTION OF SOAP AS A SURFACE ACTIVE AGENT

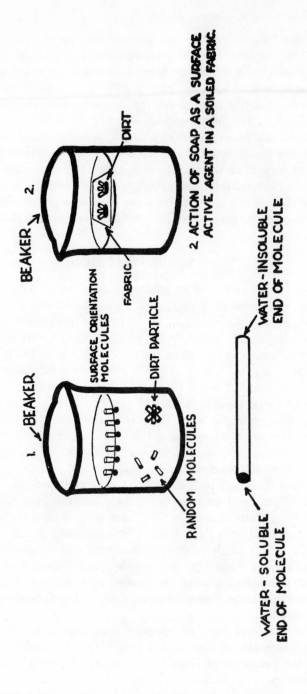

CHEMICAL ACTION

A stain which is not removed by solvent action must be treated chemically. In this way the staining substance is changed to a new one which is removed by solvent action, or the colored staining substance is converted to a colorless compound. With this type of treatment there is more danger of damage being done to the fiber or the color. Thus it is important to make preliminary tests to determine the effect of the chemical on the material at hand.

The material is placed on a flat surface with the stained side up. The spot is moistened with water. A pad of cloth or a blotter is used under the stain to pick up the excess chemical solution. The chemical is carefully applied, a little at a time, with a round glass rod. After a short time the chemical is neutralized by another suitable solution. For example, an alkali would be neutralized by an acid, and vice versa. It is better to have a number of short chemical treatments followed by neutralizing and rinsing, than to have one long exposure of the stain to the action of the chemical.

After the stain has been removed, the usual precautions for rings should be taken. The chemical method of stain removal is the only one suitable for certain stains. It will usually give rapid results but the danger to the fiber and color is greater.

ABSORBENT METHOD

Certain solid substances such as chalk, fuller's earth, etc., can absorb staining materials from fabrics. The stain must be wet. If dried out, it should be moistened with water. The fabric is placed on a flat surface with the stained side up. A layer of the absorbent is sprinkled on the stain and worked over until it is saturated. The absorbent is then brushed off, a new layer is applied, and the operation is repeated until no more of the stain comes out.

A final, long treatment overnight, for example, is often beneficial. Absorbents are not harmful to fiber or color. They are, however, slow in their action and usually must be followed by another treatment to remove the last traces of the stain.

DETERGENT ACTION

In addition to solvents, chemicals and absorbents, soap solution is often used to remove certain types of stains from fabrics. This can be accomplished by washing the entire fabric or garment or by sponging the affected area. The following definitions should be of value with regard to detergency action:

DETERGENT: A solution used to increase the ability of water to clean.

DETERGENCY: The act of removing soil from the surfaces by means of detergent solutions.

EMULSIFIER: Its function is to stabilize the suspension of water-insoluble particles in water.

SURFACE-ACTIVE AGENT: A chemical agent which tends to concentrate at the surface when dissolved in water.

WETTING AGENT: A chemical agent which increases the wettability of water.

SYNTHETIC DETERGENT: A surface active agent other than soap.

BUILDERS, ALKALIES, ALKALINE SALTS: Chemicals used to soften water, to neutralize acidic soils, and to improve the detergent action of soap.

The detergent action of a soap solution involves the following:

1. It wets the fabric and loosens the soil.
2. Mechanical action or agitation causes the soil to separate from the fabric being treated.
3. Soap stabilizes the suspension of the soil and prevents redepositing of the soil in the fabric.
4. The removal of the soil from the fabric by rinsing.

In detergency action ring prevention entails a final rinsing with water since soap solution acts in a manner which dissolves certain impurities and carries along other insoluble particles in a colloidal form.

Synthetic detergents, much used today, include the following:

ANIONIC: An anion is a negative ion and is opposed to a cation. Anionic action is resorted to in textile scouring, wetting, and emulsifying. Alkyl sulfates and long-chain alcohols fall in this category.

CATIONIC: This is a positive action and cannot be used with soap. It has definite mildew-proofing value since it inhibits the growth of mold or bacteria. Cationic action is nontoxic and finds great usage as a "cotton softener."

NON-IONIC: This detergent action is devoid of positive or negative charges. The action is compatible with both anionic and cationic actions and reactions. Non-ionic does not conduct electrical charge or current; it increases penetration, wetting action, and detergent action. Other features include the facts that it will not ionize and consequently works in both hard and soft waters; it is not precipitated by calcium or magnesium salts.

CARBOXY-METHYL-CELLULOSE: Also known as C.M.C., it is a compound which has the power of suspending soil to a greater degree than other emulsifiers. In a washing process the soap loosens the soil and C.M.C. will hold this soil in suspension, thereby increasing the whiteness retention of the washed material.

DIGESTION

The action of digestion is similar to that occurring in the bodies of animals. Insoluble food substances are made soluble by the action of certain materials present in the body. For example, insoluble starch is converted to sugar by the action of these so-called enzymes.

In the same manner insoluble protein foods are made soluble so that they can be absorbed by the body.

In the removal of stains by this method, some of the digesting agent is sprinkled on the warm, moist stain. In a short time the insoluble food or other stain becomes soluble and can easily be washed with water. In order for the action to take place, the spot must be neutral, warm, and moist.

LUBRICATION

This method is used to remove stains produced by insoluble substances such as lipstick, carbon, insoluble pigments, etc. A lubricant such as glycerine or a colorless grease is first rubbed onto the stain area; a solvent is then used to remove the lubricant, which carries the stain along with it.

SUMMARY

Stains may be removed by solvents, chemicals, absorbents, or by the use of detergent action of a soap solution.

Solvents dissolve the stain and the solution formed is forced out of the fabric onto some absorbent material.

By chemical action certain stains are changed to a soluble form so that the solvent method may be used; other stains are converted to colorless substances.

An absorbent draws out the wet stain by capillary action. Soap solution dissolves soluble stains and disperses the staining particles of others, which are then rinsed out with water. The formation of rings is avoided by having the center of the spot drying last and by having more liquid at that area when drying begins after the spot is removed.

TESTING

1. Define each of the following, used in the removal of spots and stains from fabrics: absorbent, solvent, and bleach.
2. Discuss in a general way the action of acids on fibers; action of bleaching agents.
3. What is the effect of acetone on a fabric composed of acetate and rayon; a union fabric?
4. What is meant by a built-up stain? By the absorbed-type of stain?
5. Name three built-up stains; three absorbed-type stains.
6. Define three of the following types of detergent action: detergent, detergency, emulsifier, surface-active agent, wetting agent, synthetic detergent; builders, alkalies, alkaline salts.
7. Explain the digestion method used to remove stains.
8. Discuss the lubrication action in removal of stains.
9. Name three methods used in the identification of textile fibers in a fabric.
10. Define the terms, "organic acid," "inorganic or mineral acid."

Part 2—Unit 31

TOPIC: REMOVAL OF SPOTS AND STAINS

Acid

a) The presence of an acid may be determined by an indicator such as litmus paper.
b) Acids are neutralized by alkalies or bases such as ammonia, washing soda, or lye. Ammonia is used whenever possible.
c) Mineral acid is an acid which does not contain the element carbon. It is inorganic in nature; examples include nitric, hydrochloric, and sulfuric acids.
d) An organic acid is one which contains carbon; examples are acetic, formic, and oxalic acids.
e) Water is used to dilute an acid stain.
f) Some common sources of acid stains are citrus fruits, and solutions used in industry.
g) If an acid stain is to be removed by the use of a base—say ammonia—the removing action is followed by a water treatment to remove the ammonia, which might do harm if allowed to remain in the fabric.

TREATMENT

1. Sponge with plain water.
2. Sponge with dilute ammonia.
3. Then sponge once more with plain water.

Alkali

a) Alkali will turn litmus paper blue.
b) Common substances are used to neutralize alkali; vinegar is much used.
c) Sources of alkali stains are ammonia, lye, washing soda.

[367]

1. The same as for acid treatment above, except neutralization with dilute acetic acid rather than ammonia.

Blood

a) A blood stain should not be treated with hot water since it coagulates the albumin.
b) The effect of hydrogen peroxide on a blood stain causes bubbles to form and to give off oxygen.

TREATMENT 1

1. Work with a pad wet with cold water.
2. Work with a warm soap solution which contains perborate.
3. Sprinkle perborate powder on the stain and allow to stand.
4. Then apply a water-wet pad.

TREATMENT 2

1. Work with cold-water pad.
2. Wet with peroxide.
3. Sprinkle with perborate.
4. Then apply a water-wet pad.

TREATMENT 3

1. Wet with warm water.
2. Sprinkle with digestion powder.
3. Keep the stain moist and warm for one-half hour.
4. Then apply a water-wet pad.

Chewing Gum

a) Water has no effect on chewing gum; no solubility.
b) Carbona is used in this action as a cleaning agent, and it does not burn.

TREATMENT 1

1. Place the fabric, stain side down, on blotting paper.
2. Work in the Carbona on the back of the stain.
3. Move the stained area to a clean part of the blotter as the gum is absorbed.
4. Rub the little remaining stain with a Carbona-wet pad.
5. Rub with water-wet pad.

TREATMENT 2

1. Use kerosene instead of Carbona.

TREATMENT 3

1. Rub the gum with ice, and then pick it off.

Chocolate, Cocoa

a) Chocolate consists of chocolate and sugar.
b) To remove the fat in chocolate or cocoa, use cleaning fluid, a solvent.
c) A bleach would be used to destroy color.

TREATMENT 1

1. Sponge with soap solution.
2. Sponge with water until free of the soap.
3. Bleach.
4. Sponge with water.

1. Wet with water.
2. Work with 25 per cent acetic acid.
3. Sponge with water.
4. Treat with ammonia and liquid soap.
5. Sponge with water.
6. Sprinkle with digestion powder.
7. Keep the spot warm and moist for one-half hour.
8. Sponge with water.
9. Bleach if necessary.
10. Sponge with water.

Coffee

a) Coffee consists of coffee, sugar, and cream or fat.
b) A solvent will remove the fat.
c) Water will remove sugar content.

TREATMENT 1

1. Sponge with Carbona to remove the fat.
2. Sponge with water to remove the sugar.
3. Work hot glycerine into the stain. Allow to stand 15 minutes.
4. Sponge with water.
5. Apply alcohol containing 10 per cent glacial acetic acid.
6. Sponge with water.
7. Bleach if necessary.
8. Sponge with water.

TREATMENT 2

1. Steps 1 and 2 are the same as in Treatment 1.
2. Sprinkle with perborate powder.
3. Keep the spot wet with peroxide until bleached.
4. Sponge with water.

Cream

TREATMENT 1

1. Sponge with soap solution and then sponge with water.

TREATMENT 2

1. Sponge with Carbona; follow with sponging with water.

Dye

a) To remove color or dye stain, care must be used, since the remover may take the color from the material partially or altogether.
b) Bear in mind that animal fibers need high temperatures for dyeing, and that vegetable fibers take dye at lower temperatures.

TREATMENT 1—ANIMAL FIBERS

1. Sponge with cold soap solution and then sponge with water. Then bleach with a suitable chemical and follow by sponging.

TREATMENT 2—VEGETABLE FIBERS AND RAYON

1. Sponge with dilute acetic acid and then sponge with water. Then bleach with a suitable chemical and follow by sponging.

Fruit

a) Fruit stains seem to be ever-prevalent—peach, berry, cherry, etc.
b) It is the color of the fruit stain that gives the most trouble.
c) Color can be removed by a bleach.
d) A bleach such as chlorine cannot be used on wool since it yellows and destroys the fibers.

TREATMENT 1

1. Work warm glycerine into the stain.
2. Sponge with water.
3. Apply alcohol containing 10 per cent glacial acetic acid.
4. Sponge with water.
5. Bleach, if necessary and possible to do so.
6. Sponge with water.

TREATMENT 2—CITRUS FRUITS

1. Sponge with water.
2. Sponge with ammonia solution and then sponge with water.

Grass

TREATMENT 1

1. Work spot with soap solution.
2. Work a few drops of amyl acetate into the stain.
3. Sponge with water.
4. Bleach, if necessary and possible to do so.
5. Sponge with water.

TREATMENT 2

1. Work stain with amyl acetate.
2. Sponge with naphtha.
3. Bleach if necessary.

TREATMENT 3

1. Work with kerosene.
2. Work with naphtha.
3. Bleach if necessary.

Gravy

TREATMENT

1. Wet with water and then apply a few drops of ammonia.
2. Work with soap solution.
3. Sponge with water.
4. If necessary, sprinkle with digestion powder.
5. Keep the stain warm and moist for one-half hour.
6. Sponge with water.

Grease

a) Sources of grease spots are food and machinery.
b) Water cannot be used as a solvent since grease is not soluble in it. Soap should remove grease since it emulsifies it.
c) Common solvents that remove grease include Carbona, benzene, lighter fluid.

TREATMENT 1

1. Sprinkle with absorbent powder.
2. Work with soap solution and then sponge with water.

1. Sponge with a drycleaning solvent.

Ice Cream

a) The three constituents in ice cream are fat, sugar, flavoring.
b) The cream, a fat, is removed by a solvent; sugar by water; and the coloring matter by a bleach.

TREATMENT 1

1. Sponge with naphtha, and then with water.
2. Bleach, if necessary and possible to do so.

TREATMENT 2

1. Sponge with soap solution, then with water, and bleach if necessary.

Ink

a) There is no one chemical that will remove all ink stains because there are many types of inks and many bases used in the manufacture of this product.

TREATMENT 1

1. Saturate with glycerine and sponge out with water.
2. Use ink remover after testing its effectiveness on the dye.
3. Sponge with water.
4. If necessary, follow through with oxalic acid solution.
5. Sponge carefully and well with water.
6. Use hydrosulfite if necessary and possible, to complete the removal action.

TREATMENT 2

1. Sponge with a mixture made of equal parts of Carbona and Lysol.

TREATMENT 3

1. Sponge with a mixture made of equal parts of glycerine, oxalic acid, and wood alcohol.

India Ink, Printing Ink

TREATMENT

1. Work a colorless grease into the stain.
2. Sponge with Carbona.

Iodine

TREATMENT 1

1. Sponge with soap solution, then rinse carefully and cleanly.

TREATMENT 2

1. Place a few drops of hypo crystals in the corner of a folded piece of cloth.
2. Soak in a 10 per cent ammonia solution.
3. Pat the stain with the wet corner until the blemish disappears.

TREATMENT 3

1. Sponge with ammonia solution. Wet an old stain with a little fresh iodine before treating it according to Treatment 2.

Iron Rust

a) Iron rust consists of iron oxide. Washing will not remove a stain of this sort since the rust is not soluble and does not emulsify.

b) The means used to remove these stains calls for chemical treatment with a suitable acid.

TREATMENT 1

1. Sponge with water.
2. Apply erusticator with a stick or glass rod, note result, and then sponge with water.

TREATMENT 2

1. Apply a drop of dilute solution of warm oxalic acid.
2. Sponge with water.

TREATMENT 3

1. Apply a dilute solution of hydrochloric acid.
2. Sponge with water, then with ammonia solution.
3. Sponge again with water.

Lipstick

a) The two main constituents of lipstick are color and grease.

b) The grease is removed by a solvent; the color by bleaching.

c) The lubrication method of stain removal causes a loosening by the lubricator of the grease. Glycerine or a greaseless jelly may serve as the lubricant.

TREATMENT 1

1. Work a colorless grease into the affected area.
2. Bunch up the material and dip it into Carbona.
3. Brush with solvent, then touch up with glacial acetic acid.
4. Brush once more with the solvent, and note result.

TREATMENT 2

1. Work colorless grease into the stain.
2. Dip into Carbona.
3. Bleach if necessary and possible to do so. Then sponge with water.

Mercurochrome

TREATMENT

1. Sponge with soap solution.
2. Bleach and then sponge with water.

Mildew

a) Mildew is a microscopic plant growth which forms because of dampness, poor circulation, damp walls, or staleness. This parasitic fungus or mold is found on foodstuffs and textile fabrics and garments.

b) Certain textile fibers such as cotton and linen, which are vegetable fibers, can be attacked by mildew. It has no effect on acetate or nylon.

TREATMENT

1. Use a soap solution carefully over the area.
2. Bleach and then rinse well. Check action well.

[372]

Mud

a) Mud stains can be treated by drying and then brushing, or by laundering. A **dry** mud stain should be removed by brushing.

b) A soap solution should be used to remove a stain of this sort.

TREATMENT

1. Allow the spot to dry thoroughly and then brush it.
2. Sponge the spot with soap solution.
3. Sponge with water.

Mustard

TREATMENT

1. Saturate the stain with hot glycerine, then sponge with water.
2. Apply 20 per cent acetic acid, then sponge with water.
3. Bleach; follow by sponging with water.

Paint

a) The constituents of paint are oil, color, and turpentine.

TREATMENT 1—FRESH STAIN

1. Brush with soap solution and then sponge with water.

TREATMENT 2

1. Rub lard into the fresh stain.
2. Brush with soap solution and then sponge with water.

TREATMENT 3

1. Apply ammonia solution. Then apply benzene, Carbona, or turpentine.
2. Allow to stand for fifteen minutes.
3. Then brush with soap solution, followed by sponging with water.

Scorch

a) A scorch is an area of fabric or fibers charred or burned to some degree.

b) There is no solvent that can be used for this type of blemish.

TREATMENT

1. If the area can be salvaged, which is not often the case, brush the area carefully with soap solution.
2. Then sponge with water, and bleach if necessary.

Tar

TREATMENT 1

1. Rub lard into the stain.
2. Brush with soap solution and then sponge with water.

TREATMENT 2

1. Rub lard into the stain.
2. Brush with Carbona and then sponge with the same solvent. Watch action and result carefully.

Tomato Sauce

a) The constituents are fat and color. A solvent may be used to remove the stain; the color is removed by washing and bleaching.

1. Sponge with Carbona.
2. Sponge with soap solution.
3. Bleach and then sponge with water.

Wax

1. Scrape off as much of the wax as possible. Then place the spot area between blotters.
2. Press with a hot iron.
3. Sponge with Carbona.
4. Then bleach if there is still a stain from the wax color.
5. Sponge with water.

Wine

1. Sponge with water and then with acetic acid.
2. Sponge with banana oil and lactic acid.
3. Bleach and then give a final sponging.

NOTE: A laboratory would have all the compounds and ingredients necessary for use in spot and stain removal. The following list shows items for possible use in stain removal if the work is to be done in the home:

Absorbent powder	Carbona	Lard
Acetic acid, 20 per cent	Carbon tetrachloride	Litmus paper
Alcohol	Colorless grease	Naphtha
Ammonia solution	Digestion powder	Oxalic acid
Amyl acetate	Erusticator	Perborate
Banana oil	Glycerine	Permanganate
Benzene	Hypochlorite	Peroxide
Bisulfite	Hydrosulfite	Soap solution
Bleach	Kerosene	Turpentine
	Lactic acid	

Part 2—Unit 32

EXAMINATION ON CARE OF TEXTILES AND CLOTHING— SPOT AND STAIN REMOVAL

In the following box chart for tabulations, supply under the heading "*Method One*" the means used to remove each spot or stain. If an alternate method may be used, write the answer under the heading "*Method Two*." Answers should be written as "Digestion," "Detergent," "Solvent," "Lubricant," "Mechanical," etc. In some instances the answer to be given may be "Alcohol," "Erusticator," "Turpentine," etc.

SPOT OR STAIN	METHOD ONE	METHOD TWO
1. ACID		
2. ADHESIVE		
3. BLOOD—animal fiber		
BLOOD—vegetable fiber		
BLOOD—heavy goods and wool		
4. BLUING		
5. BUTTER		
6. CANDLE WAX		
7. CANDY		
8. CHEWING GUM		
9. CHOCOLATE		
10. COCOA		
11. COFFEE		
12. DYE		
13. EGG		
14. FRUIT		
15. FURNITURE POLISH		
16. GLUE		
17. GRAPHITE		
18. GRASS		
19. GREASE, OIL		
20. GUM		
21. HAIR OIL		
22. ICE CREAM		
23. INDELIBLE PENCIL		
24. INDIA INK, PRINTING INK		
25. INK		
26. IODINE		
27. IRON RUST		
28. LEAD PENCIL		
29. LEATHER		
30. LINSEED OIL		
31. LIPSTICK		
32. MEDICINE		
33. MERCUROCHROME		
34. METALLIC STAINS		
35. MILDEW		
36. MILK		
37. MUD		
38. MUSTARD		
39. OLD PAINT, OLD VARNISH		
40. PAINT		
41. PENCIL MARKS		
42. PERSPIRATION		
43. SALAD DRESSING		
44. SCORCH		

SPOT OR STAIN	METHOD ONE	METHOD TWO
45. SHELLAC		
46. SUGAR		
47. TAR, ROAD OIL, CREOSOTE OIL		
48. TEA		
49. TIN FOIL		
50. TOBACCO		
51. TOMATO		
52. VARNISH		
53. VASELINE		
54. WATER		
55. WATER COLORS		
56. WAX		
57. WHITE SAUCES		

POSSIBLE ANSWERS IN EXAMINATION ON CARE OF CLOTHING— SPOT AND STAIN REMOVAL

SPOT OR STAIN	METHOD ONE	METHOD TWO
1. ACID	Water and ammonia	
2. ADHESIVE	Solvent—carbon tetrachloride	
3. BLOOD—all types	Solvent—saline solution	Digestion or Absorbent
BLOOD—all types	Digestion—solvase in solution	Absorbent or Solvent
BLOOD—heavy fabrics and woolens	Absorbent—raw starch paste	Solvent or Digestion
4. BLUING	Detergent	
5. BUTTER	Solvent—Carbona	Detergent
6. CANDLE WAX	Solvent—Carbona	
7. CANDY	Detergent	
8. CHEWING GUM	Solvent—Carbona	
9. CHOCOLATE	Detergent	Digestion
10. COCOA	Detergent	Digestion
11. COFFEE	Detergent	
12. DYE	Detergent	Bleach
13. EGG	Detergent	
14. FRUIT	Detergent	
15. FURNITURE POLISH	Soap solution, water	
16. GLUE	Detergent	
17. GRAPHITE	Dry spotting soap	
18. GRASS	Solvent—alcohol	
19. GREASE, OIL	Solvent—Carbona	
20. GUM	Solvent—Carbona	
21. HAIR OIL	Dry spotting agent	
22. ICE CREAM	Detergent	
23. INDELIBLE PENCIL	Alcohol or soap solution	
24. INDIA INK	Detergent	
25. INK—Blue, black on white goods	Ink eradicator	
INK—Blue, black on dyed goods	Detergent	
26. IODINE	Chemical—hypo solution	Detergent
27. IRON RUST—Cotton and Linen	Weak solution of oxalic acid, and ammonia, then rinse	

SPOT OR STAIN	METHOD ONE	METHOD TWO
28. LEAD PENCIL	Mechanical—erasing Soap solution	
29. LEATHER	Detergent	Detergent
30. LINSEED OIL	Solvent	Detergent
31. LIPSTICK	Lubrication and solvent	Solvent—alcohol
32. MEDICINE	Detergent	
33. MERCUROCHROME	Detergent	
34. METALLIC STAINS	Solvent—acetic or citric acid	
35. MILDEW	Detergent and bleach	Bleach on white goods
36. MILK	Detergent	
37. MUD	Mechanical—dry and then brush off	
38. MUSTARD	Detergent	
39. OLD PAINT, OLD-VARNISH	Turpentine	
40. PAINT	Turpentine	Detergent
41. PENCIL MARKS	Mechanical—erase	Detergent
42. PERSPIRATION	Detergent	
43. SALAD DRESSING	Solvent—Carbona	Detergent
44. SCORCH	Detergent and bleach	
45. SHELLAC	Solvent—alcohol or benzene	
46. SUGAR	Water	Detergent
47. TAR, ROAD OIL, CREO-SOTE OIL	Solvent—Carbona	
48. TEA	Water with some borax in it	
49. TIN FOIL	Soap and water	
50. TOBACCO	Soap solution	
51. TOMATO	Detergent	
52. VARNISH	Solvent—alcohol or benzene	
53. VASELINE	Solvent—alcohol or benzene	
54. WATER	Steam entire garment with care	Wash and launder, if necessary
55. WATER COLORS	Soap solution	Water
56. WAX	Solvent—Carbona	
57. WHITE SAUCES	Soap solution	

REFERENCE BOX CHART FOR SPOT AND STAIN REMOVAL IN CARE OF CLOTHING

The following chart is for ready reference in a general way. The following notations should be kept in mind:
1. Bleaching agents should not be used on dyed fabrics.
2. For a bleach on animal fibers, use peroxide; chlorine should never be used as a bleach on animal fibers.
3. For a bleach on vegetable fibers, use any bleach such as peroxide or chlorine.

SPOT OR STAIN	MATERIAL	TREATMENT	PROCEDURE
1. ACID	Any	Water and household ammonia	Sponge
2. ADHESIVE	Any	Carbon tetrachloride	Sponge, then rub
3. BLOOD	Any	Lukewarm saline solution	Immediately soak and then use regular laundry methods
BLOOD	Any	Solvase in solution	Immediately soak and then use regular laundry methods

SPOT OR STAIN	MATERIAL	TREATMENT	PROCEDURE
BLOOD	Heavy goods and wool	Use raw starch paste as absorbent	Keep applying to spot until it disappears
4. BLUING	Any	Soap solution; use solution of soap and water or sulfonated oil and water. If made in stock solution, the addition of 1 part of ether to 30 parts of solution will be of value in spot removal.	Rub carefully
5. BUTTER	Any	Carbon tetrachloride	Sponge and rub
6. CANDLE WAX	Any	Carbon tetrachloride	Sponge and rub
7. CANDY	Any	Water and soap solution	Sponge and rub
8. CHEWING GUM	Any	Carbon tetrachloride	Sponge and rub back of stain
9. CHOCOLATE	Any	Water, soap, and then bleach	Sponge and rub
10. COCOA	Any	Water, soap, and then bleach	Sponge and rub
11. COFFEE	Any	Water, soap, and then bleach	Sponge and rub
12. DYE	Any	Water, soap, and then bleach, if possible	Sponge and rub
13. EGG	Any	Water and soap	Sponge after scraping
14. FRUIT	Any	Soap solution, then bleach	Sponge and rub
15. FURNITURE POLISH	Any	Soap solution, then water	Sponge and rub
16. GLUE	Any	Soap solution	Sponge and rub
17. GRAPHITE	Any	Dry spotting soap; 2 parts oleic acid, 1 each of chloroform, carbon tetrachloride and benzol; ⅓ part denatured alcohol, ¼ part of 26% ammonia. Keep in corked bottle.	Sponge and rub
18. GRASS	Any	Alcohol	Sponge and rub
19. GREASE, OIL	Any	Carbon tetrachloride	Sponge and rub
20. GUM	Any	Carbon tetrachloride	Sponge—from back of fabric first
21. HAIR OIL	Any	Dry spotting agent; 1 part each of chloroform, benzol, and carbon tetrachloride.	Sponge and rub
22. ICE CREAM	Any	Water, soap, and then bleach	Sponge in sequence
23. INDELIBLE PENCIL	Any	Alcohol or soap solution	Sponge and rub well
24. INDIA INK	White goods	Soap solution	Sponge and rub the fresh stain

SPOT OR STAIN	MATERIAL	TREATMENT	PROCEDURE
25. INK	Any	Water, soap, and then bleach	Sponge and rub
26. IODINE	Any	Hypo- (sodium thiosulfate)	Sponge carefully
27. IRON RUST	Cotton, linen	Treat with weak solution of oxalic acid and then with ammonia	Acid applied to stain with glass rod; on disappearance of stain apply ammonia and rinse with water
28. LEAD PENCIL	Any	Try erasing. Soap solution	Sponge carefully
29. LEATHER	Any	Soap and water	Sponge vigorously but with care
30. LINSEED OIL	Any	Carbon tetrachloride	Sponge and rub
31. LIPSTICK	Any	Use colorless grease such as petroleum jelly or vaseline. Follow with carbon tetrachloride. Use care.	Rub in the grease; then sponge well but evenly
32. MEDICINE	Any	Alcohol, soap solution	Sponge very carefully
33. MERCUROCHROME	Any	Soap solution, bleach and then water	Sponge well
34. METALLIC STAINS	Any	Acetic acid	Sponge carefully
35. MILDEW	Any	Soap and then bleach	Wash well before using bleaching agent
36. MILK	Any	Soap solution	Sponge and rub
37. MUD	Any	Allow to dry, brush, sponge from back with soap solution	Sponge with water
38. MUSTARD	Any	Hot glycerine, sponge with water, apply 20% acetic acid and then sponge with water. Bleach and sponge again with water.	Sponge with water
39. OLD PAINT, OLD VARNISH	Any	Equal parts of alcohol and benzene, or use turpentine	Sponge vigorously but with care
40. PAINT	Any	Turpentine or benzene	Sponge vigorously
41. PENCIL MARKS	Any	Try erasing the marks. Soap and water may help.	Rub the detergent used on goods carefully
42. PERSPIRATION	Any	Difficult stain to remove. Use a soap-and-water solution. If peroxide is used, take particular notice of the bleaching properties involved.	Sponge with utmost care
43. SALAD DRESSING	Any	Carbon tetrachloride	Sponge carefully

| --- | --- | --- | --- |
44. SCORCH	Any	Soap solution and bleach	Sponge
45. SHELLAC	Any	Alcohol or benzene	Sponge with care
46. SUGAR	Any	Warm to hot water	Sponge well
47. TAR, ROAD OIL, CREOSOTE OIL	Any	Carbon tetrachloride	Sponge with care
48. TEA	Any	Soap solution (difficult spot to remove since it is tannic acid)	Sponge immediately
49. TIN FOIL	Any	Soap and water	Sponge
50. TOBACCO	Any	Hot water and soap; bleach, if necessary	Sponge; the degree of intensity depends on depth of stain
51. TOMATO	Any	Soap solution	Sponge and rub
52. VARNISH	Any	Alcohol or benzene	Sponge with care
53. VASELINE	Any	Carbon tetrachloride	Sponge with care
54. WATER	Any	None	Steam carefully—wash entire garment
55. WATER COLORS	Any	Soap solution	Sponge and rub
56. WAX	Any	Carbon tetrachloride	Sponge and rub
57. WHITE SAUCES	Any	Soap and water	Sponge carefully

Part 2—Unit 33

TOPIC: DRYCLEANING

Professional cleaning services for wearing apparel, household furnishings, and other textile materials were offered by textile dyers and processors as far back as the early years of the Christian era. It is said that in Roman times cleaning services were performed by a "fuller," a processor of wool fabrics. These services were based on the expert use of water and soap, and often necessitated redyeing. Organic solvents, as we know them today for drycleaning, did not come into use until the middle of the nineteenth century. The modern term for the skilled use of water and soap for the care of some textile products by professional drycleaners is called "wetcleaning." It may be said, therefore, that those who rendered cleaning services were wetcleaners long before they adopted the use of "dry" solvents and became known as they are today—as DRYCLEANERS.

The first organic solvent used for stain removal to supplement wetcleaning procedure was an organic solvent used for medicinal purposes called spirits of turpentine. In the early 1800's this solvent was refined as a lamp fuel known as camphene. In this form it was low enough in price to use as a complete cleaning medium in which the whole garments were washed, thus eliminating the hazards of shrinkage and color loss inherent in the use of water. Benzene came into use in due course of time.

With this change in the basic technology of cleaning services, obviating to a great degree the need for redyeing, the fields of textile dyeing and cleaning services became distinctly separate. Concurrently, a synthetic dyestuff industry was born, based on discoveries by Sir William Perkin in 1856, who was assisted significantly in his early work by one of the famous cleaning and dyeing firms of that day which is still in existence today—Pullar's of Perth, Scotland.

An early term for wetcleaning was "scouring," and wool-garment scourers operated large enterprises as early as 1825 in the United States. All these firms ultimately became drycleaners around the turn of the century by using gasoline, a by-product of kerosene manufacture, as an inexpensive organic solvent. In 1928, a government standard for a specifically refined petroleum solvent for drycleaning was adopted, and solvents produced under this standard specification are commonly known as Stoddard solvents in honor of a leader in the drycleaning industry who paved the way for this significant development, W. J. Stoddard. In the 1930's carbon tetrachloride and trichlorethylene were introduced in the United States for drycleaning purposes, both of which have given way completely to a more suitable synthetic hydrocarbon known chemically as tetrachloroethylene, or more popularly referred to as perchlorethylene.

Every country in the world today offers drycleaning services, and in the United States there are more than 37,000 drycleaning plants, including divisions of commercial laundry firms. The aggregate drycleaning business volume here is well over two billion dollars annually.

IMPORTANT DATES IN THE HISTORY OF CLEANING SERVICES

1532: Publication of *The Allerley Mackel*, the first known book on spot and stain removal, in Mayence, Germany.

1690: The first published reference to the use of spirits of turpentine for the removal of "tar and varnish from fabrics."

1716: Believed to be the time of the earliest regular use in cleaning services of turpentine as a "drycleaner" for grease and oil stains to supplement wetcleaning processes. Down through the ages, turpentine, a distillation of pine pitch, appears as having had several names, as follows: oil of turpentine, spirits of turpentine, spirits of terebenthene, camphene, and "turps."

1799: Even before the general use of organic solvents for cleaning by immersion methods, the cleaner of clothes was known as a "degraisseur," a degreaser of textiles able to remove grease and fat stains from cloth. The French name for cleaner was *Teinturier-degraisseur* (a dyer-degreaser). "Degraisseur" was the common term applied to a master dyer who specialized in both dyeing and cleaning garments. Spirits of turpentine was then generally used professionally as a stain-removal agent, though its use was known to French and German housewives for perhaps hundreds of years prior to this time.

1808: The noted French chemist M. J. A. Chaptal stated, "I know that the profession of cleaner does not occupy a very eminent place among the arts and crafts, but I also know that there is scarcely any other in which the operations are so essentially founded on a knowledge of chemistry. One does not deny that the profession of cleaner is not of as great interest to society as that of the dyer who decorates the fabrics which are used for our clothes with brilliant and fast

[381]

colors. Nevertheless, the cleaner who rehabilitates these changed colors does not deserve any less consideration."

1825: The discovery of benzene by Michael Faraday (1791–1867) who also discovered the electromagnetic induction principle. This coal-tar derivative, benzene, did not come into commercial production for another thirty years, when it was found that it could be widely used as a drycleaning solvent. Called "Benzole," it formed an essential and important part in the manufacture of synthetic dyestuffs.

1839: Spirits of turpentine was now easily available as a lamp fuel and was called "camphene." Its use as a drycleaning solvent in place of water was to follow in the next decade.

1848: The firm of Jolly-Belin in Paris, France, is credited with spearheading the first successful use of spirits of turpentine as a commercial drycleaning solvent, a technological innovation which spread quickly to other countries on the Continent and later to the British Isles. John Pullar and Sons, Perth, Scotland, led the introduction of drycleaning services in the English-speaking countries, where the term "French Cleaning" became popular because of the earlier reputation and fame gained in France for solvent cleaning methods. The term is still used as a connotation of special, highly skilled handwork. The same mechanical processes involved in any commercial drycleaning operation may be used but special attention and care to detail should be given to justify the generally higher prices associated with the term.

1849: The development of Benzole (benzene) as a drycleaning solvent.

1892: The first use of a "drycleaning soap" in Germany, a neutral magnesia soap. Later on potassium oleate was widely used.

1907: Establishment of the National Association of Dyers and Cleaners in Milwaukee, Wisconsin, known today as the National Institute of Drycleaning, Silver Spring, Maryland, and New York City, with more than ten thousand members in the United States and over fifty foreign countries. Included in the membership are machinery and chemical suppliers, textile and garment-manufacturing concerns and retailers. Production companies and retail firms avail themselves of the research services of the Institute through affiliate membership.

1928: Development of Stoddard solvent (U.S. Commercial Standard 3-40), a distillate of crude petroleum refined especially to meet requirements for safety and odorless cleaning. Later, a high-flashpoint petroleum, called "140° F. Solvent" was introduced. The flashpoint of Stoddard solvent is 100° F. Mineral spirits sold in paint stores as a paint diluent and all-purpose solvent are virtually the same as Stoddard solvent in the basic properties.

1932: Introduction of chlorinated hydrocarbon solvents in the United States—trichlorethylene, carbon tetrachloride, and later, perchlorethylene. Only the latter is in common use at present.

1933: Introduction of the "charged-system" method of dissolving minute quantities of water in a solvent to vastly improve the cleaning performance. Initially based on oil-soluble, petroleum sulfonate compounds, other chemical types are used today, including amine sulfonates, phosphate esters, and certain non-ionic products. Virtually all cleaners use some form of the charged system.

1939: The introduction of self-service coin-operated drycleaning systems based on the use of perchlorethylene in completely automatic machines.

Stain Removal

A process of removing heavy concentrations of soil and solvent-resistant stains which require separate treatment either before or after the drycleaning process:

PRE-SPOTTING: This is the treatment before the drycleaning of heavily soiled areas with a specially prepared solvent-detergent solution to help the regular drycleaning process perform its function in a thorough manner.

SPOTTING: The process of removing soil or stains independent of the drycleaning cycle. For the removal of water-soluble stains, steam is commonly used to condense a fine spray of warm water onto the stained area. Chemicals are used for the treatment of "chemical-type stains."

The drycleaner or other person who applies chemicals for spotting or pre-spotting purposes other than water and drycleaning solvents to fabrics or garments assumes the risk of the effect these might have on the fiber, finish, and/or color. The fabric is expected to be resistant to contact with plain water and drycleaning solvents.

Finishing

The use of any of the various procedures used to restore an article to good appearance. Three basic types of equipment are used and combinations of these may be employed—GRID-HEAD PRESS, STEAM-AIR FORMER, and the HOT-HEAD PRESS.

WOOL FINISHING (PRESSING): A term which relates to the finishing of suiting-type fabrics which contain natural or manmade fibers using steam-heated equipment. The basic types of equipment used are a grid-head press and a steam-air former.

Both units use steam for conditioning of the cloth, pressure to smooth it, and air-drying. A grid-head press molds or "presses" the fabric between a covered head-plate and a padded table or buck, both of which emit steam. A vacuum exhaust in the table causes the dry air to move through the cloth to cool it and to remove some of the moisture left from the steam.

In a steam-air former, often used in combination with a press, the article is "dressed" onto the former, then steam pressure is forced through the inflated bag of the body, and finally dry air is forced through. The pressure of the air and the steam holds the article in an inflated condition until "finished." The steam comes from a boiler operated at a pressure of 65 to 75 pounds per square inch, gauge. The temperature of steam pressing is around 250° F., and somewhat below this in steam-air formers.

SILK FINISHING (PRESSING): This caption concerns the finishing of cotton, rayon, silk, wool, worsted, and the manmade fibers treated by the use of steam-air formers, hot-head presses, and hand irons. Unlike the covered grid-head press, the head is smooth metal (uncovered) and heated by steam but does not actually emit steam. Only the buck or the table is equipped to emit steam. The temperature for pressing on hot-head equipment is around 315° F. In the case of hand ironing the user sets the temperature at the appropriate marking on the iron according to the fabric being finished.

EXPLANATION OF TERMS USED IN DRYCLEANING

Drycleaning

A process of cleaning with organic solvents. Two types of terms are used:

1. UNRESTRICTED TERMS: Terms such as "Drycleanable," "Dryclean," and similar terms with regard to drycleanability mean that the article can be drycleaned in a machine with either a petroleum solvent or perchlorethylene and a synthetic detergent, extracted by centrifugal action to remove the solvent, deodorized in a tumble dryer, and then restored to good appearance on a steam-heated press or on steam-air finishing equipment. The solvent-relative humidity shall not exceed 75 per cent. The temperature of the solvent shall not exceed 90° F. A drycleanable product is also resistant to contact with water as required for the removal of stains.

2. RESTRICTED TERMS: These limit or qualify the method of drycleaning and shall be strictly interpreted according to the limited meaning—"Dryclean—do not tumble"; "Dryclean in Stoddard Solvent Only"; etc. All procedures as specified for unrestricted terms are applicable except to the extent of the limitation.

Wetcleaning

A process similar to hand laundering performed professionally by a drycleaner using water, soap, or a synthetic detergent, and in some instances, other additives if deemed necessary.

The article to be cleaned is laid on a table, brushed gently with detergent solution and then rinsed in cool water. At other times, such as with glass-fiber fabrics, the item is immersed in water not above 105° F., with a neutral soap or detergent, and allowed to soak for a period of time, followed by rinses in cool water.

To stabilize colors, common salt or mild-acid treatments, such as acetic acid or formic acid, may be added to the water. The article is then dried by air or the drying may be accelerated by passing a strong flow of hot air through the garment on a special device known as a wind-whip at a temperature of about 120° F.

Drying, Deodorizing

The methods follow:

1. TUMBLE-DRY: A process which uses a heated tumble-drying machine in which hot air is circulated through the load at various temperatures depending on the type of load. The time cycle of a tumbler varies according to the size of the load, load classification, temperature, the type of solvent, and equipment A typical cycle will run from twenty to forty minutes. Tumble-drying temperatures normally applicable in this process range up to 160° F.

2. TUMBLE-COLD: A process which uses a tumbler without application of heat The air temperature at the intake is the same as the room temperature.

3. AIR-DRY, CABINET-DRY: A method of drying or deodorizing in which there is no movement of the article being dried. Hot air circulates around it as it hangs in a closed area until dry. Temperatures used are the same as in tumble-dry The time cycle extends up to several hours, depending on the bulkiness of the article in question.

[384]

TESTING

1. Define an organic solvent.
2. How does an organic compound differ from an inorganic compound?
3. Define the term, "wetcleaning"; "drycleaning."
4. Name four solvents that have been used in drycleaning.
5. Name a contribution to drycleaning made by two of the following persons: (1) Sir William Perkin; (2) M. J. A. Chaptal; (3) Michael Faraday; (4) Jolly-Belin; (5) W. J. Stoddard.
6. Define pre-spotting; spotting.
7. What are unrestricted terms used in the drycleaning industry? restricted terms?
8. Discuss drying, deodorizing in drycleaning.

REFERENCES

Paper entitled "Camphene et le Degraisseur" by Dr. Sidney Edelstein. *American Dye-stuff Reporter*, January 14, 1957; Howes Publishing Company, Inc., New York City.
"National Fair Claims Guide for Consumer Textile Products," published by National Institute of Drycleaning, August 1964; Albert E. Johnson, 101 West 31st Street, New York City.
"CIBA Review," January 1964; CIBA Ltd., Basle, Switzerland.
"Remembering the Years," by Edna Michelsen, NID, 1957.

TEXTILE BIBLIOGRAPHY
OUTLINE OF TOPICS

1. KNIT GOODS

American Knitting Machines, M. A. Metcalf, 502 pages. Textile American Publishing Company, Boston, Massachusetts, 1928.
Calculations and Costings for Knitted Fabrics, W. Davis, 226 pages. Pitman and Sons, Ltd., London, 1930.
Cost Control for Knit Underwear Factories, The Associated Knit Underwear Manufacturers of America, 259 pages. Ronald Press, New York, 1924.
Cost Finding in Knitting Mills, S. R. Gordon for the *Textile World,* 204 pages. McGraw-Hill Book Company, Inc., New York, 1930.
Flat Machine Knitting and Fabrics, H. D. Buck, 147 pages. McGraw-Hill Book Company, Inc., New York City, 1921.
Hosiery for Women, U. S. Government Printing Office, Washington, D. C.
Hosiery Manufacture, W. Davis, 136 pages. Has 61 illustrations including many original photo-micrographs. Pitman and Sons, Ltd., New York, 1920.
Hosiery, Hidden Value Series, Consumer Education Division, Sears Roebuck and Company, Chicago, Illinois.
Hosiery, Knit Underwear, and Gloves, Natalie Kneeland, 126 pages. A. W. Shaw Company, New York, 1924.
Knitted Fabrics, booklet, Beaunit Corporation, 261 Madison Ave., New York City.
Knitted Fabrics, Chamberlain and Quilter, 145 pages. Pitman and Sons, Ltd., New York, 1919.

Knitting Full Fashioned Hosiery, M. C. Miller. McGraw-Hill Book Company, Inc., 330 West 42nd Street, New York City, 1936.

Knitting, Its Products and Processes, raw material to finished merchandise, Jessie F. Caplin, 93 pages. Dry Goods Economist, New York, 1927.

Manufacture of Knitted Undergarments, Union Special Machine Company, Cincinnati, Ohio.

Principles of Knitting, M. C. Miller, 234 pages. McGraw-Hill Book Company, Inc., New York, 1931.

Standard Sizes for Knit Underwear, Underwear Institute, Two Park Avenue, New York City.

Standards of Construction and Inspection for Ladies' Full-Fashioned Hosiery, National Association of Hosiery Manufacturers, New York, 1936.

The Hose We Buy and Wear, National Association of Hosiery Manufacturers, New York, 1937.

The Knitting Equipment of the Seamless Hosiery Industry, G. W. Taylor and G. Allan Dash, Jr., 144 pages. Wharton School of Finance and Commerce, University of Pennsylvania, Philadelphia, Pennsylvania, 1934.

The Manufacture of Hosiery and Its Problems, E. M. Schenke, 94 pages. National Association of Hosiery Manufacturers, New York, 1935.

Warp Knitting and Glove Manufacture, from articles for the *Textile World*, by G. R. Merrill, Edward Murden, and Joseph Rowan, 125 pages. Bragdon, Lord, and Nagle Company, McGraw-Hill Book Company, Inc., New York City, 1925.

2. CARPETS, RUGS, DRAPERIES, AND UPHOLSTERY

American Carpet and Upholstery Journal, monthly. Trades Publishing Company, 1050 Drexel Building, Philadelphia, Pennsylvania.

Carpet Manufacturing, F. Bradbury, 301 pages. Lord and Nagle Publishing Company, 1904.

Carpets, R. S. Brinton, 148 pages. Trades Publishing Company, 1050 Drexel Building, Philadelphia, Pennsylvania.

Carpets and Rugs, Booklets on; Mohasco Industries, Inc., Amsterdam, N. Y.

Carpets and Rugs, Roberts Beaumont, 410 pages. D. Van Nostrand Company, Princeton, N. J.

Carpets and Rugs, Madge E. Dilts. The Hoover Company, North Canton, Ohio.

Chinese Rug Book, Mary C. Ripley, 66 pages. Frederick A. Stokes Publishing Company, 1927.

Cotton Rugs, U. S. Tariff Commission, Government Printing Office, Washington, D. C.

Decorative Draperies and Upholstery, H. W. Frohne. Garden City Publishing Company, Inc., New York, 1937.

Decoratively Speaking; Gladys Miller, Doubleday & Company, Inc., New York, 1939.

Development of Various Decorative and Upholstery Fabrics, F. Schumacher and Company, 58 West 40th Street, New York.

Fabric Magic; Fabrics, the Key to Successful Decoration, F. Schumacher and Company, 58 West 40th Street, New York.

Floor Coverings, Household Finance Corporation, Chicago, Illinois.

Home Furnishings, Hidden Value Series, Sears Roebuck and Company, Chicago, Illinois.

Homecraft Rugs, Walker. F. A. Stokes Publishing Company, New York.

How to Make Draperies, Slip Covers, Cushions, and Other Home Furnishings, Singer Sewing Machine Company, Inc., New York.

How to Make Rugs, Wheeler. Doubleday & Company, Inc., New York.

How to Use Modern Color in Your Rooms, The Hoover Company, North Canton, Ohio.

Maintenance and Care of Wool Carpets and Rugs, Institute of Carpet Manufacturers of America, Inc., 1907.

Oriental Rug Magazine, monthly. 12 East 30th Street, New York.

Oriental Rugs and Carpets, Arthur A. Dilley. Charles Scribner's Sons, New York, 1931.

Picture Book of Rug and Carpet Making, Bigelow Sanford Carpet Company, Inc., 140 Madison Avenue, New York.

The Carpet and Upholstery Trade Review, semi-monthly. Review Publishing Company, East Stroudsburg, Pennsylvania.

The Mohawk Carpet and Rug Manual, Mohasco Industries, Inc., Amsterdam, New York.

The Upholsterer and Interior Decorator, monthly. Clifford and Lawton, New York.

3. DYEING AND PRINTING

A Manual of Dyeing, E. Knecht, C. Rawson, R. Lowenthal, two volumes. London, 1920.

Acetate Silk and Its Dyes, C. E. Mullin. D. Van Nostrand Company, Princeton, N. J., 1927.

Allen's Commercial Organic Analysis, volume six; Colorimetry. Dyes and Colouring Matters, the Synthetic Dyestuffs and the Analysis of Colouring Matters, 5th edition, S. S. Sadtler, E. C. Lathrop, C. A. Mitchell, editors. Blakiston, Ltd., London, 1928.

Ancient and Medieval Dyes, William F. Leggett. New York, 1945.

Aniline Black and Its Application to Dyeing and Printing, E. Noelting and A. Lehne. Translated by A. Morris. Heywood, Ltd., London, 1909.

Application of Dyestuff to Textiles, Paper, Leather and Other Materials, J. Merritt Matthews. John Wiley and Sons, New York, 1920.

Aromatic Diazo Compounds and Their Technical Applications, K. H. Saunders. Longmans, Green Company, New York, 1936.

Artificial Dyestuffs, Their Nature, Manufacture and Uses, A. R. J. Ramsay and H. C. Weston. London, 1917.

Batik and Other Pattern Dyeing, Baker. Atkinson, Mentzer Company.

Batik, First Lessons in, Lewis. Prang Company.

Batiks and How to Make Them, Mijer. Dodd, Mead and Company, New York.

Bleaching and Dyeing of Vegetable Fibrous Materials, J. Huebner. Constable and Company, Ltd., London, 1927.

Bleaching and Related Processes, J. M. Matthews. Chemical Catalog, New York, 1921.

Bleaching Powder and Its Action in Bleaching, R. L. Taylor. Heywood, Ltd., London, 1922.

Bleaching, Dyeing, Printing, and Finishing, McMyn. Pitman and Sons, Ltd., London.

British Launderers' Yearbook. Institute of British Launderers, London.

Calico Printing and Dyeing, O'Neill, London, 1862.

Cellulose Chemistry, E. J. Heuser. McGraw-Hill Book Company, Inc., New York, 1924.

Chemistry and Physics of Dyeing, W. P. Draper. Blakiston, Ltd., London, 1906.

Chemistry and Practice of Finishing, P. Bean and W. McCleary. Hutton, Hartley, Ltd., London, 1905, 1926.

Chemistry and Practice of Sizing, P. Bean and F. Schrisbrick. 6th edition. Manchester, England, 1910.

Chemistry and Technology of Artificial Silk, A. J. Hall. London, 1928.

Chemistry in Industry, 392 pages. Wynkoop, Hallenbeck, and Crawford, New York, 1925.

Chemistry in Use, Brownlee, Fuller, Hancock, and Whitsit, 655 pages. Allyn and Bacon Company, Boston, Massachusetts, 1939.

Chemistry of Coal Tar Dyes, I. W. Fay. Second edition. D. Van Nostrand Company, Princeton, N. J., 1919.

Chemistry of Dyeing, J. K. Wood. Second edition. D. Van Nostrand Company, Princeton, N. J., 1926.

Chemistry of Dyestuffs, M. Fort and L. L. Lloyd. Cambridge University Press, England, 1917.

Chemistry of Dyestuffs, G. von Georgievics and E. Grandmougin. Translated by F. A. Mason. E. Benn and Company, Ltd., London, 1927.

Chemistry of Laundry Materials, D. N. Jackman. Longmans, Green Company, Ltd., New York and London, 1934.

Chintz Book, Percival. Rand McNally Company, Chicago, Illinois.

Cleaning and Dyeing of Celanese and Rayon, E. Foster, 1929.

Color Matching on Textiles, D. Paterson. Scott, Greenwood and Sons, Ltd., London, 1909.

Colour in Relation to Chemical Constitution, E. R. Watson. Longmans, Green Company, Ltd., London, 1918.

Colour Index, F. M. Rowe, editor. Society of Dyers and Colourists, London, 1924.

Comprehensive Survey of Starch Chemistry, R. P. Walton, editor. Chemical Catalog Company, New York, 1928.

Cotton Cellulose, Its Chemistry and Technology, A. J. Hall. D. Van Nostrand Company, London, 1924.

Cotton Warp Sizing Handbook. Research Staff of E. F. Houghton Company, Philadelphia, Pennsylvania. First edition, 1938.

Denney's Complete Spotting Guide, including Wetcleaning and Bleaching, R. Denney, Cleaning and Dyeing World, 1937.

Development of the Chemistry of Commercial Synthetic Dyes, F. M. Rowe. Institute of Chemistry, London, 1929.

Dressings and Finishings for Textile Fabrics and Their Application, F. Polleyn. Translated by C. Salter. Scott, Greenwood and Company, Ltd., London, 1911.

Dyeing and Textile Chemistry, Laboratory of, A. M. Matthews, New York, 1908.

Dyeing of Cotton Fabrics, F. Beech and A. J. Hall. Third edition. E. Benn and Company, Ltd., London, 1927.

Dyeing of Textile Fibers, R. S. Horsfall and L. G. Lawrie. E. Benn and Company, Ltd., London, 1927.

Dyeing of the Textile Fibers, Hummel. London, 1896.

Dyeing of Woolen Fabrics, F. Beech. London, 1913.

Dyeing of Viscose with D.C. Dyestuffs. Courtaulds, Ltd., London, 1927.

Dyeing with Coal Tar Dyestuffs, C. M. Whittaker and C. C. Wilcock. Third edition. Longmans, Green Company, Ltd., London, 1939.

Dyes Classified by Intermediates, R. N. Shreve, W. N. Watson, and A. R. Willis. Chemical Catalog Company, Ltd., London, 1922.

Dyestuffs and Coal Tar Products, G. Martin. Lockwood and Company, Ltd., London, 1928.

Dyes, F. M. Rowe. Institute of Chemistry, London, 1929.

Dyes and Dyeing, Pellow. Low, Marston Company, Ltd., London, 1928.

Fast Dyeing and Dyes, Morton. Constable, Ltd., Edinburgh, Scotland.

Finishing Materials, J. A. Clark. Second edition. W. R. C. Smith Publishing Company, Atlanta, Georgia, 1926, 1940.

Finishing of Textile Fabrics, Roberts Beaumont. E. Benn and Company, Ltd., London, 1926.

Finishing of Woven Fabrics, E. Midgley. Longmans, Green Company, Ltd., London, 1930.

Fundamental Processes of Dye Chemistry, H. E. Fierz-David. Translated by F. A. Mason. Churchill, Ltd., London, 1921.

History of Bleaching, S. H. Higgins. Longmans, Green Company, Ltd., London, 1924.

Introduction to the Chemistry of Cellulose, J. T. Meush and F. C. Word. D. Van Nostrand Company, Princeton, New Jersey.

Khaki on Cotton and Other Textile Materials, F. C. Theis. Heywood, Ltd., London, 1903.

Manual on the Chemistry of Laundry Materials and Methods, A. Harvey. Second edition. Technical Press, Ltd., London, 1935.

Manual on the Standard Practice for the Power Laundry Washroom, Laundry Owners' National Association, 1927.

Methods of Cellulose Chemistry, C. Doree. D. Van Nostrand Company, Princeton, N. J., 1933.

Modern Soap and Detergent Industry, G. Martin. Chemical Catalog Company, 1932.

Monsanto Chemicals, 26th Edition. Monsanto Chemical Company, St. Louis, Missouri, and Springfield, Massachusetts, 1942.

Natural Organic Colouring Matters, A. G. Perkins and A. E. Everest. Longmans, Green Company, Ltd., London, 1918.

Practical Treatise on the Bleaching of Linen and Cotton Yarn and Fabrics, L. Tailfer. Translated by J. G. MacIntosh, Second edition. Scott, Greenwood Company, Ltd., London, 1917.

Principles and Practices of Textile Printing, E. Knecht and J. B. Fothergill. Third edition. Griffin Company, Ltd., London, 1936.

Principles of Bleaching and Finishing of Cotton, S. R. Trotman and E. L. Thorpe. Griffin and Company, Ltd., London, 1911 and 1927.

Principles of Dyeing, G. S. Fraps. Macmillan Company Ltd., London, 1903.

Processing and Finishing Cottons, J. F. Monoghan. F. P. Bennett Company, Boston, Massachusetts, 1935.

Rayon Dyeing and Finishing, B. L. Hathorne. Howes Publishing Company, New York, 1934.

Remedies for Dyehouse Troubles, W. C. Dodson. D. Van Nostrand Company, Princeton, New Jersey, 1922.

Researches on Cellulose IV, C. F. Cross and C. Doree. Longmans, Green Company, Ltd., London, 1922.

Silk Screen Printing Process, J. I. Biegeleisen and E. J. Busenbark. McGraw-Hill Book Company, New York, 1938.

Soap, Its Composition, Manufacture and Properties, W. H. Simmons. Fourth edition. Pitman and Sons, Ltd., London, 1936.

Starch, Its Chemistry, Technology, and Uses, L. Eynon and J. H. Lane. Hiffer Company, Ltd., London, 1906.

Studies in Bleachery Management, B. F. Perkins and Sons, Inc. Frank P. Bennett Company, Boston, Massachusetts, 1925.

Supplement to Colour Index, F. M. Rowe, editor. Society of Dyers and Colourists, London, 1928.

Synthetic Colouring Materials, J. F. Thorpe and C. K. Ingold. Longmans, Green Company, Ltd., London, 1923.

Technology of Textile Fibers, Chemical; G. von Georgievics, 431 pages.

Textbook of Cellulose Chemistry, E. Heuser. Translated by C. J. West and G. G. Esselen. D. Van Nostrand Company, Princeton, New Jersey, and London, 1938.

Textile Bleaching, A. B. Stevens. Pitman and Sons, Ltd., London, 1921.

Textile Chemistry and Dyeing, Part One, Chemical Technology of the Fibers, seventh edition. Lowell Technological Institute Cooperative Society, Lowell, Massachusetts, 1937.

Textile Chemistry, Introduction to, Harper. Macmillan Company, New York.

Textile Fabrics, Their Selection and Care from the Standpoint of Use, Wear and Launderability, G. H. Johnson. Harper & Row, Publishers, Inc., New York, 1927.

Textile Fiber Atlas, Werner Von Bergen and Walter Krauss. American Wool Handbook Company, 303 Fifth Avenue, New York, 1942.
Textile Handbook, Cotton Edition; E. F. Houghton and Company, Philadelphia, Pennsylvania, 1925.
Textile Oils and Soaps, F. H. Hurst and W. H. Simmons. Scott, Greenwood Company, Ltd., London, 1921.
Textile Printing, Dyeing, and Finishing, A. J. Hall. E. Benn and Company, Ltd., London, 1926.
The Bleaching, Dyeing, and Chemical Technology of Textile Fibers, S. R. Trotman and E. R. Trotman, 610 pages. C. Griffin and Company, Ltd., London, 1925.
The Chemical Formulary, Volumes 1 to 6, H. Bennett, F.A.I.C., Chemical Publishing Company, Brooklyn and New York.
The Printing of Textiles, R. Capey. Chapman, Hall Company, Ltd., London, 1930.
Theory of Sizing, H. Nisbet. Emmott Company, Ltd., London, 1912.
Treatise on Colour Manufacture, G. Zerr and R. Ruebencamp. Translated by C. Mayer. C. Griffin and Company, Ltd., London, 1908.
Vegetable Dyes, E. M. Mairet. Faber and Faber Company, Ltd., London, 1939.
Waterproofing of Fabrics, S. Mierzinski. Translated by A. Morris and H. Rolson, third edition. Scott, Greenwood Company, Ltd., London, 1930.
Waterproofing Textile Fabrics, H. P. Pearson. Chemical Catalog Company, 1924.
Wool Dyeing, Gardner. Philadelphia, 1896.

4. APPLIED TEXTILES, BASIC TEXTILES, MISCELLANEOUS BOOKS

A Guidebook for Homemaking, Evelyn M. Herrington. Meredith Press, Inc., New York City, 1935.
Adventures with the Microscope, J. D. Carrington, 455 pages. Bausch and Lomb Optical Company, Rochester, New York, 1934.
Air Conditioning in Textile Mills, Albert W. Thompson, 497 pages. Parks-Cramer Company, Fitchburg, Massachusetts, 1925.
America's Fabrics, Bendure and Pfeiffer, 688 pages. Macmillan Company, New York City, 1946.
American Cotton Handbook, G. R. Merrill and A. R. Macormac. Rayon Publishing Company, 303 Fifth Avenue, New York City.
Antique Textiles, Tiffany Studios, New York City.
Applied Textiles with Lesson Plans for Teachers, George E. Linton and Louis F. Friedman. State Department of Education, Education Building, Albany, New York, 1939, 1941.
Appliqué Design and Methods, Kathleen Mann. Macmillan Company, New York City, 1937.
Art in Home and Clothing, Trilling and Williams. J. B. Lippincott and Company, Philadelphia, Pennsylvania, 1936.
Art in Industry, Richards. Macmillan Company, New York City.
Art Weaving, Frieda Kean. D. C. Heath Company, New York City, 1937.
Asbestos, Cirkel. Ottawa, Ontario, Dominion of Canada, 1905.
Bobbins of Belgium, Charlotte Kellogg. Funk and Wagnalls, New York City, 1920.
Calculations in Yarns and Fabrics, Bradbury. Belfast, Ireland, 1906.
Clothing, Jordan. Barrows Publishing Company.
Clothing and Health, Kinne and Cooley. Macmillan Company, New York City.
Clothing Construction, Brown. Ginn and Company, New York City.
Cloths and the Cloth Trade, Hunter. Pitman and Sons, Ltd., London, England.
Color and Design in the Decorative Arts, Elizabeth Burris-Meyer. Prentice Hall, Inc., Englewood Cliffs, New Jersey, 1935.
Color in Woven Design, Beaumont. Whittaker Company, London, England.
Cost Control and Accounting for Textile Mills, Eugene Szepesi, 441 pages. Bragdon, Lord and Nagle Publishing Company, New York City, 1922.
Costume Design, Bradley. International Textbook Company, Scranton, Pennsylvania.
Costume Throughout the Ages, Mary Evans. J. B. Lippincott Company, Philadelphia, Pennsylvania.
Cotton, W. Johnson. Macmillan Company, New York City.
Creative Chemistry, Edwin E. Slosson, 331 pages. Century Company, New York City, 1919.
Credit and International Trade—How They Work in Practice; B. Ellinger, 189 pages. Macmillan and Company, Ltd., London, England, 1934.
Design and Manufacture of Towels and Toweling, Wodehouse. Pitman and Sons, Ltd., London, England.
Design in Textile Fabrics, Ashenhurst. Cassell Publishing Company.
Directory of Commercial Textile Testing Laboratories, 13 pages. Textile Foundation, Commerce Building, Washington, D. C., 1933.

Distribution of Textiles, 190 pages. Bureau of Business Research, Harvard University, Cambridge, Massachusetts, 1926.

Early American Textiles, Little. Century Company, New York City.

Elementary Textile Design and Fabric Structure, John Read. Edward Arnold and Company, 1931.

Elementary Textile Microscopy, J. H. Skinkle, 144 pages. Howes Publishing Company, New York City, 1930.

Embroidery Design and Stitches, Kathleen Mann. Macmillan Company, New York City, 1937.

Embroidery in Wools, O. P. Couch. Sir Isaac Pitman and Sons, Ltd., London, England.

English Needlework, A. Kendrick. Black Publishing, Ltd., London, England, 1933.

Étude sur les Fibres Textiles, Barille. Strasbourg, 1868.

Fabric Analysis, Covering Wool, Worsted, Silk, Cotton, Artificial Silks, etc., F. A. Posselt, 231 pages. Textile Publishing Company, Philadelphia, Pennsylvania, 1920.

Finishing Materials, J. Andrew Clark, 113 pages. Textile Industries, Inc., Atlanta, Georgia, 1926.

Finishing of Woven Fabrics, E. Midgley. Longmans Green Company, New York City, 1929.

Foot-Power Loom Weaving, E. F. Worst. Bruce Publishing Company, New York City, 1943.

Fundamentals of Fibre Structure, W. T. Astbury, 187 pages. Oxford University Press, London, England, 1933.

Fundamentals of Home Economics, Jense, Jensen and Ziller. Macmillan Company, New York City, 1935.

Fundamentals of Textiles, E. A. Jacobsen and H. E. McCullough. John Wiley and Sons Inc., 605 Third Avenue, New York City, 1937.

Getting Ahead in Retailing, Nathan M. Ohrbach, 266 pages. McGraw-Hill Book Company Inc., New York City, 1936.

Handbook of Industrial Fabrics, Dr. Ernest R. Kaswell. Wellington Sears Company, Inc., Subsidiary of West Point-Pepperell Mfg. Co., Inc., West Point, Georgia, and New York City, 1963.

History of Manufactures in the United States, V. S. Clark, 3 volumes. McGraw-Hill Book Company, Inc., New York City, 1929.

History of Silk, Cotton, Linen and Wool, Gilroy. Harper & Row, Publishers, Inc., New York City.

History of the Basic Trades, H. Kay. Macmillan Company, 60 Fifth Ave., New York City, 1936.

Home and Family, Jordan, Zeller and Brown. Macmillan Company, New York, 1935.

Home Decoration—Its Problems and Solutions, Ross Steward and John Gerald. Garden City Publishing Company, Garden City, Long Island, New York City, 1938.

Home Furnishing, A. H. Ruff. John Wiley and Sons, New York, 1936.

Homespun Handcraft, Bowles. J. B. Lippincott and Company, Philadelphia, Pennsylvania, 1935.

How the World Is Clothed, Carpenter. American Book Company, New York City.

How to Decorate Textiles, Branch. Dodd, Mead Company, New York City.

How to Know Textiles, Cassie Paine Small, 394 pages. Ginn and Company, New York City, 1932.

How We Are Clothed, Chamberlain. Macmillan Company, New York City.

Industrial Fibres, Imperial Economic Committee, 113 pages. London, England, 1938.

Introduction to Textile Chemistry, H. Harper. Macmillan Company, New York City, 1931.

Laboratory Manual, Stanley and Cline. Ginn and Company, New York, 1935.

Les Fibres Textiles d'Origine Animale, Zolla. Paris, 1910.

Les Tissus Indiens de Vieux Pérou, Harcourt, France.

Management of a Textile Business, C. C. Balderston and Victor Karabasz, 228 pages. Textile Foundation, Commerce Building, Washington, D. C., 1938.

Management's Handbook, L. P. Alford, 1607 pages. Ronald Press, New York, 1924.

Manual of Winding, Warping, and Quilling, I. Kline. John Wiley and Sons, New York City, 1926.

Manufacture of Narrow Woven Fabrics, E. E. Posselt, 198 pages. McGraw-Hill Book Company, Inc., New York, 1917.

Marketing of Textiles, Reavis Cox, 390 pages. Textile Foundation, Commerce Building, Washington, D. C., 1938.

Millinery, Aiken. Ronald Press, New York City.

Millinery, Brown. Ginn and Company, New York City.

Millinery, Loewen. Macmillan Company, New York City.

Modern Needlecraft, D. C. Minter. Blackie and Sons, Ltd., London, England, 1932.

Modern Textile Microscopy, J. M. Preston, 315 pages. Emmott and Company, Ltd., London, England, 1933.

Musée Historique des Tissues, D'Hennesel. Laurens Company.

Nomenclature Nouvelle des 550 Fibres Textiles, Bernardin. Ghent, Belgium, 1872.

Ornamentation and Textile Design, Barker. Stokes Publishing Company, New York City.
One World of Fashion, M. D. C. Crawford, Fairchild Publishing Company, 7 East 12th St.,
New York City, 1946.
Plain and Fancy Weaving, Brickett. International Correspondence Company, Scranton, Penn-
sylvania.
Plastics, A. J. Lockrey, 233 pages. D. Van Nostrand Company, Princeton, New Jersey, 3rd edi-
tion, 1943.
Principles of Woolen Spinning, H. Priestman. Longmans, Green Company, New York City, 1924.
Prints and Patterns, Littlejohn. Pitman Publishing Company, Ltd., New York City, London,
England.
Problems in Textiles, Hess and Bruner. J. B. Lippincott and Company, Philadelphia, Pennsylva-
nia, 1931.
Psychology of Dress, Hurlock. Ronald Press, New York City.
Rayon Industry, M. H. Avram. D. Van Nostrand and Company, Princeton, N. J., 1927.
Romance of Design, Warren. Doubleday & Company, New York City.
Romance of French Weaving, Rodier. Tudor Publishing Company, New York City.
Romance of Textiles, E. Lewis. Macmillan Company, New York City, 1937.
Shelter and Clothing, Kinne and Cooley, 377 pages. Macmillan Company, New York City, 1913.
Some Great Commodities, Statistical Division, National Bank of Commerce in New York, 287
pages, 1922.
Standard Cloths, Beaumont. Greenwood, Ltd., London, England.
Story Book of Cotton, Maud and Miska Petersham, John C. Winston Publishing Company,
Philadelphia, Pennsylvania, 1939.
Story of Textiles, Perry Walton. Tudor Publishing Company, New York, 1936.
Story of Textiles, Watson. Harper & Row, Publishers, Inc., New York City.
Story of Weaving, L. Lamprey. Stokes Publishing Company, New York, 1939.
Student's Manual of Textiles, Wilford. Pitman and Sons, Ltd., London, England.
Study of Fabrics, Turner. D. Appleton Company, New York City.
Stuff, Beery. D. Appleton Company, New York City.
Shuttlecraft of American Hand Weaving, Atwater. Macmillan Company, New York City.
Survey of Textile Research in the United States, United States Institute of Textile Research, Inc.
65 Franklin St., Boston, Massachusetts, 1931.
Tapestry, The Mirror of Civilization, Ackerman. Oxford Press, London, England.
Technical Testing of Yarns and Textile Fabrics, Dr. J. Herzfeld, 209 pages. D. Van Nostrand
Company, Princeton, N. J., 1920.
Technology of Textile Design, E. A. Posselt. Philadelphia College of Textiles and Science, Phil-
adelphia, Pennsylvania, 1884.
Testing of Yarns and Fabrics for Manufactures, Warehousemen, and Operatives, H. P. Curtis.
Sir Isaac Pitman and Sons, Ltd., London, England, 1930.
Textile Analysis, S. R. Trotman and E. R. Trotman, 301 pages. J. B. Lippincott Company,
Philadelphia, Pennsylvania, 1932.
Textile Costing an Aid to Management, J. Lockwood and A. D. Maxwell, 300 pages. Textile
Foundation, Commerce Building, Washington, D. C., 1938.
Textile Design, Brickett. International Textbook Company, Scranton, Pennsylvania.
Textile Design, Woodhouse and Milne. Macmillan Company, New York City.
Textile Design, A Bibliography and Directory, 29 pages. Textile Foundation, Commerce Build-
ing, Washington, D. C., 1932.
Textile Design, Grammar of; Nesbit. D. Van Nostrand Company, Princeton, N. J.
Textile Fabrics, Elizabeth Dyer. Houghton Mifflin Company, Boston, Massachusetts, 1926.
Textile Fabrics, Historical; Glazier. Charles Scribner's Sons, New York City.
Textile Fabrics, Their Selection and Care from the Standpoint of Use, Wear, and Launderability.
G. H. Johnson, 385 pages. Harper & Row, Publishers, Inc., New York City, 1927.
Textile Factory Organization and Management, D. R. H. Williams, 89 pages. Emmott and Com-
pany, Ltd., Manchester, England, 1934.
Textile Fibers and Their Uses, Katherine Hess, 354 pages. J. B. Lippincott Company, Phila-
delphia, Pennsylvania, 1936, and revisions.
Textile Fibers of Commerce, Hannan. London, England, 1902.
Textile Fibers, Their Physical, Microscopical and Chemical Properties, J. Merritt Matthews,
630 pages. John Wiley and Sons Company, New York City, 1908.
Textile Fibers, Yarns, and Fabrics, Bray. Century Company, New York.
Textile Problems for the Consumer, T. N. Carver, Mary S. Woolman, and Ellen B. McGowan,
175 pages. Macmillan Company, New York City, 1935.

Textile Raw Materials, Zipser. Scott, Greenwood, Ltd., London, England.

Textile Waste Treatment and Recovery, J. C. Geyer and W. A. Perry. Textile Foundation, Commerce Building, Washington, D. C., 1938.

Textiles, Barker. Macmillan Company, New York.

Textiles, Paul H. Nystrom, 335 pages. D. Appleton and Company, New York, 1916.

Textiles, Woolman and McGowan, 572 pages. Macmillan Company, New York City, 1926.

Textiles and Clothing, McGowan and Waite, 344 pages. Macmillan Company, New York City, 1931.

Textiles and Clothing, E. Sage. Charles Scribner's Sons, New York, 1930.

Textiles and Clothing, Watson. American School of Home Economics.

Textiles and Origin of Their Names, Megrew. Private printing, 1906.

Textiles and the Microscope, E. R. Schwarz, 329 pages. McGraw-Hill Book Company, Inc., New York City, 1934.

Textiles for Salesmen, E. Ostick. Sir Isaac Pitman and Sons, Ltd., London, England. 1931.

Textiles, Guide To; Evans and McGowan, 233 pages. John Wiley and Sons Company, New York, 1939.

The Big Book of Needlecraft, Annie A. Patterson. Charles Scribner's Sons, New York.

The Conservation of Textiles, 162 pages. Laundry Owners National Association, La Salle, Illinois, 1923.

The Heritage of Cotton, M. D. C. Crawford. Grosset & Dunlap, Inc., New York City.

The Home Economics Omnibus, Harris and Huston. Little Brown and Company, Boston, Massachusetts, 1935.

The Instructor in Garment Cleaning, C. C. Hubbard, 318 pages. National Association of Dyers and Cleaners, Railway Exchange Building, St. Louis, Missouri.

The Location of Manufacturers in the United States, 1899–1929, 105 pages. F. B. Carver, F. M. Boddy, and A. J. Nixon. University of Minnesota Press, Minneapolis, Minnesota.

The Mechanics of Textile Machinery, W. A. Hanton, 236 pages. Longmans, Green and Company, New York, 1924.

The Mode in Dress and Home, D. G. Donovan. Allyn and Bacon, Boston, Massachusetts, 1935.

The New Elementary Home Economics, M. L. Matthews. Little Brown and Company, Boston, Massachusetts.

The Printing of Textiles, R. Capel, 145 pages. Chapman and Hall, Ltd., London, England, 1930.

The Standard Handbook of Textiles, A. J. Hall, F. T. I., 296 pages. D. Van Nostrand Co., Princeton, New Jersey, 1946.

The Story of Weaving, L. Lamprey, 278 pages. Stokes Publishing Company, New York, 1939.

The Textile Industries—An Economic Analysis, H. E. Michl, 304 pages. Textile Foundation, Commerce Building, Washington, D. C., 1938.

The Training of Men for the Textile Industry, 47 pages. Textile Foundation, Commerce Building, Washington, D. C., 1934.

Training in Textile Information, Research Bureau of Retail Training, University of Pittsburgh Press, Pittsburgh, Pennsylvania.

United States Testing Company, 1415 Park Avenue, Hoboken, New Jersey. Many valuable pamphlets, booklets, charts, etc., in all phases of textiles and textile testing.

Various Needlecrafts, Vera C. Alexander. Sir Isaac Pitman and Sons, Ltd., New York City, London, England.

Vertical Integration in the Textile Industries, Hiram S. Davis, G. W. Taylor, C. C. Balderston, and Anne Bezanson, 132 pages. Wharton School of Finance and Commerce, and Textile Foundation, Commerce Building, Washington, D. C., 1938.

Weaves, Handbook of; Oelsner. Macmillan Company, New York City, 1941.

What You Should Know About Rayon Yarn. Prepared by the Rayon Institute, New York City, 1940.

World Resources and Industries, E. W. Zimmerman, 842 pages. Harper & Row, Publishers, Inc., New York, 1933.

Yarn and Cloth Making, An Economic Study, Mary Louise Kissel, 252 pages. Macmillan Company, New York, 1913.

5. WOMEN'S READY-TO-WEAR AND INFANTS' WEAR

A Century of Fashion, Jean Philippe Worth. Little Brown and Company, Inc., Boston, Massachusetts, 1938.

Any Girl Can Be Good Looking. Cades. Appleton Company, New York City.

Clothes and Personality, Ryan. Appleton Company, New York City.

Clothes for Girls, Todd. Little, Brown and Company, Boston, Mass., 1935.

Clothing, Friant, Turner and Miller. Collegiate Press, Ames, Iowa, 1936.

Clothing, M. Friend and Hazel Schultz. D. Appleton Century Company, New York City, 1933.

Clothing, Choice, Care and Cost, Mary S. Woolman. J. B. Lippincott and Company, Philadelphia, Pennsylvania, 1926.

Clothing, Fundamental Problems of, Louise Jordan and E. Bulger. Barrows Company, 1927.

Clothing Introductory College Course, Latzke and Quinlan. J. B. Lippincott and Company, Philadelphia, Pennsylvania, 1935.

Clothing, Selection and Care of, Mary L. Matthews. Little Brown and Company, Boston, Massachusetts.

Clothing, Selection and Purchase of, Lillian C. W. Baker. Macmillan Company, New York City, 1932.

Clothing and Style, William H. Dooley. D. C. Heath Company, New York City, 1930.

Clothing for Women, Laura Baldt. J. B. Lippincott and Company, Philadelphia, Pennsylvania, 1929.

Clothing for the High School Girl, Laura Baldt. J. B. Lippincott and Company, Philadelphia, Pennsylvania, 1933.

Clothing Study, A Workbook for High School Girls, Trilling and Nicholas. J. B. Lippincott and Company, Philadelphia, Pennsylvania, 1935.

Color and Design in Apparel, Bernice G. Chambers, 627 pages. Prwentice-Hall, Inc., Englewood Cliffs, New Jersey, 1944.

Color and Line in Dress, Laurene Hempstead. Prentice-Hall, Inc., Englewood Cliffs, New Jersey, 1931.

Complete Dressmaker with Simple Directions for Home Millinery, Loughlin. D. Appleton and Company, New York City.

Consumer Goods, Reich and Siegler, 526 pages. American Book Company, New York City, 1937.

Designing and Decorating Clothes, The Women's Institute, International Textbook Company, Scranton, Pennsylvania, 1932.

Designing Women, Margaretta Byers and Consuelo Kamholz. Simon and Schuster, New York City, 1938.

Distinctive Clothes, Frances H. Consalus. Ronald Press, New York City, 1940.

Domestic Art in Women's Education, Cooley. Charles Scribner's Sons, New York City.

Draping and Dress Design, Mary Evans. Edwards Company.

Dress and Home Workbook, Dulcie G. Donovan. Allyn and Bacon Company, Boston, Massachusetts, 1935.

Dress and Look Slender, Wells. Personal Arts Company.

Dress Construction With the Aid of Patterns, Butterick Company, New York City.

Dress Design and Selection, Margaret H. Hopkins. Macmillan Company, New York City, 1937.

Dress, Blouse and Costume Clothes, Beaumont and Hill. Pitman and Sons, Ltd., New York City, London, England.

Dresses, Ringo. A. W. Shaw Company.

Dressmaking, Fales. Charles Scribner's Sons, New York City.

Economics of Fashion, Paul H. Nystrom. Ronald Press, New York City.

Elements of Costume Design for High School Students, Downs and O'Leary, Bruce Publishing Company, New York City.

Embroidery and Design in the New Stitching, Foster. Pitman and Sons, Ltd., New York City, London, England.

Embroidery Design, Molly Booker. Studio Publications Company.

Embroidery or the Craft of the Needle. Townsend. Truslove and Hanson, Ltd., London, England.

Essentials of Sewing, Rosamond C. Cook. Manual Arts Press.

Everyday Living for Girls, Adelaide Van Duzer. J. B. Lippincott Company, Philadelphia, Pennsylvania, 1941.

Fabrics and Clothing, McBride. Macmillan Company, New York City, 1932.

Fabrics and Dress, Rathbone and Tarpley. Houghton Mifflin Company, Boston, Massachusetts.

Fashion Drawing, H. R. Dotin. Harper & Row, Publishers, Inc., New York City, 1939.

Fashion Is Spinach, Elizabeth Hawes, 337 pages. Random House, New York City, 1938.

Fashion Merchandising, Paul H. Nystrom. Ronald Press, New York City.

Fashions Since Their Debut, Wilson. International Textbook Company, Scranton, Pennsylvania.

From Thimble to Gown, Van Gilder. Allyn and Bacon, Inc., Boston, Massachusetts.

Fundamentals of Dress, Marietta Kettunen. McGraw-Hill Book Co., Inc., New York City, 1941.

Fundamentals of Dress Construction, Manning and Donaldson. Macmillan Company, New York City, 1926.

Fundamentals of Sewing, Carrie Crane Ingalls. Bruce Publishing Company, New York City, 1928.

Fur, Max Bachrach. Prentice-Hall Company, Inc., Englewood Cliffs, New Jersey, 1937.

Girls' Problems in Home Economics, Trilling and Williams. J. B. Lippincott Company, Philadelphia, Pennsylvania.

Good Looks for Girls, Cades. Harcourt Brace Company, New York City.

Good Taste in Dress, F. W. McFarland. Manual Arts Press, Peoria, Illinois, 1936.

Handbook of Elementary Sewing, A. M. Miall. Pitman and Sons, Ltd., New York City, London, England.

Help Wanted–Female, Byers. Julian Messner Company, New York City, 1941.

History of American Costume, Elizabeth McClennan. Tudor Publishing Company, New York City, 1937.

How the Fashion World Works, Margaretta Stevenson. Harper & Row, Publishers, Inc., New York City, 1938.

How to Draw Fashion Figures, Ruth Conerly. Bridgman Publishing Company, 1936.

How We Are Clothed, James F. Chamberlain. Macmillan Company, New York, 1936.

Individuality and Clothes, Margaret Story. Funk and Wagnalls, New York, 1930.

Introduction to French Civilization, Whiting. Thrift Press, Ithaca, New York, 1938.

Junior Clothing, K. W. Kinyon and L. T. Hopkins. Sanborn Company, New York, 1937.

Language of Fashion, Mary B. Picken. Funk and Wagnalls Company, New York.

Making Smart Clothes, Butterick Company, New York City.

Mode in Dress and Home, Donovan. Allyn and Bacon Company, Boston, Massachusetts.

Modern Clothing, Laura Baxter and Alpha Latzke. J. B. Lippincott and Company, Philadelphia, Pennsylvania, 1938.

Modern Dressmaking, Mary B. Picken. McKay Publishing Company, New York City.

New Butterick Dressmaker, Butterick Company, New York City.

New Dressmaker, Butterick Company, New York City.

One World of Fashion, M. D. C. Crawford, Fairchild Publishing Company, 7 East 12th Street, New York City, 1946.

Pattern and Dress Design, Josephine Eddy and Elizabeth C. B. Wiley. Houghton Mifflin Company, New York City, 1932.

Powers Girls, John Robert Powers. E. P. Dutton and Company, Inc., New York City, 1941.

Practical Dress Design, Mabel D. Erwin. Macmillan Company, New York City, 1941.

Principles of Clothing Selection, Helen G. Buttrick. Macmillan Company, New York City, 1936.

Principles of Dress, Winterburn. Harper & Row, Publishers, Inc., New York City.

School Sewing, Burton. Ginn and Company, New York City.

Scovil's Lady Book, Cora Scovil. Harrison Hilton Brooks, Inc., New York City, 1940.

Secrets of Distinctive Dress, Mary B. Picken. International Textbook Press, Scranton, Pennsylvania.

Sewing and Textiles, Turner. D. Appleton and Company, New York City.

Sewing Handicraft for Girls, McGlauflin. Manual Arts Press, Peoria, Illinois.

Sewing Materials, 267 pages. Women's Institute of Domestic Arts and Sciences, Scranton, Pennsylvania, 1928.

Student's Manual of Fashion Drawing, E. Young. John Wiley and Sons, New York City, 1930.

Study Guide to Problems of Fabrics and Dress, L. Rathbone. Houghton Mifflin Company, Boston, Massachusetts, 1937.

Style and the Woman, Cary. Dry Goods Economist, New York City.

The Story of Costume, Beele Northrup. Art Education Press, Inc., New York City, 1935.

The Story of Lace and Embroidery, David E. Schwab. Fairchild Publications, Inc., New York City, Schiffli Embroidery Institute, Jersey City, New Jersey.

The Ways of Fashion, M. D. C. Crawford, 320 pages. G. P. Putnam's Sons, New York City, 1941.

The Women's Garment Workers, Louis Levine. B. W. Huebsch, Inc., New York City, 1924.

Well Dressed Woman, Rittenhouse. Harper & Row, Publishers, Inc., New York City.

When Sally Sews, Helen Perry Curtis. Macmillan Company, New York City, 1929.

Workbook for Clothing, Elnora Culbert. Economy Company, Oklahoma City, Oklahoma, 1933.

Your Clothes and Personality, Mildred G. Ryan. Appleton Century Company, New York City, 1937.

6. HOME ECONOMICS AND THE HOME

Accessories of Dress, K. M. Lester and B. V. Oerke. Manual Arts Press, Peoria, Illinois.

Antique Jewelry and Trinkets, Burgess. Tudor Publishing Company, New York.

Art Metalwork, Payne. Manual Arts Press, Peoria, Illinois.

Art in Needlework, Day. B. T. Batsford, Ltd., London.

Artificial Flower Making, Baskin. Pitman and Sons, Ltd., New York.

Bedding, Hidden Value Series, Sears Roebuck and Company, Chicago, Illinois.
Consumer Goods, Reich and Siegler. American Book Company, New York, 1937.
Decorating the Home, Ethel Lewis, 574 pages. Macmillan Company, New York, 1942.
Decoratively Speaking, Gladys Miller. Doubleday & Company, Inc., Garden City, New York, 1939.
Embroidery and Tapestry, Christie. Hogg, Ltd., London.
Embroidery Book, Mary Thomas. William Morrow and Company, Inc., New York, 1936.
Encyclopedia of Needlework, Therese de Dillmont, 813 pages plus appendix. D M C Library, Mulhouse, France. Printed by the Société Anonyme, Dollfus-Mieg & Cie., Mulhouse, France.
Gem and Gem Materials, E. H. Kraus and C. B. Slawson. McGraw-Hill Book Company, Inc., New York, 1939.
Hats and How to Make Them, Patty. Rand McNally Company, Chicago, Ill.
Home Fashions Reporter, monthly, Reporter Publications, New York.
Homecraft Rugs, Walker. Frederick A. Stokes Publishing Company, New York.
How to Make Lace, Roberts. Dry Goods Economist, New York City.
Individuality and Clothes, Margaret Story. Funk and Wagnalls, New York, 1940.
Interesting Art Needlework, Lukowitz. Bruce Publishing Company, New York.
Lace Books, The; Jessie F. Caplin. Macmillan Company, New York, 1932.
Lace Making, Page. J. B. Lippincott & Company, Philadelphia, Pa.
Metalcraft and Jewelry, Kronquist. Manual Arts Press, Peoria, Ill.
Period Influences in Interior Decorations, W. R. Storey. Harper & Row, Publishers, Inc., New York, 1937.
Point and Pillow Lace, Sharp. E. P. Dutton Company, New York.
Product Standards and Labeling for Consumers, Alice L. Edwards. Ronald Press, New York, 1940.
Pottery, Cox. Macmillan Company, New York.
Selling Home Furnishings Successfully, Samuel W. Reyburn. Prentice-Hall, Inc., Englewood Cliffs, New Jersey, 1938.
Shopping Guide, E. B. Weiss. Whittlesey House, New York, 1937.
Varied Occupations in String Work, Walker. Macmillan Company, New York.

7. PERIODICALS FOR TEXTILE INFORMATION, TRADE JOURNALS, AND GENERAL INFORMATION ON ALL MAJOR FIBERS

American Dyestuff Reporter, monthly, Howes Publishing Co., 44 East 23rd St., New York City.
American Exporter, monthly, Johnston Export Publishing Company, 386 Fourth Avenue, New York City.
American Fabrics Magazine, quarterly, Doric Publishing Co., Inc., 24 East 38th St., New York City.
America's Textile Reporter, weekly (since 1887), Frank P. Bennett Company, Boston, Massachusetts.
Daily News Record, Fairchild Publications, 7 East 12th Street, New York.
Export Trade and Shipper, weekly. Export Shipper Publishing Company, New York City.
Industrial Standards and Commercial Standards Monthly. American Standards Association, 70 E. 45th Street, New York.
Modern Textiles Magazine, Rayon Publishing Co., Inc., 303 Fifth Avenue, New York City.
Packing and Shipping, monthly, Bonnell Publications, 30 Church Street, New York.
Textile Bulletin, weekly, Clark Publishing Company, Charlotte, North Carolina.
Textile Industries Magazine, Atlanta, Georgia.
Textile Research, monthly, Textile Research Institute, Princeton, New Jersey.
Textile World, monthly, McGraw-Hill Book Company, Inc., New York.
The Industrial Arts Index, monthly, H. W. Wilson Company, 950 University Avenue, New York.
The New York Times Index, New York Times Monthly Publication, New York Times, Times Square, New York.
The Readers Guide to Periodical Literature, monthly, H. W. Wilson Company, 950 University Avenue, New York.
Waste Trade Journal, weekly, Atlas Publishing Company, 150 Lafayette Street, New York.

8. FOR COTTON

American Cotton Grower, monthly. The American Cotton Grower Publishing Company, 713 Glen Street, Atlanta, Georgia.
American Ginner and Cotton Oil Miller, monthly, Box 504, Little Rock, Arkansas.

America's Textile Reporter, weekly, Frank P. Bennett Company, Inc., 286 Congress Street, Boston, Massachusetts.

Cotton, monthly, Textile Industries, Inc., Atlanta, Georgia.

Cotton and Cotton Oil Press, weekly, 3116 Commerce Street, Dallas, Texas.

Cotton Digest, weekly, Cotton Exchange Building, Houston, Texas.

The Cotton Oil Press, monthly, Memphis, Tennessee.

The Cotton Trade Journal, weekly, Cotton Exchange Bldg., New Orleans, Louisiana.

The Oil Mill Gazetteer, monthly, H. E. Wilson Company, Wharton, Texas.

The Oil Miller and Cotton Ginner, monthly, Oil Miller Publishing Company, Atlanta, Georgia.

9. FOR MANMADE FIBERS

Manmade Fiber Producers Association, Inc., 350 Fifth Avenue, New York City.

Modern Textiles Magazine, Rayon Publishing Company, 303 Fifth Avenue, New York.

Textile Organon, monthly, Stanley B. Hunt, Textile Economics Bureau Incorporated, 10 East 40th Street, New York.

10. FOR MISCELLANEOUS FIBERS

American Society for Testing Materials Bulletin, monthly, (A.S.T.M.), Philadelphia, Pennsylvania.

America's Textile Reporter, weekly, Frank P. Bennett Company, 286 Congress Street, Boston, Massachusetts.

Associated Wool Industries, monthly, 386 Fourth Avenue, New York.

Bags, monthly, Atlas Publishing Company, New York.

Broom and Broom Corn News, weekly, Arcola, Illinois.

Brooms, Brushes, and Mops, monthly, Montgomery Bldg., Milwaukee, Wisconsin.

Cord Age, monthly, Cord Age, 114 East 32nd Street, New York.

Cordage Trade Journal, semi-monthly, 132 Nassau St., New York.

Daily Mill Stock Reporter, information on wool, burlap, cotton, and wastes, Atlas Publishing Company, New York.

Linens and Domestics, monthly, Haire Publishing Company, East Stroudsburg, Pennsylvania.

Monthly Statistics of Wool Manufacture, National Association of Wool Manufacturers, 80 Federal Street, Boston, Massachusetts.

National Canvas Goods Manufacturers Review, monthly, 532 Endicott Building, St. Paul, Minnesota.

The Bedding Manufacturer, monthly, Better Bedding Alliance of America, 608 South Dearborn Street, Chicago, Illinois.

11. FOR KNIT GOODS

Gloves, monthly, Gloversville, New York.

Knit Goods Weekly, Howes Publishing Company, 44 East 23rd St., New York City.

Knitted Outerwear Age, monthly, Knit Goods Publishing Corporation, New York City.

Knitted Outerwear Times, weekly, National Knitted Outerwear Association, 51 Madison Ave., New York City. Also publishes annual Year Book.

Underwear and Hosiery Review, monthly, Knit Goods Publishing Company, 34 North Crystal Street, East Stroudsburg, Pennsylvania.

12. FOR WOMEN'S READY-TO-WEAR AND INFANTS' WEAR

American Lady's Tailor and Les Parisiennes, monthly, American-Mitchel Style Corporation, 145 West 28th St., New York.

Black Fox Magazine, monthly, 152 West 42nd Street, New York.

Central Furrier, monthly, 185 North Wabash Avenue, Chicago, Illinois.

Corset and Underwear Review, monthly, Haire Publishing Co., 1170 Broadway, New York.

Corsets and Brassieres, monthly, Bowman Publishing Company, 267 Fifth Avenue, New York.

Fur Animals, monthly, 201 B. M. A. Building, Kansas City, Missouri.

Fur Reporter, weekly, Atlas Publishing Company, Inc., 150 Lafayette Street, New York.

Fur Trade Review, monthly, 370 Seventh Avenue, New York.

Furs, monthly, Atlas Publishing Company, Inc., 150 Lafayette Street, New York.

Los Angeles Modes and Apparel Gazette, monthly, 857 South San Pedro Street, Los Angeles, California.

Midwest Retailer, monthly, Savoy Hotel, Kansas City, Missouri.

The Review, monthly, Garment Trade Review Company, 151 West 40th Street, New York.

Sportswear Magazine, monthly, Ranney Publishing Company, 1170 Broadway, New York.

Style Trend, monthly, Modes and Fabrics, Inc., 307 Fifth Avenue, New York.

The Fur Journal, monthly, 72 Columbia Street, Seattle, Washington.
The Illustrated Milliner, monthly, 105 West 40th St., New York.
Women's Wear Daily, Fairchild Publishing Company, 7 East 12th Street, New York.

13. FOR LAUNDRY TRADES, CLEANING AND DYEING

American Dyestuff Reporter, monthly, Howes Publishing Company, 44 East 23rd Street, New York.
Cleaning and Dyeing World, monthly, Kates-Boyleston Publishers, Inc., 1697 Broadway, New York.
Dyestuffs, quarterly, National Aniline and Chemical Company, Inc., 40 Rector Street, New York.
Laundry Year Book, annual, Laundry Age Publishing Co., New York.
National Cleaner and Dyer, monthly, National Cleaners and Dyers Publishing Corporation, National Institute of Drycleaning, Silver Spring, Maryland.
Starchroom Laundry Journal, monthly, R. H. Donnelley Corporation, 305 East 45th Street, New York.

14. FOR MEN'S AND BOYS' CLOTHING

American Gentleman and Sartorial Art Journal, monthly, 1133 Broadway, New York.
American Hatter, monthly, The Hat Trade Publishing Company, 1225 Broadway, New York.
Apparel Arts, quarterly, Apparel Arts, Publications, 919 North Michigan Avenue, Chicago, Illinois.
Apparel Manufacturer, monthly, Atlas Publishing Company, 150 Lafayette Street, New York.
Biography of a Suit—From Fiber to Fashion, Boys' Outfitter, 175 Fifth Avenue, New York City, December, 1940.
Clothing Trade Journal, monthly, Clothier Publishing Company, 307 Main Street, Kutztown, Pennsylvania.
Cotton Shirts for Men and Boys, Bulletin 1837F, U. S. Government Publishing Office, Washington, D. C.
How to Buy a Shirt, Cluett, Peabody and Company, Inc., 530 Fifth Ave., New York.
Magazine of the Merchant Tailors and Designers Association of America, 400 Madison Avenue, New York.
Men's Wear, bi-monthly, Fairchild Publishing Company, 418 South Market Street, Chicago, Illinois.
Selling Men's Evening Wear, and Other Articles, Fairchild Publishing Company, 7 East 12th Street, New York.
The Hat for the Occasion, Hat Style Council, Inc., 1123 Broadway, New York.
The National Clothier, monthly, National Clothier Publishing Company, Inc., 803 Merchandise Mart, Chicago, Illinois.

15. GENERAL TRADE AND MANUFACTURING DIRECTORIES

American Hatter Directory, bi-annual, The Hat Trade Publishing Company, 1225 Broadway, New York.
America's Textile Reporter, Annual Textile Statistics Issue (July); 286 Congress Street, Boston 10, Massachusetts.
Boy's Outfitter Directory, bi-annual, 175 Fifth Avenue, New York.
Buyers for Export, annual, Thomas Ashwell & Co., 20 Vesey St., New York.
Corset and Underwear Review's Annual Directory, Haire Publishing Company, 1170 Broadway, New York.
Cotton Fabrics Directory by Constructions and Sources, 96 pages. The Textile Committee, National Association of Purchasing Agents Daily Trade Record Company, 8 East 13th Street, New York, 1937.
Crain's Market Data Book, annual, Class and Industrial Market, 537 South Dearborn Street, Chicago, Illinois.
Davison's Cordage, Twine and Duck Trade Directory, annual, Davison Publishing Company, 50 Union Square, New York.
Davison's Knit Goods Trade, annual, Davison Publishing Company, New York.
Davison's Silk and Rayon Trades, annual, Davison Publishing Company, New York.
Davison's Textile Blue Book and Buyer's Guide, annual, Davison Publishing Company, New York.
Davison's Textile Directory for Salesmen, annual, Davison Publishing Company, New York.
Fairchild's Directory of Fabrics, Trimmings and Supplies, bi-annual, Fairchild Publishing Company, 7 East 12th Street, New York.

Fairchild's Men's Wear Directory of Chicago, semi-annual, Fairchild Publishing Company, New York.

Fairchild's Men's Wear Directory of New York, semi-annual, Fairchild Publishing Company, New York.

Fairchild's Women's Wear Directory of New York, semi-annual, Fairchild Publishing Company, New York.

International Cotton Book, annual, The Cotton and Cotton Oil News, Dallas, Texas.

Macrae's Blue Book and Hendricks' Commercial Register, Macrae's Blue Book Company, 18 East Huron Street, Chicago, Illinois.

Official American Textile Directory, annual, McGraw-Hill Book Company, Inc., New York.

Official Handbook of Textile Corporations, annual, Frank P. Bennett Company, 286 Congress St., Boston, Massachusetts.

The Directory of Branded Textile Merchandise, Textile World for Bragdon, Lord and Nagle, McGraw-Hill Book Company, New York, 1926.

Thomas' Register of American Manufacturers, annual, Thomas Publishing Company, 461 Eighth Avenue, New York.

16. TEXTILE DICTIONARIES

Callaway Textile Dictionary, W. L. Carmichael and George E. Linton, 390 pages. Callaway Mills, Inc., LaGrange, Georgia; New York Office, 295 5th Avenue, New York City, 1947.

Dan River's Dictionary of Textile Terms, Cox, Grimshaw, Hoye, Linton, Merrill, and *Good Housekeeping Magazine,* 128 pages, Dan River Mills, Inc., 111 West 40th Street, New York City. 10 editions from 1944–1964.

Dictionary of Weaves, E. A. Posselt, 85 pages with 2,000 weave constructions arranged for handy use showing the draft for each weave. S. Low, Marston & Company, Ltd., London, 1914.

Handbook of Textile Fibers (Natural and Manmade), J. Gordon Cook, Ph.D., Merrow Publishing Company, Ltd., Watford, Hirts, England, 1964. Excellent succinct coverage of all textile fibers.

Index to Manmade Fibers of the World, Peter Lennox-Kerr, Harlequin Press, Ltd., Manchester, England, 1964. Excellent for ready reference.

The "Mercury" Dictionary of Textile Terms, Staff of "Textile Mercury," Manchester, England. Excellent source book in all details, 1950.

Textile Statistics Section for the Combined Textile Industries; Annual Dictionary and Directory for data, statistics and concise information on all textile mills and plants in the United States; *America's Textile Reporter Magazine,* Frank P. Bennett, Inc., 286 Congress Street, Boston 10, Massachusetts.

17. GENERAL GOVERNMENT PUBLICATIONS RELATING TO TEXTILES

Census of Manufacturers, biennial, Bureau of the Census, U. S. Department of Commerce. Also monthly and seasonal data on cotton ginning, consumption, imports and exports.

Cotton and Cottonseed, Rachel P. Lane, 149 pages. Miscellaneous Publication No. 203, U. S. Department of Agriculture, 1934.

Cotton Literature, selected references, annual. Prepared in the Library of the Department of Agriculture.

Commerce Reports, weekly. Survey of foreign trade and industrial economic conditions in foreign countries. U. S. Department of Commerce.

Domestic Commerce, issued the 10th, 20th, and 30th of each month. Gives the latest research data on distribution problems in highly condensed form. Bureau of Foreign and Domestic Commerce, U. S. Department of Commerce.

Federal Reserve Board Indexes, monthly. Index of production, factory employment, pay rolls for textiles as a whole, and index numbers covering employment and payrolls in the fabric industry. Federal Reserve Board, Washington, D. C.

Foreign Commerce and Navigation of the United States, annual. Import and export statistics of various textiles. U. S. Department of Commerce.

Foreign Commerce Yearbook. Gives high-points of trade, production, and market conditions for many important foreign countries, tabulated and analyzed. Covers comparative world statistics on climate and population, agriculture, mining and manufacturing, transportation, international trade, and finance. U. S. Department of Commerce.

Government Publications Relating to Textiles, Alvin E. Johnson, 101 pages. Bureau of Foreign and Domestic Commerce, U. S. Department of Commerce, 1931.

Market Data Handbook of the United States. Covers facts necessary to an appraisement of markets in the profitable distribution of goods. Includes statistics on the location of textile manufacturing industries by states and counties. U. S. Department of Commerce.

Monthly Labor Review. Covers all phases of labor in specific states. Bureau of Labor Statistics, U. S. Department of Labor.

Monthly Summary of Foreign Commerce of the United States. Contains import and export figures, monthly average import prices, etc. Bureau of Labor Statistics, U. S. Department of Commerce.

Statistical Abstract of the United States, annual volume of about 800 pages, 56 numbers have been issued. Covers all forms of activity and progress in this country. U. S. Department of Commerce.

Survey of Current Business, monthly records of business conditions. Bureau of Foreign and Domestic Commerce, U. S. Department of Commerce.

Wholesale Prices, monthly which gives index numbers shown for wholesale prices of cotton goods, silk, rayon, woolen and worsted goods, and other textile products. Bureau of Labor Statistics, U. S. Department of Labor.

World Economic Review, annual which contains the outstanding economic developments, with emphasis on the general trend. Also includes statistics of international trade, a chronology of important events, a summary of important legislative acts, and a table of comparative business statistics. Bureau of Foreign and Domestic Commerce, U. S. Department of Commerce.

Year Book of Agriculture, contains information on production, prices, and trade of textile raw materials. U. S. Department of Agriculture.

APPENDIX

Important Extracts from the Textile Fiber Products Identification Act
(Announced June 3, 1959; effective March 3, 1960)

TEXTILE FIBER PRODUCTS IDENTIFICATION ACT

Public Law 85 – 897
85th Congress – 2d Session
H. R. 469
(72 Stat. 1717; 15 U.S.C. §70)

AN ACT

To protect producers and consumers against misbranding and false advertising of the fiber content of textile fiber products, and for other purposes.

Be it enacted by the Senate and House of Representatives of the United States of America in Congress assembled, That this Act may be cited as the "Textile Fiber Products Identification Act."

DEFINITIONS

Sec. 2. As used in this Act—

(a) The term "person" means an individual, partnership, corporation, association, or any other form of business enterprise.

(b) The term "fiber" or "textile fiber" means a unit of matter which is capable of being spun into a yarn or made into a fabric by bonding or by interlacing in a variety of methods including weaving, knitting, braiding, felting, twisting, or webbing, and which is the basic structural element of textile products.

(c) The term "natural fiber" means any fiber that exists as such in the natural state.

(d) The term "manufactured fiber" means any fiber derived by a process of manufacture from any substance which, at any point in the manufacturing process, is not a fiber.

(e) The term "yarn" means a strand of textile fiber in a form suitable for weaving, knitting, braiding, felting, webbing, or otherwise fabricating into a fabric.

(f) The term "fabric" means any material woven, knitted, felted, or otherwise produced from, or in combination with, any natural or manufactured fiber, yarn, or substitute therefor.

(g) The term "household textile articles" means articles of wearing apparel, costumes and accessories, draperies, floor coverings, furnishings, beddings, and other textile goods of a type customarily used in a household regardless of where used in fact.

(h) The term "textile fiber product" means—

(1) any fiber, whether in the finished or unfinished state, used or intended for use in household textile articles;

(2) any yarn or fabric, whether in the finished or unfinished state, used or intended for use in household textile articles; and

(3) any household textile article made in whole or in part of yarn or fabric; except that such term does not include a product required to be labeled under the Wool Products Labeling Act of 1939.

(i) The term "affixed" means attached to the textile fiber product in any manner.

(j) The term "Commission" means the Federal Trade Commission.

(k) The term "commerce" means commerce among the several States or with foreign nations, or in any Territory of the United States or in the District of Columbia, or between any such Territory and another, or between any such Territory and any State or foreign nation or between the District of Columbia and any State or Territory or foreign nation.

(l) The term "Territory" includes the insular possessions of the United States, and also any Territory of the United States.

(m) The term "ultimate consumer" means a person who obtains a textile fiber product by purchase or exchange with no intent to sell or exchange such textile fiber product in any form.

CRIMINAL PENALTY

Sec. 11. (a) Any person who willfully does an act which by section 3, 5, 6, 9, or 10 (b) is declared to be unlawful shall be guilty of a misdemeanor and upon conviction shall be fined not more than $5,000 or be imprisoned not more than one year, or both, in the discretion of the court: *Provided,* That nothing in this section shall limit any other provision of this Act.

(b) Whenever the Commission has reason to believe that any person is guilty of a misdemeanor under this section, it may certify all pertinent facts to the Attorney General. If, on the basis of the facts certified, the Attorney General concurs in such belief, it shall be his duty to cause appropriate proceedings to be brought for the enforcement of the provisions of this section against such person.

EXEMPTIONS

Sec. 12. (a) None of the provisions of this Act shall be construed to apply to—

(1) upholstery stuffing, except as provided in section 4 (h);

(2) outer coverings of furniture, mattresses, and box springs;

(3) linings or interlinings incorporated primarily for structural purposes and not for warmth;

(4) filling or padding incorporated primarily for structural purposes and not for warmth;

(5) stiffenings, trimmings, facings, or interfacings;

(6) backings of, and paddings or cushions to be used under, floor coverings;

(7) sewing and handicraft threads;

(8) bandages, surgical dressings, and other textile fiber products, the labeling of which is subject to the requirements of the Federal Food, Drug and Cosmetic Act of 1938, as amended;

(9) waste materials not intended for use in a textile fiber product;

(10) textile fiber products incorporated in shoes or overshoes or similar outer footwear;

(11) textile fiber products incorporated in headwear, handbags, luggage, brushes, lampshades, or toys, catamenial devices, adhesive tapes and adhesive sheets, cleaning cloths impregnated with chemicals, or diapers.

The exemptions provided for any article by paragraph (3) or (4) of this subsection shall not be applicable if any representation as to fiber content of such article is made in any advertisement, label, or other means of identification covered by section 4 of this Act.

(b) The Commission may exclude from the provisions of this Act other textile fiber products (1) which have an insignificant or inconsequential textile fiber content, or (2) with respect to which the disclosure of textile fiber content is not necessary for the protection of the ultimate consumer.

RULES AND REGULATIONS UNDER THE TEXTILE FIBER PRODUCTS IDENTIFICATION ACT

RULE 1—TERMS DEFINED

As used in these rules, unless the context otherwise specifically requires:

(a) The term "Act" means the "Textile Fiber Products Identification Act" (approved September 2, 1958, 85th Congress, 2nd Session; 15 U.S.C. §70, 72 Stat. 1717).

(b) The terms "rule," "rules," "regulations," and "rules and regulations" mean the Rules and Regulations prescribed by the Commission pursuant to Section 7(c) of the Act.

(c) The definition of terms contained in Section 2 of the Act shall be applicable also to such terms when used in rules promulgated under the Act.

(d) The term "United States" means the several States, the District of Columbia, and the Territories and possessions of the United States.

(e) The terms "required information" and "information required" mean such information as is required to be disclosed on labels or invoices and in advertising under the Act and Regulations.

(f) The terms "label," "labels," "labeled," and "labeling" mean the stamp, tag, label, or other means of identification, or authorized substitute therefor, required to be on or affixed to textile fiber products by the Act and Regulations and on which the information required is to appear.

(g) The terms "marketing or handling" and "marketed or handled," when applied to textile fiber products, mean any one or all of the transactions set forth in Section 3 of the Act.

(h) The terms "invoice" and "invoice or other paper" mean a written account, order, memorandum, list, or catalogue, which is issued to a purchaser, consignee, bailee, correspondent, agent, or any other person, in connection with the marketing or handling of any textile fiber product transported or delivered to such person.

(i) The term "outer coverings of furniture, mattresses, and box springs" means those coverings as are permanently incorporated in such articles.

(j) The term "wearing apparel" means any costume or article of clothing or covering for any part of the body worn or intended to be worn by individuals.

(k) The term "beddings" means sheets, covers, blankets, comforters, pillows, pillowcases, quilts, bedspreads, pads, and all other textile fiber products used or intended to be used on or about a bed or other place for reclining or sleeping but shall not include furniture, mattresses, or box springs.

(l) The term "headwear" means any textile fiber product worn exclusively on or about the head or face by individuals.

(m) The term "backings," when applied to floor coverings, means that part of a floor covering to which the pile, face, or outer surface is woven, tufted, hooked, knitted, or otherwise attached, and which provides the structural base of the floor covering. The term "backings" shall also include fabrics attached to the structural base of the floor covering in such a way as to form a part of such structural base, but shall not include the pile, face, or outer surface of the floor covering or any part thereof.

(n) The term "elastic material" means a fabric composed of yarn consisting of an elastomer or a covered elastomer.

(o) The term "coated fabric" means any fabric which is coated, filled, impregnated, or laminated with a continuous-film-forming polymeric composition in such a manner that the weight added to the base fabric is at least 35% of the weight of the fabric before coating, filling, impregnation, or lamination.

(p) The term "upholstered product" means articles of furniture containing stuffing and shall include mattresses and box springs.

(q) The term "ornamentation" means any fibers or yarns imparting a visibly discernible pattern or design to a yarn or fabric.

(r) The term "fiber trademark" means a word or words used by a person to identify a particular fiber produced or sold by him and to distinguish it from fibers of the same generic class produced or sold by others. Such term shall not include any trademark, product mark, house mark, trade name or other name which does not identify a particular fiber.

(s) The term "wool" means the fiber from the fleece of the sheep or lamb or hair of the Angora or Cashmere goat (and may include the so-called specialty fibers from the hair of the camel, alpaca, llama, and vicuña) which has never been reclaimed from any woven or felted wool product.

[403]

(t) The term "reprocessed wool" means the resulting fiber when wool has been woven or felted into a wool product which, without ever having been utilized in any way by the ultimate consumer, subsequently has been made into a fibrous state.

(u) The term "reused wool" means the resulting fiber when wool or reprocessed wool has been spun, woven, knitted or felted into a wool product which, after having been used in any way by the ultimate consumer, subsequently has been made into a fibrous state. (16 CFR §303. 1)

RULE 2—GENERAL REQUIREMENTS

(a) Each textile fiber product, except those exempted or excluded under Section 12 of the Act, shall be labeled or invoiced in conformity with the requirements of the Act and Regulations.

(b) Any advertising of textile fiber products subject to the Act shall be in conformity with the requirements of the Act and Regulations.

(c) The requirements of the Act and Regulations shall not be applicable to products required to be labeled under the Wool Products Labeling Act of 1939 (Public Law 76-850, 15 U.S.C. 68, 54 Stat. 1128).

(d) Any person marketing or handling textile fiber products who shall cause or direct a processor or finisher to label, invoice, or otherwise identify any textile fiber product with required information shall be responsible under the Act and Regulations for any failure of compliance with the Act and Regulations by reason of any statement or omission in such label, invoice, or other means of identification utilized in accordance with his direction, *provided* that nothing herein shall relieve the processor or finisher of any duty or liability to which he may be subject under the Act and Regulations. (16 CFR §303. 2)

RULE 3—FIBERS PRESENT IN AMOUNTS OF 5% OR LESS

In disclosing the constituent fibers in required information, no fiber present in the amount of five percentum or less of the total fiber weight shall be designated by its generic name or fiber trademark, but shall be designated as "other fiber."

Where more than one of such fibers are present in a product, they shall be designated in the aggregate as "other fibers." (16 CFR §303. 3)

RULE 4—ENGLISH LANGUAGE REQUIREMENT

All required information shall be set out in the English language. If the required information appears in a language other than English, it also shall appear in the English language. The provisions of this rule shall not apply to advertisements in foreign-language newspapers or periodicals, but such advertising shall in all other respects comply with the Act and Regulations. (16 CFR §303. 4)

RULE 5—ABBREVIATIONS, DITTO MARKS, AND ASTERISKS PROHIBITED

(a) In disclosing required information, words or terms shall not be designated by ditto marks or appear in footnotes referred to by asterisks or other symbols in required information, and shall not be abbreviated except as permitted in Rule 33(d).

(b) Where the generic name of a textile fiber is required to appear in immediate conjunction with a fiber trademark in advertising, labeling, or invoicing, a disclosure of the generic name by means of a footnote, to which reference is made by use of an asterisk or other symbol placed next to the fiber trademark, shall not be sufficient in itself to constitute compliance with the Act and Regulations. (16 CFR §303. 5)

RULE 6—GENERIC NAMES OF FIBERS TO BE USED

(1) Except where another name is permitted under the Act and Regulations, the respective generic names of all fibers present in the amount of more than five percentum of the total fiber weight of the textile fiber product shall be used when naming fibers in the required information; as for example: "cotton," "rayon," "silk," "linen," "nylon," etc.

(2) Where a textile fiber product contains hair or fiber of a fur-bearing animal present in the amount of more than five percentum of the total fiber weight of the product, the name of the animal producing such fiber may be used in setting forth the required information, provided the name of such animal is used in conjunction with the words "fiber," "hair," or "blend"; as for example:

"80% Rabbit Hair
20% Nylon"

or

"80% Silk
20% Mink Fiber"

[404]

(3) The term "fur fiber" may be used to describe the hair or fur fiber or mixtures thereof of any animal or animals other than the sheep, lamb, Angora goat, Cashmere goat, camel, alpaca, llama or vicuña where such hair or fur fiber or mixture is present in the amount of more than five percentum of the total fiber weight of the textile fiber product and no direct or indirect representations are made as to the animal or animals from which the fiber so designated was obtained, as for example:

"60% Cotton
40% Fur Fiber"

or

"50% Nylon
30% Mink Hair
20% Fur Fiber"

(4) Where textile fiber products subject to the Act contain (1) wool, (2) processed wool, or (3) reused wool in amounts of more than five percentum of the total fiber weight, such fibers shall be designated and disclosed as wool, reprocessed wool, or reused wool as the case may be. (16 CFR §303. 6)

RULE 8—PROCEDURE FOR ESTABLISHING GENERIC NAMES FOR MANUFACTURED FIBERS

Prior to the marketing or handling of a manufactured fiber for which no generic name has been established by the Commission, the manufacturer or producer thereof shall file a written application with the Commission, requesting the establishment of a generic name for such fiber, stating therein:

(a) the reasons why the applicant's fiber should not be identified by one of the generic names established by the Commission in Rule 7 of the Regulations;

(b) the chemical composition of the fiber, including the fiber-forming substances and respective percentages thereof, together with samples of the fiber;

(c) suggested names for consideration as generic, together with a proposed definition for the fiber;

(d) any other information deemed by the applicant to be pertinent to the application, including technical data in the form of test methods;

(e) the earliest date on which the applicant proposes to market or handle the fiber in commerce for other than developmental or testing purposes.

Upon receipt of the application, the Commission will, within sixty (60) days, either deny the application or assign to the fiber a numerical or alphabetical symbol for temporary use during further consideration of such application.

After taking the necessary procedure in consideration of the application, the Commission in due course shall establish a generic name or advise the applicant of its refusal to grant the application and designate the proper existing generic name for the fiber. (16 CFR §303. 8)

RULE 9—USE OF FUR-BEARING ANIMAL NAMES AND SYMBOLS PROHIBITED

(a) The advertising or the labeling of a textile fiber product shall not contain any names, words, depictions, descriptive matter, or other symbols which connote or signify a fur-bearing animal, unless such product or the part thereof in connection with which the names, words, depictions, descriptive matter, or other symbols are used is a fur product within the meaning of the Fur Products Labeling Act.

(b) Subject to the provisions of subsection (a) hereof and Rule 6 of the Regulations, a textile fiber product shall not be described or referred to in any manner in an advertisement or label with:

(1) The name or part of the name of a fur-bearing animal, whether as a single word or a combination word, or any coined word which is phonetically similar to a fur-bearing animal name, or which is only a slight variation in spelling of a fur-bearing animal name or part of the name. As for example, such terms as "Ermine," "Mink," "Persian," "Broadtail," "Beaverton," "Marmink," "Sablelon," "Lam," "Pershian," "Minx," or similar terms shall not be used.

(2) Any word or name symbolic of a fur-bearing animal by reason of conventional usage or by reason of its close relationship with fur-bearing animals. As for example, such terms as "guardhair," "underfur," and "mutation," or similar terms, shall not be used.

RULE 10—FIBER CONTENT OF ELASTIC YARN OR MATERIAL

(a) Where a textile fiber product is made wholly of elastic yarn or material, with minor parts of rigid material for structural purposes, it shall be identified as to the percentage of the elastomer, together with the percentage of all textile coverings of the elastomer and all other yarns or materials used therein.

(b) Where a textile fiber product is made in part of elastic material and in part of other fabric, the fiber content of such fabric shall be set forth sectionally by percentages as in the case of other fabrics. In such cases the elastic material may be disclosed by describing the material as elastic followed by a listing in order of predominance by weight of the fibers used in such elastic, including the elastomer, where such fibers are present by five percentum or more. An example of labeling under this subsection is:

> "Front and back rigid sections:
> 50% Acetate,
> 50% Cotton.
> Elastic: Rayon, cotton, nylon, rubber."

(16 CFR §303. 10)

RULE 11—FLOOR COVERINGS CONTAINING BACKINGS, FILLINGS, AND PADDINGS

In disclosing the required fiber content information as to floor coverings containing exempted backings, fillings, or paddings, the disclosure shall be made in such manner as to indicate that it relates only to the face, pile, or outer surface of the floor covering and not to the backing, filling, or padding. Examples of the form of marking these types of floor coverings as to fiber content are as follows:

> "100% Cotton Pile"

> "Face—60% Rayon, 40% Cotton"

> "Outer Surface—100% Wool." (16 CFR §303. 11)

Note: Where it is desired to disclose the fiber content of exempted backings of pile floor coverings, such floor coverings may be labeled in accordance with Rule 24.

RULE 14—PRODUCTS CONTAINING UNKNOWN FIBERS

(a) Where a textile fiber product is made from miscellaneous scraps, rags, odd lots, textile by-products, or waste materials of unknown, and for practical purposes, undeterminable fiber content, the required fiber content disclosure may, when truthfully applicable, indicate that such product is composed of miscellaneous scraps, rags, odd lots, textile by-products, or waste materials, as the case may be, of unknown or undetermined fiber content; as for example:

> "Made of miscellaneous scraps of undetermined fiber content."

> "Made of miscellaneous rags of undetermined fiber content."

> "Made of miscellaneous odd lots of undetermined fiber content."

> "Made of miscellaneous textile by-products of undetermined fiber content."

> "Made of miscellaneous waste materials of undetermined fiber content."

No representation as to fiber content shall be made as to any textile fiber product designated as being composed of undetermined fibers. If any representation as to fiber content is made with reference to such products, a full fiber content disclosure shall be required.

(b) Nothing contained in this rule shall excuse a full disclosure as to fiber content if the same is known or practically ascertainable. (16 CFR §303. 14)

RULE 15—LABEL AND METHOD OF AFFIXING

The label required to be on or affixed to the textile fiber product shall be such as is appropriate to the nature and type of product. Such label shall be conspicuously affixed to the product or, where permitted, its package or container in a secure manner and shall be of such durability as to remain on and attached thereto throughout the sale, resale, distribution and handling of the product, and, except where otherwise provided, shall remain on or be firmly affixed to the product or, where permitted, its package or container when sold and delivered to the ultimate consumer. (16 CFR §303. 15)

RULE 22—PRODUCTS CONTAINING LININGS, INTERLININGS, FILLINGS, AND PADDINGS

In disclosing the required information as to textile fiber products, the fiber content of any linings, interlinings, fillings, or paddings shall be set forth separately and distinctly if such linings, interlinings, fillings, or paddings are incorporated in the product for warmth rather than for structural purposes, or if any express or implied representations are made as to their fiber content. Examples are as follows:

"100% Nylon

Interlining: 100% Rayon"

"Covering: 100% Rayon

Filling: 100% Cotton." (16 CFR §303. 22)

RULE 23—TEXTILE FIBER PRODUCTS CONTAINING SUPERIMPOSED OR ADDED FIBERS

Where a textile fiber product is made wholly of one fiber or a blend of fibers with the exception of an additional fiber in minor proportion superimposed or added in certain separate and distinct areas or sections for reinforcing or other useful purposes, the product may be designated according to the fiber content of the principal fiber or blend of fibers, with an exception naming the superimposed or added fiber, giving the percentage thereof in relation to the total fiber weight of the principal fiber or blend of fibers, and indicating the area or section which contains the superimposed or added fiber. Examples of this type of fiber content disclosure, as applied to products having reinforcing fibers added to a particular area or section, are as follows:

"55% Cotton
45% Rayon
Except 5% Nylon added
to toe and heel."

"All Cotton except 1% Nylon
added to neckband." (16 CFR §303. 23)

RULE 24—PILE FABRICS AND PRODUCTS COMPOSED THEREOF

The fiber content of pile fabrics or products composed thereof may be stated on the label in such segregated form as will show the fiber content of the face or pile and of the back or base, with percentages of the respective fibers as they exist in the face or pile and in the back or base, *provided* that in such disclosure the respective percentages of the face and back be given in such manner as will show the ratio between the face and the back. Examples of the form of marking pile fabric as to fiber content provided for in this rule are as follows:

"100% Nylon Pile

100% Cotton Back

(Back constitutes 60% of
fabric and pile 40%)."

"Face—60% Rayon, 40% Nylon

Back—70% Cotton, 30% Rayon

"(Face constitutes 60% of fabric
and back 40%)." (16 CFR §303 .24)

RULE 25—SECTIONAL DISCLOSURE OF CONTENT

(a) (Permissive) Where a textile fiber product is composed of two or more sections which are of different fiber composition, the required information as to fiber content may be separated in the same label in such manner as to show the fiber composition of each section.

(b) (Mandatory) The disclosure as above provided shall be made in all instances where such form of marking is necessary to avoid deception. (16 CFR §303. 25)

RULE 26—ORNAMENTATION

(a) Where the textile fiber product contains fiber ornamentation not exceeding five per-centum of the total fiber weight of the product and the stated percentages of the fiber content are exclusive of such ornamentation, the label or any invoice used in lieu thereof shall contain a phrase or statement showing such fact; as for example:

"60% Cotton
40% Rayon
Exclusive of Ornamentation."

or

"All Cotton
Exclusive of Ornamentation."

The fiber content of such ornamentation may be disclosed where the percentage of the ornamentation in relation to the total fiber weight of the principal fiber or blend of fibers is shown; as for example:

"70% Nylon
30% Acetate
Exclusive of 4% Metallic Ornamentation."

or

"100% Rayon
Exclusive of 3% Silk Ornamentation."

(b) Where the fiber ornamentation exceeds five percentum, it shall be included in the state-ment of required percentages of fiber content.

(c) Where the ornamentation constitutes a distinct section of the product, sectional dis-closure may be made in accordance with Rule 25. (16 CFR §303. 26)

RULE 27—USE OF THE TERM "ALL" OR "100%"

Where a textile fiber product or part thereof is comprised wholly of one fiber, other than any fiber ornamentation, decoration, elastic, or trimming as to which fiber content disclosure is not required, either the word "All" or the term "100%" may be used in labeling, together with the correct generic name of the fiber and any qualifying phrase, when required; as for example: "100% Cotton," "All Rayon, Exclusive of Ornamentation," "100% Acetate, Exclusive of Decora-tion," "All Nylon, Exclusive of Elastic," etc. (16 CFR §303. 27)

RULE 35—USE OF TERMS "VIRGIN" OR "NEW"

The terms "virgin" or "new" as descriptive of a textile fiber product, or any fiber or part thereof, shall not be used when the product or part so described is not composed wholly of new or virgin fiber which has never been reclaimed from any spun, woven, knitted, felted, bonded, or similarly manufactured product. (16 CFR §303. 35)

RULE 43—FIBER CONTENT TOLERANCES

(a) A textile fiber product which contains more than one fiber shall not be deemed to be misbranded as to fiber content percentages if the percentages by weight of any fibers present in the total fiber content of the product, exclusive of permissive ornamentation, do not deviate or vary from the percentages stated on the label in excess of 3% of the total fiber weight of the product. For example, where the label indicates that a particular fiber is present in the amount of 40%, the amount of such fiber present may vary from a minimum of 37% of the total fiber weight of such product to a maximum of 43% of the total fiber weight of such product.

(b) Where the percentage of any fiber or fibers contained in a textile fiber product deviates or varies from the percentage stated on the label by more than the tolerance or variation provided in subsection (a) of this rule, such product shall be misbranded unless the person charged proves that the entire deviation or variation from the fiber content percentages stated on the label resulted from unavoidable variations in manufacture and despite the exercise of due care.

(c) Where representations are made to the effect that a textile fiber product is composed wholly of one fiber, the tolerance provided in Section 4(b)(2) of the Act and subsection (a) of this rule shall not apply except as to permissive ornamentation where the textile fiber product is represented to be composed of one fiber "exclusive of ornamentation." (16 CFR §303. 43)

RULE 44—PRODUCTS NOT INTENDED FOR USES SUBJECT TO THE ACT

Textile fiber products intended for uses not within the scope of the Act and Regulations or intended for uses in other textile fiber products which are exempted or excluded from the Act shall not be subject to the labeling and invoicing requirements of the Act and Regulations, *provided* an invoice or other paper covering the marketing or handling of such products is given, which indicates that the products are not intended for uses subject to the Textile Fiber Products Identification Act. (16 CFR §303. 44)

RULE 45—EXCLUSIONS FROM THE ACT

(a) Pursuant to Section 12(b) of the Act, the Commission hereby excludes from the operation of the Act:

(1) All textile fiber products *except:*

    (i) articles of wearing apparel;
    (ii) handkerchiefs;
    (iii) scarfs;
    (iv) beddings;
    (v) curtains and casements;
    (vi) draperies;
    (vii) tablecloths, napkins, and doilies;
    (viii) floor coverings;
    (ix) towels;
    (x) wash cloths and dish cloths;
    (xi) ironing board covers and pads;
    (xii) umbrellas and parasols;
    (xiii) batts;
    (xiv) products subject to Section 4(h) of the Act;
    (xv) flags;
    (xvi) cushions;
    (xvii) all fibers, yarns and fabrics (including narrow fabrics except packaging ribbons);
    (xviii) furniture slip covers and other covers or coverlets for furniture;
    (xix) afghans and throws;
    (xx) sleeping bags;
    (xxi) antimacassars and tidies;
    (xxii) hammocks;
    (xxiii) dresser and other furniture scarfs.

(2) Belts, suspenders, arm bands, permanently knotted neckties, garters, sanitary belts, diaper liners, labels (either required or non-required) individually and in rolls, looper clips intended for handicraft purposes, book cloth, artists' canvases, tapestry cloth, and shoelaces.

(3) All textile fiber products manufactured by the operators of company stores and offered for sale and sold exclusively to their own employees as ultimate consumers.

(4) Coated fabrics and those portions of textile fiber products made of coated fabrics.

(5) Secondhand household textile articles which are discernibly secondhand or which are marked to indicate their secondhand character.

(6) Non-woven products of a disposable nature intended for one-time use only.

(b) The exclusions provided for in subsection (a) of this rule shall not be applicable if any representations as to fiber content of such articles are made, except as to those products excluded by paragraph (6).

(c) The exclusions from the Act provided in subsection (a) hereof are in addition to the exemptions from the Act provided in Section 12(a) of the Act and shall not affect or limit such exemptions. (16 CFR §303. 45)

Promulgated and made effective by the Federal Trade Commission on March 3, 1960.

Note: The Commission on its own motion or upon the application of any interested party may initiate proceedings to revise, amend, or modify all or any part of these Rules and Regulations. Such proceedings will be conducted in accordance with the rule-making procedures prescribed in the Administrative Procedure Act (60 Stat. 237, as amended, 5 U.S.C. §§1001-1011) and in accordance with Subpart A of the Rule Making Procedures of the Federal Trade Commission. (16 CFR §§2. 1-2. 8)

AMENDMENT TO RULE 25 (C) OF THE RULES AND REGULATIONS UNDER THE WOOL PRODUCTS LABELING ACT OF 1939: "THE POINT OF ORIGIN LABEL."

RULE 25(c) AS AMENDED

(c) When any representation is made on a stamp, tag, label, or other means of identification on or attached to a wool product that the fabric contained therein is imported, the name of the country where the fabric was woven, knitted, felted, bonded, or otherwise manufactured shall be set forth on the stamp, tag, label, or other means of identification so as to clearly indicate that the fabric contained in the wool product was made in such country; as for example:

"Fabric Woven in Italy."

NOTE: Nothing in this Rule shall relieve any person subject to the Act (1) from any duty or liability under Section 4(a)(1) of the Wool Products Labeling Act of 1939 which prohibits false or deceptive labeling or (2) from compliance with Section 5 of the Federal Trade Commission Act which has been held to require disclosure of the country of origin of products or fabrics from which completed products are made where the failure to make such a disclosure has the tendency and capacity to deceive or (3) from the marking requirements of the Tariff Act and the regulations of the Bureau of Customs pursuant thereto. [16 CFR §300.25 as amended, effective May 20, 1964]

PROPERTIES AND CHARACTERISTICS OF MAJOR TEXTILE FIBERS FOR READY REFERENCE

THE PROPERTIES OF COTTON

PHYSICAL CHARACTERISTICS:

MICROSCOPICAL APPEARANCE	A flat ribbonlike fiber which has from 150 to 300 natural turns of twist per inch.
LENGTH	½" to 2", or slightly longer.
DIAMETER	.0005" to .0009".
COLOR	Ordinarily white; may be cream-colored or tinted brown.
LUSTER	In untreated condition has no pronounced luster.
STRENGTH	The single fiber will sustain a dead weight of 2 to 8 grams. Strength is temporarily increased when wet, and decreased when abnormally dried.
ELASTICITY	Not nearly as elastic as silk and wool. Spiral twists make it apparently more elastic than linen.
CONDUCTIVITY OF HEAT	Better than silk or wool, not as good as linen.
HYGROSCOPIC MOISTURE	6% to 7%.
CAPILLARITY AND PENETRABILITY	It has capillarity because of its tubular structure.
FIBER COMPOSITION	Formula is $C_6H_{10}O_5$, n or x times. Cellulose content varies from 90% to about 96%, water from 5% to 8%, natural impurities from 4% to 6%.

CHEMICAL CHARACTERISTICS:

EFFECT OF LIGHT	Pure cotton is not attacked readily.
HEAT	Withstands high temperatures well. In dry atmosphere, it can be heated to 300° F., without injury. At 475° F., the fiber will turn brown and burn.
MILDEW	If sized or treated with starches, flours, and gums, in presence of dampness will be affected by mildew, and lose strength.
WATER	Boiling water does not affect the fiber.
MINERAL ACIDS	Concentrated acids such as hydrochloric, hydrofluoric, nitric, and sulfuric will destroy the fiber. Cold dilute acids will not injure the fiber if washed out or neutralized. Dilute solutions, 3% or less of these acids, if allowed to dry, cause the fiber to become tender, and in time will destroy cotton.

[410]

VOLATILE ORGANIC ACIDS	With formic or acetic acids there is no detrimental action.
NON-VOLATILE ORGANIC ACIDS	Oxalic acid will cause a high loss in tensile strength; a low loss with tartaric acid. Citric acid will tender the fiber if not removed, and especially if heat is applied.
STRONG ALKALIES	With caustic soda there is not any injury, even if concentrated, and even if the heat is applied when the oxygen is excluded. Concentrated solutions will mercerize cotton if it is under tension; otherwise the cotton will shrink.
WEAK ALKALIES	No injurious effect upon the fiber.
OXIDIZING AGENTS	Potassium permanganate, for example, will destroy cotton if not controlled.
METALLIC SALTS	Cotton has practically no affinity for metallic salts.
AFFINITY FOR DYESTUFFS	Less than that of silk and wool.
DYES USED	Cotton is dyed by direct dyestuffs, sulfur dyes, basic dyes with a mordant, by coloring matter developed in the fiber, and by vat dyes.
BLEACHING AGENTS	Chlorine bleach or hypochlorites, when in cold dilute solution, will not injure the fiber. The bleach used, however, should be removed carefully since heat and concentrated solutions will destroy the fiber.
OTHER OXIDATION BLEACHES	Hydrogen peroxide, sodium perborate, or potassium permanganate will not injure cotton if properly controlled.
REDUCTION BLEACHES	Sulfurous acid (sulfur dioxide plus water) or hydrosulfites will cause no injury if controlled.
USES:	Cotton has more uses than any other textile fiber. It finds use, directly or indirectly, in the following: Abrasives, adhesive plaster, aircraft, aprons, armbands, artificial flowers, athletic and sporting goods, batting, duck, elastic fabrics, nets, tubing, webbing, uniforms, shirts, curtains, awnings, baby carriages, bags, bandages, bathrobes, bedspreads, belting, bias binding, blankets, bookbinding, chafer fabric, caskets, chairs and cots, cleaning cloths, cushions and pillows, electrical supplies, dressgoods of many types, flags, gloves, hose, linings, and a host of other uses too numerous to mention.

OTHER PROPERTIES AND CHARACTERISTICS OF COTTON:

1. Will shrink unless preshrunk.
2. Launders easily and well; much used in wash-and-wear garments.
3. Ideal for blending with other major fibers.
4. Is soft and comfortable next to the skin.
5. Stores well; no deterioration if well cared for.
6. Comfortable in warm weather.
7. Classed as a dead fiber; wool is a live fiber.
8. Available in large quantities.
9. Flexible; not broken when twisted.
10. Wrinkles easily but can be made wrinkle-resistant.
11. Crease-resistant finishes easily applied.
12. Makes excellent toweling because of absorbent properties.
13. Relatively inexpensive fiber.
14. Mercerized for added strength and permanent luster.
15. Lower quality yarns are carded; higher grade yarns are combed.
16. Said to have over 10,000 uses.
17. Can be spun to very high counts of yarn, 100s and higher.
18. Cool because of its power of absorption followed by evaporation.

THE PROPERTIES OF WOOLEN AND WORSTED FIBERS

PHYSICAL CHARACTERISTICS:

MICROSCOPICAL APPEARANCE	Rodlike, with surface covered with horny scales; comparable with scales on a fish, or an asparagus tip.
LENGTH	Short wool is from 1″ to 6″; long wool from 6″ to 14″ or more.
DIAMETER	.0005″ to .0009″.
COLOR	Yellowish-white to brown; some fiber brownish-black to black.
LUSTER	Low in better grades; high in coarser wools.
STRENGTH	Single fiber runs from 15 to 30 grams before rupture.
ELASTICITY	Has considerable; an average wool may stretch up to 35% of its length prior to breaking.
CONDUCTIVITY OF HEAT	Poor, but excellent generator of heat.
HYGROSCOPIC MOISTURE	Worsted about 10%, wool from 15% to 17%.
CAPILLARITY AND PENETRABILITY	Possesses both because of structure.
FIBER COMPOSITION	Varies slightly with various grades. Depends on soil, climate, and area. Average percentages are carbon, 50%; oxygen, 22%; nitrogen, 18%; hydrogen, 7%; sulfur, 2%; with slight traces of calcium, phosphorus, and iron. Somewhat resembles structure of human hair.

CHEMICAL CHARACTERISTICS:

EFFECT OF LIGHT	Chemical structure changes, thereby causing its action toward dyestuffs to differ; dye affinity is usually increased.
MILDEW	Attacked if left in damp area for any length of time. Resisting agents now on market to prevent this.
HEAT	Decomposes above 275° F., dry heat. If heated to boiling point of 212° F., in damp atmosphere, wool becomes plasticized and may be shaped, and will retain this shape when cooled.
WATER	Boiling water reduces luster and strength.
MINERAL ACIDS	Acids such as aqua, regia, hydrochloric, hydrofluoric, nitric, and sulfuric, in dilute form, will not injure wool fibers, even at the boil. Concentrated forms destroy the fiber.
VOLATILE ORGANIC ACIDS	Acetic or formic acids have no detrimental effect.
NON-VOLATILE ORGANIC ACIDS	Acids such as citric, oxalic, or tartaric will not injure fibers if removed properly and at right time.
STRONG ALKALIES	Caustic soda or soda ash in strong solutions decomposes the fiber. Dilute cold acids will not injure fiber if removed at proper time or neutralized. Soda ash, in dilute solution, may be used at lukewarm temperature but must be removed in time.
WEAK ALKALIES	Ammonia, borax, phosphate of soda, silicate of soda, or soap will not be injurious if properly controlled.
OXIDIZING AGENTS	Potassium permanganate, for example, will destroy the fiber if not controlled. Same action as on cotton.
METALLIC SALTS	Affinity for these is rated good.
AFFINITY FOR DYESTUFFS	Good to excellent when proper dyes are used.
DYES USED	Acid, some basic dyes, chrome, and direct colors.

BLEACHING AGENTS	A chlorine or hydrochlorite bleach is harmful. Under some conditions, controlled, chlorinated wool will be developed. This has high luster, and causes fiber to become unshrinkable.
OTHER OXIDATION BLEACHES	With hydrogen peroxide or sodium perborate there is not any injury to the fiber. Same action as on cotton.
REDUCTION BLEACHES	Sulfurous acid, which is sulfur dioxide plus water, or hydrosulfite, will not injure the fiber. Same action as on cotton.

THE PROPERTIES OF LINEN

PHYSICAL CHARACTERISTICS:

MICROSCOPICAL APPEARANCE	Resembles bamboo, has cross markings throughout, and appears as a group of minute fibers cemented together.
LENGTH	From a few inches up to about one yard; average runs from 15" to 20".
DIAMETER	.0047" to .0098".
COLOR	Ecru or yellowish buff to gray.
LUSTER	More natural luster than cotton; silklike inherent luster is noted.
STRENGTH	Stronger than cotton; strength increases when wet.
ELASTICITY	Classed as a nonelastic fiber.
CONDUCTIVITY OF HEAT	Good, better than cotton.
HYGROSCOPIC MOISTURE	Between 6% and 8%.
CAPILLARITY AND PENETRABILITY	Devoid of each, consequently is more difficult to dye than cotton.
FIBER COMPOSITION	Mainly composed of cellulose but has less than cotton. Natural impurities range from about 15% up to 30%.

CHEMICAL CHARACTERISTICS:

EFFECT OF LIGHT	Has more resistance to light than cotton.
MILDEW	Attacked.
HEAT	Withstands high temperatures well. Can be heated to about 300° F., without injury; around 475° F., the fiber will turn brown and burn. Very similar to cotton.
WATER	Increased moisture provides increased strength.
STRONG ACIDS	Concentrated types such as hydrochloric, hydrofluoric, nitric, and sulfuric will destroy the fiber. Cold dilute acids will not injure the fiber if washed out or neutralized. Dilute solutions, 5% or less of these acids, will cause tendering of the fiber; if allowed to dry, the fiber will decompose in time.
VOLATILE ORGANIC ACIDS	Acetic or formic acid has no detrimental effect.
NON-VOLATILE ORGANIC ACIDS	Oxalic acid causes high loss in tensile strength; a low loss with tartaric acid. Citric acid tenders the fiber, if not removed, and particularly if heat is applied. Generally about the same reactions as with cotton.
STRONG ALKALIES	With caustic soda, soda ash, there is no appreciable effect even if concentrated, and even if heat is applied with the oxygen excluded. Concentrated solutions will add some luster if under tension, otherwise some shrinkage will result.
WEAK ALKALIES	Those such as ammonia, borax, phosphate of soda, silicate of soda, and soap have no injurious effect upon the fiber.

OXIDIZING AGENTS	Potassium permanganate, for example, will destroy linen fiber unless controlled.
METALLIC SALTS	Practically no affinity for these.
AFFINITY FOR DYESTUFFS	Generally speaking, less than silk and wool.
DYES USED	Comparable with cotton but not as good. Dyes that may be used include direct, sulfur, basic dyes with a mordant, coloring matter developed in the fiber, and vat dyes.
BLEACHING AGENTS	More difficult to bleach than cotton because of natural impurities present. Bleaches used must be controlled at all times. Heat and concentrated solutions such as chlorine or hypochlorite will disintegrate the fiber.
OTHER OXIDATION BLEACHES	Hydrogen peroxide, sodium perborate, potassium permanganate plus bisulfite of soda will injure the fiber if not controlled.
REDUCTION BLEACHES	Hydrosulfite, sulfurous acid (sulfur dioxide plus water) will not cause degradation if controlled.
USES:	In the men's wear field, linen is used for summer suiting, sports jackets, caps, collars and shirting, handkerchiefs, and footwear. In the women's and children's wear it is used for dresses, handkerchiefs, suiting, beach sandals, handbags, collar and cuff sets, and bolero jackets. Household uses include bed sheets, curtains and drapes, toweling, table linen, upholstery. The flax seed which produces linseed oil is used in the manufacture of linoleum, oilcloth, patent leather, opaque window shade fabric, printer's ink, and scouring soaps.

THE PROPERTIES OF SILK

PHYSICAL CHARACTERISTICS:

MICROSCOPICAL APPEARANCE	Shows a twin filament uneven at beginning and end of reeled portions; is rather even at the center of the reeled filament. Very thin places noted throughout.
LENGTH	Dependent on type of silk, filament runs from about 500 yards up to 1,600 yards or more in finer qualities.
DIAMETER	From .0006″ to .0012″.
COLOR	Yellow through gray to white.
LUSTER	After sericin or silk gum has been removed by boiling-off, silk shows high luster.
STRENGTH	From 5 to about 28 grams before rupture.
ELASTICITY	Will stretch from 15% to 20% before rupture.
CONDUCTIVITY OF HEAT	Poor because it is an animal fiber.
HYGROSCOPIC MOISTURE	Averages about 11%, but depending on the grade may go to about 28%.
CAPILLARITY AND PENETRABILITY	Good penetrability, no capillarity.
FIBER COMPOSITION	Fiber or fibroin, 53.37%; gelatine, 20.66%; albumen, 24.43%; wax, 1.39%; coloring matter, 0.05%; resinous and fatty matter, 0.10%.

CHEMICAL CHARACTERISTICS:

EFFECT OF LIGHT	Not very good in strong light; repeated exposure to sunlight disintegrates silk faster than cotton or wool. Yellow-colored silk will fade rapidly in sunlight. Deterioration is rapid if the fiber has been weighted.

MILDEW	Affected only by extreme conditions.
HEAT	Not affected as much as wool.
WATER	No effect at all.
STRONG ACIDS	Hydrochloric, hydrofluoric, nitric, and sulfuric acids, in concentrated form, destroy the fiber. Dilute forms will not affect the fiber, even at the boil.
VOLATILE ORGANIC ACIDS	Acetic or formic acids have no detrimental effect.
NON-VOLATILE ORGANIC ACIDS	Citric, oxalic, or tartaric acids will not injure the fiber if controlled and removed.
STRONG ALKALIES	Caustic soda or soda ash will injure the fiber if in strong solution. Dilute cold solutions will not be injurious if neutralized or removed. Dilute soda ash solution may be used lukewarm but must be removed at proper time.
WEAK ALKALIES	Ammonia, borax, phosphate of soda, silicate of soda, or soap will have no effect if controlled.
OXIDIZING AGENTS	Potassium permanganate, for example, will destroy the fiber unless controlled.
METALLIC SALTS	Good affinity; used for weighting silk.
AFFINITY FOR DYESTUFFS	Good to excellent.
DYES USED	The best to use include acid, chrome, certain selected basic, and direct colors.
BLEACHING AGENTS	Chlorine or hypochlorite bleaches are not used on silk.
OTHER OXIDATION BLEACHES	Hydrogen peroxide, sodium perborate, potassium permanganate plus bisulfite of soda will not injure the fiber, if controlled.
REDUCTION BLEACHES	Hydrosulfite, sulfurous acid (sulfur dioxide plus water) will not injure fiber, if controlled.
USES:	These include women's coats, pajamas, business or street dresses, sportswear; afternoon, cocktail, and evening dresses and gowns; underwear, hosiery; in the accessory field are included gloves, handkerchiefs, headgear, shoe and slipper fabrics, scarves, and sweaters. In men's wear, silk is used for cravat fabric, cap cloth, gloves, handkerchiefs, hosiery, robes, shirtings, and underwear. Household uses include bedspreads, curtains and drapes, lampshades, scarves, table covers, and upholstery.

THE PROPERTIES OF ACETATE—CELLULOSE DERIVATIVE FIBER

MANUFACTURED BY: Celanese Corporation of America, E. I. du Pont de Nemours & Co., Inc., Eastman Chemical Products Inc., and American Viscose, Division of FMC Corporation. Du Pont and American Viscose do not manufacture the staple fiber.

MANUFACTURE: Purified cellulose is made into cellulose acetate with acetic anhydride. The cellulose acetate is dissolved in acetone and is extruded into air, where the acetone evaporates and is recovered, thereby leaving the yarn. Filaments can be cut to any desired length to produce staple stock.

PROPERTIES:

HEAT	Becomes sticky at 350° to 375° F. Softens at 400° to 445°. Melts at 500° F.
ALKALIES	Strong alkalies will saponify into regenerated cellulose.
ACIDS	Concentrated solutions of strong acids cause decomposition.

BLEACHES	Attacked by strong oxidizing agents. Not damaged by weak sodium hypochlorite or peroxide bleaching solutions. After-bleach rinsing should be done with utmost care.
ORGANIC SOLVENTS	Soluble in acetone, and in certain other organic solvents.
MILDEW-RESISTANCE	High.
SUNLIGHT	Slight weakening of tensile strength, no discoloration.
TENSILE STRENGTH (IN GRAMS PER DENIER)	1.3–1.5 standard. 0.8–1.2 wet.
ELONGATION (IN PERCENTAGE)	25–30 standard. 30–40 wet.
AVERAGE STIFFNESS (IN GRAMS PER DENIER)	5.3.
SPECIFIC GRAVITY	1.32.
WATER ABSORBENCY	14% at 95% relative humidity.
DYES USED	Dyed with disperse dyes and in a few cases with basic dyes. Acetate can also be dyed under special conditions with some vat, azoic, acid, mordant, pigment, and solvent dyes.
IDENTIFICATION	Melts prior to burning; forms a hard black bead. Ball is noted at the tip. Gives off drippings when held to flame.
LIMITATIONS:	Weakened when wet, regains strength when dry; use care in manipulation. Acetate fabrics may not be as durable as those made from some of the other fibers; keep in mind the end use of the fabric. There may be a tendency for slippage in some woven fabrics, and the possibility of drop-stitching or runs in knitted cloths. Handle fabrics gently and carefully since there may be a tendency to split or tear when cut on the bias. Uniformity or the lack of it will have an effect on even dyeing results. Always read the garment labels and be guided accordingly.
USES:	This fiber is used in dressgoods of many types, evening wear, fused fabrics, linings, lingerie. Acetate staple is often blended with other fibers for use in blanketings, carpets, fused fabrics; many types of men's and women's wear; and upholstery.

OTHER PROPERTIES:

1. Suppleness gives excellent draping qualities.
2. No natural tendency to stretch or shrink.
3. May be given special finishes.
4. Retains a permanent whiteness.
5. Acetates may be laundered and drycleaned, provided proper care and attention are given.
6. Used for cross-dyeing with other fibers to give two-tone and iridescent effects.
7. Acetate fabrics should be ironed on the wrong side or back of the material. The fabric should be slightly damp. Use a warm iron, not hot, to prevent glazing. (Acetate is thermoplastic.)
8. Fabrics of acetate will take a crease or a pleat well.
9. Texture is soft, has pleasant feel to the skin.

THE PROPERTIES OF ACRILAN—ACRYLIC FIBER

MANUFACTURED BY: The Chemstrand Co., Division of Monsanto Company, New York City.

MANUFACTURE: Acrilan is made from a polymer of acrylonitrile. The solution is made and extruded, the solvent is eliminated and the yarn obtained is then stretched. Filament form is cut easily into staple form.

PROPERTIES OF ACRILAN STAPLE:

HEAT	Char point is at 356° F. Does not have a melting point. Burns and leaves a hard black bead.
ALKALIES	Fair to good resistance.
ACIDS	Good to excellent resistance.
BLEACHES	Excellent resistance to hypochlorites and other bleaching agents.
ORGANIC SOLVENTS	Not harmed by the common solvents.
MILDEW-RESISTANCE	Resists mildew.
SUNLIGHT	Outstanding resistance in common with the other acrylics.
TENSILE STRENGTH (IN GRAMS PER DENIER)	2.5 standard. 2.0 wet.
ELONGATION (IN PERCENTAGE)	36 standard. 44 wet.
AVERAGE STIFFNESS (IN GRAMS PER DENIER)	7.00.
SPECIFIC GRAVITY	1.17.
WATER ABSORBENCY	5% after centrifuging.
DYES USED	Acid, premetalized, acetate, chrome, basics and vats, generally with ordinary dyeing procedures and dyeing time.
IDENTIFICATION	Round cross-section under the microscope. Not affected by glacial acetic acid, chloroform, acetone, or 90% formic acid. Soluble in dimethyl formamide.
USES:	Much used in the sweater trade, fine jersey fabrics, dressgoods, suitings, and other staple apparel in men's, women's, and children's wear. Also used in carpets, blankets, pile fabrics, chemically resistant materials, draperies and upholstery.

OTHER PROPERTIES:

1. Medium tenacity and abrasion-resistance.
2. High extensibility and low absorption properties.
3. Dries rapidly, washes easily and well, and has high resistance to wrinkling.
4. Has good bulking capacity; greater fabric bulk for weight of the material used.
5. Possesses a warm, full feel.
6. Crimping properties are excellent.
7. Excellent resistance to microbiological and insect degradation.

THE PROPERTIES OF ARNEL—TRIACETATE FIBER

MANUFACTURED BY: Celanese Corporation of America.

MANUFACTURE: Known as triacetate fiber and is thermoplastic.

PROPERTIES:

HEAT	Melts at approximately 572° F. When heated, will not stick at an ironing temperature of 482° F.
ALKALIES	Under normal dyeing conditions, little or no effect at 9.5 pH at 200° F., for 16 hours. Saponified by high alkali concentrations.

ACIDS	Unaffected by dilute solutions of weak acids. Strong acids may cause deterioration.
BLEACHES	Attacked by strong oxidizing agents such as potassium permanganate. Ordinary laundry bleaches such as hypochlorites and peroxides do not damage it if used in standard procedures and amounts.
ORGANIC SOLVENTS	Unaffected by common solvents; swollen by some ketones and trichlorethylene. Soluble in methylene chloride and acetone.
MILDEW-RESISTANCE	High.
SUNLIGHT	High resistance.
TENSILE STRENGTH (IN GRAMS PER DENIER)	1.1–1.2 standard. 0.8–1.0 wet.
ELONGATION (IN PERCENTAGE)	22–28 standard. 30–40 wet.
AVERAGE STIFFNESS (IN GRAMS PER DENIER)•	5.2.
SPECIFIC GRAVITY	1.3.
WATER ABSORBENCY	10% to 11%—100 R.H. centrifuge-method heat-treated Arnel.
DYES USED	With proper selection of disperse dyes, colors that do not change or stain other fibers when washed at 160° F. are obtained.
IDENTIFICATION	Soluble in methylene chloride-alcohol mixture.
LIMITATIONS:	Not as absorbent as cotton or rayon. Finishing and heat-setting are of utmost importance. Gas-fading may develop in garments; thus proper selection of dyestuffs and inhibitors is very important. Trichlorethylene should not be used as a dry-cleaning solvent or spotting agent since it will cause Arnel to swell.
USES:	Used for fabrics such as challis, faille, flannel, gabardine, sharkskin, taffeta, crepe, and other comparable fabrics for daily wear, when properly blended with other fibers. Arnel has appeal in both men's and women's wear in woven and knitted fabrics. Also used in laundry pads and in press covers.

OTHER PROPERTIES:

1. When heat-treated, resistant to glazing.
2. Iron can be set at the cotton setting.
3. Washes easily and dries quickly.
4. Can be dyed for wash-fast fabrics in a wide range of colors.
5. When properly constructed and heat-set, Arnel can be used in fabrics which are known for their colorfastness, crease- and pleat-retention, and dimensional stability.

THE PROPERTIES OF CRESLAN—ACRYLIC FIBER

MANUFACTURED BY: American Cyanamid Co., New York City.

MANUFACTURE: Creslan is a true acrylic in that it is composed of 85% or more of acrylonitrile.

PROPERTIES:

HEAT	Does not flash-burn. Sticking point 408° F.
ALKALIES	Fair to weak resistance; poor to strong; yellows.
ACIDS	No strength loss in weak acids; good resistance to strong organic acids; will dissolve in some strong inorganic acids.

BLEACHES	Can be bleached with some common bleaches.
ORGANIC SOLVENTS	Insoluble in acetone; soluble in dimethylformamide.
MILDEW-RESISTANCE	Excellent; is not attacked.
SUNLIGHT	Effect is negligible.
TENSILE STRENGTH (IN GRAMS PER DENIER)	2.7 minimum.
ELONGATION (IN PERCENTAGE)	30–35%.
AVERAGE STIFFNESS (IN GRAMS PER DENIER)	8.06.
SPECIFIC GRAVITY	1.17.
WATER ABSORBENCY	1.5% at 70° F., and 65° relative humidity.
DYES USED	Acetate, basic, chrome, direct, developed, direct after-treated, neutral milling, neutral metalized.
IDENTIFICATION	Use Calco Identification Stain #2, American Cyanamid Company.
LIMITATIONS:	May be affected by strong alkali and by dry temperatures above 400° F.
USES:	Brushed, napped, or pile fabrics, blankets, suitings, sweaters; jersey and other knit fabrics; sportswear, overcoatings, work clothing. Creslan can be used alone or in blends with natural and other manmade fibers. Especially good for union dyeing in wool blends.

THE PROPERTIES OF CUPRAMMONIUM OR BEMBERG RAYON— REGENERATED CELLULOSIC FIBER

MANUFACTURED BY: Beaunit Corporation, Fibers Division.

MANUFACTURE: Purified cellulose is dissolved in ammoniacal copper hydroxide, and through chemical processing is then regenerated into yarn. It is a stretch yarn as compared with regular viscose rayon yarn.

PROPERTIES:

HEAT	Burns like cotton, quickly. Decomposes around 300° F.
ALKALIES	Swells in alkalies, the degree of swelling depending on the concentration of the alkali solution.
ACIDS	Like viscose; little effect with cold diluted acid, weakens in hot diluted acid, and yarn disintegrates at higher concentration.
BLEACHES	About the same as for viscose.
ORGANIC SOLVENTS	Generally insoluble.
MILDEW-RESISTANCE	Attacked.
SUNLIGHT	Same as for viscose.
TENSILE STRENGTH (IN GRAMS PER DENIER)	1.7–2.3 standard. 0.95–1.25 wet.
AVERAGE STIFFNESS (IN GRAMS PER DENIER)	15.5.
SPECIFIC GRAVITY	1.52–1.54.
WATER ABSORBENCY	27% at 95% relative humidity; total retention—100% to 125%.
DYES USED	Same as for viscose.
IDENTIFICATION	Disintegrated by acids about the same as cotton; insoluble in acetone; dissolves in ammoniacal copper solution; cross-sections show round shape of filaments.

LIMITATIONS:	Same as for viscose.
USES:	Lightweight dressgoods, crepes, sheers, gloves; ninon, marquisette, voile and other sheer fine-denier fabrics. Also used in knitted fabrics, neckties, and decorative materials. Novelty yarns used for shirting, dressgoods, suitings, draperies and upholstery materials.

THE PROPERTIES OF "DACRON"—POLYESTER FIBER

MANUFACTURED BY: E. I. du Pont de Nemours & Co., Inc.

MANUFACTURE: "Dacron" * is made from petroleum, natural gas, air, and water. A chemical composition of ethylene glycol and terephthalic acid is used to make the product in which the polyester is melted, extruded through a spinnerette, and then stretched to obtain the yarn.

PROPERTIES:

HEAT	Sticking temperature is around 460° F. Melts at 480° F.
ALKALIES	Good resistance to weak alkalies; moderate to strong alkalies at room temperature; disintegrated by strong alkalies at the boiling point.
ACIDS	Good resistance to mineral acids. Dissolved with partial decomposition by concentrated solutions of sulfuric acid.
BLEACHES	Excellent resistance to hypochlorites and peroxides.
ORGANIC SOLVENTS	Generally insoluble; soluble in some hot phenolic compounds.
MILDEW-RESISTANCE	Excellent.
SUNLIGHT	Loses some strength on prolonged exposure. No discoloration. Much more resistant behind glass than in direct sunlight.
TENSILE STRENGTH (IN GRAMS PER DENIER)	4.0–6.9 standard. 4.0–6.9 wet.
ELONGATION (IN PERCENTAGE)	11–40 standard. 11–40 wet.
AVERAGE STIFFNESS (IN GRAMS PER DENIER)	23.
SPECIFIC GRAVITY	1.38.
WATER ABSORBENCY	0.5% at 95% relative humidity.
DYES USED	Disperse (acetate) and developed (azoic) with carrier, or at high temperatures.
IDENTIFICATION	Melts prior to burning, burns slowly. Fabric after 30 days at 300° F. retains about 75% original strength. Soluble in hot metacreosol. Not soluble in acetone or in concentrated formic acid.
LIMITATIONS:	Too hot an iron will affect the fabric. May create static electricity unless fabric treated against it. Fabric does not absorb perspiration well.
USES:	Blouses, shirts, suitings, curtains, slacks, hosiery, sewing thread.

OTHER PROPERTIES:

1. Does not shrink or stretch.
2. Sensitive to high heat; if ironing is necessary, press with a rayon setting so that the shape will not become distorted.
3. Washes easily and well, dries quickly, needs little ironing, and holds shape very well.

* "Dacron" is the Du Pont Company's registered trademark for its polyester fiber.

4. Noted for wrinkle-resistance.
5. Pleats may be heat-set into fabric and are lasting in nature.
6. Allows for quick, easy removal of water-borne spots and stains such as coffee, tea, lemonade, etc.

THE PROPERTIES OF DARVAN (TRAVIS OUTSIDE U.S.A.)—
NYTRIL FIBER

MANUFACTURED BY: Celanese Corporation of America.

MANUFACTURE: A composition of matter * whose basic constituent is vinylidene dinitrile. Available only in staple form.

PROPERTIES:

HEAT	Outstanding resistance to dry heat degradation. Zero tenacity loss noted after 195 days at 300° F. Less than 4% warp shrinkage after 126 days at 300° F.
ALKALIES	Fair resistance to cold dilute caustic; degraded by strong alkalies.
ACIDS	Good to excellent resistance to hot or cold acids.
BLEACHES	May be bleached using acidic sodium or calcium hypochlorite or sodium chlorite. Not affected by acidic hydrogen peroxide.
ORGANIC SOLVENTS	Insoluble in acetone; soluble in dimethylformamide.
MILDEW-RESISTANCE	No evidence of failure in standard tests.
SUNLIGHT	Outstanding resistance to outdoor weathering in direct sunlight. After two years direct Florida exposure, 88% strength retained.
TENSILE STRENGTH (IN GRAMS PER DENIER)	1.75 standard. 1.50 wet.
ELONGATION (IN PERCENTAGE)	30 standard. 30 wet.
AVERAGE STIFFNESS (IN GRAMS PER DENIER)	5.8.
SPECIFIC GRAVITY	1.18.
MOISTURE REGAIN	2%–3% at 65% relative humidity, 70° F.
DYES USED	Pastels obtained with disperse dyestuffs. Disperse or cationic dyes, with a carrier, for medium or deep shades; also azoid dyes developed with beta-oxynaphthoic acid for deep shades. Limited affinity for vat, solubilized vat, or selected acid dyes, the latter applied by the cuprous ion method. No affinity for direct, acid, metalized, or chrome dyestuffs.
IDENTIFICATION	May be separated from protein or cellulosic fibers by dissolving the Darvan in dimethylformamide. Stained pale mint green using Identification Stain GDC (General Dyestuff Corporation) or light purple-gray using Calco Identification Stain Number 2 (American Cyanamid Company).
LIMITATIONS:	Strong alkaline conditions, dry temperatures above 315° F., or wet temperatures above 250° F. should be avoided.
USES:	Men's and women's apparel, pile fabrics, hand-knitting yarns, sweaters, industrial fabrics.

* U.S. Patent Number 2,615,866 originally assigned to The B. F. Goodrich Company, Avon Lake, Ohio.

THE PROPERTIES OF DYNEL—MODACRYLIC FIBER

MANUFACTURED BY: Union Carbide Corporation, Fibers & Fabrics Division, New York City.

MANUFACTURE: Dynel is made from a copolymer of acrylonitrile and vinyl chloride; the co-polymer is dissolved in acetone, filtered well, and then spun somewhat similar to acetate. Made in tow form and cut as desired.

PROPERTIES:

HEAT	Will burn on contact with an open flame but is self-extinguishing when flame is removed. Does not melt or drip.
ALKALIES	Little effect at high concentration.
ACIDS	Little effect at high concentration.
BLEACHES	No effect.
ORGANIC SOLVENTS	Softened and dissolved by acetone and certain other ketones.
MILDEW-RESISTANCE	Excellent; is not attacked.
SUNLIGHT	Darkens after hundreds of hours of exposure.
TENSILE STRENGTH (IN GRAMS PER DENIER)	3.0 standard. 3.0 wet.
ELONGATION (IN PERCENTAGE)	36 standard. 36 wet.
AVERAGE STIFFNESS (IN GRAMS PER DENIER)	8.2.
SPECIFIC GRAVITY	1.30 at 25° C.
MOISTURE REGAIN	Less than 0.4% at 70° F. and 65% R.H.
DYES USED	Selected acetate, premetalized, direct and acid dyes; certain soluble vat dyes and basic colors, as well.
IDENTIFICATION	Will not support combustion, shrinks from flame. If held in flame, burns with acrid odor.
LIMITATIONS:	Because of its initial shrinkage point of 250° F., Dynel can be ironed with a bare iron only at temperatures below acetate setting. It can be boiled; piece-dyed fabrics are generally subjected to boiling above 205° F. for 1–1½ hours. Unless blended with acetate, rayon, or the natural fibers, there will be susceptibility to high temperatures. Fabrics must be finished properly lest there be a possibility of shrinkage in laundering.
USES:	Work clothing, auto fender covers, pile fabrics, napped fabrics, draperies, and industrial goods. When blended with cotton, rayon, wool, or other manmade fibers, it is used for suitings, dresses, underwear, and military fabrics.

OTHER PROPERTIES:

1. Soft, warm hand, excellent drapeability, wrinkle-resistance.
2. Basically wool-like in nature, but possesses considerably higher tenacity and abrasion-resistance.
3. Can be spun on any of the known commercial systems.
4. Provides good wear, has excellent shape, pleat, and crease-resistance.
5. Washes easily and well, and the wet strength is 100% of the dry strength.
6. Not affected by moths or mildew.
7. Can be dyed any color that fashion stylists decree.
8. Unaffected by drycleaning solvents.
9. Basic raw materials are natural gas, salt, air, water, and limestone.
10. Provides bulk without added weight.

THE PROPERTIES OF NYLON—POLYAMIDE FIBER

MANUFACTURED BY: Nylon Type 6 by Allied Chemical Corp., American Enka Corp., Beaunit Corp., Firestone Synthetic Fibers Co., IRC Division of Midland Ross Corp. Nylon Type 66 by E. I. du Pont de Nemours & Co., Inc., Chemstrand Co., Fiber Industries Company of Celanese Corp. of America, National Plastic Products Co., Inc.

MANUFACTURE: Type 66 is made from hexamethylene diamine and adipic acid. It is polyhexamethylene adipamide. Type 6 is polycaprolactam (polyaminocaproamide).

PROPERTIES:	TYPE 66	TYPE 6
HEAT	Melts at 482° F.; yellows slightly at 300° F., when held for 5 hours.	Melts at 420° F.; yellows at 300° F., when held for 5 hours.
ALKALIES	Both show little effect, substantially inert.	
ACIDS	Boiling in 5% hydrochloric acid causes disintegration; dissolves with at least partial decomposition in cold concentrated solutions of hydrochloric, sulfuric, and nitric acids.	Oxidizing agents and mineral acids such as hydrochloric and sulfuric cause degradation. Others such as benzoic and oxalic will cause loss in tenacity and elongation depending upon time and the concentrations.
BLEACHES	Good resistance to normal hypochlorite and peroxide bleaches.	
ORGANIC SOLVENTS	Both are generally insoluble; soluble, however, in phenolic compounds, and in concentrated formic acid.	
MILDEW-RESISTANCE	Not attacked.	Not attacked.
SUNLIGHT	Loses strength on long exposure; no discoloration. Bright yarn is more resistant than semi-dull yarn.	Strength is lost on long exposure, but there is no discoloration.
TENSILE STRENGTH (IN GRAMS PER DENIER)	4.3–8.8 standard. 3.8–7.6 wet.	4.6–5.8 standard. 4.0–5.1 wet.
ELONGATION (IN PERCENTAGE)	18 to 45 standard. 21 to 52 wet.	26–32 standard. 30–37 wet.
AVERAGE STIFFNESS (IN GRAMS PER DENIER)	32.	18.
SPECIFIC GRAVITY	1.14	1.14
WATER ABSORBENCY	Both are 8% at 95% relative humidity.	
DYES USED	Disperse and acid dyes are preferred.	
IDENTIFICATION	Both melt prior to burning. Give off odor of celery when burned. Insoluble in acetone. Soluble in xylenol.	
LIMITATIONS:	Absorbency and coolness depend primarily on yarn and fabric construction.	
USES:	Curtains, draperies, dressgoods, floor coverings, hosiery, lingerie, socks, sportswear, summer suitings, sweaters, slips, upholstery, transportation fabrics.	

OTHER PROPERTIES:

1. High abrasion-resistance.
2. Washes easily, dries quickly, needs little ironing, holds shape well, and does not stretch or shrink.
3. Takes creases and pleats well; these may be heat-set in fabric for durability.
4. Possesses excellent wet strength.
5. Elastic and flexible.
6. If ironing is necessary, press with rayon setting or the fabric may tend to fuse.

THE PROPERTIES OF "ORLON"—ACRYLIC FIBER

MANUFACTURED BY: E. I. du Pont de Nemours & Co., Inc.

MANUFACTURE: "Orlon" * acrylic fiber is made from a polymer of acrylonitrile. The solution is then made and extruded, the solvent is eliminated, and the yarn obtained is then stretched. The filament form is cut easily into staple form. Made only in staple form at present.

PROPERTIES:

HEAT	Sticking point is 445° F., on copper-block method. Retains 100% strength after 32 days in air at 257° F. Does not have a practical melting point, but will burn.
ALKALIES	Fair to good resistance to weak alkalies.
ACIDS	Good to excellent resistance to mineral acids.
BLEACHES	Excellent resistance to hypochlorites and other bleaching agents.
ORGANIC SOLVENTS	Not harmed by common solvents.
MILDEW-RESISTANCE	Resists mildew.
SUNLIGHT	Very little effect.
TENSILE STRENGTH (IN GRAMS PER DENIER)	1.9–2.3 standard. 1.8–2.2. wet.
ELONGATION (IN PERCENTAGE)	20–25 standard. 20–25 wet.
AVERAGE STIFFNESS (IN GRAMS PER DENIER)	9.
SPECIFIC GRAVITY	1.14–1.17.
WATER ABSORBENCY	2.5% at 95% relative humidity.
DYES USED	Dyed with cationic and disperse dyes and with acid dyes by the cuprous ion method.
IDENTIFICATION	Melts and burns; leaves hard black bead. Not affected by glacial acetic acid, chloroform, acetone, or 88% formic acid.
LIMITATIONS:	Too hot an iron may glaze or discolor the fabric. Does not come in clear white (chalk). Likely to build up static electricity.
USES:	Good for use in outdoor fabrics where cold temperatures prevail. Used considerably in sweaters and pleated garments. In blends, the fiber is used for suiting, apparel fabrics, dressgoods, work clothes. The fiber is very good for use in fabrics where strength and a low stretch point is necessary. Much used in curtainings and in certain specific garments when it is necessary to have the material of such a nature as to be able to withstand extreme conditions, particularly changing weather. Laboratory coats, aprons, etc., have met with much favor where there is a possibility of coming in contact with acids, corrosive chemicals, and substances that would normally deteriorate cotton garments.

OTHER PROPERTIES:

1. Noted for its high tenacity and strength which enable it to withstand rugged wear.
2. Dries rapidly and possesses a decided resistance to wrinkling.
3. Washes easily and requires little ironing.
4. Has a soft hand and good draping qualities.
5. Has a warmer feel when compared with nylon.
6. Can be made in soft textures and feels warm next to the skin.
7. Takes creases and pleats well. These may be set into fabrics; durable in nature.
8. Sensitive to high heat; press with rayon setting on the iron.
9. Avoid high temperature in tumbling.
10. Provides bulkiness without added weight; easily napped for certain surface effects.

* "Orlon" is the Du Pont Company's registered trademark for its acrylic fiber.

THE PROPERTIES OF SARAN—VINYLIDENE CHLORIDE FIBER

MANUFACTURED BY: The Dow Chemical Co. has licensed the following companies to produce Saran fibers:

1. MULTIFILAMENTS, STAPLE AND MONOFILAMENTS, DIAMETER LESS THAN FOUR MILS:
   The Saran Yarns Co., Odenton, Maryland.
   Firestone Synthetic Fibers Co., New York City.
   Vectra Division of National Plastic Products Co., Inc., Odenton, Maryland.

2. MONOFILAMENTS, MINIMUM DIAMETER OF FOUR MILS:
   Dawbarn Brothers, Inc., Waynesboro, Virginia; trade name of Dawbarn.
   Firestone Plastics Co., Pottstown, Pennsylvania; trade name of Velon.
   Southern Lus-Trus Corporation, Jacksonville, Florida; trade name of Lus-Trus.
   National Plastic Products Co., Inc., Odenton, Maryland; trade name of Vectra.
   Oriented Plastics, Ridgefield, Connecticut; trade name of Oriented.

MANUFACTURE: The vinylidene chloride monomer is prepared by chlorinating ethylene. This monomer is mixed with approximately 10% to 15% vinyl chloride monomer and polymerized.

This copolymer is in the form of a powder which is melted and extruded in filament form. The filaments are oriented to give the desirable tensile properties. A staple length can be made in the neighborhood of one to six inches.

PROPERTIES:

HEAT	Self-extinguishable. Softens at 240° F. to 280° F., and melts at 340° F. to 350° F.
ALKALIES	Saran fibers have outstanding resistance with the exception of ammonium hydroxide.
ACIDS	Excellent resistance.
BLEACHES	Safe to use at low temperatures—120° F.
ORGANIC SOLVENTS	Not affected by alcohols or aromatic hydrocarbons, halogenated hydrocarbons, or ketones. Esters and ethers may be detrimental in varying degrees.
MILDEW-RESISTANCE	High.
SUNLIGHT	Darkens slightly.
TENSILE STRENGTH (IN GRAMS PER DENIER)	Up to 2 for monofilaments, dry. No loss of strength when fiber is wet.
ELONGATION (IN PERCENTAGE)	15% to 25% at break.
AVERAGE STIFFNESS (IN GRAMS PER DENIER)	8 to 12 grams per denier.
SPECIFIC GRAVITY	1.70 plus/minus 0.05.
MOISTURE ABSORBENCY	Less than 1/10 of 1% after 24-hour immersion.
DYES USED	Saran fibers can be mass-pigmented; colors are built in during fiber manufacture; each fine fiber is colored solidly all the way through. This factor contributes to increased color stability and fade-resistance in the finished fabric.
IDENTIFICATION	When exposed to a flame, the fibers will soften and char but will not support combustion. When combined with flammable fibers, Saran acts as a fire-retardant (e.g., a yarn spun of 50% Saran and 50% flammable fiber will not support a flame). Flameproof properties of Saran conform to the standards of the flammable fabrics act. Insoluble in acetone; dissolves in dioxan at elevated temperatures.
USES:	**Monofilament:** Original automotive upholstery, curtains, heavy-mesh open cloths, screening, auto seat covers, filter cloth, decorative fabrics, luggage, outdoor furniture, car seats, etc.
	Multifilament: Carpet pile, protective clothing, blankets, outerwear, imitation fur, scouring pads, upholstery and drapery fabrics.

OTHER PROPERTIES:

1. Unaffected by moths.
2. The same strength wet or dry.
3. Oils have little effect.
4. Good resistance to light.

THE PROPERTIES OF VEREL—MODACRYLIC FIBER

MANUFACTURED BY: Tennessee Eastman Co., Division of Eastman Kodak Co., and sold through its sales representative Eastman Chemical Products, Inc.

MANUFACTURE: Modified acrylic fiber.

PROPERTIES:

HEAT — Verel is available in both stabilized and shrinkable forms. The stabilized or non-shrinking fiber will show only a small percentage of shrinkage (2%–3%) when subjected either to boiling water or hot air (250°–275° F.).

Type I Verel has moderate shrinking characteristics (10%–12%) at conditions stated above. Yarns made from Type I are adapted to pile fabric, upholstery backing, et al.

Type II is the maximum shrinking member (20%–25%) and is applicable to high-bulk needs.

ALKALIES — Slight effect on tensile properties from sodium hydroxide and comparable alkalies.

ACIDS — Little or no effect from hydrochloric or nitric acids, phenol, aqua regia, etc., even at high temperatures.

BLEACHES — Hydrogen peroxide at 30% concentration will show no effect. Clorox at 5% concentration will show a slight bleaching.

ORGANIC SOLVENTS — Unaffected by drycleaning solvents and common organic solvents. Soluble in warm acetone.

MILDEW-RESISTANCE — Highly resistant to mildew and microorganisms.

SUNLIGHT — Highly resistant; suffers no appreciable loss in strength or coloration.

TENSILE STRENGTH (IN GRAMS PER DENIER) — 2.5–2.8 standard.
2.4–2.7 wet.

ELONGATION (IN PERCENTAGE) — 33–35 standard.
33–35 wet.

AVERAGE STIFFNESS (IN GRAMS PER DENIER) — 8.0.

SPECIFIC GRAVITY — 1.37.

MOISTURE REGAIN — 3.5%–4.0% at standard conditions.

DYES USED — Neutral-dyeing, premetalized, disperse (acetate), and in some cases the basic or cationic dyes.

IDENTIFICATION — Verel is not soluble in acetic acid at room temperature, nor is it soluble in cyclohexanone. Soluble in warm acetone.

An excellent test for the qualitative detection of Verel is to place a small amount of scoured fiber in a test tube which contains pyridine, and then heat it over a steam bath for two or three minutes. If Verel is present, the fiber takes on a deep reddish-brown color and the solution becomes pale pink. The Verel is not soluble in this specific test.

The fiber is blended with other fibers in woven and knitted fabrics such as dress and sportswear fabrics, sweaters, men's hosiery, and flannel-type men's suitings. Other uses include pile fabrics in which Verel may be used for either the face or the back of the fabric.

Verel can be mixed with cotton to produce lightweight fabric such as batiste, and with wool for dense industrial materials.

In the non-apparel field, it can be used in blankets, paint rollers, wash mitts, toys, and polishing fabrics because of high resistance to chemicals and non-flammability. Draperies, fire curtain shields, and work clothing are also made with Verel.

OTHER PROPERTIES:

1. White color in its natural state, thereby not requiring bleaching.
2. Soft, pleasant, and appealing hand.
3. Easily dyed; excellent chemical resistance.
4. Good wrinkle-retention as well as press- and shape-retention.
5. Withstands repeated launderings.
6. Good dimensional stability and little tendency toward pilling.

THE PROPERTIES OF VISCOSE RAYON—REGENERATED CELLULOSIC FIBER

MANUFACTURED BY: American Enka Corp., American Viscose, Division of FMC Corporation, Beaunit Corporation, Celanese Corporation of America, Courtaulds North America, Inc., IRC Division of Midland Ross Corp., New Bedford Rayon Co., a Division of Mohasco Industries, Inc., and E. I. du Pont de Nemours & Co., Inc.

MANUFACTURE: Purified cellulose is made into a solution and then regenerated (from solid to liquid and then back to a solid formation) into yarn by chemical procedures. Stretching produces high-tenacity type rayon. Filaments can be cut into suitable lengths to produce the stable fiber.

PROPERTIES: There are three types of viscose rayon. The main differences are given below:

	REGULAR VISCOSE	MEDIUM VISCOSE	HIGH TENACITY VISCOSE
HEAT	All three types burn like cotton, do not melt.		
ALKALIES	Strong solutions cause swelling and reduce strength.		
ACIDS	Act about the same as with cotton. Hot diluted or cold concentrated solutions cause disintegration.		
BLEACHES	Not damaged by weak hypochlorite or peroxide bleaches. Make sure to rinse after bleaching.		
ORGANIC SOLVENTS	Generally insoluble except in cuprammonium and comparable compounds.		
MILDEW-RESISTANCE	May be attacked by mildew.		
SUNLIGHT	There is a tensile strength loss following long exposure; very little discoloration.		
TENSILE STRENGTH (IN GRAMS PER DENIER)	1.5–2.4 standard. 0.7–1.2 wet.	2.4–3.0 standard. 1.2–1.7 wet.	3.0–4.6 standard. 1.9–3.0 wet.
ELONGATION (IN PERCENTAGE)	15–30 standard. 20–35 wet.	15–20 standard. 17–30 wet.	9–17 standard. 14–20 wet.
AVERAGE STIFFNESS (IN GRAMS PER DENIER)	11.1.	16.6.	25.5.
SPECIFIC GRAVITY	1.50–1.54.	1.50–1.54.	1.50–1.54.
WATER ABSORBENCY	27% at 95% relative humidity for each type.		
DYES USED	All three types use the same classes as used on cotton; note that medium- and high-tenacity rayons do not dye as readily as regular viscose rayon.		

Viscose burns quickly without melting or forming a bead, leaving a black or grayish skeleton ash. Bemberg, cotton, linen, kapok, and other cellulosic fibers burn in a similar manner.

In a staining test use Texchrome and/or Testfabrics Identification Stain. These are excellent staining agents for identification of viscose. It will stain lavender in Texchrome; and blackish blue in Testfabrics Identification Stain.

In a chemical test the most common test accepted is the 60% sulfuric acid (by weight) method. Viscose is soluble in a 60% solution.

LIMITATIONS:

Exercise care against mildew formation. Watch for stretch in garments in handling and in laundering. When wet, tensile strength is diminished but returns when dry.

USES:

Woven and knitted fabrics of 100% viscose rayon in filament or staple, or in blends with wool, cotton, and other manmade fibers and filaments. It is used in many types of apparel in all fields; carpets and rugs, blankets, upholstery, suiting, etc.

Viscose rayon is used considerably in particular fabrics such as crepe, faille, grosgrain, bengaline, lining, plush, velvet, etc.

OTHER PROPERTIES:

1. Age has little effect on viscose rayon.
2. Will remain white permanently.
3. Resistant to moths.
4. Viscose rayon is a smooth filament, comes in bright, dull, or pigmented lusters, and sheds dirt readily.
5. Good absorptive qualities. Moisture content may vary from 3% to 11%. Moisture regain is 11% commercial standard and 13% standard condition.
6. Viscose rayon is never weighted. Its draping qualities are good.
7. Crepe effects are obtained easily.

THE PROPERTIES OF ZEFRAN—ACRYLIC FIBER

MANUFACTURED BY: The Dow Chemical Co., Textile Fibers Dept., Williamsburg, Virginia.

MANUFACTURE: A nitrile alloy based on acrylonitrile.

PROPERTIES:

HEAT	Sticking point is 490° F.
ALKALIES	Fair; resistant to weak alkali.
ACIDS	Good to excellent resistance.
BLEACHES	Excellent white obtained with sodium chlorite.
ORGANIC SOLVENTS	Not affected by the common solvents.
MILDEW-RESISTANCE	Not attacked.
SUNLIGHT	Good resistance.
TENSILE STRENGTH (IN GRAMS PER DENIER)	3.5 standard. 3.1 wet.
ELONGATION (IN PERCENTAGE)	33% wet or dry.
SPECIFIC GRAVITY	1.19.
AVERAGE STIFFNESS (IN GRAMS PER DENIER)	11.

| MOISTURE REGAIN | 2.5% at 70° F. at 65% relative humidity. |
| | 4.7% at 70° F. at 95% relative humidity. |

DYES USED — Takes a wide range of colors with vat, naphthol, sulfur, after-treated direct, and neutral premetalized dyes.

IDENTIFICATION — Under the microscope reveals a round cross-section. Melts and leaves a hard black bead when flame is applied.

In a staining test it is dyed at room temperature for three minutes with 1.0% (owf) Fastusol Pink BRA. Other fibers are left white or slightly stained. In a solvent test it is similar to other acrylic fibers. Ammonium thiocyanate is used to separate acrylics and Zefran is insoluble.

USES: — General apparel and household uses such as for suiting, sportswear, dresswear, knitwear, rainwear, outerwear, blankets, carpeting, pile fabrics, and industrial fabrics.

SCIENCES USED IN THE TEXTILE INDUSTRY

All items of trade science are based on some principle of one of the basic sciences—physics, chemistry, or biology. The science of physics will be better understood when thought of in terms of its various phases, as heat, light, sound, mechanics, and gases. Biology can be considered more effectively under the headings of botany and zoology.

In all phases of an analysis one should find it advantageous to examine only one division or part at a time, in order to follow the scientific information in proper sequence. In scientific problems the chemistry, the physics or the biology of the problem has to be carefully considered.

CHEMISTRY

Chemistry is a study of the composition of substances and the changes that may take place in them. Chemistry has made it possible for us to know that ordinary table salt ($NaCl$) is composed of equal parts of the elements sodium and chlorine, that water is made by combining one part of oxygen with two parts of hydrogen, (H_2O); that sulfuric acid (H_2SO_4) is composed of two parts of hydrogen, one part of sulfur, and four parts of oxygen; and that, for example, the deadly fumes from a gas engine, carbon monoxide (CO), is made up of one part of oxygen and one part of carbon; while carbon dioxide (CO_2) so essential for plant life, is made up of one part of carbon and two parts of oxygen.

CHEMICAL CHANGE

When a substance undergoes a change in its composition it is said that a "chemical change" has taken place—for example, when iron is exposed to air for a period of time we say it rusts; in reality, the oxygen in the air has united with some of the iron to form a new substance, iron oxide. When oxygen unites with a substance rapidly enough to release sufficient energy to produce considerable heat, we say that "combustion" takes place, or that the material is "burning." The development of power by burning gasoline in an automobile engine, or even the heat that we obtain from a gas stove, is explained by this chemical process of oxidation.

EXAMPLES OF CHEMICAL CHANGES FOUND IN TRADES

Other examples of chemical changes are found in baking of food; the generation of electricity by electrolysis; the softening of water; the dissolving of substances to form solutions such as zinc chloride for a soldering flux; preparation of dyes from coal-tar derivatives; and the manufacturing of countless synthetic products such as rayon, acetate, celluloid, cellophane, mercerized fabric, nylon, Vinyon, Fiberglas, "Dacron," and rubber.

Many trade tests are chemical tests; for example, textile fibers are found to be either animal or vegetable as to origin by simple chemical tests of solubility in an alkaline or acid solution; cloth is burned to determine its contents; metals are etched to reveal their true appearance; and the presence of obnoxious gases in the air are determined by the reaction of a controlled flame.

PHYSICAL CHANGE

All changes in a substance, however, are not of a chemical nature: some are merely physical; that is, the composition has not changed although the apparent form becomes different in appearance. The melting of glass, the evaporation of water, the dissolving of salt, and the dilution of oil with gasoline are physical rather than chemical changes. The physical state has changed rather than the chemical composition even though the visual identity may be lost. In general, physical changes may be recognized by the possibility of restoring the material to its previous form; for instance, water may be frozen, but easily returned to its original state by melting the ice formed by freezing; this is a physical change. Wood once consumed by fire is forever beyond recovery in its original form; this is a chemical change.

CHECK TRADE PROCESSES FOR APPLICATIONS OF CHEMISTRY

Examine the processes and the materials of your trade, vocation, calling, or profession as a means of calling to mind instances where a knowledge of the underlying principles of science are needed by, or would be helpful to, the worker in doing his job. Think of these items in the form of units and try to recall to mind the findings.

PHYSICS

Physics includes several phases of scientific investigation and knowledge; namely, heat, light, sound, electricity, mechanics and mechanical devices, hydraulics and gases. For purposes of analyzing your work it is well to examine it with reference to each of the fields of science. Following this examination it is well to transfer the prior learning to the subject at hand in the fields of textiles, textile testing, dyeing, chemistry, etc.

BIOLOGY

Biology is the study of living things including both plant and animal life. Those vocations which utilize plant and animal materials and whose services deal with living things must turn to biology for part of its underyling information of a scientific nature. Companies which use silk, wool, cotton, flax, ramie, jute, hemp, worsted, mohair, alpaca, asbestos, glass fibers, etc., use materials whose sources are animal, vegetable, or mineral matter.

For the purposes of classification, biology is grouped under two headings:

BOTANY: the study of plant life.

ZOOLOGY: the study of animal life.

To assist one further in analyzing his or her trade or profession for items of trade science, several suggestions are given under the headings of Botany and Zoology:

BOTANY

1. The story of cotton.
2. Flax and its structure.
3. Linen and what it is made from.
4. How plants used for textiles grow.
5. Plant structure.
6. Testing of plant fibers.
7. Vegetable oils and their uses in textiles.
8. How rubber is obtained and what it is.
9. The raw materials used in rayon and acetate.
10. A study of the bast fibers.

ZOOLOGY

1. Wool, its nature, and its source.
2. The nature of vicuña.
3. A study of the hair fiber animals used in textiles.
4. Differences between woolen and worsted fibers.
5. Human hair, its characteristics and nature.
6. The story of leather.
7. The story of silk.
8. How silk differs from wool in chemical, physical, and biological testing.
9. Bacteriology: explanation of diseases peculiar to wool- and hair-bearing animals.

Some Important Dates in the Early History of the Knitting Industry in the United States

1775: Germantown, Philadelphia, Pennsylvania, and Brandywine, a nearby settlement, had about 150 knitting machines in operation. By 1800 the number had increased to over 200 frames.

1818: A Lee type knitting machine was smuggled out of England and sent to Watertown, Massachusetts, and then to Ipswich, Massachusetts. The machine was owned by Benjamin Fewkes and George Warner.

1822: Ipswich, Massachusetts became the first knitting area in the United States.

1825: Germantown, Philadelphia, Pennsylvania was now a knitting center, under the aegis of Thomas R. Fisher.

1831: Timothy Bailey, Albany, New York, is credited with having driven the first Lee knitting frame by power.

1832: Cohoes, New York, was now a knitting center.

1834: James and Sanford Peatfield, Ipswich, Massachusetts, set up a rotary-warp knitting machine factory. A stocking mill was also in operation in Newburyport, Massachusetts, the Newburyport Hose Manufacturing Company. About this time the Wildman Machine, named for its inventor, came into being; it was capable of knitting a dozen hose at one time on one frame. Shortly thereafter the frames were used in Manchester, England and were considered the last word in frames of this type.

1839: Richard Walker, Portsmouth, New Hampshire, invented a rotary-powered knitting frame to make stockings, named because of the rotary motion of the cam shaft on the machine.

1846: Tompkins Brothers, Inc., now in Syracuse, New York, but founded in Troy, New York, is the oldest knitting company in the United States. It makes circular spring needle knitting machines and its most recent models are a 54- and a 70-inch frame especially set up to make carpets, carpet backing, and tufted scrim. The nephews of the founders sold the company to the Ingalls family of Syracuse and it is still owned by this family.

1850: Thomas Thompson was the first to adopt the circular knitting frame so that it would produce ribbed fabric. An Englishman, Appleton, and an American, John Pepper of Portsmouth, New Hampshire, disputed the Thompson claim.

1858: W. C. Gist invented a circular knitting machine that had eight feeds and made successfully striped fabrics which he patented in England, where the machines received great acclaim.

1859: E. E. Kilbourn brought out the earliest automatic knitting machine to make full-fashioned fabrics. However, the British claimed that this type of frame was invented in England in 1816, but details are lacking for verification.

1860: Canton, Massachusetts, was the home of the Draper & Townsend Company for the manufacture of latch needles. Mr. Draper was a member of the famous Draper family of Hopedale, Massachusetts, which today maintain the Draper Corporation, one of the two largest loom concerns in the United States.

About this time Walter Aiken, the son of Herrick Aiken, of Franklin, New Hampshire, sued Townsend for patent infringement and won the case. Townsend had argued that the latch needle had first been brought out in France decades earlier. It was not until 1940 that he was proved to be correct when the Smithsonian Institution discovered that Pierre Jeandreau had patented a latch needle in 1803 in France.

Woolen and Worsted Fabrics Used in the Apparel Industry and in Home Furnishings

MEN'S OVERCOATING FABRICS

Albert cloth	Donegal tweed	Kersey	Polo cloth
Beaver	Double cloths	Kerseymere	Reefer fabric
Bouclé	Fearnaught	Mackinac cloth	Scotch tweed
Broadcloth	Forestry cloth	Melton	Shetland
Buffalo cloth	Frieze	Meltonette	Tattersall
Cadet cloth	Harris Tweed	Montagnac	Ulster
Camel hair	Heather mixtures	Moscow	Whitney
Cashmere	Herringbone effects	Overplaids	Windbreaker cloth
Cheviot tweed	Homespun	Pilot cloth	Worumbo
Chinchilla	Irish tweed	Plaid-back coating	

MEN'S TOPCOATINGS

Albert cloth	Cravenette	Harris Tweed	Overplaids
Balmacaan	Donegal tweed	Herringbone effects	Plaid-backs
Bedford cord	Elastique	Homespun	Scotch tweed
Camel hair cloth	Forestry cloth	Irish tweed	Shetland
Cavalry twill	Gabardine	Kerseymere	Tweed
Cheviot	Glengarry	Melton	Whipcord
Covert	Gun club check	Meltonette	

MEN'S HATS

Felted wool　　　Felted fur

MEN'S SUITINGS

Alpaca	Cheviot	Filling-back serge	Herringbones
Banjo stripes	Clay serge	French-back	Homespun
Bannockburn	Cotton-warp unions	French serge	Irish tweed
Bedford cord	Diagonal worsted	French-back serge	Kerseymere
Broadcloth	Donegal tweed	Gabardine	Norfolk effects
Broché effects	Double serge	Glengarry	Oxfords
Cashmere	Drap d'été	Gun club check	Palm Beach
Cassimere	Dress worsted	Hairline effects	Panama
Cavalry twill	Elastique	Harris Tweed	Tropical
Chain-break worsted	Flannel	Heathers	

HOSIERY AND UNDERWEAR

Knitted all-wool	Wool-cotton	Miscellaneous wool mixes
Wool-nylon	Wool-rayon	

ROBES

Flannels of many types　　　Wool-mixture fabrics

NECKWEAR

Knitted all-wool	Worsted tie fabric	Wool-silk
Wool-cotton clubs	Wool-rayon	Wool-mohair

WOMEN'S COATS, SUITS, AND DRESSES

Albatross	Duvetyne	Jersey-woven/knitted	Shaker flannel
Baize	Elastique	Kersey	Sharkskin
Bolivia	Eolienne	Kerseymere	Shepherd's checks
Brilliantine	Epingle	Lace effects	Shetland
Broche	Eponge	Marvella	Silvertone
Brushed wool	Flannel	Mousseline de Laine	Stockinette
Camel hair	Florentine twill	Nun's veiling	Suede
Camel suede	French serge	Overplaids	Tartan plaid
Cashmere	Filling-back serge	Pebble cheviot	Tree-bark effect
Challis	French-back serge	Pencil stripes	Tricotine
Cheviot tweed	Georgette wool crepes	Pepper-and-salt	Tropical
Chiffon velvet	Goldtone	Poiret twill	Union fabric
Color-effects	Gun club checks	Poplin	Velour
Covert	Hairline effects	Prunella	Velour check
Crepe	Harris Tweed	Rabbit hair cloth	Voile
Crepon	Heathers	Ratine	Wool-rayon mixes
Donegal tweed	Homespun	Rib-weave effects	Wool-silk mixes
Double serge	Honeycomb	Saxony	Zephyr flannel
Drap d'été	Hound's tooth effects	Scotch tweed	
Dress worsted	Irish tweed	Serge	

WOMEN'S HOSIERY AND UNDERWEAR

Knitted all-wool; wool-cotton; miscellaneous mixtures of wool and manmade fibers.

WOMEN'S ROBES

Flannel of many types　　　Mixture cloths

Homespun	Flannel	Knitted cloths

MILLINERY

Duvetyne	Jersey	Velvet
Felt mixtures	Plush	Wool mixtures
Homespun	Tweed	

GLOVES

Wool fabrics of several types—made of soft-twisted or hard-twisted yarns.

BOYS' WEAR

Cheviot	Meltonette	Much re-used and re-manu-
Chinchilla	Serge	factured fabrics are used in
Homespun	Shetland	boys' wear. Vary consider-
Jersey	Tweed	ably in price and grade.
Mackinac	Whipcord	
Melton	Worsteds of varying types	

GIRLS' WEAR

Challis	Poiret twill	Twill
Crepe	Poplin	Union fabric
Dress flannel	Prunella	Zephyr flannel
Florentine twill	Serge	Most coatings similar to
Henrietta	Stockinette	women's wear but cheaper
Homespun	Tartan	in price and type.
Meltonette	Tweed	
Mixes of many types and qualities		

INFANTS' WEAR

Baby flannel	Dress flannel	Poplin	Sheer woolen
Bombazine	Eiderdown	Prunella	Stockinette
Cashmere	Flannel of many types	Ratine	Tartan plaid
Challis	Henrietta	Serge	Zephyr flannel
Crepe	Nun's veiling	Shaker flannel	

THE USE OF WOOL IN HOME FURNISHINGS

BED COVERINGS

Blankets and afghans	Comfortables with animal	All-wool blankets
Comfortables	fiber stuffing	Part-wool blankets

DRAPERIES

Damask	Frise	Velvet
Denim	Mohair	Wool mixtures of many types
Frieze	Mohair mixes	either in plain or Jacquard
Friezette	Velour	designs

RUGS AND CARPETS

Orientals and Domestics may be made wholly of wool or with a wool-pile effect on the face of the fabric with a backing made of another textile fiber.

Axminster	Genuine Orientals	Tapestry
Broadloom	Sheen-type American	Velvet
Brussels	Orientals	Wilton
Chenille	Smyrna	

UPHOLSTERY

Damask	Rep	Combination mixtures of
Denim	Velour	fibers in which wool is the
Frieze	Velvet	basic fiber
Friezette	Whipcord	
Frise	Tapestry	

Basic Terms Used in Women's Apparel

ACCESSORIES

Bags	Fads	Hoods	Scarfs
Belts	Gilets	Jerkins	Shoes
Bows	Gloves	Jewelry	Sweaters
Buttons	Halter-dickeys	Kerchiefs	Stoles
Collar and cuff sets	Hats	Neckwear	Vestees
Cover-ups			

BLOUSES

Asymmetric	Peasant	Stovepipe	Tunic
Draped	Peplum	Tailored	Tuck-in
Overblouse	Rhumba		

COATS

Belted tunic	Cutaway	Peignoir	Straight-line
Bloused	Double-breasted	Princess	Swagger
Box	Dressmaker	Ruana cape	Tailored
Cape	Duster	Redingote	Topper
Chesterfield	Fitted	Reefer	Trench
Coolie	Mandarin	Reversible	Tuxedo
Cruise			

COLLARS

Asymmetric	Fichu	Mandarin	Shawl
Bertha or cape	Flared standing	Notched	Standing
Choir boy	Flared ripple	Peter Pan	Turnover
Convertible	Johnny	Plastron	Tuxedo
Double Peter Pan	Lapel and collar in one	Reverse rolled	Wing
Draped	Lord Byron	Sailor	Yoke and collar in one

CUFFS

French	Hanging fluffed	Straight band
Hanging flared	Shaped band	Turn back straight, flared, or shaped

DRESSES

Apron effect	Empire	Maternity	Suit dress
Basque	Flared tunic	Pinafore	Tunic straight or flared
Coat	Jumper	Redingote	
Chemise	Long torso	Sari-sarong	

FOUNDATION GARMENTS

Bra	Cinch waist	Garter belt	Pantie girdle
Combination	Corset	Girdle	Strapless bra

HISTORIC COSTUMES

Directoire	Grecian	Victorian
Egyptian	Modern	

JACKETS

Blazer	Kiltie	Pea	Tailored
Bolero	Lumberjack	Semi-tailored	Tuxedo
Cardigan	Mandarin	Shirtwaist	Waistcoat
Dressmaker	Midway	Short	
Eton	Miss-tailored	Swagger	

NECKLINES

Asymmetric	Crew	Keyhole	Square
Bateau or boat	Decolleté	Off-shoulder	Surplice
Cameo	Diamond	Plunging "V"	Sweetheart
Camisole	Draped	Portrait	Turtle
Cardigan	Harlequin	Round	Wishbone
Cowl	Heart-shaped	Slashed	

NEGLIGEES

Bed jackets
Ensembles—
  robes and
  nightgowns or
  pajamas

Lounging garments—
  robes or
  pajamas

Sleeping garments—
  to include long or short
  nightgowns or pajamas

PLAYCLOTHES

Active clothes—
  riding habits
  skating dresses
  ski suits
  swim suits
  tennis dresses

Beach robes
Bras
Cabana suits
Culottes
Halters
Pedal pushers

Shorts
Slacks
T-shirts

SKIRTS

Asymmetric
Barrel
Bias
Bias gored
Bouffant
Built-up
Circular
Directoire
Dirndl
Draped—
  bustle
  center-front

center-back
pannier
peg-top
polonaise
side
Empire
Flounce
Frothy hemline
Godet
Gored
Kiltie
Lampshade

Lantern
Panel and yoke
Pencil slim
Peplum
Pleated—
  box
  group
  inverted
  kick
  side
  sunburst:
    flat

accordion
unpressed
Pleated gore
Sectional
Shirred
Straight or full
Swing
Tiered
Tunic
Wrap-around
Yoke
Zigzag

SLEEVES

Asymmetric
Balloon
Bishop
Bloomer
Cap
Cape
Circular
Convertible
Detached

Dolman
Draped
Drop shoulder
Epaulet
Fitted
Kimono
Lantern
Leg-of-mutton

Mousquetaire
One-piece or two-piece
Peasant
Petal
Puffed
Raglan
Saddle
Sectional

Shirred
Shirtwaist
Short
Sleeve-mitts
Three-quarter
Tiered
Tulip
Yoke and sleeve in one

SUITS

Bolero
Classic

Convertible
Dressmaker

Semi-tailored
Tailored-tailleur

Weskit

THEATRICAL COSTUMES

Fantastic

Historic

Modern

TRIMMINGS

Air tucking
Appliqué
Beading

Embroidery:
  includes Bonnaz
  and Schiffli

Passementerie
Quilting
Jabot frills

Rococo
Smocking
All-over tucking

UNDERGARMENTS

Bloomers
Bras
Chemise
Panties

Petticoats
Slips—
  princess line
  tailored

Tailored

WAISTS

Asymmetric
Basque
Draped—
  darts
  shirring
  tucks
  twists

Fitted
Fullness—yokes
  darts
  shirring
  tucks
Kimono
Shirtwaist

Surplice

Some Major Types of Skirts and Dresses

The word "silhouette," when applied to apparel, means the outline or contour of a figure or costume. The new silhouette of any fashion season means the general contour in fashion at the particular time, with special reference to length and width of skirt, shoulder width, etc., in contrast to the popular and accepted silhouettes of the previous season. The silhouette, a profile shadow projected on a reflecting surface, or the outline of a person or object filled in with color, solid or otherwise, became a popular word in Paris around 1759, associated with M. Étienne de Silhouette, who was minister of finance in France.

The origin of the word "Shirt," which is linked to the word "Skirt," is probably the Scandinavian root *skar*, which means "to cut off," and is applied to a garment that reaches to the area of the waist. The Icelandic word for a short garment is *skyrte* and the Danish word is *skiorte*, both derived from *skar*. Thus, it may be gleaned that a shirt is for the covering of the upper part of the body while a skirt serves the same purpose for the lower part of the body.

See PRINCESS, SHEATH, SHIFT, SHIRTWAIST, VARIATIONS OF SKIRTS (illus.).

PRINCESS: This very popular dress features the following high points: (1) It is created by seaming and dart effects. (2) Vertical seaming, which begins at the neckline-armhole-shoulder area, crosses the point of the bust and continues downward to the waistline, hipline, or hemline to constitute what is known as the "princess line." (3) The amount of snugness or ease to a princess-line fit is determined by the degree of shaping used on the seams. (4) Princess-line garments may be pencil-slim or fuller than a circular skirt. (4) The amount of flare used to create the varied princess silhouette is added to the basic body contour fit. (5) Flare may be added at any level of the garment: under the bust, at the waist, on the hipline, from the knee. This creates a dual silhouette, as noted, for example, in the empire-princess type of garment.

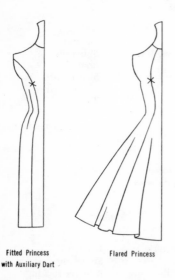  

| Fitted Princess with Auxiliary Dart | Flared Princess | Empire Princess Dual Silhouette | Knee - Flare Princess or Trumpet Styling |

Sketches pages 436-439 courtesy Edmund Roberts, F.I.T., New York City

SHEATH: A woman's dress made with the following high points: (1) It is always made with the vertical dart fit. (2) The vertical darts are used in single or multiple (group) darts. (3) The sheath can also be used in combination with a horizontal dart. (4) It may or may not be fitted to the contours of the figure. (5) The amount of the "dart pick-up" (depth of the dart) creates the ease or lightness of a sheath. Thus the sheath may be described as a type of slim garment, with or without a waistline seam, which is fitted rather snugly to the figure. *See* SILHOUETTE.

SHIFT: This "no-fit" dress features the following points: (1) Only the horizontal dart fit is used in this type of dress. (2) The shaping (if any) flare and the fall of the garment are directly controlled by the amount of the "dart pick-up." (3) Shifts which hit the hipline level are called "pullovers" or shells" and are controlled and constructed on the same lines as dress-length shifts.

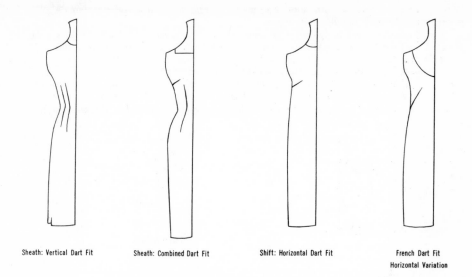

Sheath: Vertical Dart Fit   Sheath: Combined Dart Fit   Shift: Horizontal Dart Fit   French Dart Fit
Horizontal Variation

The shift is a garment that hangs loosely from the shoulder or is semifitted, and has no definite waistline. There are several modifications, as noted above, and generally speaking it is not very attractive on the wearer and often reminds one of a man's long shirt. The sides of the garment are often slashed for effect, with the slashes running from short to considerable length.

Shift: The Pullover

Shift: Flared

Two Very Popular Shirtwaist Styles of 1960's

1. The dropped waistline, which shows the influence of the 1920's.
2. Empire waistline, raised.
Note that all the components of the shirtwaist dress are featured in each sketch.

SHIRTWAIST: This type of dress is truly a concept of American designers and it is continually adapted and adopted by Continental designers. The shirtwaist was conceived and perfected by the creativeness of "Seventh Avenue" in New York City.

It was originated about 1893, it reached great heights in 1905, and has been a staple item in the apparel field ever since. It is in every woman's wardrobe, even to the present time. The popularity of the shirtwaist dress took on further impetus in the early 1960's, and it gives promise of marching along into the twenty-first century with a one-hundred-year heritage of styling, taste, and excellent fit, since it seems to be one of the few styles in female attire that is exceptionally well suited to the figure.

The shirtwaist dress is made up of seven component parts: (1) Back-shoulder yoke. (2) Bloused back-bodice. (3) Semifitted bloused front bodice. (4) Convertible collar. (5) Tab front closing. (6) Easy fit or full skirt, which is often pleated or in circular-type flare. (7) Shirtwaist mounted into an armscye always cuffed or banded (full at the wrist when long).

Note: The Tab Closing is the most positive "pure feature" of a real or genuine shirtwaist dress. The tab is a closing which is cut or slashed into an area of the garment where no seam is located. This slashing is a tailored quality or "classic touch" observed in shirtwaist styling.

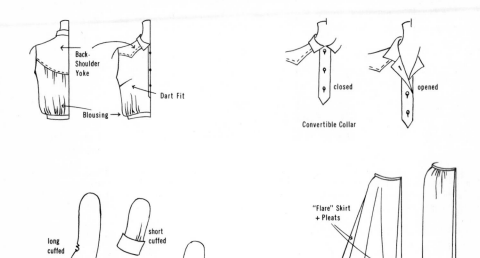

The American shirtwaist style no longer reflects the uniform of an office-girl worker. It is now used for all occasions—office, patio, at home, cocktail hour, dinner gown, golf and other sports apparel, evening gown, house dress, etc.

Practically any and all fabrics are suitable for shirtwaist styling. The ingenuity, deftness, élan and éclat of the designer determine whether or not his product is to be merely a fad or a good winner in the field of fashion.

Some popular fabrics used in the shirtwaist dress:

EVENING GOWNS	COCKTAIL DRESSES	SPORTSWEAR
Satin	Chiffon	Linen and simulated linen
Brocade	Organza	Denim
Lamé	Douppioni—true silk or	Gingham, broadcloth,
Matelassé	manmade fiber fabric	madras, etc.
Moiré (taffeta, faille, etc.)	Wool crepe	Piqué of any type
	Beaded knitwear fabric	Seersucker

As to price range, the shirtwaist dress may run from the $6.95 range in the bargain basement to around $1,200 in the exclusive salons of the leading couturiers and stores.

SOME "CAPSULE NUMBERS" APPLIED TO TEXTILES AND APPAREL

1. THE TEN "M'S" OF INDUSTRY

Men	Management and Methods
Material	Manipulation
Machinery	Millwrighting
Money	Marketing
Mill Engineering	Merchandising

2. THE EIGHT NECESSITIES OF LIFE

Food	Fuel
Shelter	Tools
Clothing	Accessories
Transportation	Adornments

3. THE FOUR WAYS IN WHICH TEXTILES DIFFER: Raw Material, Construction, Color, and Finish.

4. THE FOUR "F'S" IN TEXTILES AND APPAREL: Fiber, Fabric, Finish, and Fashion.

5. FOUR-SEASON FABRIC OR GARMENT: Spring, Summer, Autumn, and Winter.

6. THREE-WAY FABRIC OR GARMENT: For men's wear, women's wear, and children's wear.

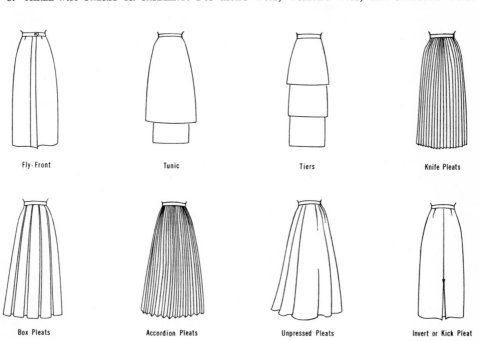

Fly-Front   Tunic   Tiers   Knife Pleats

Box Pleats   Accordion Pleats   Unpressed Pleats   Invert or Kick Pleat

FACTORS TO BE CONSIDERED IN BUYING A DRESS

The factors that should be considered in the purchase of a dress, and many other items of apparel as well, are of interest to the consumer. The proper sequence of considerations in most purchases of apparel follows:

1. SIZE

a) Above other considerations, the dress or other item must be of correct size in order to assure a satisfactory fit.

b) Necessary changes or alterations should not spoil the effectiveness of the garment on the wearer. Artistic and construction lines should not be sacrificed.

2. COLOR

a) Serious thought should be given to the color of the garment, for several reasons. First of all, the garment should be suited to the complexion—auburn, blond, brunette, swarthy, sallow, pallid, or flushed. Also, the wearer of properly selected clothes should consider the synchronizing between the garment and the hair, eyes, or figure.

b) The color should be such that it will add brightness and cheeriness to the wearer. Doleful, drab, or somber colors will not add to one's appearance under most circumstances. Of course, it must be realized that dark shades, tones, casts, and hues of color, when they are in fashion or chosen to withstand soil, or for occasions such as mourning, should be worn in good taste.

c) The color of the garment should suit the purpose for which it is to be worn and used.

d) Care should be taken that the color chosen is one which will not become tiresome and outmoded. People discard the stronger colors sooner than the lighter ones.

e) The dress or ensemble should blend and harmonize with other apparel and accessories that are worn—shoes and stockings, coat, purse, gloves, costume jewelry, headgear, etc.

3. QUALITY

a) Make sure that the quality of the dress is satisfactory.

b) Design, workmanship, price, and general make-up of the article are important. You should be satisfied, after due consideration has been given to the fabric, that the garment is suitable from all possible angles.

c) Make a close inspection of the garment with regard to hems, zippers, hooks, and eyes; seams, stitching, fastenings, etc.

d) Consideration should be given to decorations and embellishments. The article should be attractive. Keep in mind that the placing of buttons, lace, belt, shoulder formation, and lines will "make or break" the item. A belt, particularly, is most important in setting off the garment. Check placing of all accessories and decorations, since these should be in harmony and proper balance at all times.

e) The fabric and garment should wear well and suit your purpose, taste, and pocketbook.

4. APPEARANCE

a) A comfortable, well-fitting dress adds to one's appearance.

b) The outline or silhouette will make the wearer appear taller or shorter, slimmer or stouter, depending on the design, cut, drape, clinginess, the fabric used, the color, and whether the dress is form-revealing or form-concealing. Stripes of all types (pin, chalk, banjo), plaids, checks, overplaids, plain goods, plus the finish on the fabric and the surface effect or texture of the material, are items that should be borne in mind when buying practically anything new. The "hand" or feel of the goods is also a good determining factor when buying, especially when purchasing a dress for some definite purpose or use.

c) Attention to details is very important. The hemline, waistline, and the fashion and style for the particular season of the year should be studied prior to the purchase. These, along with all other items, should not be out of place or unsuited to the wearer.

d) Plan ahead of time on anything that you are about to purchase. All purchases should be considered as an investment, since it is your money that is to be spent. Think of all the good points, as well as those points which may not appeal to you. There are, of course, a great many types of fashions and styles in particular articles; in addition, there are many types of individuals and persons as well. You should be sure that you have a good conception of your type or the purposes for which your purchases are best suited. This may be determined by the following factors—complexion, height, weight, posture, manner of walking, disposition, purpose of the garment.

The figure—after the personality—is, naturally, the most important thing in summing up these elements which go to make this or that type of human being, as apart from other humans. No two of us are identical and there is some individuality in all of us. This is a very important factor to bear in mind.

e) Choose the dress or garment that appeals most to you, all things considered. You have to wear it, after purchase, and have bought it with your money. Do not be swayed by pressure talk, sales gibberish, or the sugar-coated words of a glib sales person. Be master of your own convictions and suspend final judgments until you are fully satisfied that the purchase will be worthwhile. Do not be rushed or stampeded into any purchase.

The individual has to be the one to decide on this or that dress, coat, hat, ensemble, evening dress, sports clothes, etc.

Ask yourself the following questions:

a) What will my intimate friends think of my purchase?
b) Will they approve or disapprove of the purchase?
c) Will it be becoming on me when they see it for the first time?
d) Is my selection suited to their taste as well as my own?
e) Have I made a "good buy" or a "poor buy"?

5. PSYCHOLOGICAL PHASES

a) In your own mind, the dress should express and fit what is referred to as "your own personality." Your dress should "look like you." The choice should make you feel happy, contented, and serene. Of course, everyone has, at some time or other, bought things and soon felt sorry that he made the purchase. Thus, we learn by trial and success, trial and error; and all of us have profited from both success and error, even in the purchase of a dress or any other item of apparel—coat, hat, shoes, neckwear.

Who Is to Blame for Faulty Fabrics and Garments?

Who is at fault or to blame when the customer or consumer complains about piece goods or garments that have been purchased and that do not give good performance, service, utility or satisfaction? Throughout the nation in every department store, haberdashery, apparel shop, drycleaning plant, and wherever fabrics and garments or apparel are sold, there is a constant flow of complaints—some warranted, some not warranted—concerning poor color, unsatisfactory drape, poor crease-resistance, sagginess, faulty buttonholes, and a host of other factors that require attention of the textile and apparel industries.

The fiber and yarn producers, weavers or knitters, dyers, finishers, garment manufacturers, retailers, sales personnel, the dry cleaner, the laundryman, and lastly, the consumer of the merchandise—all these agencies are involved and "implicated." And all these are interested in better fabric performance and longer-lasting apparel and garments. The following is an attempt to indicate some of the instances where a fabric or garment may go awry. Thus the trouble may be caused by any of the following:

1. FIBER AND YARN PRODUCER

The yarn may have lack of proper cohesion of the fibers, faulty elongation, crimp, fineness, flexibility, resiliency or ply.

Improper staple length of the fibers, variation in fiber diameter, faulty yarn twist.

Moisture content in fiber or yarn may be detrimental, thereby giving a negative effect in the finished fabric.

Tensile strength may be such that the yarn or fabric does not come up to specifications or requirements.

There may be too much foreign matter in the stock or yarn.

"Upgrading," which places the fibers in a class to which they do not belong or fit.

Carding and/or combing processes may have been curtailed or omitted in order to save time or make a "short-cut" in the yarn manufacture, or possibly to cut down labor costs.

Yarn twist that has been set poorly and not spaced well in the yarn.

Grease on machines that has been transferred to the fibers or yarns.

2. THE WEAVER OR KNITTER

Faulty selvages on woven cloth, such as missing threads, knots, slubs, excessive tightness of the yarns which causes "belling-out" of the fabric between selvages, and which gives much trouble to the cutter of the fabric for manufacture into a garment.

Broken ends or picks, bowed filling, missing plies in ply-yarn, loops or knots, etc., in woven goods.

Mistakes that have occurred in the drawing-in and the reeding-in of the warp yarns.

Missing loops, holes, and other factors that make for unevenness in knitted goods.

Uneven sizing, starching, or other treatments that are supposed to improve weaving or knitting yarns in manipulation.

Improper storage, poor care, and failure to keep machine parts in good working order; faulty or careless oiling of machine parts, which results in stains, streaks, and causes the material to become unsightly. Carelessness on the part of operatives who come in contact with the article from raw material through the finished apparel or garment.

Poor supervision in the mill or apparel house; failure to check constantly.

Faulty actions by the loom or knitting frame which necessitates, at times, calling the fabric a "second."

3. THE DYER

Poor color matching for proper shade; substitution of less expensive dyes for those which would give a longer life to the article.

Improper or careless bleaching of white ground before printing the goods; unclean dye kettles used for dyeing or printing with regard to proper consistency for the coloring matters used, especially when light shades are wanted.

Use of water of doubtful purity; hardness of water readily affects some dyes.

Faulty preparation for dyeing or printing goods, such as singeing, embossing, boiling-out of the goods, and the caustic-soda bath for cottons and some other types of fabrics.

Improper temperatures, poor timing, carelessness in the use of auxiliary agents of many types used in coloring textile goods.

4. THE FINISHER

Improper washing of the goods in scouring, boiling-out, etc. Poor application of finishing agents used on many fabrics, either mechanical or chemical in nature. Excessive bleaching that causes tendering of the material. Not using chlorine bleaches carefully, thereby causing irregularities in the goods.

Failure to cure properly, at prescribed temperatures; poor application of resin finishes with the result that the material will become less durable. Although time and heat may be saved here, customer satisfaction will become lost.

Chemical and lacquer coatings should be applied according to directions. Poor inspection throughout processing; a casual "look-over" should never be resorted to at any time.

Lack of proper quality control, and careless testing, whether physical or chemical. The finisher must apply his skills to the fabrics sent to him for finishing, although many cuts or bolts of fabric are not what they should be by the time they arrive in the finishing plant.

5. MANUFACTURE OF GARMENTS

Seams not cut on the true bias when so designated will result in sagging, unsightly stretching, etc. Provide protection against ravelings.

Pattern parts poorly matched, especially in prints, plaids, and checks.

The use of piping and other trims which are not washable or drycleanable.

Thread that is either weak and will break at once under wear and strain, or that which is not fast in color and will "bleed" on adjacent material. Color migration spoils many garments.

The addition of cheap, low-priced belts to low-priced dresses in which the belts have a backing that will not wash or dry-clean.

The use of buttons which melt under the first encounter with laundering, ironing, or drycleaning. Use of inferior padding or stuffing in shoulder pads in dresses.

Poor quilting or stitching in many types of women's apparel; the use of too wide stitches in smocking or quilting, which, when under tension, will break or snap shortly after the garment has been worn.

6. THE RETAILER

Does not press and check on his garments for display; crowding of garments in the show window or on the racks so that they do not appear in the best light.

Removal of brand names, labels, etc., so that the customer cannot relate the garment to the manufacturer of whom she may be cognizant from advertising in the newspapers, magazines, on television or radio.

Failure to instruct the sales force about the salient features and points of the garments to be displayed and sold. The store may conduct a sales session before selling hours to brief the personnel on the selling points of the merchandise. Unfortunately, by and large, this procedure is usually resented by the salespersons. One of the reasons given is that the information is usually disseminated in a haphazard manner and is only partially assimilated by the sales people.

Failure to assure that the purchasers are thoroughly impressed with the sales points other than fashion, eye appeal, and buy appeal. Positive selling points in many garments are not made known to the salespersons. Very often the store buyer does not know very much himself about the merchandise he purchases.

Failure to stock full sizes for selection by the public, although this is often intimated in the advertising of the merchandise.

Sales people cannot tell the customer how to care for a garment. When asked, they usually look surprised and say, "We do not know that." However, every customer should read well the attached labels on all merchandise. Unfortunately, the public seems to have little interest, all told, as to the text on the various labels about fiber content, washing and laundering instructions, etc.

It seems, generally speaking, that there are too many "Dryclean Only" labels or tags on garments that could be washed, thereby saving money for the customer.

7. THE SALESCLERK

Poor information on what or where the stock is located in the department.

Indifference to the customer and a lack of interest in the needs of the consumer concerning the particular merchandise. No apparent comprehension of how to tell the customer the correct way to care for the garment, despite the tags on the article.

Lack of knowledge on how to measure for sizes.

Inability to talk about and differentiate among the fibers, especially the manmade fibers. Failure to know anything about the most publicized fibers, fabrics, finishes on fabrics, etc. Will give incorrect information about items such as water-repellent, durable finish, crease-resistance, shrinkage-resistance, etc. Does not know if a vat dye is good or not. Knows little or nothing at all with regard to testing of fabrics about which a store may advertise. In fact, has not even read the advertisement when a special departmental promotion is being conducted that day—all of this based on the newspaper, radio, or television advertising.

The attitude of sales people is often very callous and indifferent; they just do not, for the most part, seem to have much interest in the customer, merchandise, the store, and, at times, even themselves. Some sales personnel often appear to be nothing more than necessary evils, and sometimes not necessary. Many are poorly equipped in the matter of dress, manners, courtesy, stance, cooperation, service, etc.

8. THE DRYCLEANER

Failure to use clean fluids and tendency to run garments through fluid until a sludge is too prevalent.

Does not prespot, that is, remove spots and stains before running through the general solution.

Does not check the garment for fiber content before cleaning. Very often, he "takes a chance and trusts to luck," and this often leads to disaster.

May use a drying process after cleaning that is too high in temperature, thereby ruining some of the fabric or garment, especially those of manmade fiber blends. In addition, shrinkage may also result.

Pressing of some articles too heavily or too long so that shine is evident in the seams and in parts of the garment where there are double folds. At times, the entire garment may take on this undesirable sheen.

Failure to know which fabrics or blends should not be subjected to steam pressure in pressing.

Has no knowledge of fibers, chiefly the newer types. Thus, he is unable to return the garment in the "good-as-new-condition."

When asked to apply nondurable or retreatable water-repellent, the dry cleaner very likely will have no knowledge of what you are requesting. Or, if he does know what you desire, chances are that the application of the agent will cause the garment to come out stiff and unwearable. Utmost care must be used when dealing with drycleaners as to guarantee that your garment will come back to you in a good condition.

9. THE LAUNDRYMAN

Little or no knowledge of textile fibers, even in a general way. Thus the laundryman may use a bleach that is too strong on whatever he considers to be cotton. Even if the article is of cotton, it will soon deteriorate.

Starching, when needed, such as in shirt collars, is very unreliable; one time stiffness will result; another time, limpness.

Repeated calls and notes sent to laundries are apparently not given too much attention. Very often, the help seems to be untrained and uninformed about practically anything they handle.

Although all good laundries say they can handle rayon slips, nightgowns, etc., these garments are often returned looking like a ghost or shell of their former selves—limp, out of shape, etc.

Although an ordinary laundry today should be able to handle "tumble-dry" terry towels and bath mats, they often are returned with deep creases in them and with the pile matted down to considerable degree.

Has thrown away the hang tags, labels, etc., which indicate the care that should be given the article. And, likely, has cast aside the sales slip. Thus, many errors arise because of sheer carelessness. Labels should be kept at all times and the directions for ease of care followed to the letter.

Does not tell the laundry or drycleaner the fiber content of the item. This trends for mis-handling which causes the customer to become vexed and possibly leads to some argumentation. He may also fail to inform them about the type or types of spots and stains that may be on the article. When returned with the spots still in them, the customer will often blame the laundry or drycleaner.

The consumer at home washes garments in water of improper temperature, notably woolens, which should be washed in lukewarm water throughout both washing and rinsing to prevent shrinkage.

The consumer may, for example, wash nylon garments at home, expecting not to iron them, and then wring them out "hard" in both directions in washing and ironing, thereby putting in wrinkles that are most difficult to remove in any way. Then he wonders why the garment wrinkles.

Many consumers do not ask the salesperson about the care of the garment, for during the buying period the customer seems to be absorbed only with the fashion and style angles. Women seem to care little for the internals in a garment; they seem only interested with the externals and the fashion whims.

The consumer uses too hot an iron in pressing without first trying the iron on an incon-spicuous part, as she may have been told. The result is that the article may become "jellied," shrunken, seared, etc. And, of course, she is not to blame.

The consumer may soak a garment which she has been told "to wash quickly by hand." Thus, delicate garments and delicate color shades are harmed. Improper or careless washing and failure to follow instructions on hand tags and labels are two of the reasons why stores have to listen to a host of complaints for which they should be held blameless.

HISTORY OF COSTUME

OUTLINE

1. INTRODUCTION.
2. HISTORY OF COSTUME.

    I. Oriental Period: Egyptians, Assyrians, Persians, Hebrews, 2680 B.C. to A.D. 638.
    II. Classical Period: Greeks, Romans, 2800 B.C. to A.D. 476.
    III. Germanic Period or Gallo-Roman Period: 500 B.C. to A.D. 476.
    IV. Franco-Merovingian Period: 476–752.
    V. Carolingian Period: 751–987.
    VI. Capetian Period: 987–1328.
    VII. Hispano-Moresque Period: 711–1500.
    VIII. Middle Ages: 1100–c.1600.
    IX. Italian Gothic: 1300–1450.
    X. Flemish Textiles and German Gothic: 1150–1500.
    XI. Renaissance: c.1450–c.1600.
    XII. Louis XIII: 1610–43.
    XIII. Louis XIV: 1643–1715.
    XIV. English Commonwealth: 1649–64.
    XV. Louis XV: 1715–74.
    XVI. Louis XVI: 1774–93.
    XVII. Directoire Period: 1795–99.
    XVIII. Consulate Period: 1800–04.
    XIX. Empire Period 1804–14.
    XX. American Colonial and Post-Revolutionary Periods: 1714–c.1820.
    XXI. French Restoration Period: 1814–30.
    XXII. Louis Philippe: 1830–48.
    XXIII. Second Republic Period: 1848–52.
    XXIV. Second Empire Period: 1852–70.
    XXV. Mid-Nineteenth Century in America: 1820–c.75.
    XXVI. Third Republic of France: 1871–1940.
    XXVII. American Fashions Come of Age: 1875 to present.

Man, in many ways, is the great exception in the realm of living creatures. Among most of the other genre, through no desire on their own part, the male of the species is the gaudier or has the more elaborate adornment since he, instinctively, is the aggressor in the race for "boy gets girl." For Homo sapiens, perhaps because he is a thinking man, the situation has been reversed since the beginning of civilization.

True, there have been times when the male has worn pastel shades of elaborate materials, lavishly embellished with laces and embroidery, but his wife has always out-glamoured him. Then the pendulum would swing to the other extreme, and male attire would become as drab as that of Jenny Wren. Today, once again, the male is breaking out of his chrysalis and is attempting to emulate the butterfly—at least in what he dons for sportswear. ·

The history of costume may be traced through various ages or periods in world history. The first garb worn by men was made of animal skins. This was followed, in due course of time, by the use of pressed or felted goat's hair and sheep's wool, in the colder areas of the world, while fabrics of linen, silk, and cotton provided body covering for those who dwelt in the warmer sections. Sometimes the body and/or fabrics were stained by leaves and berries.

In colder climates, dress shape was of the pelt hung from the shoulders over the body; the various parts of the skins were held together by strips of tough skin and muscle.

In the warmer sections, the first garments consisted of a cloth made of grass or reeds, or of linen or cotton suspended from the hips to the knees. A belt or girdle was used to hold the material in place.

The women of the colder areas often wore, in addition to the foregoing, a fur or leather jacket or covering for greater warmth. In the warmer areas, women were addicted to long, flowing garments for greater comfort.

As time progressed, the dress of early civilizations began to express the spirit, temperament, customs, and traditions of the various peoples or tribes. The three earliest eras in the history of costume may be classed as Oriental, Classical, and Germanic.

THE ORIENTAL PERIOD, 2680 B.C.–A.D. 638

This is represented by the dress of the Egyptians, Assyrians, Persians, and Hebrews. The Egyptians apparently contributed more to the history of costume than the other three nations. This period began with the Old Kingdom, which flourished in the years 2680–2258 B.C., coinciding with the development of stone architecture, and ended with the Byzantine-Coptic Era, A.D. 395–638. This span of time included the following: the Middle Kingdom Period; the New Kingdom Period; the Late Period, which included the building of Carthage; the Persian Era; the Ptolemaic Period; and the Roman Period ranging from about 30 B.C. to A.D. 395. The Christianization of Egypt, and the Age of Cleopatra, 69–30 B.C., are included in the Roman Period.

Using the Egyptian mode of dress as the example, it would appear that the people wore much linen fabric, which was draped in a long, circular effect to cover the lower half of the body. Fabric lengths varied, and the folds in the cloth were the forerunner of the skirt of today. Another item of apparel at this time was the triangular, short, plaited petticoat, which was a forerunner of the present-day kilt worn by the Scots.

Later on in the Egyptian Era, men and women wore over this skirt effect a loose, flowing garment which extended from the neck to the feet. Higher-textured linens and cottons appeared in due time, and these materials were worn by the higher castes. Loops of fabric, belts, or girdles, and draped folds became popular. Ornamentation and soft collars made their debut in the latter part of the Oriental Period.

THE CLASSICAL PERIOD, 2800 B.C.–A.D. 476

This includes the dress of the Greeks and Romans. The period began with the Pre-Hellenic Era, 2800–1200 B.C., through the Homeric Era, the Age of Aristotle, 384–322 B.C., the Persian Wars, and the conquest of Greece by the Romans, 146 B.C.

The Greeks had plain, simple tastes in apparel and did not adopt any of the highly colored and embellished costumes of the oriental nations. The dress of the Greeks consisted of a garment made of a rectangular piece of fabric which was measured to be both twice the height and the width of the body. The cloth was folded and allowed to drape from the left shoulder, where it was fastened at first by a thorn and later on by clasps, pins, or buttons. A broad, cloaklike piece of fabric was worn in loose fold form by men of higher rank.

The clothing of men and women was about the same, except that the latter wore theirs in somewhat looser form and with more grace. White cotton or linen fabric was the favored fabric but, as time went on, purple and gold colorings became prime favorites.

The Roman costume was on the order of the Grecian attire and at first consisted of a single garment, called a tunic. The men, in time, adopted the loose garment known as a toga, which was thrown in folds about the person. Many women also wore comparable attire plus a shawl which was large enough in measurement to cover the entire body.

In the halcyon days of the Romans, during both the Empire and the Republic, clothing was considered expensive and those who could afford to do so went to extremes with woolen, fine cotton, linen, and silk fabrics, all of which were elaborately trimmed. Jewelry and personal ornamentation were favored by women of the times.

THE GERMANIC PERIOD OR GALLO-ROMAN PERIOD, 500 B.C–A.D. 476

It is the third major period in dress attire. The period began with the first appearance of the Gauls around 500 B.C., and may be said to have ended around the year A.D. 450. That part of Europe which is now France was formerly known as Gaul, and it was conquered by the Romans under Caesar (58–51 B.C.). The hordes of Franks crossed the Rhine into Gaul in A.D. 276, and the French Kingdom was set up by Clovis in A.D. 486.

The Romans introduced their customs, manners, traditions, and dress to the Gauls with some modifications. Gallic women, after the conquest, wore many and elaborate costumes. Wealth may have been estimated by the number of costumes owned by the individual.

The high points of the era in women's wear included the following:

1. The tunic reached to the ground and was gathered by a belt or girdle at the waist; a band was used to adjust it to the bosom. The garment fell in folds and only the top of the footwear could be seen.

2. Boneless corsets supported the bosom.

3. Some women wore a chemise of cotton, linen, or silk, often scalloped around the edge.

4. Embroidered aprons made their debut and a veiling or mantilla was used to cover the face or to serve as a scarf for the head.

5. Plain and embroidered handkerchiefs came into vogue and there was considerable use of the narrow fabric now known as ribbon.

6. Women went in for much coloring and design in dressing gowns and robes of various types. Ceremonial robes were very vivid with color and embroidery.

THE FRANCO-MEROVINGIAN PERIOD, A.D. 476–752

Rome, as an empire, fell in A.D. 476, and Clovis, as previously stated, established the Frankish Kingdom ten years later. The Germanic tribes of Franks, Vandals, and Goths established themselves after the collapse of the Roman Empire. Clovis, a Frank, made Paris his capital. He did all he could to stifle everything Roman, particularly in dress. Frankish women wore a long black gown with an opening for the head and slits for the arms. A girdle held the gown in place; arms and the bosom were mostly uncovered. A piece of cloth was wrapped around the man's body and it was fastened over the right shoulder. The use of color, embroidery, and splendor in dress was very slow in progress among these peoples.

In the latter part of the era, knee-length trousers, tunics held at the waist by girdles, leggings, strapped shoes, short mantles or cloaks, and hoods or small caps made their appearance.

THE CAROLINGIAN PERIOD, 751–987

Two of the great historical happenings of the era were the reign of Charlemagne and the Treaty of Verdun. The kingdom of the Franks was now well established, and time could be given to other than martial matters. Dress became more elaborate and richer under the kings of the era. Men wore a short linen tunic, which was worn under the well-known woolen tunic. Matching embroidery was much used on long, flowing sleeves. Precious stones and girdles of gold and silver came into popular favor. Fabrics were made of better texture, and the surface effect was improved on wool, silk, linen, and cotton.

THE CAPETIAN PERIOD, 987–1328

This included the Crusades, travels of Marco Polo, and the rise of Gothic art. To about 1100 the era is often known as the Feudal Period. Clothing of this era, chiefly that worn by women, was form-revealing. Complete neck coverage was popular, while the long tunic was fastened at the waist and closed at the wrist.

Following the First Crusade, 1095, kimono sleeves made their appearance. A type of stocking began to replace the time-worn legging. The stocking was made of fabric cut to fit the leg. Shoes were of the pointed type, while hats appeared square in shape; mantles became longer and cumbersome. Men appeared in short trousers, forerunner of the modern knickerbockers; these were worn underneath the long linen tunic and the outer tunic, which was unlike the type worn in prior centuries.

It was during the latter part of this period that the bliaud or transformed tunic made its appearance. The bliaud had fullness in the skirt caused by the use of gores at the sides of the garment. Veils were used to partially conceal the flowing hair which was in vogue at the time.

HISPANO-MORESQUE PERIOD, 711–1500

The Saracens conquered Spain in 711. Of all Islamic textiles, those woven in medieval Spain rank foremost in interest today. Sericulture seems to have been unknown in Spain before the Mohammedan conquest—yet, shortly afterwards, great quantities of raw silk were brought into Spain and it was not long before Spanish silks were in great demand throughout Europe.

The creation of the Western Umayyad Caliphate led to new and friendly relations with Syria and from this came a great exchange of ideas, commerce, goods, and fashions. The tiraz, a fine gauzelike fabric, became popular, and much of it was produced on Spanish looms. Elaborate tapestry borders were woven in silk and gold threads. By the ninth century Spain was making good strides in silk manufacture.

Although there are many Hispano-Moresque fabrics designed with animal motifs, and some few with designs of the human body, on the whole the textile design of this era seemed to be limited to geometric and arabesque motifs, which predominated in all Moorish crafts. Their appeal is due largely to the jewel-like quality of the colors. Many silks were made with gold or silver threads interspersed throughout the fabric.

The thirteenth century, often referred to as "the greatest of centuries," brought out in Spain a wide variety of the star and lacéria motifs which predominated. In the fifteenth century, while still elaborating horizontally striped geometric patterns, there arose the idea of combining these with Kufic inscriptions in bands or cartouches. This led to the Mudejar style, in which there was a clever blending of Gothic and Moorish motifs.

This style survived the Fall of Granada in 1493, while the pure Moorish style found a last nostalgic expression in certain fabrics woven in Morocco in the sixteenth and seventeenth centuries.

In the sixteenth century the Spanish were influenced by the doleful, gloomy Philip II. Somber dignity and conservativeness of line and color were in vogue during the last half of this century. Black velvet, considered an item of great smartness, was favored among the courtiers. Pins, a Spanish invention, were put to use. This time is known as the Age of the Spanish Cloak. It was of the usual shape, semicircular, short-waisted or hip-length. For travel or for older men, it was cut long to the ankles. The collar was rather wide and rounded over the top. Muffs became fashionable for women.

Thus, after eight centuries of rule by the Saracens, little by little the Spaniards regained their country, but the Moors, who possessed a much higher culture, had left an indelible influence on their living, art, customs, manners, and dress. They gave to Europe the ruche, the ruff, the short cape, and the corset; the hoop, the bombast style of the padded doublet and trunk hose, followed by the unpadded trunks or breeches. Silk knit stockings were a Spanish invention, and for many years the Spanish hosiery surpassed that made elsewhere.

THE MIDDLE AGES, 1100–c.1600

Also known as the Moyen Age. Various historians have taken different views as to when it actually began. The usual dates seem to be from the Fall of Rome in A.D. 476 to either 1500 or 1600. Thus the Franco-Merovingian, the Carolingian, and the Capetian are really a part of the Moyen Age. Considering the year 1100 as a beginning for the purposes of costume design, the changes of major import up to about 1550 include the following:

1. The tendency to overdress; women wore long, tight-fitting robes and gowns with a decorated band or collar. Large hoods to which were attached flowing veils were very popular. Women wore external corsets made of silk with elaborate decoration interspersed throughout.

2. Fancy headdresses and accessories were very common.

3. Sleeves were slashed at the shoulder to reveal undergarments. Furs and velvets were worn indoors for warmth.

4. Clothing for men was elaborate—breeches, coats, shoes and stockings, greatcoats. Long sleeves were in fashion for men.

5. All garments were stiffly padded and were hot, uncomfortable, and cumbersome.

6. People in the warmer nations wore loose, flowing dresses made of soft-textured fabrics featuring wide sleeves, square necklines, and girdles at the waist.

The so-called Middle Ages are looked upon today as the springboard for present-day costume design, fashion, and style. As a carry-over from this period to present-day style, the following will prove the point: Today's use of the close-fitting bodices which follow the natural lines of the figure to the hips and are held close to the figure by a band or belt of some sort. In addition, we find the free use of embroidery, the use of a girdle, and the revival, periodically, of a great many of the favorite fashions taken from the era of the Middle Ages.

ITALIAN GOTHIC, 1300–1450

At this time, the bliaud, the full overtunic of the men, had shortened to the knees and by the latter part of the eleventh century young men wore them "shockingly short." The tunic hung straight or belted, with a skirt of only a few inches below the waist. Hip-length stockings or tights were worn, of bias material, usually red, and with gold and jeweled garters, accompanied by soft leather shoes.

Both sexes wore sumptuous, loose, full mantles. The feminine tunic invariably had a train and many attempts were made to regulate its length. Early in the fourteenth century there was a new style of feminine robe which brought about a second advent of the corset. (The first use of the corset was in prehistoric Greece.)

FLEMISH TEXTILES AND GERMAN GOTHIC, 1150–1500

Weavers and fabric fullers were in business in Ghent by the tenth century. Flanders was thoroughly Gothic in influence in the fourteenth and fifteenth centuries. Features included the long tunic, slashings, puffings, starched fabrics, and the use of steel needles.

By the fifteen century the best woolens in the world were produced in Flanders. North of the Alps there was a great impetus in textile art. Linen damask tablecloths and napkins to simulate silk damask came in vogue. The flax-growing regions of Saxony, Flanders, and northern France profited from this rise in linen cloths. Holland was to profit in due time.

A special style of design was evolved, possibly by borrowing from the early woodcuts of the Flemish and German schools. The subjects were chosen chiefly from the Old and New Testaments, and often resembled the woven orphreys of Florence. Armorial devices and trophies, sometimes accompanied by lengthy inscriptions, were woven to the taste of patrons.

Red, blue, yellow, black and white, along with metallic colors, were favorites from the standpoint of color and motif, the reds running from pink to deep crimson and bright scarlet.

Cloaks were richly lined and turned back to show the lining of the garment. Decoration, in open-work braid effect, was applied along the seams of the underarm, the sleeve, and breeches. Silver brocade and satin fabrics were used by the upper classes.

It is interesting to note that during the Middle Ages women's arms were never bare. In the fourteenth and the fifteenth century, low necks and very bare shoulders were the vogue, but it was rigid rule that the arms be covered. In the fifteenth century, cuffs concealed the hands to the second knuckle of the fingers while, at the same time, décolletage was hardly above the waistline.

The Italian Gothic Era ended earlier than in other countries of Europe, about 1300. The Renaissance was slower to spread in Flanders and Germany because they were hostile to anything that had a Roman tinge.

THE RENAISSANCE, c.1450–c.1600

There is little doubt that the latter part of the Moyen Age and the Renaissance intermingled to a considerable degree. There seems to be no exact line of demarcation. Modern fashion is said to be taken mainly from this great era in world history.

It should be kept in mind that in Italy, where this "rebirth of culture" began, art reached the Golden Age under the patronage of the Medici, Borgia, and other reigning princely families. The paintings and sculpture, mostly religious, by such men as Da Vinci, Titian, and Michelangelo, have left us a remarkable picture of the fashions, both male and female, of prince and peasant; while the writings of men like Dante and Machiavelli have done much to give some impression of the daily life of the time. The influence of the Italian Renaissance ultimately spread to other European countries, led to the Reformation and an interest in the humanities, and culminated in the Elizabethan Era in England.

Three historical events of the era, in France, were the Field of the Cloth of Gold, 1520, the Massacre of St. Bartholomew, 1572, and the Edict of Nantes, 1598. This was the era of Rabelais, Clouet, Ronsard, and Montaigne. It was the time of other world luminaries who have been given historical posterity—Francis I, King of France (1515–1547), the Father of the Silk Industry in France, who established the industry in Lyons, Paris, and other French centers, where it is still flourishing; the age of Anne of Brittany, Catherine de Médicis, her daughter-in-law, Mary Stuart, her niece, Marie de Médicis, Mme. d'Estampes and Diane de Poiters. Each of the foregoing women still has an influence on present-day fashion and style in the women's wear field.

Historically, this was also the era of the Reformation and Counter-Reformation, the era of Luther, The Council of Trent, The Peace of Augsburg, Zwingli, Calvin, Henry IV of France, Henry VIII of England, Queen Mary of England, the daughter of Henry VIII and Catherine of Aragon, Queen Elizabeth, Pope Gregory XIII, Cesare Borgia, St. Ignatius of Loyola, Erasmus, and a host of other great figures, men and women, too numerous to mention here.

Some of the outstanding contributions to fashion and style of the era which have influenced present-day attire include:

1. The purpoint, full-skirted doublet which retained its broad neckline and was cut with a full, knee-length skirt held in at the waist by a sword-type belt.

2. Sleeves were long and roomy, and slashed to permit rich and colored linings to be pulled out between the slashes.

3. Jeweled pins and other costume jewelry were used to add color to the ensemble.

4. Women wore sleeves to the elbow, loose and richly ornamented. The waist was long and pointed. Large skirts were gathered at the waist and trimmed around the bottom with embroidery, often raised, slashed or cut to show a petticoat of rich fabric. Incidentally, the overskirt and sheer embroidered underskirt of today are taken from this idea.

5. Catherine de Médicis introduced the ruff collar worn at the neck. She was the widow of Henry II, King of France, but was of Italian birth. Thus it seems only natural that she should have had such a great influence in the fashions of France. Catherine de Médicis had a sixth sense when it came to fabrics, and she relied on her native Italy for the importation of the most exquisite materials from that country to make the French people the best dressed in the world at this time, an era of extravagance in dress.

6. During the reign of Henry VIII, King of England, men's dress reached the acme of elaboration and embellishment. The use of plain and untrimmed frills at the neck and the wrists came into vogue and the general effect seemed to make the lower part of the body rather broad.

7. Mary, Queen of Scots, has given posterity the well-known Mary Stuart collar.

8. The hoopskirt came into being during this era of lavishness. Stiff cottons were used chiefly to obtain the effect. The long-waisted, pointed bodice effect was also introduced, and it is still popular, at times, in women's dress today.

LOUIS XIII, 1610–43

Louis XIII of France and his contemporaries, James I (1603–25) and Charles I (1625–49), kings of England, whose reigns are sometimes referred to as the Stuart Period, made the following contributions to the history of costume:

1. The picturesque costumes of the Cavaliers of England and the Mousquetaires of France. Broad velvet hats became the rage. Adorned by an ostrich plume, they were worn over the face of the wearer who usually sported a pointed beard and long, curly locks.

2. Falling, unstarched ruffles of lace and embroidery were favored; shoulder widths were increased by curved epaulets. An ornamented belt supported the sword.

3. Breeches were loose and tied at the knee by means of ribbon. Long gauntlets and a short cloak, trimmed with lace and with silk lining, completed the ensemble.

4. "Slashed garments" seemed to be more or less the order of the times; breeches, shoes, skirts, gowns—all were slashed to bring out varying effects.

5. Frilled skirts, tight at the waist, were worn over rich fabric used for petticoating; hips were padded with whalebone or steel.

6. Ruffs were popular with both men and women. Wide-brimmed hats were worn by the men. Overcoats had snug-fitting sleeves.

7. Velvets, damasks, brocades, brocatelles, and other silk fabrics were eagerly sought for by the affluent people of the times.

His wife was Maria Theresa of Austria. Known in history as "Le Grand Monarque," he was the son of Louis XIII and he warred with England, Austria, and Spain. The period was one of exaggeration in style; men wore wigs and large, round castor hats trimmed with feathers. The tight-fitting body garment had increased in length and was decorated with gold lace or comparable material. It was buttoned from the neck to the waist. The coat was made without collar or lapel and was open at the neck to show the waistcoat. A lace cravat was carelessly knotted around the throat.

Coat sleeves were rather loose and were turned up so as to be rather short and thus show ruffled shirt sleeves of fine cambric material. Breeches were made of moderate width and were tied at the knees with ribbons. Low shoes replaced high shoes and gold or silver buckles were in great favor. Toward the end of the period, men's dress did become simpler and more comfortable, but elaborate trimmings still held.

The corsage of the women was of the décolleté variety; the bodice was rather pointed, and sleeves were made of shorter than elbow length with long folds of lace. Long gloves became fashionable. Skirts were full, rather simple, short in the front and with fullness given at the sides and the back by the use of an overskirt open at the front. The hairdressing of men and women was about the same. The simply arranged curls about the temples which had been fostered by Ninon de l'Enclos were superseded by elaborate headdresses composed of lace, ribbons, and flowers wired to great height and introduced by one of the king's favorites, Mlle. de Fontanges. Muffs were worn by both men and women. Court plaster was used as a "beauty mark." Gloves of kidskin or net replaced the ill-shaped leather gloves of the prior period. The draped bustle was extensively used by women of the day.

France, after the Renaissance had run its course, made a definite move to become the art center of the world. Kings, queens, nobility were all interested keenly in developing things artistic. Textiles received their share of attention. The first great patron of art after the Renaissance was Louis XIV. He fostered many establishments devoted to fine fabrics; his patronage of the Gobelin family was outstanding. He sought skilled textile workers not only from France, but from other countries as well. Louis was very desirous of obtaining expert weavers and encouraged other patrons to do the same.

While the characteristic motif of the Renaissance period was the repetition of the acanthus plant, the ornament for the capital of a Corinthian column, and vases, the age of Louis XIV brought a refinement of this with motifs of scroll effect in a masculine strain that was classic and serious.

ENGLISH COMMONWEALTH, 1649–64

It should be recalled that, with the advent of the Commonwealth in England under Oliver Cromwell, the era of John Milton, simplicity ruled and a rigid regime resulted. Because of the religious belief and the revolt against the ornateness of the first Stuart Period, bright colors, embellished materials, fancy cuts in both men's and women's wear, and elaborate hair-dos were banished by law, as were all forms of entertainment and their concomitant fancy dress.

Women wore gray or black, tightwaisted dresses relieved by a white triangular kerchief, and tight gray or white bonnets. The men wore gray or black knee breeches with silver buckles, three-quarter-length matching coats with white circular collars, and stovepipe hats with narrow brims. They cut their hair, which gave rise to their nickname of "Roundheads."

Silver buckles were worn on the front of these hats while similar large silver buckles adorned their sturdy shoes. It was this type of Puritan garb that came to the New World with the Pilgrims and may be still seen, to some extent today, in the clothes of the Shakers, Mennonites, Amish, and other such sects. We also still see reversion to some of these styles in contemporary fashions.

LOUIS XV, 1715–74

He was the king who ceded Canada to England. His Queen was Maria Leszczynska. Men's dress retained the knee breeches, the long coat, the doublet and the wig from the period of Louis XIV. These, as time went on, were modified considerably. The skirts of the coat, with pleats at the sides, became fuller and were held out from the body at the sides and the back by the insertion of stiffened materials and whalebone. Both coat and waistcoat were of low-neck cut and revealed the soft, lacy finish of the shirt. Lace ruffles were still conspicuous. Wigs died out by about 1740. Men dressed their hair in a few long curls which fell down the back of the neck only, and a black ribbon was used to hold the queue in place.

In women's wear, the draping and lifting of the skirts brought out a silhouette that was broad and broken. The panier or hoopskirt effect was much in favor; the draped bustle remained in fashion and was greatly used.

Mme de Pompadour, the power behind the throne, introduced the combed-back hair style. Bodices were of the décolleté type and were trimmed around the edges with small floral motifs. The paintings of Watteau and the printed cambrics of Oberkampf exemplified the trends of the times. Silk, flowers, fur, gauze, lace, and ribbon were extensively used on skirts and gowns for formal wear. Fabrics were rich in texture and motif and truly represented this era of frills and extravagances.

LOUIS XVI, 1774–93

Born in 1754, this grandson of Louis XV was king of France from 1774 until guillotined in 1793. His queen was Marie Antoinette. Men's attire during his reign did not undergo too radical a change from the time of Louis XV.

Coats were cut away at the bottom, skirts lost much of their fullness and flare, while the coat sleeve was made longer and fitted closer to the wrist. High heels became passé and the tricorne felt or velvet hat became popular with the cocarde or cockade of ribbon which replaced the feathers formerly in style. The redingote became a favorite with its long swirling skirt effect, long tight sleeves and shoulder-cape effect.

In women's wear, the dress was full, comfortable, and loose-fitting. It hung from the shoulders with the back fullness caught into a deep box pleat from the neck to the waist. The polonaise was another favorite dress. This was a one-piece dress with a close, tight waist; the usual short sleeves and a skirt which was draped at the sides into the shape of two broad wings while a third, and somewhat larger one, was at the back. Silk stockings and satin slippers were always shown to advantage.

Flounce effects became extremely popular. The figure became narrower and the bust and the bustle were exaggerated toward the end of the period.

The years 1789 to 1793 in the regin of Louis XVI are known as the era of the French Revolution. These few years wrought a complete change in France; art, design, weaving, fabrics, all went through drastic changes. This great turning point in the history of the world is still felt and has done much to promote modern ideas in fabrics and apparel. Simplicity in dress replaced the extravagance, show, and formality of the kings. Men began to wear long trousers in dull and somber colors, which were known as "sans culottes" ("without breeches"—i.e. forerunners of the present-day lady's culottes or pedal pushers). Long greatcoats, cutaway coats, and dark hats also came on the scene. Clothes of the time were arranged poorly, fitted badly, and were form-concealing.

Women of the day wore simple, short-waisted dresses with a kerchief around the neck which was crossed over the bosom and knotted at the back of the waist.

DIRECTOIRE PERIOD, 1795–99

Following the French Revolution there was a three-year span known as the First Republic, 1792–95. English sailors' trousers inspired the new style for men, which decreed that these garments reach halfway between the knee and the ankle. By 1793, the trouser reached to the shoe top. Russian boots came into favor. Women's silhouettes were broad and broken and the exaggeration of the bust made its appearance. Hoops were discarded but hairdressing received much attention. The First Republic was a time of uncertainty and chaos.

The Directoire reverted to the revival of Greek fashion and style. Sheer, transparent materials became popular with women; trailing skirts were slit from the hem to the knee, some were even slit to the waist. Women had their hair cut to current style and took to wearing wigs. The Directoire coat for men came into being; it had a short front with cutaway lines. The period was one in which the economic living standards were low because of the heavy costs of war. Accessories, however, were important.

CONSULATE PERIOD, 1800–04

The atrocious fashions and styles of the Directoire Period were abolished and simple plain clothes, in which white was the favorite color, came into favor. It was the influence of the so-called Neo-Classicists which prevailed. Women wore tunics of color and texture at variance with the foundation dress. Satin, muslin, velvet, and lace were the favorite materials worn. Tunics were not made with any regularity as to length.

EMPIRE PERIOD, 1804–14

This was the era of Napoleon, Josephine de Beauharnais, and Marie Louise. Napoleon had absolute control and the period is noted for its poor taste in dress, culture, and manners. Greek fashion prevailed with the short-waisted effect which received the name of Empire Fashion. Gowns and dresses were long, simple in cut, while the waist was very short and very low and plunging in effect. Headgear of all types was ugly, large, off balance, and profusely trimmed with artificial flowers. All told, the period was somber, dull, and listless.

AMERICAN COLONIAL AND POST-REVOLUTIONARY PERIODS, 1714–c.1820

The periods from that of Louis XV through that of the French Empire correspond roughly with the Georgian Period (1714–1820) in England, and our own late Colonial and Post-Revolutionary Periods. What France dictated, the rest of the fashionable world copied, whether one lived just across the border or Channel or amidst the hardships of the New World. Milady and her spouse waited anxiously for the latest fashion magazines from Paris and had the garments copied, even though the style might be inappropriate to the climate or the other exigencies of life in the Colonies.

The clothes of the Cavaliers in the Virginia Colonies lacked nothing of the elaborateness of their homeland brothers. Other colonists, however, like the Pilgrims in New England and the Dutch in New Amsterdam, had brought their own styles along, so that when the various groups met and mixed, some modifications resulted and many of the unnecessary furbelows were eliminated. Simple homespuns and printed fabrics replaced the rich silks, satins, and brocades, and dress, too, became simpler.

FRENCH RESTORATION PERIOD, 1814–30

At this time in France, the styles were a carry-over from the Empire Period—long shoulder effects and large sleeve effects which ended at the elbow. Hoops were in favor and these distorted the form and silhouette. Short, full skirts were the order of the day. Hair was worn parted in the center with long curls at the sides of the head.

The effects of the Industrial Revolution were now being felt and machine-made materials caused the attire of the more affluent people to be easily and readily copied or pirated. Then, as now, changes were frequent because fear of obsolescence seems to be the psychology of the female mind in fashion and style, and anticipation seems to prevail over realization. Changes were the order of the day.

The period, however, marked the end of the frills of the prior periods in men's wear; gone forever were satins, lace effects, powdered wigs, and so on.

Around 1820, the corset returned to favor, thereby causing the waistline to become smaller. Broad belts came into prominence. The large sleeve effects were held from the arm by boning or padding and gloves became very popular, either colored or white.

LOUIS PHILIPPE, 1830–48

Known as the Romantic Period, this era saw the advent of the bertha collar, the scarf, and the small shoulder cape to accentuate the long drooping shoulder which was the last word in fashion appeal in women's wear. Low, straight-cut necklines were used in evening wear, and these tended to give a broad effect to the wearer. Skirts were wide at the bottom and the hem was several inches from the ground; only the shoes or slippers were revealed by the skirts of the day. All types of flounces, ruffles, and tucks were in vogue.

In men's wear, some of the features of the times included the wearing of two vests, one short and one long; starched shirts with high collars, small ties, tight pantaloons which were long and strapped in gaiter fashion under the shoe, as well as the introduction of the corset or basque to make men's waists slender. The short jacket and the chimney-pot type of hat were in style.

SECOND REPUBLIC PERIOD, 1848–52

Costumes of this period were a continuation of the Restoration Period and the Louis Philippe Period with some modifications. These included longer shoulder lines and smaller waists. Black lace became extremely popular and black velvet bands for the wrist and throat also were in demand.

SECOND EMPIRE PERIOD, 1852–70

The days of Napoleon III and of the famous Eugénie (1826–1920), Empress of France (1853–70). Her name was Eugénie Marie de Montijo de Guzman. Under the direction of Empress Eugénie, many changes took place in fashion and style. A new era came into existence. Extravagance seemed to become the keynote. Worth, the famous fashion house of France, still in existence, made the clothes for Eugénie. Soft shades of blue, gray, mauve, and sapphire-blue were color favorites. Tulle and gauze were used; long, full skirts with many flounces were held out by hoops. Starched and ruffled petticoats were also in style. Tight, pointed bodices, buttoned to the neck, had small turn-down collars. Sleeves were set in a low armscye and were long and tight, or bell-shaped with lace and muslin undersleeves. Off-the-shoulder necklines and short puff sleeves were used in evening wear. Accessories included small bonnets, lace mantillas worn as shawls, and lace gloves. Incidentally, in the 1930's, the Empress Eugénie hat with its side plume was revived and achieved a great deal of popularity for quite some time.

It was during this period that the bathing suit for men was introduced. From the late years of the seventeenth century, the bustle was revived; and it soon transformed the entire silhouette.

MID-NINETEENTH CENTURY IN AMERICA, 1820–c.75

After the War of 1812, American styles, while still influenced by Europe, took on a flavor all their own. Publications like *Graham's Magazine* and *Godey's Lady's Book* contained the fashions now worn by the ladies of the young Republic. With the establishment of long trousers and duller colors for men, their fashions have remained static until the present time, when some bright notes are being added by the Hollywood and Hawaiian influences on sports and evening wear.

In the early 1830's, the lady's silhouette was still quite extravagant, but it softened into a bell shape in the forties and early fifties, with the use of sloping shoulders, tight waistlines and full skirts made of silk, satin, velvet, woolen cloth, muslin, and cambric. The rural and pioneer women created more practical styles that conformed more closely to the figure and made much of printed cottons.

In the late 1850's, the hemline opened to its widest with the help of crinoline and the hoop, while the waistline was kept small enough for a man to grasp in his two hands and the sleeves were made full, going to three-quarters or wrist length.

Because of the War Between the States, women's styles varied throughout the country, but certain basic changes were noted in the early sixties, primarily the shrinkage of the hem's circumference from 17 or 20 yards of cloth to 10 or 12 yards, and the slimming and simplification of the sleeves, which were now wrist length and sometimes had an epaulet effect.

Black was considered elegant for cloaks, both in summer and winter. Bonnets, which had been worn on the back of the head, were replaced by flatter hats, which were tied under the chin. By the late sixties, further modification of the hem led to extravagant trains, a belt line and sashes were introduced, and there was a trend to have the entire garment of the same color and material. Hair styles began to be more elaborate, with curls and/or chignons being added. As a result, the hat or cap practically disappeared, and was replaced by various types of ornaments which were interlaced in the hair-dos. Dress materials ran the gamut of all types, while costly furs were also used.

THIRD REPUBLIC OF FRANCE, 1871–1940

With Paris and Lyons, and later on, New York and Hollywood, all centers of fashion and style, apparel and clothing from this time forward have seen many changes in women's styles. Some of the changes early in the period included the skirt, made plain and pulled back by a cord to insure snugness in the front, much ornamentation on dresses, the demise of the hoop, and greater freedom than was formerly the case. Taffeta came into its own in favorite shades of blue, green, yellow, and magenta; black was also in favor for some occasions.

Tight bodices were set off with jabots of lace, and the polonaise—a waist and an overskirt in one piece, became popular. The mannish tailored suit made in somber colors also made its debut. Dolman sleeves were used on jackets and coats. Small headgear, pleated fans, and fancy parasols were popular accessories.

From about 1870 to the present time, there has been comparatively little change in men's wear. The French Revolution dealt a serious blow to fashion in men's apparel in so far as the lavish tastes prior to the Revolution were banished and they have not returned. Present-day men's wear may be said to be a carry-over from the days of the early seventies in France.

[453]

AMERICAN FASHIONS COME OF AGE, 1875 TO PRESENT

Styles in America were already looking back and copying those of the Colonial Period as the country prepared to celebrate its centennial in 1876. Instead of the side panniers, however, the back bustle was introduced. Waistlines were higher and skirts hung to the ground.

Hair styles became even more elaborate, while hats became smaller with a yet wider variety of trimmings. At this time, too, coats and jackets became very tailored, often in dramatic contrast with the elaborate and trained skirts.

In the 1880's, the silhouette changed greatly so that the figure was revealed. Women were not expected to be active, so skirts were narrow at both the knee and the hemline, which frequently had several rows of ruffles protruding from it. An even wider variety of materials and colors was used. Bathing "dresses" began to appear and the corset took on great importance because it held the figure tight and nipped in the waistline to conform to the dictates of fashion.

The Gay Nineties were characterized by what came to be known as the "leg-o'-mutton" sleeve and skirts with fullness in the back. Bonnets were smaller and flatter, while hats were wider in the front and turned up behind. Side plackets appeared in dresses and the first dress was specially designed for sport-bicycling. Then, as now, the theater influenced style, and the Juliet cap and Flora Dora parasols, among other items, gained great popularity. As "Society" emerged, so did styles change again, and the 1900's saw the return of the back bustle with skirts ending in elaborate trains.

Emphasis was given to the bustline by ruffles and jabots. Embroidery was a favorite pastime, so its product appeared on both lingerie and outerwear. Accessories became important and the earliest discussions of maternity wear were printed. A new century for women's wear had dawned.

The past fifty years have seen some drastic changes in styles. Artists such as Charles Dana Gibson and Howard Chandler Christy created the fashions at the beginning of the century. The advent of the automobile introduced the duster and hats with long veils. The top-heavy hair-dos and the hobbled skirts of 1912–14 changed quickly when women were needed to do their part in World War I. Skirts became shorter and fuller because of the need for greater mobility.

Home-knit sweaters and skirts became popular, while middies and bloomers became the approved thing for gymnasium and outdoor sports activities. This, in turn, led to the rise of the "flapper" and her own peculiar uniform of mannish clothing, felt hat, and open galoshes. The teen-ager was asserting herself as a result of the greater freedom for women. This period, too, saw the introduction of manmade fibers, and attention was given to molding the figure rather than confining it.

One of the most drastic revolutions to hit the fashion world came with the Roaring Twenties. Everything changed. The hair was cut in mannish style, the figure was flattened to a sexless silhouette, waistline and hemline almost met, the one being lowered too far, while the other rose to the knees. All wore the same styles, whether they were becoming or not. All sorts of make-up was worn. Good taste had fled. True, outfits were designed specifically for every activity of milady, but all along the same basic pattern. Such a trend could not last.

The only bright spot was in hosiery, with the changes from black to beige and tan, and from cotton to silk.

Rayons began to appear in hosiery colors that seemed to go well with the ensemble. Fortunately, the age of nylon was just around the corner.

The 1930's saw a return of artistic taste. Because of the depression, women took to making their own clothes because dress materials were so low in price. Then ready-to-wear garments also fell in price. Hemlines dropped a bit here and there, until they straightened out to a more graceful length, where they have remained, with slight variations such as a plunge with the "New Look," until now. Slide fasteners came into use, as did a limitless variety of materials. A greater individuality appeared, influenced by world events.

And then World War II began. This froze styles and cut the amount of material to be used in each garment. Skirts were short because of the lack of fabric, and the era became a period of static, inartistic style. Shoulders were padded, flattering only the slender, youthful figure. Old and young, slim and stout, all wore exactly the same things.

After the shortages caused by the war had been overcome, the late forties saw a rapid swing away from the frozen, too-short skirt and the too-wide shoulder. Skirts became very long and full, hips were padded, and the bustline was emphasized. Garments were designed for ease of motion and comfort. The "New Look" from Paris had arrived.

Today, the Colonel's Lady and Judy O'Grady both can look equally smart and stylish, for both wear clothes designed by New York, Paris, or Hollywood designers. The use of nylon and other new textile fibers and fabrics has inspired many new styles so that each may have what is becoming to her. The influence of Hollywood is noticeable.

Since the flapper first declared her independence, more attention has been paid to fashions for the young. For countless centuries children were simply miniature adults—whereas during the past thirty years, all this has changed, and there are specialists designing for the different age groups.

Particular attention is given to the teen-ager with her constantly changing proportions, and there are even fashion magazines geared to her needs. Today, if she will, the adolescent can look and feel as comfortable and stylish as her mother. Unfortunately, however, she has developed a uniform of her own—her brother's plaid shirt worn outside of her sloppy blue jeans with their turned-up bottoms, slacks, jackets, stretch garments, windbreakers, etc.

Her brother is now beginning to copy her, while his father is getting away from dull colors, thanks to Hollywood, and is wearing bright solid colors or printed shirts for sports and bright bathing trunks. Even his suits are taking on a brighter tinge.

What the future history of costume will be, only the designers know—and that's a trade secret.

Reference: *Mode in Costume*, R. Turner Wilcox, 2nd edition, Charles Scribner's Sons, New York City.

FASHION AND STYLE

Prior to 1913, the last normal year that the present-day world has witnessed, textile mills which made men's wear and women's wear had little difficulty in keeping their looms running to supply the demands of the textile, apparel, and allied trades. What the mill decreed as to weave, construction, weight, color, finish, and types of stocks used was accepted by the buying public. Fashion and style, in their present stature, were practically unknown before World War I.

The year 1913 was the last year of peace before the world was plunged into chaos, storm, stress, and strife by the onset of World War I, conditions from which it has not recovered to the present day. Those born after 1913 have been born in what might be termed the age of chaos and uncertainty.

Following World War I and beginning in 1920, the entire scheme of things for the textile world began changing to a great degree. These changes are still taking place. At present, the acceptance of the fabrics made by mills is based solely upon the choice of the consumer, who follows the prevailing fashion as more or less decreed by fashion writers, fashion coordinators, fashion magazines, and "clothes consciousness" on the public's part.

Standards of living, as well, have had much influence on this item called fashion, which is nothing more than a prevailing style. In other words, the textile plants began to learn that they could no longer obtain a long run on their somewhat staid, staple fabrics, and that unless they made what the consumer desired, the mills faced serious difficulties.

Thus, going back to 1913, and more particularly since 1920, the mills which make apparel fabrics, especially in the women's wear field, have found it increasingly difficult to produce goods which are of positive consumer acceptance, unless they have followed the elements and dictates of fashion and style.

Successful mills of today must adapt themselves to the quick, ever-changing demands of fashion. If a plant is flexible and well managed, it should be able to produce easily and readily materials for the style markets without having fabric left on hand at the end of the season. Goods carried from season to season usually bring a lower price than the original price asked, and thus arises the problem of distressed merchandise and excessive inventory.

When one looks closely and examines this thing called fashion, with all of its workings, ramifications, tangibles, and intangibles, one learns that fashion is a logical element, certain and predictable. Fashion comes from the Latin *factio,* "a making." It can be considered as a prevalent style, or mode, in dress or attire, the general practice by what is considered as good society at some particular time. Fashion trends are followed to a successful conclusion: namely, in the making of goods that will meet the demands of such fashion and trade trends. When wool crepes, for example, of 9-ounce weight per yard are popular and in demand for dresses, would it not be foolish for a mill to run on, say, 12-ounce "red flannel"? Likewise, when fashion, custom, vogue, or usage later on sponsors wool and some manmade fiber in the material, would it not be wise to cease to manufacture wool crepe?

This anticipation of fashion trends, when successfully carried out, will make profit for the mill, and its selling force will keep the looms humming while labor is actively engaged in continuous work.

Style may be said to be a fashion, a manner, or a way of expression in the use of this or that textile fabric—the popularity of covert, Venetian, gabardine, Scotch tartans and Scottish district checks, seersucker, combinations of blended fabrics, homespuns, tweeds, etc. This may be expressed by the latest fashion in coatings for women being successful in the distributive and consumer trades.

To differentiate between fashion and style, consider a few examples: bustles, hoopskirts, dirndl dresses, high-button shoes, powdered wigs. All of these are styles, but surely all of these are not in fashion at present. At some future time, however, any one of the foregoing may become a fashion in the cycle of apparel. At times, a trend of fashion will revive for a season or for a year or sometimes even longer. In 1933, for example, the very popular and chic Empress Eugénie hats were a fashion, as they had been for many years in France; and from time to time they are accepted by the headgear trade and become a favorite with the consumer millinery trade.

All merchandise and fabrics are styles. Only those, however, that are in actual consumer demand are considered fashions. Style is part and parcel, or an inherent characteristic, of an object or an action. Only those styles in demand and accepted by a majority of the people at the present time are true fashions of the day. Not all new styles marketed are accepted, and only those that are genuine become fashion. Years ago fashion existed as it does today, but it should be borne in mind that in the so-called good old days fashion was not nearly the dominating factor that it is today in the ways and the standards of living.

Today, styles become fashion very quickly—almost overnight, so it seems at times. These styles become fashion if they are in harmony with fashion trends; if they are not in harmony with other fashions they will soon expire. Some styles in fabrics not in accordance with the trends of the times are discarded by textile mills shortly after the fabric lines are opened. Years ago, different sections of the country had quite different fashion ideas. Merchandise unsalable in one section of the nation could be disposed of very quickly in some other area.

The reasons for the speedier acceptance of certain styles are obvious: scientific development and progress with fibers, old and new; advances in research, yarns, design and design development, production, dyeing, printing, and finishing have been little short of miraculous. In addition, the automobile, radio, television, talking pictures, streamlined trains, faster travel, the photogravure sections of newspapers, fashion magazines, movie shorts, and so on, have all been important in bringing fashion to all corners of the nation and the world. People in the rural areas can drive to nearby towns and buy fabrics, clothes, and accessories that are the last word in fashion—instead of relying on the backwoods or country store to furnish them with a dress length of goods, the design or pattern of which might not be fashionable.

Truly, the automobile, radio, and television have done much to bring the rural population into direct and close touch with fashion that is right up to the minute. A new fashion trend soon spreads all over the nation in an incredibly short time. Any particular style which happens to become fashionable, or the "last word," develops into a piece of volume production. It is of great importance, therefore, that mills making fabrics that will be popular must know the factors and the underlying psychological principles which cause a style to become a good-selling fashion.

Mill management and good labor relations are vital factors. Fashions are a direct reflection and interpretation of the modes and the manners of living and the thoughts of the times. Mills must be keenly aware of these reflections and interpretations. They reflect the moral, economic, religious, political, and social phases and conditions of the period.

Sports clothes play an important part in our lives today, not only in active-sports garments but in spectator sports clothes, as well. It is the custom today to wear the proper and correct apparel when taking part in sports or in viewing sports events. Recall to mind the clothes worn for the polo game, tennis, football, college campus, fishing and hunting, beach sports, resorts for summer and winter, the cruise.

It has often been stated that the higher-priced fashions in garments will probably be the fashions in the lower-priced fields the following season. This is true to a great degree. Fashion and style are sought by the masses as well as by the wealthy and leisure class. Fashion permeates every city, town, village, and hamlet in the land. These groups of consumers follow fashion and style to the bitter end. Fashion and style are eagerly followed all the way from the "Colonel's Lady to Judy O'Grady."

Consider for the moment the fashion and style for New York City. It percolates from 57th Street, the most exclusive buying area in the world, to upper and lower Fifth Avenue, to 34th Street, to 14th Street, and to the Lower East Side. The exclusive-creation shops of 57th Street set the prevailing fashions for the four seasons of the year. The other areas follow suit. And every city, town, village, and hamlet has its Fifth Avenue and its Lower East Side, its "railroad tracks." Fashion marches on!

This series of facts bears out the impression that the people of today are more and more style- and fashion-conscious than ever before. Everyone, so it seems, wants to be dressed in correct fashion. Clothing and apparel must be correct and in keeping with the trends of the times, regardless of the price paid in many instances. Is not obsolescence, after all, the psychology of the female mind in fashion and style? Is not anticipation greater than realization in fashion and style?

Fashion surely runs the successful mills of today, whether they be making woolens, cottons, rayons, linens, silks, blends, or combinations. Textile mills, large and small, have to follow closely the fashion markets in order to keep abreast of the times. To disregard or overlook the questions and problems of fashion and style wuld be pure suicide for the textile plant.

BASIC OR KEY WORDS AND TERMS USED IN THE WORLD OF FASHION AND STYLE

These terms serve as the background or core for fashion writers, department store advertising, magazine writers on all types of apparel, etc. Close examination of the writing in this field will reveal that they seem to be used over and over again, along with some slight variations.

ACHIEVED: Accomplished, gained, completed; the final garment effect ready for comment, acclaim, and criticism.

ALLURING: Pleasing, attractive, and a temptingly attractive garment, usually along form-revealing lines.

ABOUNDING: Plentifully supplied or considerable abundance, especially of the amount of fabric used in the finished article. Refers to a garment with considerable "gingerbread," or may have some allure and zestfulness.

APPEALING: To have "appearance and looks," attract attention and interest, and convey its purpose; desirable and suitable for the occasion.

BALANCE: Poise, may be a symmetrical garment that is in even order and does not border on the bizarre or the outlandish.

BEAUTIFUL: Excelling in color, line, form, silhouette, balance, attractiveness.

BEJEWEL: Ornamented or embellished as in the case of sequins and other articles used to make the article more attractive; may border on the bizarre.

BIZARRE: Singular in appearance, style or general character; whimsically strange and a type of garment that can be worn attractively by only few persons.

BUCOLIC: Of or pertaining to the countryside; rustic or rural effect.

BOUFFANT: Puffed, puffed-out, raised, blister effect, quilted; full, as in the drape of a skirt, a puffed sleeve, or quilted house gown for leisure wear.

CHIC: Natty, neat, smart, stylish; tasteful, sleek, smooth, pert type of garb.

CHARACTER: A distinctive mark or merit noted in a garment; prepossessing, having distinction and individuality; sets off the appearance of the wearer.

CONTRAST: Opposite, dissimilitude, and effective but different effect observed. Often used with regard to color contrasts, a new fashion or counter to a prevailing style.

DAINTY: Neat effect as the result of intricate or detailed work as noted on many types of apparel for both innerwear and outerwear. A chic effect.

DEBONAIR: Gentle in effect, courageous, suave, elegant, smooth, jaunty.

DEBUT: The first entrance of a new style that has become fashion and remains so for a time that is short or long in duration. The effect and silhouette have much to do on how long a style will last after its debut.

DÉCOLLETAGE: A dress or suit—evening wear—with bare neck and shoulders to provide a flimsy, low-cut effect, often a plunging neckline which may border on the daring and even seems to be "out of line."

DEFIES DESCRIPTION: Beyond actual description, sensational; must be seen to be appreciated; the "out-of-this-world" type of attire.

DELICACY: Luxuriant, graceful, refined, and a consideration of being delicate and apart from the usual order of what might be expected; the niceties of a particular garment.

DELICATE: Tender, frail, dainty, easily injured by handling; borders on the flimsy, zephyr-like type of garb.

DIAPHANOUS: Transparent, as chiffons, sheers, and comparable materials used in dresses and gowns. Sometimes referred to as the "peek-a-boo" type.

DIFFERENT: Unlike and often implies a new effect in a garment; dissimilar.

DISCOTHÈQUE: This rather fantastic, lasting phenomenon was born in bizarre St. Tropez, the sophisticated resort in the Nice-Cannes area in the French Riviera, in 1963. It burgeoned in the rest of France, went to the British Isles, and finally arrived in the United States, where it has had a sensational reception. Originally the term meant a night club, private or public, where the habituées, frustrated and otherwise, whiled away the evenings to phonograph records. In these low-lighted or candle-lighted dens of pleasure were born the frug, sired by the twist, which was also responsible for the monkey, hitchhiker, the fish, the watusi, and other forms of bodily effort.

The fashion industry soon adopted the term, and the dress of this name is recognized by its low neck and short hem; to add to the ensemble black lace stockings and a suitable make-up were adopted to set off the configuration of the individual. As an item of apparel there are several modifications and offshoots with all of these using the popular catch-all word "discothèque."

DISCREET: Prudent, conservative; a well-cared-for-effect and in good taste.

ELABORATE: To perfect or develop by labor operations embellishments for a pronounced effect. Often carried to extremes, out of the ordinary, and often used to more or less describe the so-called "new look," in some particular article of apparel.

ELEGANCE: Polish, regality, daintiness; demands a second look. May be gorgeous in effect, scintillating, commanding, and of high class, such as observed in a creation, a classic, or a haute couture.

EXEMPLIFIED: To illustrate a new departure or a new development in fashion, style, vogue, or demand with an example.

EXCITING: Stirring; attracts attention by its conservativeness or its daring effect, usually the latter. Out of the ordinary, at times fantastic.

EXPERTLY: Done in a very skillful manner as to detail, final finish, and effect in some item of apparel. Effectively completed in minute detail.

EXOTIC: Delicate, strange; or something that reveals a new departure, often on the bizarre or sensuous side. Attracts attention because of its daringness or extremes.

EXQUISITE: Dainty, delicate, neat and appealing, refined with regard to appeal, approval or taste; done in proper balance and decorum.

EYE-CATCHING: Immediately attracts optical inspection and a second glance. "Fills the eye" because of its beauty or attractiveness and may be of the breathtaking type. Brought about by color, line, form, silhouette, cut-fit-and-trim, and, at times, by revealing phases of the article.

FANFARE: Much ado, flourish, great preparation, much commotion, etc.

FAVORITE: Preferred, the best-liked, popular, the choice, "tops"; the choice from a group.

FEMININE: Female, delicate, effeminate, ladylike and without any form of masculinity in lines, cut, fit, or trim.

FIGURE-CLINGING: Form-fitting, form-revealing, alluring, exotic; especially with regard to satins and comparable materials used in evening wear.

FLIRTATIOUS: Inclined to flirt, coy, demure, "cute," and to attract attention.

FLUTTERED: Moving rapidly; unsteady, confused, wavering.

FORM-CONCEALING: To hide the figure or the shape, opposite to form-revealing. Taffeta and similar fabrics are used in form-concealing women's apparel.

FRESHNESS: Vigorous, clean, natty, neat, spotless, not blemished; often used with regard to organdies and other cottons which always seem to have a fresh appearance.

FRILLINESS: Ruffled, flounced, and may be on the fastidious side; implies too much embellishment in which excesses tend to spoil the effect of the article.

FRIVOLOUS: Trifling, petty, even silly to some of the extremes seen at times in some fashions. Also known as the "frou-frou type."

GLAMOUR: Alluring and often illusory charm or fascination; enchanting. Probably the most used and often the most abused, word in fashion and style; seems to cover a multitude of "sins of commission and omission" with reference to fashions, styles, vogues and demands, especially in women's fashions. For want of a better word, glamour is often used, since the word adroitly expresses what the writer or speaker has in mind.

GENTLY SLOPING: Inclining gradually with ease and grace, softness.

GORGEOUS: Splendid, arresting, eye-catching, regal and rich in color. Its use is often overdone when there is nothing at all that is gorgeous in the particular article. "Gorgeous" seems to have more appeal than the word "bizarre," which might describe the article in a better way.

GRACIOUS: Affable, kindly, in good taste and done with care, élan and éclat.

HANDSOME: Pleasing to the eye, graceful, liberal to some degree in fashion. A man may be handsome; a woman may be beautiful.

IMAGINATION: The power to imagine, design or develop, fanciful. The use of the mind and the senses "to create" or to develop something "new."

INTERESTING: Exciting to the point where one desires the details.

INTRICATE: Entangled or done with much dainty detail. May be complicated but effective because of the working out of the detailed effect or effects.

INTRIGUING: Done with determined effectiveness, captivating, beguiling, accomplished. An attractive garment planned with definite thoughtfulness and positive imagination.

LONG TORSO: The trunk of the body without head and hands; being long or great in linear extent.

LOOSE: Swinging or hanging detached, as in a flared or swinging skirt.

MASTERFUL: Authoritative, well done, good work and excellent execution.

METHOD: Orderly and systematic, done with care and thought, well planned.

MINIMIZED: Reduced or modified somewhat in favor of other features currently in favor in other items of apparel.

MOLDED: Shaped, formed, form-fitting in order to improve the appearance of the wearer of the article.

MOTIF: Design or pattern, period of design, planned result, effect.

NATURAL: Not artificial, inborn, done in a natural manner, gives the so-called "natural look" to the wearer.

NIFTY: One of the most used and most abused words in the field of fashion and style, extending from describing a creation, classic, haute couture, gown, frock, all the way down to what all these are—dresses. It encompasses expressions such as fine, clever, divine, smart, stylish, chic, etc. This "easy" term covers a very wide range of expressions all in favor of the article being superb in all respects. Nifty is used by fashion editors, writers, co-ordinators, buyers, and sellers, and even by operatives and the "pusher-boys" who steer their dress-carts from one door to the next one. Many items of apparel are nifty but many, as is obvious, do not seem to truly fall into that category. Ranks with "terrific," "swell," "looks like a million," "great," etc.

NOSTALGIC: Homelike, homely, to think of home; causes one to think and to philosophize, often of the good old days and the good old fashions and styles of yesteryear.

POISED: Balanced and with some dignity; bearing of carriage or poise.

RESTRAINT: Confined, sober, somber and not liberalized; checked and done with care and decorum. Devoid of flourishes and embellishments.

RICH: Done in elaborate design, a rich or regal type of fabric used in a garment, especially in evening wear.

RHYTHM: Done with confidence, balanced and symmetrical in form and shape.

SANS: French for "without," such as without a collar, etc.

SEDUCTIVE: Alluring, daring, inviting, enticing, exotic, sensual. May be an attractive garment; a good conversational word to use in fashion and style.

SILHOUETTE: Used to imply the profile or configuration—from the top of the head to the tip of the toe. May include color, line, form, shape, etc. Named after the Frenchman, Étienne de Silhouette.

SLEEK: Smooth, slinky, glossy, lustrous, alluring; clean-cut and streamlined. Applied to form-fitting and even tight-fitting attire.

SMARTEST: Done with great care and shrewdness to achieve the utmost in clever and neat results on completion of the article in question.

SOPHISTICATION: Wise, and may be an artificial disillusion. Ideas, tastes, or ways developed through education, worldliness. A change from the natural character or simplicity into what at times may develop into "nasty niceness." A sophisticated gown is one that is right up to the minute in detail, cut, and design.

STRAPLESS DÉCOLLETAGE: A garment without straps to reveal the neck and shoulders, and often the bosom. May or may not be appealing to the wearer and to the observer; usually daring and the latest item in vogue. Actually may be in good taste and, at times, in poor taste, since it does not seem to do anything for the wearer.

SUAVE: Affable, bland, easily overdone, gracious, smoothly suitable for the occasion. Often worn in a nonchalant manner and does attract attention if the garment is genuinely suited to the wearer.

SWINGING RHYTHM: A type of attire that seems to provide rhythm to the wearer; usually observed on persons "who know how to wear clothes."

TASTE: The general character, manner or style as showing perception or lack of it as to what is beautiful, desirable or well fitting with regard to apparel. Expresses the characteristics of prevailing style or fashion. In some respects it may be stated that taste is really indefinable; what one person calls good taste, another may think is atrocious. The following questions on taste are thought-provoking, in a way indefinable, and many hours could be spent on coming to a solution for each question—if that is possible:

1. Define GOOD TASTE.
2. Define BAD TASTE.
3. Is TASTE active or passive?
4. Is TASTE an activity or a quality?

5. Is TASTE dependent upon the time factor? If so, in what way?
6. Can anyone have TASTE? Can it be implanted if not already existing?
7. How is TASTE related to FASHION? To STYLE?
8. How do we account for the unevenness of TASTE?
9. GOOD TASTE is better than BAD TASTE.
10. BAD TASTE is better than NO TASTE AT ALL.
11. Analyze your own TASTE pertinent to the apparel you wear.

TIERED: Done in folds, flounces, or in a series of repeated forms. May imply one above the other, banked. Should be done effectively at all times.

TREMENDOUS: Like the word "terrific," it is much overdone in the garment industries. Implies "large," "overpowering," "powerful," "commanding." Also means "great demand." Like the words "swell" and "terrific" in American English, it is used for want of some better adjective or description in speaking of items of apparel.

INFORMATION SOURCES ON TEXTILES

MAGAZINES:

1. *American Fabrics Magazine,* quarterly, 24 E. 38th St., New York City. The outstanding magazine devoted to textiles and apparel, fashion and style, vogue and demand, and current trends.
2. *American Dyestuff Reporter,* bi-monthly, 44 E. 23rd St., New York City. Devoted to textile chemistry, dyeing and printing, color and finishing.
3. *America's Textile Reporter,* weekly, 286 Congress St., Boston, Massachusetts. A weekly since 1887, and a leader on current trends, developments, and what is going on in all phases of the textile industry.
4. *Modern Textile Magazine,* monthly, 303 Fifth Ave., New York City. The manmade textile fibers and filaments—entire coverage in these fields.
5. *Textile Industries,* monthly, 1760 Peachtree Road, N.W., Atlanta, Georgia.
6. *Textile World,* 330 W. 42nd St., New York City. This long-established monthly magazine covers all phases of the industry from raw material through finished fabrics. Excellent for developments on machinery.
7. Fairchild Publications, 7 E. 12th St., New York City. Publishers of *Daily News Record* and *Women's Wear Daily.* Both papers cover all details of textiles and apparel, fashion and style; merchandising, buying and selling, and marketing. Up-to-the-minute reporting on trends and business conditions.

COMPANIES THAT SERVE AND SERVICE THE TEXTILE INDUSTRIES: Many manufacturers will furnish excellent material such as charts, literature, exhibits, and visual aids on their products. There is a nominal charge for some items, others are free. Ideal for display, objective material, reading, discussion groups, and training programs of many types.

1. American Bemberg and Beaunit Fibers, Division of Beaunit Corporation, 261 Madison Ave., New York City. (Bemberg) rayon, novelty yarns, sheers; nylon, olefin, polyester.
2. American Cyanamid Co., 111 W. 40th St., New York City. Creslan, chemicals, finishes, resins, etc.
3. American Enka Corp., 350 Fifth Ave., New York City. Enka, Jetspun, rayon, Nylon 6.
4. American Viscose, Division of FMC Corporation, 1617 Pennsylvania Blvd., Philadelphia, Pa. Avisco products, acetate, Colorspun, Vinyon HH, cellophane.
5. Joseph Bancroft & Sons Co., Wilmington 99, Del. Everglaze, Ban-Lon, Banflame.
6. The Carpet Institute, 350 Fifth Ave., New York City. Carpets and rugs.
7. Celanese Corporation of America, 522 Fifth Ave., New York City. Acetate, Arnel, Celaperm, Fortisan, Fortisan-36, Quilticel, Rayon, Darvan-Travis.
8. Chemstrand Co., Division of Monsanto Company, 350 Fifth Ave., New York City. Acrilan, Nylon 66.
9. Courtaulds North America, Inc., 104 W. 40th St., New York City. Rayon, Fibro, Coloray.
10. Deering Milliken Co., 1045 Sixth Avenue, New York City. Agilon, Lorette, Milium, Belfast wash-and-wear fabrics.
11. Dobeckmun Co., 3301 Monroe Ave., Cleveland, Ohio. Division of Dow Chemical Co. Lurex metallic yarns.
12. Dow Chemical Co., Midland, Michigan; Williamsburg, Virginia. Zefran.
13. E. I. du Pont de Nemours & Co., Inc., Wilmington 98, Delaware. Viscose rayon, acetate, Nylon 66, "Orlon" acrylic fiber, "Dacron" polyester fiber, Teflon, Mylar polyester film, Taslan, Color-sealed, Lycra, Corfam, Cantrece.

14. Eastman Chemical Products, Division of Eastman Kodak Co.—Tennessee Eastman Co., 260 Madison Ave., New York City. Chromspun, Estron, Kodel, Verel.
15. Owens-Corning Fiberglas Corp., 717 Fifth Ave., New York City. Fiberglas.
16. Firestone Synthetic Fibers Company, Division of Firestone Tire & Rubber Company, 45 Rockefeller Plaza, New York City. Saran, Velon.
17. B. F. Goodrich Chemical Co., Division of B. F. Goodrich Co., Cleveland, Ohio. Chemicals.
18. Heberlein Patent Corp., 350 Fifth Ave., New York City. Helanca.
19. Industrial Rayon, Division of Midland Ross Corp., 500 Fifth Ave., New York City. Viscose rayon, Nylon 6.
20. International Silk Assn., 185 Madison Ave., New York City. Silk.
21. Metlon Corp., Subsidiary of Acme Backing Corp., 432 Park Ave. S., New York City. Metlon metallic yarns.
22. National Cotton Council of America, Memphis, Tennessee. Cotton.
23. National Plastic Products Co., Inc., Odenton, Maryland. Saran.
24. Union Carbide Corporation, Fibers & Fabrics Division, 270 Park Ave., New York City. Dynel.
25. The Wool Bureau, 360 Lexington Ave., New York City. Wool, worsted, hair fibers.

Selected List of the Better Semitechnical and Technical Books on Textiles for Your Library

TITLE	AUTHOR	PUBLISHER
American Fabrics Magazine and AF Encyclopedia of Textiles	Staff	Doric Publishing Co., Inc., 24 East 38th Street, New York City
Apparel Manufacturing Analysis	Jacob Solinger	John Wiley & Sons, Inc., 605 Third Avenue, New York City
Calculations, Yarn and Cloth	L. H. Jackson	Textile Book Publishers, Inc., 257 Park Avenue South, New York City
Cellulose; The Chemical That Grows	William Haynes	Doubleday & Company, Inc., Garden City, New York
Chemistry & Dyeing of Textiles	Olney	Spaulding Co., Boston, Massachusetts
Costume, The Book of	Davenport	Crown Publishers, 419 Park Avenue South, New York City
Cotton, Growing	Cardozier	McGraw-Hill Book Co., 330 West 42nd Street, New York City
Cotton Handbook, American	Merrill, Macormac, Mauersberger	Textile Book Publishers, Inc., 257 Park Avenue South, New York City
Cotton, Heritage	M. D. C. Crawford	Fairchild Publications, Inc., 7 East 12th Street, New York City
Dictionary, Modern Textile	George E. Linton	Duell, Sloan & Pearce 60 East 42nd Street, New York City
Diderot Pictorial Encyclopedia of Trades & Industry	Denis Diderot	Dover Publications, Inc., 180 Varick Street, New York City
Dress, How to Look and	Garson	McGraw-Hill Book Co., 330 West 42nd Street, New York City

Fabric Defects	J. B. Goldberg	J. B. Goldberg, Textile Consultant, 11 West 42nd Street, New York City
Fabrics, Focus on	Dr. Dorothy S. Lyle	National Institute of Drycleaning, Inc., Silver Spring, Maryland
Fashion, The Woman in	Langley Moore	Batesford, Ltd., London, England
Finishing, Textile	March	John Wiley & Sons, Inc., 605 Third Avenue, New York City
Handbook of Textile Fibers	Dr. Milton Harris	John Wiley & Sons, Inc., 605 Third Avenue, New York City
Handbook of Industrial Fabrics—Wellington Sears Company, Inc. (1963)	Ernest R. Kaswell	Wellington Sears Co., 111 West 40th Street, New York City
Index to Manmade Fibers of the World	Peter Lennox-Kerr	Harlequin Press, Ltd., Manchester, England
Lace and Embroidery, The Story of	D. E. Schwab	Fairchild Publications, Inc., 7 East 12th Street, New York City
Man-Made Textile Encyclopedia	J. J. Press, Editor	Textile Book Publishers, Inc., 257 Park Avenue South, New York City
"Mercury" Dictionary of Textile Terms (1950)	Staff of "Textile" Mercury	Textile Mercury, Ltd., 41 Spring Gardens, Manchester 2, England
Mode in Costume, The	R. Turner Wilcox	Charles Scribner's Sons, 597 Fifth Avenue, New York City
Nylon Technology	Karl Inderfurth	McGraw-Hill Book Co., 330 West 42nd Street, New York City
Printing, Textile	Fred F. Jacobs	Chartwell House, Inc., 11 Broadway, New York City
Rayon Technology	Staff Members	American Viscose Company, 1617 Pennsylvania Blvd., Philadelphia, Pennsylvania
Rug and Carpet Book, The	Mildred O'Brien	McGraw-Hill Book Co., 330 West 42nd Street, New York City
Sewing Machine Book, Singer	Mary Brooks Picken	McGraw-Hill Book Co., 330 West 42nd Street, New York City
Tailors, Textiles for	House of James Hare Staff	House of James Hare, Ltd., London, England
Textile Design, Advanced	William Watson	Longmans, Green & Company, (David McKay Co., Inc.), 750 Third Avenue, New York City

Textile Design and Color	William Watson	Longmans, Green & Company, (David McKay Co., Inc.), 750 Third Avenue, New York City
Textile Fibers, Structure of	A. R. Urquhart & P. O. Howitt	Textile Institute, Manchester, England
Textile Fibers, Yarns, and Fabrics (1964)	Ernest R. Kaswell	Reinhold Publishing Company, Inc., New York City
Textile Fibers, Sixth Edition of	Matthews and Mauersberger	John Wiley & Sons, Inc., 605 Third Avenue, New York City
Textile Materials, Identification of	Staff of Textile Institute	Textile Institute, Manchester, England
Textile Testing	Skinkle	Lowell Technological Institute, Lowell, Massachusetts
Wool Handbook, American	Von Bergen and Mauersberger	Textile Book Publishers, Inc., 257 Park Avenue South, New York City

RECENT DEVELOPMENTS

ALTER-EASE: Durable press garments may be altered by the use of this chemical spray, available in aerosol cans. The technique consists of spraying and then pressing the portion of the garment to be altered. Existing creases can be removed and new ones introduced when desired. No change is needed in existing durable press technology to accommodate this development of J. P. Stevens & Co., Inc., New York City.

LASTRILE: A manufactured fiber in which the fiber-forming substance is (1) a hydrocarbon, such as natural rubber, polyisoprene, polybutadiene, copolymers of dienes and hydrocarbons of amorphous (crystalline) polyolefins; (2) a copolymer of acrylonitrile and a diene (such as butadiene) composed of not more than 50 per cent but at least 10 per cent by weight of acrylonitrile units; (3) a polychloroprene or a copolymer of chloroprene in which 35 per cent by weight of fiber-forming substances are composed of chloroprene units. The term "Lastrile" is the seventeenth generic term decreed by the Federal Trade Commission, Washington, D.C., March, 1966. Lastrile falls into category (2), above. The first sixteen generic terms for Manufactured Fibers became effective March 3, 1960.

WOOL GRADES, OFFICIAL STANDARD: Established by the Federal Register of August 21, 1965, Title 7, Chapter 1, Part 31.

Grade	Limits for average fiber diameter (microns) *	Limit for standard deviation maximum (microns)
Finer than 80s	Under 17.70	3.59
80s	17.70 to 19.14	4.09
70s	19.15 to 20.59	4.59
64s	20.60 to 22.04	5.19
62s	22.05 to 23.49	5.89
60s	23.50 to 24.94	6.49
58s	24.95 to 26.39	7.09
56s	26.40 to 27.84	7.59
54s	27.85 to 29.29	8.19
50s	29.30 to 30.99	8.69
48s	31.00 to 32.69	9.09
46s	32.70 to 34.39	9.59
44s	34.40 to 36.19	10.09
40s	36.20 to 38.09	10.69
36s	38.10 to 40.20	11.19
Coarser than 36s	Over 40.20	—

* A micron is 1/25,400 of an inch.

Index

uses for, 115
Nottingham lace machine, 106
Novelty dress goods, 58
Nylon:
  burning test for, 11
  chemical test for, 12
  definition of, 4
  properties of, 14-15, 423

Oil and grease in textiles, determination of amount of, 354
Oldknow, James, 106
Olefin fibers, 7, 14-15
Organic acid, definition of, 359
Organic, definition of, 359
Organic solvent, 362
Oriental lace, 104
Oriental rugs:
  American, 250
  genuine, 250
Orlon:
  burning test for, 11
  chemical test for, 12
  properties of, 13-14, 424
Overprinting, 221
Oxidation base dye, 203
Oxycellulose test, 361

Pantograph, 215-216
Parts of a fabric, names and definition of, 42
Parts of a loom, 46-47
Pattern motion, 47
Percentage of acetate in a union fabric, 353-355
Permanent or Durable Press:
  abrasion resistance, 244
  basic terms used in, 244-246
  batch cure, 244
  catalyst, 244
  chlorine resistant, 244
  compressive shrinking, 244
  continuous cure, 244
  crease, pleat, and wrinkle in, 240-244
  cross-linking agent, 244
  curing, 241, 244
  curing oven, 243
  deferred cure, 240, 242, 244
  dimensional stability, 245
  durable crease, 245
  "fabric memory," 245
  fibrillation, 245
  findings, 245
  flat curing, 245
  Graniteville Mills, Inc., 240
  hand builder, 245
  history of, 240-241
  hot head press, 245
  imidazolidine, 245
  impregnation, 241, 245
  Koratron Company, Inc., 240-243
  Levi Strauss Company, Inc., 242
  National Cotton Council, 240
  odor, 243
  padding solution, 245
  Perma-fresh 183, 243
  permanent press, 240, 245
  pre-cure process, 240-241
  progressive curing, 245
  puckering in, 246
  reactant, 246
  resin, 246
  Sanforized Company, Inc., 243
  sensitized, 246
  shrinkage in, 243
  softener in, 246
  spontaneous curing, 242-243, 246

storage stability, 246
tear strength, 246
thermosetting resin in, 246
trademarks in, some prominent, 247
uses of, 243
woolens, durable creased, 244
Permanent Press, some major trademarks of:
  "Burmi-Crease," 247
  "Coneprest," 247
  "Dan-Press," 247
  "Koratron," 247
  "Never-Press," 248
  "Penn-Prest," 248
  "Primatized," 248
  "Reeve-Set," 248
  "Sharp-Shape," 248
  "Super-Crease," 248
Permeability of fabrics, air and water, 338-339
Perspiration, fastness of dyed materials to, 348-349
Phenols, 356
Photographic printing, 222
Picking motion on loom, 47
Piece dyeing, 210
Piece goods yarn, 128
Pigment colors dye, 203
Pigment primaries, 195
Pile Fabric:
  definition of: 71
  sketches, 162
  some properties and characteristics of, 164
  weave in, 161-163
Pillowcases, 266
Pique weaves, 157-158, 179
Placket, knitted shirt, 79
Plain stitch, knitting, 73
Plain weave, 144-147
Plaited fabrics, 240-244
Plaiting, definition of, 43, 46
Plastic, 134
Plating, definition of, 71
"Plus-X," 134
Ply-yarn, definition of, 43
Polo knitted shirt, 79
Polyester, definition of, 6
Porosity, 8
Princess dress, 436
Princess lace, 104
Principles applied to textiles, xxx-xxxi
Printing:
  definition of, 213, 215
  operation of machine in, 216
  side view of machine for:
    calender, cylinder, 219
    direct or roller, 219
Printing, major methods in:
  blotch, 220
  calender, cylinder, 219-220
  direct or roller, 220, 224
  resist, 220
  resist and discharge, summary of, 220
Printing, minor methods in:
  application, 221
  block, 221
  burn-out, 221
  commercial, 221
  duplex or register, 221
  flock, flocking, flocked, 221, 225-228
  India print, 221
  overprinting, 221
  photographic, 222
  print-on-print or dyed fabric, 222
  rotary screen printing, 224

screen or stencil, 222, 224
shadow, 223
stipple-effect, 223
Tjap, 223
Toile de Jouy, 223
warp, 223-224
Wedgwood, 224
Properties and characteristics of major tetxile fibers, 410-428
Pucci, Emilio, 128
Pullover sweater, 79

Qualitative tests, 335
Quality control, 315-316
Quantitative tests, 335
Quaternary ammonium salts, 357

Rando-feeder, 113
Random dyeing, 212
Random-tumble pilling tester machine, 336-337
Rando-webber, 113
Raw stock dyeing, 213
Rayon staple, 427
Rayon, viscose:
  burning test for, 10
  chemical test for, 11
  manufacturers of, 427
  properties and characteristics of, 427-428
  staining test for identification, 428
  viscose method, Cross and Bevan, 34-35
Reactive dye, 204
Réaumur, René de, 34
Reed, and dents in, 59-60
Reed marks in warp direction in woven goods, 59-60
Regains for major fabrics, standard, 15
Regis, S. J., Father, 100
Relative humidity:
  absorbency in, 284
  definition of, 283
  moisture regain in, 284
  table for percentage regain in, 284
Residual shrinkage testing, 315
Resiliency, 9
Resin bonding for nonwoven fabrics, 112
Resin, definition of, 6
Resist printing, 220
"Restora," 134
Reversible fabric, 64
Ribbed fabric, 67
Rib weaves, 155-156
Rigid fiber or fabric, 134
Rigmel-Shrunk, 236
Rose point lace, 104
Rugs, see Carpets

Saint Feutre, 86
Saint Gall or Gallen, Switzerland, 106, 108
Sanforized, 237
Saran:
  burning test for, 11
  chemical test for, 12
  properties of, 424-425
Satin, definition of, 153
Satin, silk, 61
Satin weave, 144, 151, 177
Schiffli embroidery, 108-109
Schreinerizing, cotton, 237
Sciences used in textile industry, 429-430
Screen printing, 224
Seamless hosiery, 84
Selvage, definition of, 46

[469]